S0-AVS-511

INTERNATIONAL TABLE OF ATOMIC WEIGHTS

(1971, including 1973 corrected values)

Based on the assigned relative atomic mass of $^{12}C = 12$.

The following values apply to elements as they exist in materials of terrestrial origin and to certain artificial elements. When used with the footnotes, they are reliable to ±1 in the last digit, or ±3 if that digit is in small type.

	Symbol	Atomic number	Atomic weight
Actinium	Ac	89	
Aluminum	Al	13	26.98154[a]
Americium	Am	95	
Antimony	Sb	51	121.7_5
Argon	Ar	18	39.94_8[b,c,d,g]
Arsenic	As	33	74.9216[a]
Astatine	At	85	
Barium	Ba	56	137.3_4
Berkelium	Bk	97	
Beryllium	Be	4	9.01218[a]
Bismuth	Bi	83	208.9804[a]
Boron	B	5	10.81[c,d,e]
Bromine	Br	35	79.904[c]
Cadmium	Cd	48	112.40
Calcium	Ca	20	40.08[g]
Californium	Cf	98	
Carbon	C	6	12.011[b,d]
Cerium	Ce	58	140.12
Cesium	Cs	55	132.9054[a]
Chlorine	Cl	17	35.453[c]
Chromium	Cr	24	51.996[c]
Cobalt	Co	27	58.9332[a]
Copper	Cu	29	63.54_6[c,d]
Curium	Cm	96	
Dysprosium	Dy	66	162.5_0
Einsteinium	Es	99	
Erbium	Er	68	167.2_6
Europium	Eu	63	151.96
Fermium	Fm	100	
Fluorine	F	9	18.99840[a]
Francium	Fr	87	
Gadolinium	Gd	64	157.2_5
Gallium	Ga	31	69.72
Germanium	Ge	32	72.5_9
Gold	Au	79	196.9665[a]
Hafnium	Hf	72	178.4_9
Helium	He	2	4.00260[b,c]
Holmium	Ho	67	164.9304[a]
Hydrogen	H	1	1.0079[b,d]
Indium	In	49	114.82
Iodine	I	53	126.9045[a]
Iridium	Ir	77	192.2_2
Iron	Fe	26	55.84_7
Krypton	Kr	36	83.80
Lanthanum	La	57	138.905_5[b]
Lawrencium	Lr	103	
Lead	Pb	82	207.2[d,g]
Lithium	Li	3	6.94_1[c,d,e,g]
Lutetium	Lu	71	174.97
Magnesium	Mg	12	24.305[c,g]
Manganese	Mn	25	54.9380[a]
Mendelevium	Md	101	
Mercury	Hg	80	200.5_9
Molybdenum	Mo	42	95.9_4
Neodymium	Nd	60	144.2_4
Neon	Ne	10	20.17_9[c]
Neptunium	Np	93	237.0482[f]
Nickel	Ni	28	58.70
Niobium	Nb	41	92.9064[a]
Nitrogen	N	7	14.0067[b,c]
Nobelium	No	102	
Osmium	Os	76	190.2
Oxygen	O	8	15.999_4[b,c,d]
Palladium	Pd	46	106.4
Phosphorus	P	15	30.97376[a]
Platinum	Pt	78	195.0_9
Plutonium	Pu	94	
Polonium	Po	84	
Potassium	K	19	39.09_8
Praseodymium	Pr	59	140.9077[a]
Promethium	Pm	61	
Protactinium	Pa	91	231.0359[a,f]
Radium	Ra	88	226.0254[f,g]
Radon	Rn	86	
Rhenium	Re	75	186.207
Rhodium	Rh	45	102.9055[a]
Rubidium	Rb	37	85.467_8[c]
Ruthenium	Ru	44	101.0_7
Samarium	Sm	62	150.4
Scandium	Sc	21	44.9559[a]
Selenium	Se	34	78.9_6
Silicon	Si	14	28.08_6[d]
Silver	Ag	47	107.868[c]
Sodium	Na	11	22.98977[a]
Strontium	Sr	38	87.62[g]
Sulfur	S	16	32.06[d]
Tantalum	Ta	73	180.947_9[b]
Technetium	Tc	43	98.9062[f]
Tellurium	Te	52	127.6_0
Terbium	Tb	65	158.9254[a]
Thallium	Tl	81	204.3_7
Thorium	Th	90	232.0381[f]
Thulium	Tm	69	168.9342[a]
Tin	Sn	50	118.6_9
Titanium	Ti	22	47.9_0
Tungsten	W	74	183.8_5
Uranium	U	92	238.029[b,c,e]
Vanadium	V	23	50.941_4[b,c]
Wolfram		(see Tungsten)	
Xenon	Xe	54	131.30
Ytterbium	Yb	70	173.0_4
Yttrium	Y	30	88.9059[a]
Zinc	Zn	30	65.38
Zirconium	Zr	40	91.22

[a] Mononuclidic element.

[b] Element with one predominant isotope (about 99 to 100% abundance).

[c] Element for which the atomic weight is based on calibrated measurements by comparing with synthetic mixtures of known isotopic composition.

[d] Element for which known variation in isotopic abundance in terrestrial samples limits the precision of the atomic weight given.

[e] Element for which users are cautioned against the possibility of large variations in atomic weight due to inadvertent or undisclosed artificial isotopic separation in commercially available materials.

[f] Most commonly available long-lived isotope.

[g] In some geological specimens this element has a highly anomalous isotopic composition, corresponding to an atomic weight significantly different from that given.

Physical Science with Environmental and Other Practical Applications

Second Edition

Jonathan Turk, Ph. D.
Bozeman, Montana

Amos Turk, Ph. D.
Professor, Department of Chemistry
The City College of the City University of New York

SAUNDERS GOLDEN SUNBURST SERIES

SAUNDERS COLLEGE PUBLISHING
Philadelphia New York Chicago San Francisco Montreal Toronto
London Sydney Tokyo Mexico City Rio de Janeiro Madrid

Address orders to:
383 Madison Avenue
New York, NY 10017
Address editorial correspondence to:
West Washington Square
Philadelphia, PA 19105

This book was set in Melior by York Graphics Services, Inc.
The editors were John Vondeling, Patrice Smith and Karen Comerford.
The art director, cover and text designer was Nancy E. J. Grossman.
The production manager was Tom O'Connor.
New artwork was drawn by Jan Logan and Mario Neves.
The printer was Hampshire Press.

Cover photo: "Old limber pine and the Cathedral group, Grand Teton National Park, Wyoming." by David Sumner
Title page photo: "Mount Changabang, India" by Dakers Gowans.

PHYSICAL SCIENCE ISBN 0-03-057782-9

 Library of Congress catalog card number 80-53940.

34 032 9876543

CBS COLLEGE PUBLISHING
Saunders College Publishing
Holt, Rinehart and Winston
The Dryden Press

PREFACE

It is difficult to teach the elements of physics, chemistry, geology, and astronomy in a single course. Each teacher will necessarily emphasize certain areas and topics in preference to others. As a result, every physical science course in every classroom is somewhat unique. In fact, many instructors have found that the needs, backgrounds, and interests of their students change from year to year, and the course content must be varied accordingly. However, certain factors remain constant. Primarily, any course must be grounded in basics. A discussion of motion and energy, Newton's laws, the fundamentals of electricity and magnetism, the structure of the atom and the nature of the chemical bond, and other standard topics must all be presented clearly. But an unbroken discussion of theory alone can strain a student's attention. Students are interested in applications of science and technology to their daily lives. Therefore, we have included *environmental and other practical applications* as an integral part of the text. Much of this material is to be found in no other introductory science text of any kind, whether for science or non-science majors. We trust that this innovation will enhance the student's motivation to learn and, incidentally, provide much interesting and useful information. However, while we have added a great deal of applied science and technology, we have always been conscious of the fact that the book is first and foremost a physical science text and that discussions of practical applications must always integrate with and support the primacy of the physical science theme.

These broad guidelines do not, by themselves, construct an outline for a course. Many specific questions must be answered. Some, such as "How much mathematics should be required?" apply to all topics. Others refer to particular subjects: "Should a greater emphasis be placed on discussions of local weather patterns or on global climate change?" "Should more space be devoted to an explanation of the motion of the celestial bodies as seen from Earth, or to a brief introduction to the mysteries of pulsars, black holes, and quasars?" The choices seem virtually endless. To offer the widest rein in such matters, we have tried to make the text as flexible as possible. Some sections that deal with specific applications or with other special topics can be omitted without interrupting the general flow. For example, Chapter 9, Environmental Chemistry, consists of a series of chemical case histories. Each section introduces fundamental chemical principles through the study of a practical chemical problem. The chapter is modular so that addition or deletion can be easily made at the teacher's discretion.

In all chapters, additional material has been set aside in separate boxes. These boxes contain background material, special examples, or additional explanations or information and can be included or omitted.

The use of mathematics is held to a minimum in the text itself. Where it is used, it is in the form of simple equations such as Ohm's Law. For those instructors who elect to introduce a more rigorous approach, a series of simple worked-out mathematical examples are available at the ends of many chapters. Additional mathematical material is found in the Appendix.

This edition also includes a greatly expanded emphasis on world energy supplies, a discussion of the incident at Three Mile Island, and other timely topics as well as many of the practical and environmental examples that were included in the first edition. Other pedagogic tools used in the book include the following:

Chapter Openings and Summaries. Each chapter is prefaced with a short introduction which explains the type of material that will be discussed. A summary of chapter objectives at the end of the chapter serves as an aid for easy review of the text. This summary is supplemented with a checklist of key words.

Take-Home Experiments. Simple laboratory experiments are also provided. These experiments are designed to illustrate various topics in the chapter and to require no more, or very little more, equipment and supplies than are commonly available in the household. They will, we hope, also be fun to do.

Study Problems. A generous supply of various types is provided. Some are straightforward applications of the material in the chapters; others invite more imaginative interpretations. The answers to numerical problems appear at the end of the text.

Glossary. An extensive glossary of terms used in the text is provided at the end of the book.

Appendix. The Appendix explains significant figures and proportionality. The text itself does not demand the use of significant figures so that the instructor may exercise the option as to whether or not to do so. The Appendix also includes temperature conversion formulas, a simple derivation of the kinetic energy equation, a slightly more mathematical treatment of the decibel scale, and tables of conversion factors, atomic weights, and three-place logarithms.

ACKNOWLEDGMENTS

A very incisive, careful, and thorough group of reviewers gave us the benefit of their comments and suggestions on the manuscript, and we thank them all most sincerely. They are: Robert Backes, Pittsburgh State University; Harold Brower, Highline Community College; Vernon Burger, Cuyahoga Community College; Adrian B. Cooley, Sam Houston University; Theodore C. Foster, California Polytechnic State University; Donald E. Holmes, California State University at Fresno; Philip Kasimer; Donald Marchand, Old Dominion University; Keith F. Oles, Oregon State University; Jay M. Pasachoff, Williams College; W. C. Shellenberger, Northern Montana College; Stephen G. Wukovitz, Bloomsburg State College.

Many others have helped: Evelyn Manacek and Patricia Deyling Renn typed most of the manuscript, Jan Logan drew many of the illustrations, Pearl Turk secured photographs, and our friends at Saunders College Publishing helped put the book together.

JONATHAN TURK
AMOS TURK

TABLE OF CONTENTS

CHAPTER 1

Many scientific concepts can be understood intuitively. Even a lion or a wolf can judge the speed and direction of a fleeing animal and plan a course to intercept it. Modern science is based on conceptual understanding but demands precision of measurement and exact calculations as well. This chapter discusses measurement and introduces the International System of Units. It also shows how one type of unit is converted to another and discusses scientific notation.

INTUITION AND SCIENTIFIC REASONING

1.1 INTRODUCTION

Let us start by telling a short true story. Not long ago, the younger Turk (Jon) and a friend, Ken Brewer, were paddling a canoe northward along the coast from Vancouver, British Columbia, to Glacier Bay, Alaska. We were starting to cross a dangerous stretch of water, Dixon Entrance, just north of Prince Rupert, from Flewin Point to Garnett Point, as shown on the map in Figure 1–1. Suddenly a strong wind picked up from the east, blowing us westward out to sea. If we had continued to aim the canoe directly toward our destination, we never would have made it; instead we would have found ourselves far from land, drifting out toward the open ocean. So we aimed the canoe almost due north, which meant that we bent further into the wind. The happy result was that we headed to the safety of Garnett Point and not out to sea. The motion of the boat was really a combination of two independent motions; we were paddling north while simultaneously being blown due west. As a result, the net motion was northwest, as shown in the diagram.

We did not have to consult a book to plan our course and steer the boat. By combining a little common sense with a good healthy dose of fear of the open seas, we were able to understand what had to be done. We chose our route intuitively, by the feel of the situation, but the problem also could have been solved mathematically, using elementary physics. In fact, in the next chapter we will study vector analysis in more detail. But why bother, if we can solve a real life problem without ever touching pencil to paper. In this case, there would have been no reason whatsoever to solve the problem mathematically, but suppose that next time we decide to sail a larger boat and travel across the Pacific from Seattle to Hawaii. Imagine, now, that as we left Seattle a wind arose from the south and blew the boat northward off course. Since we could not see Hawaii, it would be impossible to plot a correct course by intuition. In such a case mathematical analysis and elementary physics are essential.

Few people actually sail boats across the Pacific or study navigation, and in most everyday situations our informal experience and our intuitive feelings for the world about us are entirely sufficient. You don't need to be a chemist to bake bread, you can build a garage without being an engineer, and hardly any canoeists major in physics. Think of all the things you do

Figure 1–1. Crossing Dixon entrance.

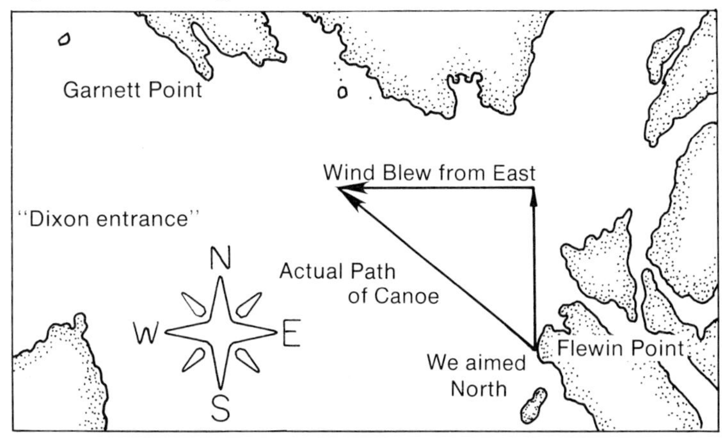

Canoeing in the Inland Passage. Preparing to set out into the Straits of Georgia on a rainy morning.

in your everyday life that require an intuitive understanding of fundamental physical properties. Perhaps you shift gears on your bicycle, adjust the tension on a sewing machine, tune a motorcycle, ski, or ride a skateboard. Although most events in our lives can be dealt with using knowledge gained without formal training, there is a wider domain of problems for which our everyday experience is insufficient. The purpose of this book is to teach the principles necessary for an understanding of some broader and more complex issues that we face today.

For example, we would like to know what happened during the accident at the Three Mile Island nuclear facility. Who was at fault, if anyone, and is such an accident likely to happen again? What are the advantages and disadvantages of the alternatives to a nuclear future? How can technological solutions aid our efforts to conserve energy without disrupting our lives?

Even some seemingly simple problems cannot always be solved intuitively. Many of the people who live in small towns in various rural regions burn wood as a source of heat. Pot-bellied stoves have become symbols of a new way of life; people save money and energy and enjoy fall forays after firewood. But small stoves are often smoky, and during the winter months this smoke accumulates and often causes noticeable air pollution in some areas. Two central questions have been raised. (1) Is the smoke harmful to human health? (2) If it is, what can be done about it? Neither of these questions is easy to answer. In subsequent chapters, we will study chemistry, including the chemistry of air pollution, and some aspects of the relationship between pollution and human health. Problems related to depletion of fossil fuel supplies and the use of renewable fuels such as wood are discussed in

Telluride, Colorado: The air in this isolated mountain town is heavily polluted from smoke from wood stoves and dust from the unpaved streets.

Splitting firewood on a wintry day. Homeowners save money and conserve fuel by burning firewood, but fireplaces are nearly always smoky and polluting.

Chapter 3. The possibility that pollution may affect local or global climate is discussed in Chapter 13. In other chapters, technical approaches to energy conservation will be considered. These methods include construction of energy-efficient houses that use less fuel, use of solar collectors, or installation of heat pumps that extract heat from the earth. It may also be possible to reduce pollution through the use of air purification devices mounted on chimneys or stoves. Some people suggest it might be simpler and better to build a nuclear generating plant and supply all the houses in the region with electric heat.

1.2 SYSTEMS OF MEASUREMENT

Measurement is fundamental not only to experimental science but also to our whole technological way of life. Thus, while cooks used to fire their ovens until they were "about hot enough," baking is now done at carefully measured and monitored temperatures. Similarly, we measure distances with a much higher degree of accuracy than was used previously. The distance between two cities, for example, is expressed in kilometers (or miles) rather than in such vague terms as "two days' journey" or "an afternoon's ride."

A carpenter uses a metal ruler to measure distances during house construction.

A mass spectrometer. This device is used in chemistry and physics laboratories to measure the masses of molecular fragments.

Measurement is essential to our modern way of life. The instrumental panel of a Boeing 747 jet, shown here, is studded with gauges of all types.

Measuring devices are all around us: clocks, thermometers, rulers, and bathroom scales are present in most homes, and automobiles are equipped with speedometers, pressure gauges, and electrical current meters.

A measurement must include both a quantity and a description of what is being measured. Thus, it is meaningless to say that an animal is 3. The quantity, by itself, doesn't give us enough information. The animal could be 3 years old, 3 meters tall, or have a mass of 3 kilograms. Years, meters (m), and kilograms (kg) are all units. If you are asked to measure the distance between point A and point B below, you must note its length and the units used to express it. It is obviously meaningless to say that A is 6.2 away from B, for the number 6.2, by itself, has no meaning in this context. The distance between point A and point B is 6.2 centimeters (cm). We could also express the same distance in other units, because 6.2 cm is equal to 2.44 inches (in), 0.062 m, or 0.203 foot (ft).

A • ←—— 6.2 cm ——→ • B

It is much easier for different observers to communicate with one another if everyone uses the same system of measurement. The metric system (Système International d'Unités, abbreviated SI) is internationally recognized and is now used in nearly all the nations in the world. The use of a universal measuring "language" facilitates international communications.

The fundamental metric units are standardized by the International Bureau of Weights and Measures in Sèvres, France. The meter originally was defined as one ten-millionth of the distance between the North Pole and the Equator. Since it is nearly impossible to calibrate our ordinary measuring devices directly against such a global standard, a more manageable meter was created by placing two marks on a platinum-alloy bar, which was called the International Prototype Meter. More recently there has been a return to a "natural" standard for the meter, based on the wavelength of light emitted by the krypton atom.

The standard kilogram is the mass of a block of platinum alloy, also stored in Sèvres, and is almost exactly equal to the mass of 1000 cubic centimeters (cm^3) of water at a temperature of 3.98° C.

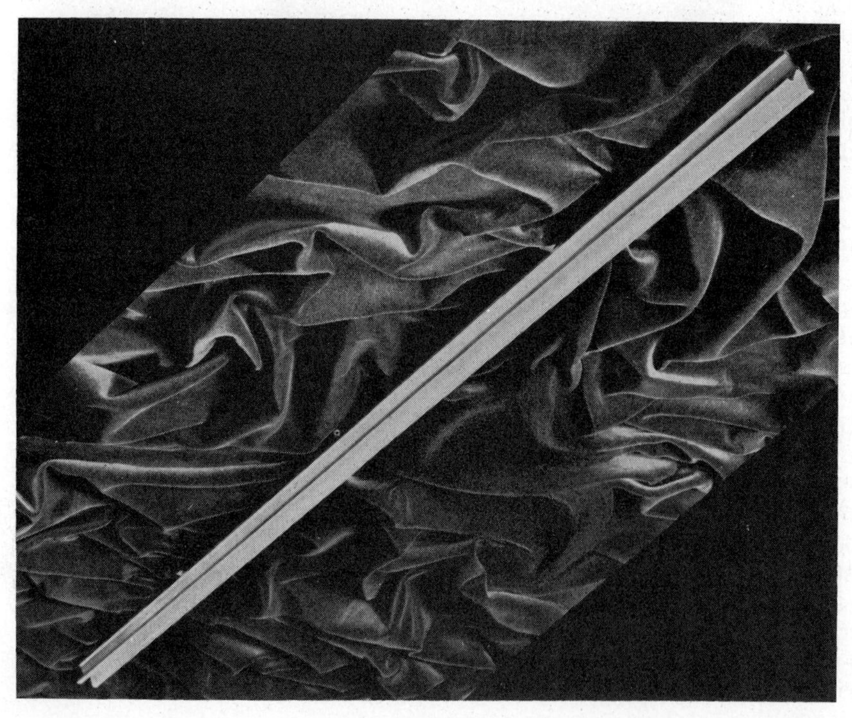

The United States copy of the Standard Meter, Prototype Meter No. 27, was delivered from France in 1890. (Courtesy of National Bureau of Standards.)

Prototype Kilogram No. 20, the national standard of mass for the United States. It is a platinum-iridium cylinder 39 millimeters in diameter and 39 millimeters high. (Courtesy of National Bureau of Standards.)

The standard second (sec) originally was defined as 1/86,400 of a mean solar day of the year 1900, but since the solar day is not constant, the second has been redefined in terms of a particular molecular vibration. Other standard units will be discussed in later chapters.

The United States traditionally has used what is called the **British system** of units, although it is now converting to the metric system to be compatible with most of the nations in the world. The British system is derived largely from old usages in commerce, industry, and navigation that are hard to remember and that are not decimal multiples of each other. As shown in the accompanying box, these units are related to each other in rather haphazard ways.

The International System (SI) is particularly convenient because units are expressed as multiples of 10. Thus, for example, there are 100 cm in 1 m, and 1000 m in 1 kilometer (km).

The SI values are based on seven well-defined, independent units from which all other units can be derived. The seven units, called the **base units** are listed in Table 1–1. Various combinations of these base units give us a large variety of derived units. For example, area is measured as a length times a length and can be expressed as meter × meter or meter² (m^2). Similarly, speed is a length divided by a time and can be expressed as $\frac{\text{meter}}{\text{second}}$.

TABLE 1–1. SI BASE UNITS

Quantity	Name	Symbol
length	meter	m
mass	kilogram	kg
time	second	s
electric current	ampere	A
temperature	Kelvin	K
luminous intensity	candela	cd
amount of substance	mole	mol

The SI rules specify that the symbols are not followed by periods, nor are they changed in the plural. Therefore, we write "the beaker contains 5 g of mercury." (*not* "5 g. of mercury" or "5 gs of mercury.") The SI symbol for second, which is s, is often replaced by the unofficial sec because an expression like "10 s" is easily misread as "tens." In this text we use sec for second. Another older symbol, still used in some books, is amp for ampere.

COMMON AND UNCOMMON BRITISH UNITS

Length

1 yard = 0.9144 meter

1 foot = $\frac{1}{3}$ yard = 12 inches

1 hand = 4 inches

1 span = 9 inches

1 fathom = 8 spans

1 rod = $5\frac{1}{2}$ yards

1 furlong = 40 rods

1 mile = 8 furlongs = 5280 feet

Volume

1 cubic foot = 28316.847 cubic centimeters
= 2.296×10^{-5} acre feet
= 12 board feet
= 6.428 U.S. dry gallons
= 7.48 liquid gallons
= 0.0078125 cord (wood)

1.3 CONVERSION FACTORS

Both scientists and lay people alike frequently find it necessary to change a quantity expressed in one unit to the same quantity expressed in another. For example, if you are traveling in France, your restaurant bill may come to 80 francs and you might wish to know how much that is equal to in dollars. Or, if you are baking a pie in your kitchen at home, you might find it necessary to convert tablespoons to cups; a physicist might measure something in centimeters and wish to express it in meters. The mathematical manipulations do not change the cost of a dinner or the size of an object, they only change the units that we express them in.

To start with very familiar units, we ask, "How many seconds are there in 1.5 minutes (min)?" You know immediately that the answer is 90 sec, but let us examine the reasoning process. We start with the equation

$$60 \text{ sec} = 1 \text{ min}$$

Dividing both sides by 1 min, we have

$$\frac{60 \text{ sec}}{1 \text{ min}} = \frac{1 \text{ min}}{1 \text{ min}} = 1$$

The fraction $\frac{60 \text{ sec}}{1 \text{ min}}$ is called a "conversion factor" because it can be used to "convert" minutes to seconds. Since this factor has a value of 1, its reciprocal, $\frac{1 \text{ min}}{60 \text{ sec}}$, also has a value of 1 and is an equally correct conversion factor that can be used to "convert" seconds to minutes. Multiplying (or dividing) anything by 1 does not change its value, so it is correct to carry out such operations. How do we decide which of these two factors will give the correct answer to the problem? Let us try both to show which is right and which is wrong:

$$1.5 \cancel{\text{min}} \times \frac{60 \text{ sec}}{1 \cancel{\text{min}}} = 90 \text{ sec}$$

(correct answer)

$$1.5 \text{ min} \times \frac{1 \text{ min}}{60 \text{ sec}} = 0.025 \frac{\text{min}^2}{\text{sec}}$$

(incorrect answer)

The second answer cannot be correct because the units are wrong. It is impossible for an incorrect use of a conversion factor to give a correct answer.

Table 1–2 gives the names and symbols of the prefixes that form decimal multiples or fractions of SI units. Table 1–3 gives some common conversion factors between metric and British units. A longer list is given in Appendix E. Use of the conversion tables is illustrated in the following examples.

Example 1.1
Long-distance runners run a 10,000-m race. How far is that in (a) km, (b) miles (mi)?

Answer: (a) The conversion from meters to kilometers is 1 km = 1000 m or

$$\frac{1 \text{ km}}{1000 \text{ m}} = 1$$

therefore, $10{,}000 \text{ m} \times \frac{1 \text{ km}}{1000 \text{ m}} = 10 \text{ km}$

Measuring devices.

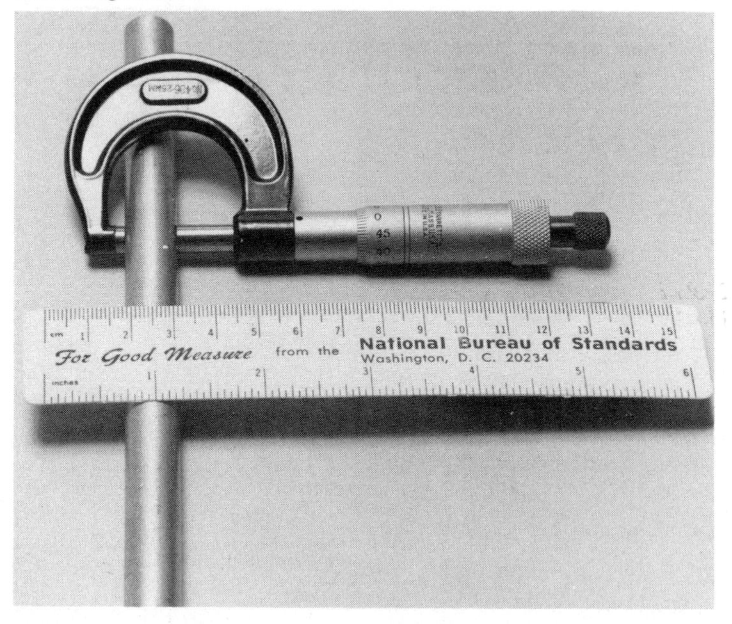

(b) The conversion factor from Table 1–3 is

$$\frac{1 \text{ mi}}{1.61 \text{ km}} = 1$$

therefore,

$$10 \text{ km} \times \frac{1 \text{ mi}}{1.61 \text{ km}} = 6.21 \text{ mi}$$

Example 1.2
A diesel car can travel 800 km on a tank of fuel. How far is that in miles?

Answer: The conversion factor, from Table 1–2, is

$$\frac{1 \text{ mi}}{1.61 \text{ km}}$$

Thus, $800 \text{ km} \times \dfrac{1 \text{ mi}}{1.61 \text{ km}} = 497 \text{ mi}$

Example 1.3
Suppose that a race car travels at an average speed of $240 \dfrac{\text{km}}{\text{hour}}$. What is its speed in $\dfrac{\text{miles}}{\text{hour}}$?

Answer:

$$\frac{240 \text{ km}}{1 \text{ hour}} \times \frac{0.62 \text{ mi}}{1 \text{ km}} = 149 \frac{\text{mi}}{\text{hour}}$$

Example 1.4
(a) A human who is 3 ft tall is probably a child; is a person who is 3 m tall a child? (b) A weightlifter can just lift 150 pounds (lb); can he lift 150 kg?

Answer: These problems are designed to give you an intuitive feel for the metric system. We need not solve the mathematics exactly.

(a) Since there are approximately 3 ft in a meter, a person who is 3 m tall is approximately 9 ft tall, and is not a child but a giant.

(b) There are approximately 2.2 lb in a kilogram, or a kilogram is more than twice as large as a pound.* Thus, a weightlifter who can just lift 150 lb could not lift 150 kg.

*The relationship 2.2 lb = 1 kg is valid only on Earth at sea level, because a pound is a unit of force and a kilogram is a unit of mass. This difference will be discussed in Chapter 2.

TABLE 1—2. NAMES AND SYMBOLS FOR METRIC PREFIXES

Prefix	Symbol	Multiply by
tera	T	10^{12}, or one trillion
giga	G	10^{9}, or one billion
*mega	M	10^{6}, or one million
*kilo	k	10^{3}, or one thousand
deci	d	10^{-1}, or one tenth
*centi	c	10^{-2}, or one hundredth
*milli	m	10^{-3}, or one thousandth
*micro	μ	10^{-6}, or one millionth
nano	n	10^{-9}, or one billionth
pico	p	10^{-12}, or one trillionth

*Most commonly used.

TABLE 1—3. HANDY CONVERSION FACTORS*

To Convert from		Multiply by the Conversion Factor	
centimeters	inches	0.394	in/cm
feet	centimeters	30.5	cm/ft
	meters	0.305	m/ft
grams	pounds (avdp.)	0.0022	lb/g
inches	centimeters	2.54	cm/in
kilograms	pounds (avdp.)	2.20	lb/kg
kilometers	miles	0.621	mi/km
liters	quarts (U.S., liq.)	1.06	qt/L
meters	feet	3.28	ft/m
miles (statute)	kilometers	1.61	km/mi
pounds (avdp.)	kilograms	0.454	kg/lb

*A more complete list is given in Appendix E.

TABLE 1—4. SOME USEFUL METRIC RELATIONSHIPS

A centimeter is shorter than an inch.	There are 2.54 cm in an inch.
A kilometer is shorter than a mile.	There are approximately 1.6 km in a mile.
A gram is much lighter than a pound.	There are 454 g in a pound.
A pound is slightly less than half a kilogram	There are 2.2 lb in a kilogram.
A quart is slightly less than a liter.	There are 1.1 qt in a liter.

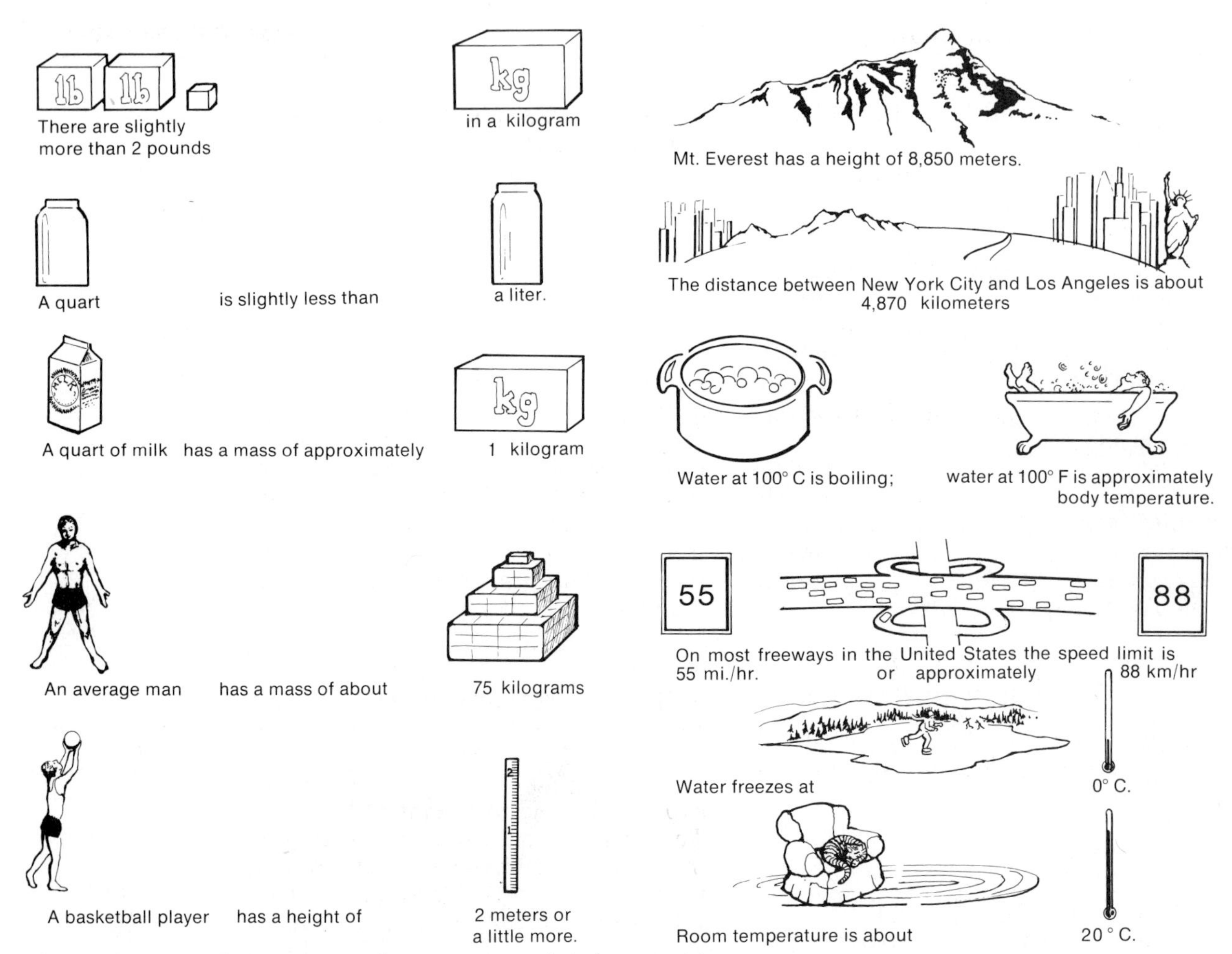

Since we are now changing to metric measurement, it is important to "think metric." Some useful rule-of-thumb relationships are shown.

1.4 SCIENTIFIC NOTATION

Scientific measurements frequently involve very large or very small numbers. For example, the number expressing the mass of the Earth—approximately 3,120,000,000,000,000,000,000,000 kg—requires so many digits that it is cumbersome to work with. Very small numbers, such as the mass of a hydrogen atom, which is approximately 0.000000000000000000000017 g, are also cumbersome. To make matters easier, we adopt a system called scientific notation. This system is based on exponents of 10, which are shorthand notations for repeated multiplications or divisions.

A positive exponent tells us that a number is to be multiplied by itself a given number of times. Thus, the number 10^2 (read "ten squared" or "ten to the second power") is exponential notation for $10 \times 10 = 100$. Similarly, $3^4 = 3 \times 3 \times 3 \times 3 = 81$. A negative exponent means that we take the reciprocal of the expression. Thus,

$$10^{-2} = \frac{1}{10^2} = \frac{1}{100} = 0.01.$$

Positive and negative powers of 10 are shown below:

$10^4 = 10 \cdot 10 \cdot 10 \cdot 10 = 10000$ (4 digits to the right)

$10^3 = 10 \cdot 10 \cdot 10 = 1000$ (3 digits)

$10^2 = 10 \cdot 10 = 100$ (2 digits)

$10^1 = 10 = 10$ (1 digit)

$10^0 = 1$ (0 digits)

$10^{-1} = \frac{1}{10} = 0.1$ (1 digit to the left)

$$10^{-2} = \frac{1}{10 \cdot 10} = 0.01 \text{ (2 digits)}$$

$$10^{-3} = \frac{1}{10 \cdot 10 \cdot 10} = 0.001 \text{ (3 digits)}$$

$$10^{-4} = \frac{1}{10 \cdot 10 \cdot 10 \cdot 10} = 0.0001 \text{ (4 digits)}$$

Notice that to write 10^4 in longhand form we simply start with the number 1 and move the decimal four places to the right: 10000. Similarly, to write 10^{-4} we start we start with the number 1 and move the decimal four places to the left: 0.0001.

It is just as easy to go the other way—that is, to convert a number written in longhand form to an exponential expression. Thus, the decimal place of the number 1,000,000 is six places to the right of 1.

$$1\,\underbrace{000\,000}_{6\text{ digits}} = 10^6$$

Similarly, the decimal place of the nummer 0.000001 is six places to the left of 1 and

$$0.\underbrace{000001}_{6\text{ digits}} = 10^{-6}$$

What about a number like 3,000,000? If you write it $3 \times 1{,}000{,}000$, the exponential expression is simply 3×10^6. Thus, the mass of the Earth, which was expressed in long numerical form at the beginning of this section, can be written more conveniently as 3.12×10^{24} kg.

Using the techniques you just learned, check for yourself that the mass of a hydrogen atom can be written as 1.7×10^{-24} g.

To multiply numbers in scientific notation, we add the exponents. To divide, we subtract the exponents.

$$10^4 \times 10^3 = 10^7$$

$$\frac{10^5}{10^3} = 10^5 \times 10^{-3} = 10^2$$

Scientific notation is used frequently with numbers in the metric system. Thus, there are 100 cm in a meter and we write, "there are 10^2 cm in a meter." A kilometer is 1000 m, which can be written as 10^3 m. Similarly, a milligram (mg) is 10^{-3} g, or 0.001 g. There are 1000, or 10^3, mg in a g and 10^3 g in a kg.

Example 1.5
(a) The distance from the center of the Earth to the center of the Moon is approximately 3.8×10^5 km. How many meters is this? Write your answer in exponential and in longhand form. (b) The distance between two hydrogen nuclei in a hydrogen molecule is approximately 0.000000007 cm. Write this number in exponential notation.

Answer: (a) There are 1,000, or 10^3, m in a km. Converting, we have

$$3.8 \times 10^5 \text{ km} \times \frac{10^3 \text{ m}}{1 \text{ km}} = 3.8 \times 10^8 \text{ m}$$

This can be written as 380,000,000 m.

$$\text{(b) } 0.\underbrace{000000007}_{9\text{ digits}} \text{ cm} = 7 \times 10^{-9} \text{ cm}$$

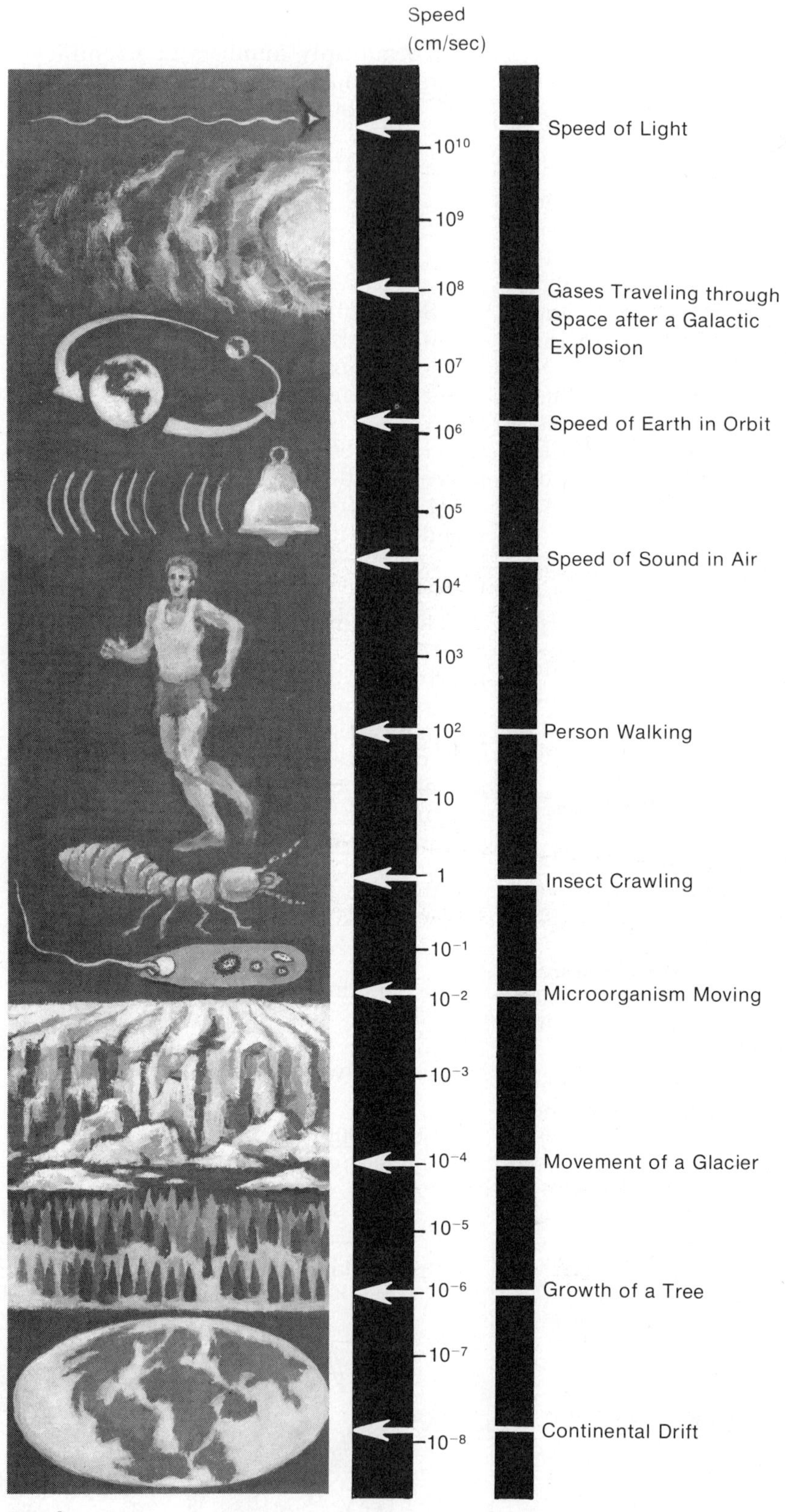

Speed
(cm/sec)
10^{10}
10^{9}
10^{8}
10^{7}
10^{6}
10^{5}
10^{4}
10^{3}
10^{2}
10
1
10^{-1}
10^{-2}
10^{-3}
10^{-4}
10^{-5}
10^{-6}
10^{-7}
10^{-8}
Speed of Light
Gases Traveling through Space after a Galactic Explosion
Speed of Earth in Orbit
Speed of Sound in Air
Person Walking
Insect Crawling
Microorganism Moving
Movement of a Glacier
Growth of a Tree
Continental Drift

Speeds.

Size
(cm)
10^{24}
Diameter of Andromeda Galaxy
10^{22}
10^{20}
Distance from the Sun to the Nearest Star
10^{18}
10^{16}
Diameter of Solar System
10^{14}
10^{12}
Diameter of Sun
10^{10}
Diameter of Earth
10^{8}
Height of Mt. Everest
10^{6}
Height of World Trade Center in New York
10^{4}
Height of a Person
10^{2}
Length of Insect
1
10^{-2}
Length of Bacterium
10^{-4}
Large Molecule
10^{-6}
A Simple Atom
10^{-8}
10^{-10}
Proton and Electron
10^{-12}

Lengths.

CHAPTER OBJECTIVES

Given a measurement expressed in one type of unit, you must be able to convert it to another. You should have learned to convert British units to metric units and also be able to convert numbers expressed in one metric unit to numbers expressed in another. Given a number in exponential notation, you should be able to express that number in conventional form or vice versa.

TAKE-HOME EXPERIMENTS

1. **Length.** Cut a piece of string that is 1 m long and another that is 1 ft long. Compare them. Cut a piece of string that is 1 cm long and another that is 1 in long, and compare them.

2. **Mass.** Weigh out 1 kg of some commodity such as rice, coffee, or flour; then weigh 1 lb of the same commodity. Compare the two piles.

3. **Temperature.** Using a Celsius thermometer, record the temperature in (a) your house, (b) the refrigerator, (c) the outside air. Now without converting Celsius to Fahrenheit, answer the following questions. What kind of clothes would you wear if the outside temperature were 0° C; 15° C; 20° C; 30° C? What would be a typical Celsius temperature in your city in January; April; July; October?

PROBLEMS

1. **Conversions.** How many (a) milligrams are there in a gram, (b) centimeters in a meter, (c) grams in a kilogram, (d) micrometers in a meter, (e) meters in a kilometer?

2. **Systems of measurement.** Give two reasons why the SI is easier to use than the British system.

3. **Conversions.** If a gallon of gasoline costs $1.25, how much would a liter cost?

4. **Conversions.** The speed of light is approximately 3×10^8 m/sec. How many cm/sec is that? Write the number in exponential and in longhand form.

5. **Conversions.** A European dress pattern calls for 3 m of fabric. How many yards would you have to buy to make the dress?

6. **Conversions.** The super-tanker Globtik Tokyo is approximately 1243 ft long. How long is that in meters? Express your answer in longhand and in exponential notation.

7. **Conversions.** There are approximately 32,000 aluminum cans in a ton of scrap. How many cans are there in 100 tons? Express your answer in exponential notation.

8. **Metric system.** Identify an object in your everyday experience that has: (a) a mass of 1 to 2 kg; (b) a mass of 1 to 2 g; (c) a length of 1 to 2 mm; (d) a length of 1 to 2 cm; (e) a length of 1 to 2 m; (f) a length of 1 to 2 km; (g) a volume of 1 to 2 cm^3; (h) a volume of 1 to 2 m^3.

9. **Conversions.** A football player is 6 ft tall; how tall is he in meters? in centimeters?

10. **Conversions.** The distance between New York and San Francisco is approximately 3000 mi. How far is that in kilometers?

11. **Conversions.** (a) A man can run a mile in 4 min; can he run a km in 4 min? (b) In the supermarket, hamburger costs about $1.50/lb. If you saw a kg of hamburger for sale for $1.50, would you buy it? (c) Would five people fit comfortably in a 10-ft boat? What about a 10-m boat?

12. **Metric system.** Imagine that a truck has a legal load capacity of 10,000 lb. How many 100-kg boxes could be carried within this load limit?

13. **Exponential notation.** (a) Write the following numbers in long numerical form: The diameter of a bacterium is about 10^{-4} cm. The radius of the Sun is 6.9×10^5 km. There are approximately 10^{11} stars in the Milky Way galaxy. (b) Write the following in exponential form: The temperature of the core of the Sun is approximately 15,000,000° C. The outer region of the Sun's atmosphere has a density of about 0.000000001 times that of the Earth's atmosphere.

CHAPTER 2

Motion is fundamental to all life, all being, and all change, for it is only through motion that small particles or large objects come together, interact, and diversify. The chapter opens with discussions of speed, velocity, and acceleration. The concept of force is then introduced. Newton's laws and the interrelationships among force, velocity, and acceleration are explored. Finally, two special cases, rotational and gravitational acceleration, are discussed.

MOTION

2.1 INTRODUCTION

When we approach the topic of motion we are all indeed in a fortunate position. Everyone who reads this book already understands most of the fundamental concepts of motion intuitively, and all that we must do here is to organize that understanding and define it more precisely. For example, everyone knows that it is harder to start or stop a freight train than a sports car. Why? Because the train is bigger, heavier, more massive. Later in this chapter we will introduce Newton's Second Law and will define the relationship between mass and acceleration concisely and exactly. This more precise treatment adds to our intuitive understanding, but, in learning the mathematics, let us not forget what we already know.

Ancient science was pursued by two different groups of people, often with little communication between them. On the one hand were the practical technologists—metallurgists who developed new alloys for harder tools and sharper weapons, architects who planned stronger and loftier structures, shipwrights who designed faster and sturdier boats. On the other hand were the philosophers, who dealt with what seemed to be less practical matters. In Athens, for example, Aristotle and his students pondered the question, "Why do planets and other celestial bodies appear to move in curves, while falling stones or flying arrows tend to move in more or less straight lines?" Aristotle reasoned that some objects had an "essence" that impelled them to move in circular paths, while the "essence" of other objects kept their paths straight. But thinking about the flight of arrows did not help an archer to shoot better. Later, in 1686, Sir Isaac Newton published his great work, *Principia*, in which he showed that all motion of all objects under any conditions obeys a few simple, readily understandable natural laws. The idea that a single set of laws simultaneously describes a planet in orbit and an arrow in flight and that the universe operates in an orderly and predictable fashion has been one of the greatest of all philosophical and scientific concepts. Not only was Newton's work a milestone in philosophy but also it established the mathematical framework for classical physics and for engineering.

Sir Isaac Newton

ARISTOTLE (384–322 BC)

Aristotle was a Greek philosopher, scientist, and educator. He was a student of the great philosopher Plato and the teacher of Alexander the Great, the man who was to conquer all the western world. Later in his life, Aristotle moved to Athens, where he taught for many years until he was exiled for his association with Alexander. Aristotle possessed a wide range of interests, and his writings covered such diverse topics as logic, ethics, politics, literary criticism, metaphysics, and natural science and philosophy. He constantly searched for unifying theories that explained diverse natural phenomena in terms of a few simple concepts. Unfortunately, many of his observations and experiments were incomplete, and some of his theories were erroneous. Even though many of his theories were later discarded, many of his observations, especially those in the biological sciences, were accurate, and his curiosity opened people's minds. The logic that Aristotle developed was an important step in the progression of science.

GALILEO GALILEI (1564–1642)

Galileo was an Italian mathematician, astronomer, and physicist who made three extremely important contributions to modern science. Perhaps the most significant was his realization that the laws of nature must be understood through experimentation and mathematical analysis. This concept ultimately freed scientists from the confining principles of Aristotelian thought and marked the beginning of modern physics. Using his own methods, Galileo informally stated certain laws of motion, including Newton's first two laws, and did pioneering work on the laws of gravitation. He was also the first man to use the telescope to study the skies. His work led him to the conclusion that the Earth revolves around the Sun and is not the center of the Universe.

In this chapter we will discuss three fundamental types of motion. **Translational motion** is the movement of an object from one place to another, like an arrow in flight. **Rotational motion** is exemplified by a spinning object such as a top, which does not actually travel from place to place. Instead the matter in the top moves around and around. A third type of motion is exhibited by an object such as a tuning fork or a guitar string, which can vibrate without being permanently displaced from its fixed position; this is **vibrational motion.**

2.2 SPEED

Average speed is defined simply as the distance an object moves divided by the time needed to travel this distance.

$$\text{Speed} = \frac{\text{distance}}{\text{time}} \qquad [2.1]$$

Scientists express speed in units like m/sec, cm/sec, km/hr, and mi/hr.

If an automobile travels 80 km in 1 hr, its average speed is 80 km per hr (80 km/hr). Of course a person in a car can travel 80 km in 1 hr by any of a variety of different driving modes. An expert driver on an open stretch of road might keep the car moving at exactly

Speed

80 km/hr all the time. His speed at any moment, or his **instantaneous speed,** is always 80 km/hr, and at the end of the hour he has traveled 80 km. An impatient driver operating in heavy traffic might be slowed down to 50 km/hr at times and then speed along at 100 km/hr for a while. If at the end of an hour he has traveled 80 km, we know that his **average speed** during that time was 80 km/hr although his instantaneous speed, registered by the speedometer on the car, varied considerably.

2.3 VELOCITY

The **velocity** of an object is a description of its *speed and the direction* in which it is moving. Thus if we say that a car is traveling at 80 km/hr, we are describing its speed, whereas if we say a car is traveling at 80 km/hr due east, we are describing its velocity. An object travels at a constant speed when its speed is unchanging, but it travels at a constant velocity only if speed and direction are both constant. Thus, if the speedometer of your car registers exactly 50 km/hr when rounding a curve, your speed is constant, but your velocity is changing.

The numerical component of velocity can be treated by using the same equations that we used to describe speed.

$$\overrightarrow{\text{Velocity}} = \frac{\overrightarrow{\text{distance}}}{\text{time}} \qquad [2.2]$$

or,

$$\vec{v} = \frac{\vec{d}}{t}$$

where

$\vec{v} = \overrightarrow{\text{velocity}}$
$\vec{d} = \overrightarrow{\text{distance}}$
$t = \text{time}$

We draw an arrow above the word velocity to remind us that to describe the velocity of an object we must describe both the speed and the *direction* in which that object is traveling.

Since velocity is a combination of speed and direction, we cannot describe velocity through the use of numbers alone. **Vector notation** has been developed as a convenient shorthand to describe magnitude and direction simultaneously. A vector quantity is simply a number representing magnitude combined with an arrow indicating direction. Thus the motion of a boat

SIR ISAAC NEWTON (1642–1727)

One of the greatest physicists of all times, Newton was the first person to recognize the law of universal gravitation. He developed the mathematics of calculus, formulated the basic laws of motion, and made great advances in the study of light, optics, and color. Combining his interest in optics with his studies of motion, he built the first reflecting telescope and used it in many astronomical studies.

Most of Newton's significant achievements were produced in a short period of time when he was in his early forties. As a child and later as a college student he was undistinguished. After publication of the studies of motion and optics, Newton avoided the scientific debate his theories aroused. He became a member of Parliament and master of the British mint, a job he held until his death.

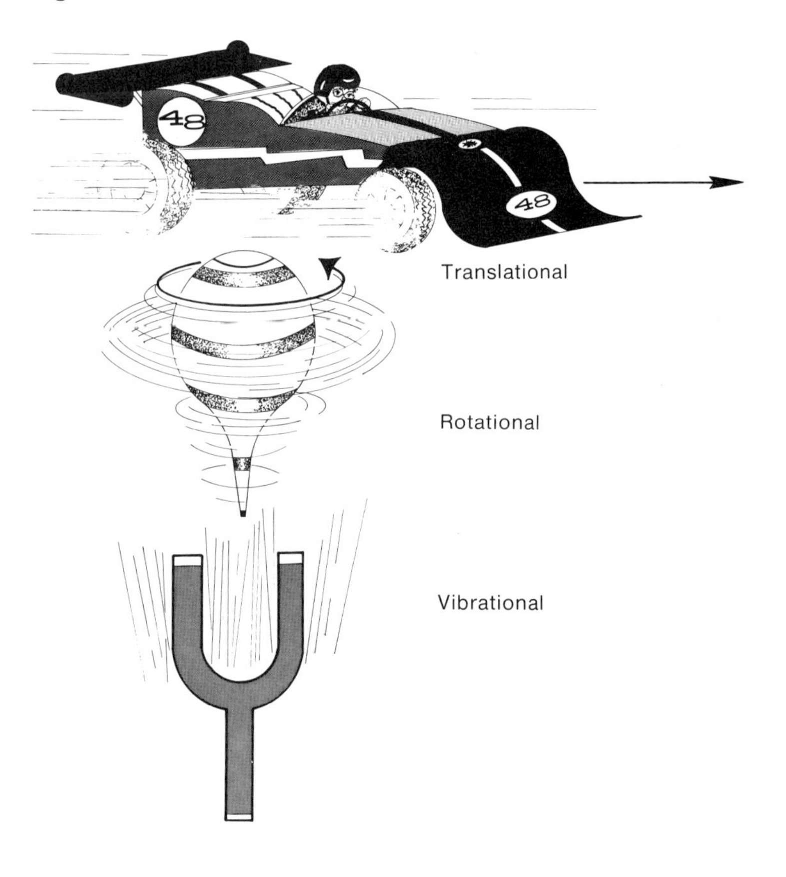

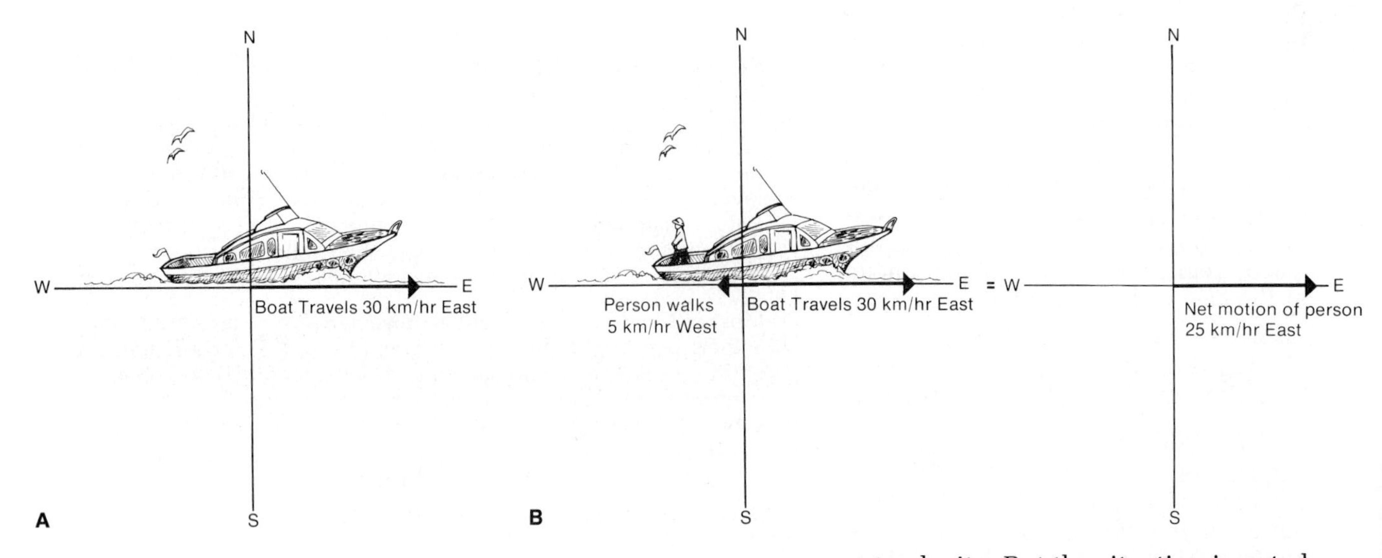

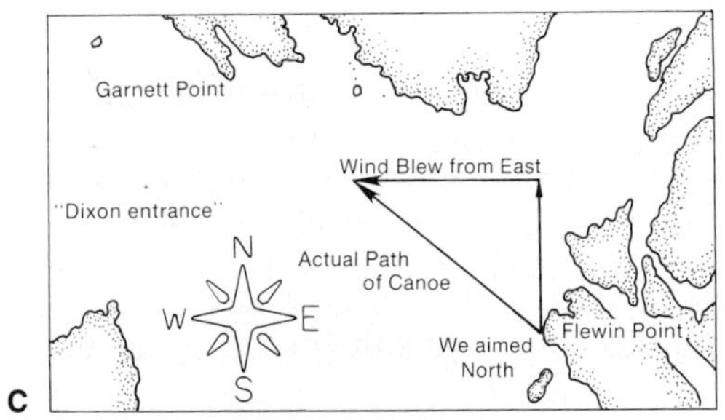

Figure 2–1. Vector notation.

traveling 30 km/hr east can be described on a graph as shown in Figure 2–1*A*.

Vectors can be added or subtracted to calculate more complex types of motion. Suppose, for example, that you are sailing on the boat just mentioned. The boat is traveling at a rate of 30 km/hr east. Now imagine that you are on deck, walking westward at a rate of 5 km/hr. Your motion with respect to an observer on land is a result of two movements, one eastward and one westward. Therefore, your net motion can be calculated by combining the vectors as shown in Figure 2–1*B*.

30 km/hr east − 5 km/hr west
= 25 km/hr east

In the previous example the two component velocities were directly opposite each other. Therefore we could subtract the two to calculate the resultant velocity. But the situation is not always so simple. Let us return to the example of our canoe crossing Dixon Entrance as discussed in Chapter 1. We were paddling due north while being blown westward. We paddled at a rate independent of the wind velocity and were blown along at a rate that did not depend on the forward speed. In this case, the two motions are not opposite; they are at right angles to each other. Obviously, if a canoeist is paddling northward and the wind is blowing westward, the canoe will travel toward the northwest. To calculate this velocity, we draw two component vectors, one northward and the other westward, as shown in Figure 2–1*C*. The *length* of each arrow represents the speed in the direction indicated by the arrow. Notice that the head of one component vector is connected to the tail of the other. To estimate the resultant velocity, we draw a third arrow from the base of one component vector to the point of the other. The direction of this resultant vector shows us that the canoe was traveling roughly northwest. Of course, the boat did not move first northward and then westward, it traveled in a straight path, as shown by the diagonal arrow in the figure.

To estimate the actual resultant velocity, draw the component vectors on a sheet of graph paper. Let the northward component be 3.5 cm long and the westward one 4.8 cm. Draw the resultant vector and measure it with your ruler. It will be about 5.9 cm long, showing that the resultant velocity of the canoe was 5.9 km/hr northwest.

2.4 ACCELERATION

Acceleration is the change in velocity per unit of time. If a body is moving at 30 km/hr in some given direction, and reaches a speed of 80 km/hr in the same direction 1 hr later, its velocity has increased by 50 km/hr in 1 hr. We say that its acceleration has been 50 km per hr in an hr, on 50 km per hr per hr, or 50 km/hr^2. In equation form,

$$\overrightarrow{\text{acceleration}} = \frac{\overrightarrow{\text{change in velocity}}}{\text{time}} \qquad [2.3]$$

Most people are familiar with the fact that an object is accelerating when it is "speeding up." We call the gas pedal on a car the accelerator because we use that device to make the car go faster. To the physicist, however, slowing down is also a form of acceleration. In common usage we say that an object which is slowing down is decelerating. In other words, if an object speeds up from 30 km/hr to 80 km/hr in 1 hr, its acceleration is +50 km per hr per hr (+50 km/hr^2). If the same object slows down from 80 km/hr to 30 km/hr in 1 hr, its acceleration is −50 km per hr per hr (−50 km/hr^2).

Recall that velocity is a description of the speed and direction of an object. Therefore, if an object moving at constant speed changes direction, the velocity also changes. Since acceleration is a change in velocity, a body moving at constant speed around a curve is accelerating. This concept may seem confusing at first until we think of it in human terms. We will learn in a later section that an object will accelerate only if forced to do so. Think of a situation in which you are changing direction. Perhaps you may recall sitting in a bus, car, or train when it is rounding a corner. You may feel the sides of the vehicle press against your shoulder as various forces cause you to change your direction and therefore your velocity. Starting, stopping, and turning are all forms of acceleration.

A drag racer accelerating. (Courtesy of Petersen Publishing Co.)

There is an organ inside the human ear that senses acceleration and relays that sensation to the brain. It is interesting to note, however, that the ear cannot differentiate among various forms of acceleration. For example, in the absence of other stimuli, you cannot tell whether you are speeding up or turning. People who ski the open treeless expanses of tall mountains occasionally become engulfed in such heavy, white fog that they have no visual reference points and must ski as if they were blind. If ever in that situation, you will suddenly realize that it is difficult to tell whether you are turning or skiing straight downhill. Your senses indicate that you are accelerating, but without sight you can't tell

It is easy to remember that speeding up is *plus* and slowing down is *minus*. But if this convention sounds mysterious to you, and you prefer to be more logical, then we can simply define a *change in velocity* as follows:

$$\text{change in velocity} = \text{final velocity} - \text{initial velocity}$$

and therefore,

$$\text{acceleration} = \frac{\text{final velocity} - \text{initial velocity}}{\text{time}}$$

In the speeding-up example,

$$\text{acceleration} = \frac{80\ \text{km/hr} - 30\ \text{km/hr}}{1\ \text{hr}} = +50\ \text{km/hr}^2$$

In the slowing-down example,

$$\text{acceleration} = \frac{30\ \text{km/hr} - 80\ \text{km/hr}}{1\ \text{hr}} = -50\ \text{km/hr}^2$$

whether the acceleration is forward or angular. I, Jon, have been caught in such a fog and simply didn't know in which direction my skis were pointing with respect to the slope of the hill, didn't know how to distribute my weight to maintain balance, and frequently found myself toppling over unexpectedly. Airplane pilots experience the same sensation. A pilot who is flying through a cloud out of sight of land without the use of instruments cannot distinguish between the sensation of turning and accelerating.

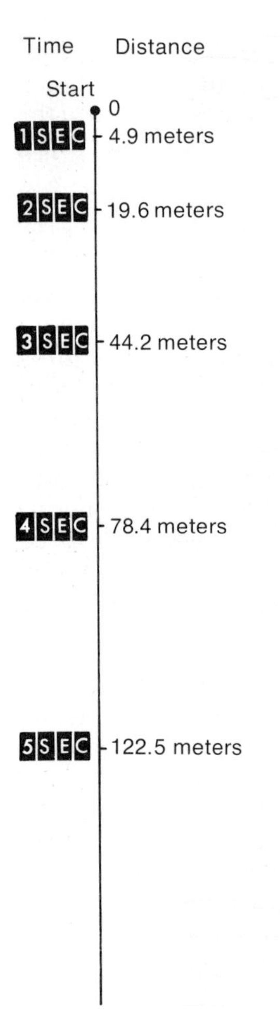

Distance traveled by a falling object.

2.5 ACCELERATION OF A FALLING OBJECT

A popular legend tells how Sir Isaac Newton was sitting under an apple tree one day when an apple fell on his head and—presto—he discovered gravity. Of course, people knew long before Sir Isaac Newton was born that unsupported objects fall to the ground. Exactly what, then, did he discover? Newton was the first person to recognize gravity as a universal force. He realized that a single equation could be used to describe the motion of both terrestrial objects such as apples falling to Earth and much larger objects such as planets in orbit. Much of the early work on the motion of small objects falling to Earth was solved earlier by Galileo. In Section 2.6 we will discuss some of the consequences of Newton's realizations that gravitation is a universal force, but now we are concerned with the motion of a free-falling body.

Imagine that there is some object suspended in the air, such as an apple hanging on a branch. Since it is stationary, its velocity is zero. Then at some instant the stem breaks and the apple starts falling. As it falls its velocity constantly increases; it is moving faster after 2 sec than after 1 sec, and faster still after 3 sec. In fact, its velocity is increasing from instant to instant. The instantaneous velocity of a body falling freely from rest can be calculated according to the equation:

$$\overrightarrow{\text{velocity}} = \overrightarrow{\begin{matrix}\text{(acceleration} \\ \text{due to gravity)}\end{matrix}} \times \text{time} \quad [2.4]$$

Physicists use the letter g to represent the acceleration due to gravity and t to represent time. Thus, the equation above can be written:

$$v = g \times t$$

At the surface of the Earth the acceleration due to gravity is a constant and is equal to $\dfrac{9.8\,\dfrac{\text{m}}{\text{sec}}}{\text{sec}}$, or 9.8 m/sec². Thus the velocity* after 1 sec is:

$$v = 9.8\,\frac{\text{m}}{\text{sec}^2} \times 1\ \text{sec} = 9.8\ \text{m/sec}$$

*All these velocity vectors are directed straight downward. These figures do not take air resistance into account. They apply accurately in a vacuum.

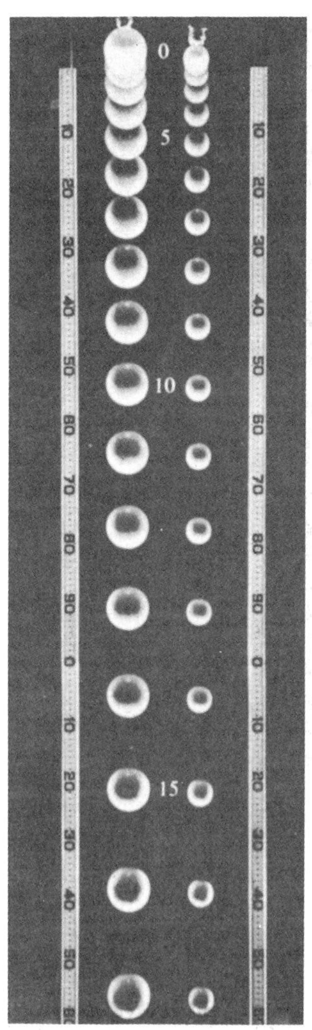

A stroboscopic photograph of a baseball and a golf ball released simultaneously. The time interval between photographs was 1/30 second. (From *PSSC Physics,* D. C. Heath and Company, Lexington, Mass., 1965.)

after 1.1 sec,

$$v = 9.8 \frac{m}{sec^2} \times 1.1 \text{ sec} = 10.8 \text{ m/sec}$$

after 2.0 sec,

$$v = 9.8 \frac{m}{sec^2} \times 2.0 \text{ sec} = 19.6 \text{ m/sec}$$

after 3.0 sec,

$$v = 9.8 \frac{m}{sec^2} \times 3.0 \text{ sec} = 29.4 \text{ m/sec}$$

after 4.0 sec,

$$v = 9.8 \frac{m}{sec^2} \times 4.0 \text{ sec} = 39.2 \text{ m/sec}$$

and after 10 sec,

$$v = 9.8 \frac{m}{sec^2} \times 10 \text{ sec} = 98.0 \text{ m/sec}$$

Let us focus our attention for the moment on the constant term g, the acceleration due to gravity. The value of g, which has been determined experimentally, tells us that the velocity of any freely falling body on the earth will increase by 9.8 m/sec every second. There is an interesting story behind this number. The great Greek philosopher Aristotle believed that natural laws could be understood by logical reasoning alone and that experimentation was largely unnecessary. Aristotle reasoned that a heavy body must necessarily fall faster than a light body, and his reasoning was held to be fact. Two thousand years later, the Italian scientist Galileo Galilei questioned this conclusion and decided to test it by a direct experiment. It is said that he took two objects, a heavy one and a light one, up to the top of the Leaning Tower of Pisa and dropped them together. They both hit the earth at the same

Heavy objects and light objects fall at the same rate.

time. In other words, the acceleration of a freely falling body is not determined by the weight of the object but is equal for all objects. Galileo realized that fluttery objects like feathers or paper fall more slowly than compact objects like blocks of wood or stone, but he concluded correctly that air resistance and wind currents retarded the fall of the fluttery objects and that in the absence of air, feathers would fall as rapidly as stones. In fact, one common laboratory demonstration is to place a marble and a feather inside an evacuated glass tube. The tube is then flipped upside down and a person can observe how quickly the two objects fall. Since there is no air in the tube, both the marble and the feather fall at the same rate and hit the bottom at exactly the same time.

2.6 INERTIA, FORCE, AND THE FIRST LAW OF MOTION

Most of the objects that we deal with in our everyday lives—cars, boats, washing machines, billiard balls, people—lie at rest at least part of the time. Since many of them move on occasion, they must start up and slow down. In other words, they must accelerate from a zero velocity at rest to some other velocity and then decelerate back to zero. We are interested in the physics of starting and stopping. Think of anything lying at rest—the electronic calculator on your desk, or a round ball on a smooth table. You watch it and watch it and it doesn't move. If you want it to move, you have to push it. In fact, no object will ever start to move spontaneously; it must be acted upon first by some push or pull. In more scientific terms, the pushes and pulls that make things move are called **forces,** and an object at rest will remain at rest until it is forced to move.

Now, what happens to an object once it has been set into motion? We know from experience that all objects stop after a while. The Greek philosophers concluded that it was natural for objects to be at rest and that therefore all objects eventually stopped moving in order to resume their natural static state. But Galileo, and later Newton, were puzzled. If a force was required to give an object a positive acceleration, wouldn't a force also be required to give it a negative acceleration? Since one force was required to push a block of wood across a level floor, another force must be required to stop it. This stopping force might be exerted by a person or an obstacle. Thus, if a block of wood is sliding across the floor, a person who wished to stop it would be required to push (exert a force) against it. But even in the absence of such ob-

A, An object at rest remains at rest—until acted upon by some outside force (B).

TIGER

vious forces, the block of wood eventually will be brought to rest. The invisible force producing this result is called **friction.**

What is friction? Friction is a force that always acts to oppose motion. It occurs because objects are never perfectly smooth. Suppose, for example, that we magnified the surfaces of a block of wood and the floor on which it was sliding. Both surfaces would be jagged and irregular, as shown in Figure 2–2. For the block to slide it must either rise over the bumps or break them off, and either act requires force. Even very smooth objects have tiny, molecular or atomic-sized irregularities. As one object is moved across the other, the atoms themselves can cling together and oppose the motion.

Imagine what would happen if there were no friction. Think of a block of wood sliding across an infinitely long and perfectly smooth floor in a vacuum. It would slide and slide in a straight line and never stop. If we wanted to stop it, we would have to exert a force against it. Similarly, a force must be exerted against the block to change its direction. Newton recognized that a body accelerates only when a force is applied to it. This observation was summarized in his First Law of Motion, which can be stated as follows:

A body at rest remains at rest, and a body in uniform motion in a straight line remains in such motion, unless acted upon by some outside force.

All matter has this built-in quality, which compels it to remain at rest or at constant velocity (constant speed and direction) unless forced to change. This quality or property of matter is known as **inertia.**

Inertia is closely related to mass. A large, massive object has more inertia than a smaller, less massive one. This relationship will be discussed further in the next section.

Let us examine a few consequences of inertia. Imagine that you are standing in a bus. As long as the bus remains motionless (0 velocity) you can stand at ease. Now what happens if the bus starts to move (accelerate) rapidly? The standing passengers appear to "fall" backwards. Why does this happen? Actually, the passengers aren't "falling" anywhere. When both the passenger and the bus are at rest, each tends to remain at rest, according to the First Law. When the driver presses down on the gas pedal, the engine forces the bus to move. However, the bus doesn't exert enough force on the passenger to accelerate him at the same rate, and the vehicle tends to slide out from under the person. The passenger doesn't accelerate as fast as the bus, and therefore, to an outside observer, it appears that the passenger is falling backwards.

Figure 2–2. Magnified view of surfaces of floor and block of wood.

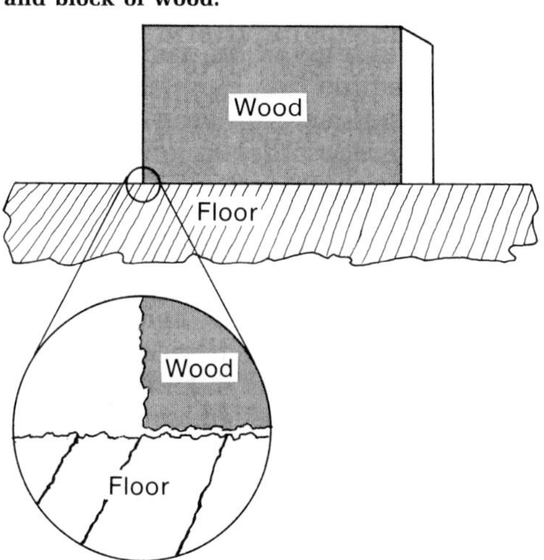

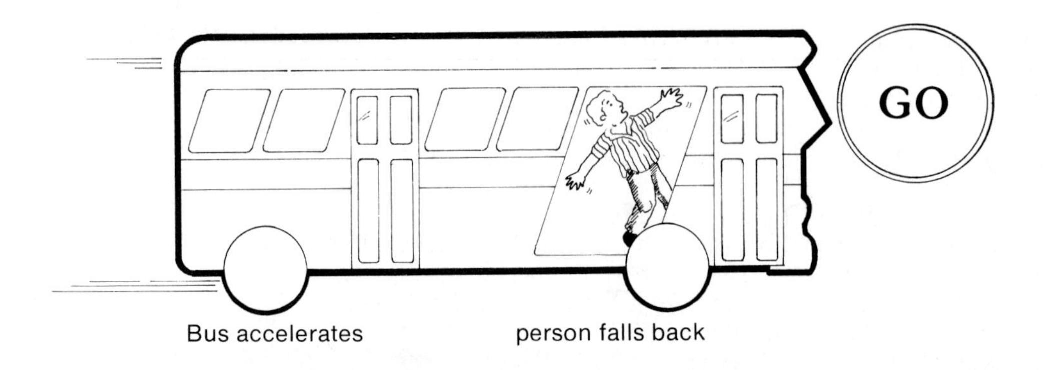

The acceleration of the bus affects the passengers inside.

After the bus has reached a constant velocity, say 70 km/hr down a straight road, the passenger can stand at ease once again. The person and the bus are moving along together and according to the First Law, "a body in uniform motion in a straight line remains in such motion." If the bus slows down suddenly, the person would appear to be thrown forward. Once again, the rider isn't thrown anywhere, the brakes exert a force on the bus but the person continues to move at a constant velocity until forced to slow down. If the bus were to stop very suddenly, as by hitting a stone wall, the inertia of the unlucky passenger would cause him to fly through the air in a straight line until he hit something that resisted him. Similarly, when the bus turns sharply, the person tends to continue to move in a straight line and he sways sideways with respect to the bus. In each case the motion of the person in the bus is affected by the acceleration of the bus. Remember, starting stopping, and turning are all forms of acceleration.

Many aspects and consequences of inertia were understood long before Newton formulated his laws of motion. However, people did not appreciate the fact that all objects have inertia. For centuries, astronomers had known that various heavenly bodies move in curved orbits, but as mentioned earlier, Aristotle had decreed that circular motion was "natural" for these bodies. What Newton realized was that the laws of motion must be the same for all objects, large and small, and therefore that all moving bodies "naturally" tend to travel in straight paths. If planets have an inertial drive to move in straight lines, why do they, in fact, move in nearly circular orbits? Newton reasoned that something must be continuously forcing them to turn and that this mysterious force must be the gravitational pull of the Sun. This realization that the same universal force that causes an apple to fall also causes the planets to orbit was a milestone in physics.

2.7 FORCE AND MOTION—NEWTON'S SECOND LAW

Knowing that a body will accelerate only if forced to do so is valuable in itself, but then we ask ourselves, "How much force is required to cause a given object to accelerate at a given rate?" We realize that even in the absence of friction, more force is required to move a stalled automobile than a toy wagon. Generalizing, we realize intuitively that massive objects are harder to accelerate than are smaller, less massive ones. Therefore, the massive objects have more inertia. The **mass** of an object is defined as the quantity of matter in it, as determined by its inertia—its resistance to change in velocity. An object that can be forced to change velocity easily has a small mass, and an object that changes velocity slowly when acted upon by that same outside force has a large mass.

Notice that we have not defined mass in terms of weight, even though an object with a lot of mass is also heavy. *Mass and weight are different.* Weight is the force of gravity upon an object. When that object has escaped the force of gravity, it becomes weightless. But a weightless object still has mass.

To illustrate the distinction between mass and weight, imagine two astronauts. One is a woman with a mass of 50 kg, and the other is a man with a mass of 75 kg. Before they leave Earth for a mission to the far reaches of outer space, they are each given ice skates, taken to a perfectly smooth frozen pond, and asked to position themselves against a stone wall. There are two equally coiled springs on the wall, as shown in Figure 2–3. The springs are

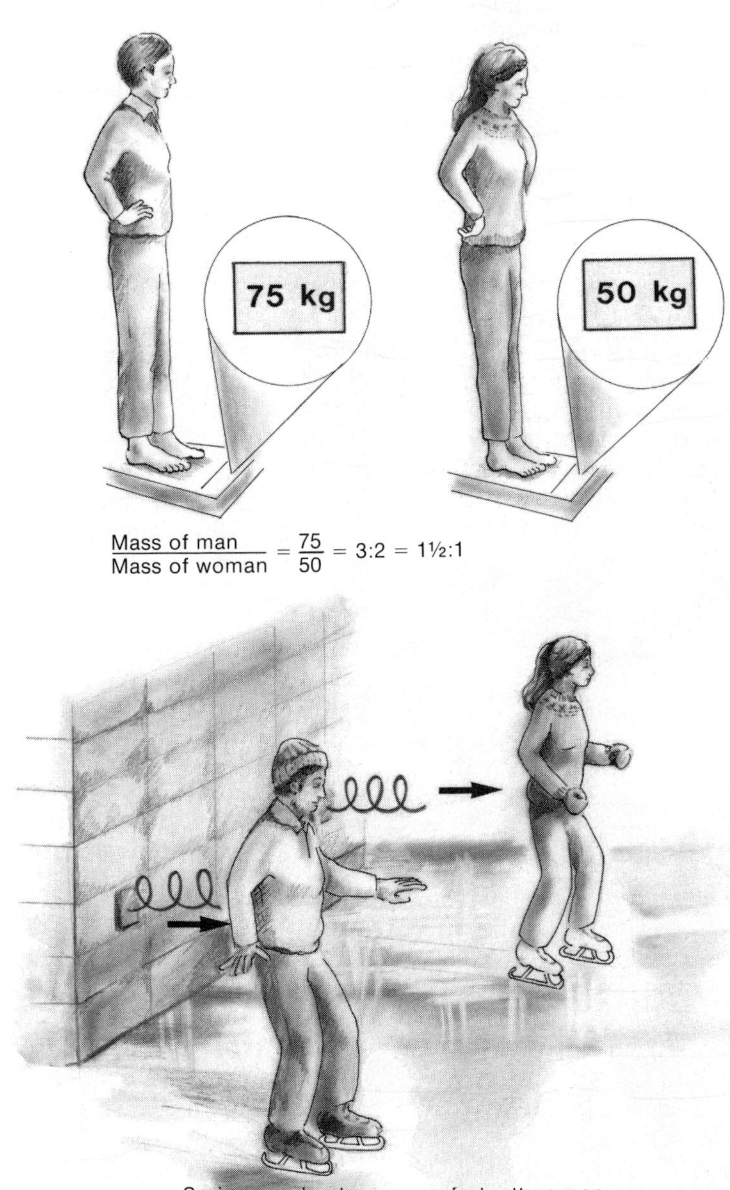

Figure 2–3. Mass and weight.

released, pushing the two astronauts forward across the ice. The woman will accelerate across the ice faster than the man does because she is less massive, and a given force will accelerate her faster. Now both astronauts board the rocket ship and take off for parts unknown. Once they are in free space, both are weightless. But neither has lost any mass. They have not gotten skinnier; they still have inertia. If there were two coiled springs on one wall of the spaceship and the astronauts were placed against the springs and both were released simultaneously, the woman would again be accelerated faster than her partner. In fact, the mass and inertia of both people would be the same in the rocket as it was on Earth. To carry the principle one step further, the gravitation pull on the Moon is only one sixth as great as that on Earth. Both people weigh less on the Moon than they do on Earth, but their mass and

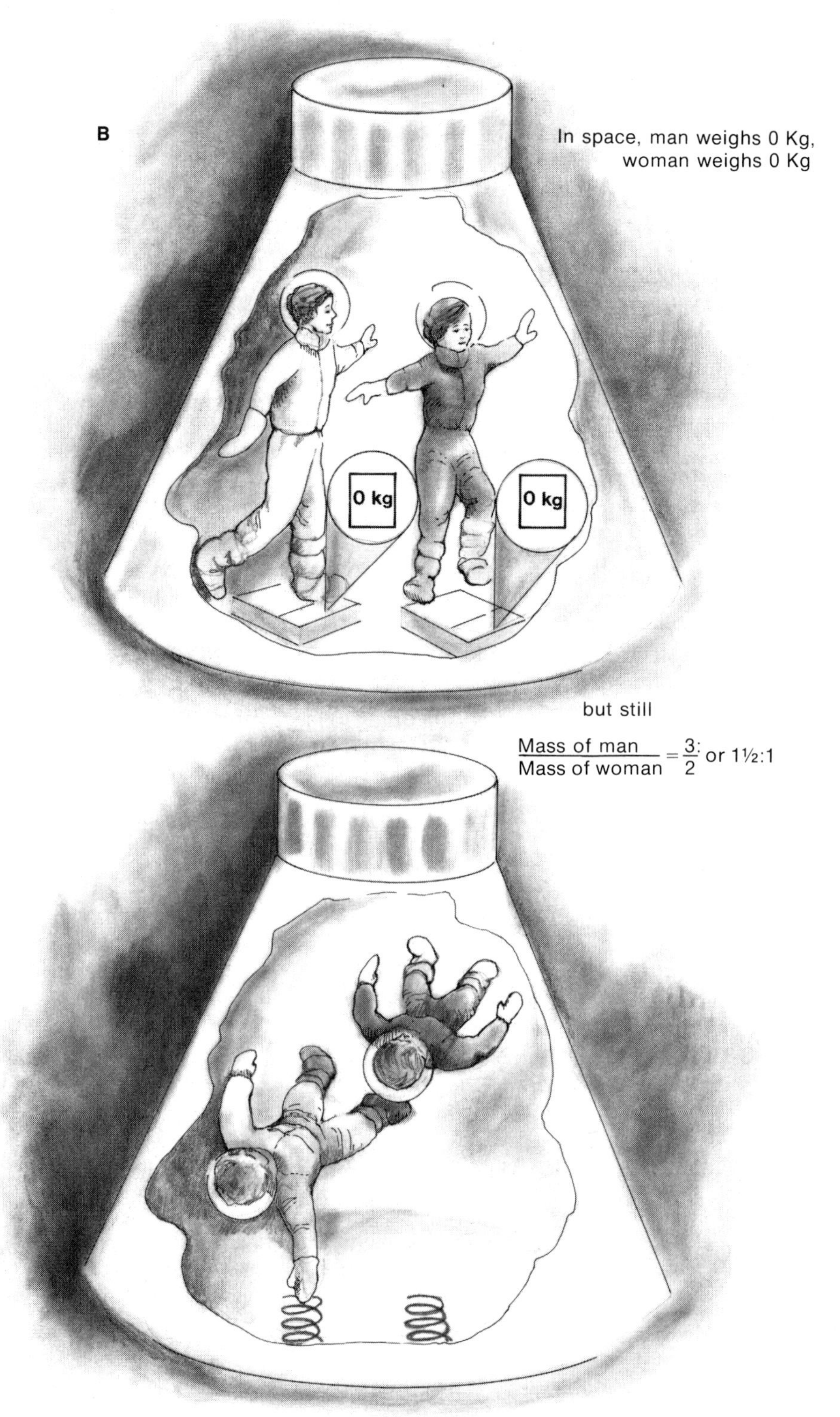

Spring accelerates woman faster than man

A man standing on the Moon weighs only 1/6 as much as he weighs on Earth, but his mass is unchanged. (Courtesy of NASA.)

inertia are the same as on the Earth or in free space.

It should now be obvious that the weight of an object is dependent on its location, whereas its mass is an inherent property. The weight of an object is the *force* exerted on it by the Earth's gravity.

In our discussion so far we have defined acceleration as a rate of change in the velocity of an object. When we came to describe force and mass we had to describe these concepts in terms of acceleration. A force is a push or a pull that causes something to accelerate. The mass of an object is defined as its inertia, or its resistance to acceleration. Newton recognized the interrelationships among force, mass, and acceleration and summarized them in his Second Law of Motion.

The acceleration of an object is directly proportional to the net force acting upon it and inversely proportional to the mass of the object.

If the proper units are selected, Newton's Second Law can be stated in equation form:

$$\overrightarrow{\text{acceleration}} = \frac{\overrightarrow{\text{force}}}{\text{mass}} \qquad [2.5]$$

or

$$\overrightarrow{\text{force}} = \text{mass} \times \overrightarrow{\text{acceleration}} \qquad [2.6]$$

or, in symbols,

$$\vec{F} = m\,\vec{a}$$

If mass is expressed in kilograms, and acceleration is expressed in m/sec^2, force will be expressed in newtons. One newton is the force needed to give

---

The relationship between mass and weight can be shown clearly using Newton's Second Law. If you are standing on Earth you are accelerated downward by the acceleration of gravity, g. Therefore, you exert a force on the Earth equal to

$$F = mg$$

Note that this is just a special case of the Second Law, where the acceleration is a constant, g. But the force in this case is simply your weight, so we can rewrite the equation as

$$\text{Weight} = \text{mass} \times \text{acceleration due to gravity}$$

or

$$W = mg$$

---

a mass of 1 kg an acceleration of 1 m/sec^2.

$$\text{force} = \text{mass} \times \text{acceleration}$$

$$1 \text{ newton} = 1 \text{ kg} \times \frac{\text{m}}{\text{sec}^2}$$

A newton (N) is the metric unit of force, and as such can be compared with the British unit of force, the pound. There is some confusion in comparing British and metric units of force and mass because people in the United States commonly buy commodities such as meat and vegetables by the pound, whereas Europeans buy these same goods by the kilogram. A pound is a unit of force, and therefore a unit of weight, and a kilogram is a unit of mass. The two can be compared on Earth at sea level, but in any other place in the Universe the comparison is invalid.

One N = 0.225 lb; or a 1 lb loaf of bread weighs approximately 4 N.

If we push an object with a slight force, it will accelerate slowly; if we push the same object with a greater force, it will accelerate more rapidly. Conversely, if we have two objects, a light one and a heavy one, and we push them with the same force, the light object will accelerate faster than the heavy one. Of course, this idea was well understood and utilized in practical ways long before Newton developed it mathematically. For example, since ancient times people have known that one could separate a mixture of light and heavy objects by applying equal forces to all of them and collecting the objects of different masses at various distances from the applied force. Inertial separators have been used since the beginning of recorded history. When wheat is harvested, the wheat berry is encased in a small husk and surrounded by leaves and other inedible plant parts. To thresh the grain, the farmer must separate the heavier, denser berry from the lighter, fluffier chaff. Traditionally, this has been done in a two-step operation. First the farmer beats the wheat stalks, thereby breaking up the plant and disconnecting the wheat berry from the other plant parts. Now the farmer has a mixed pile of wheat kernels and various pieces of chaff. He could pick out the kernels by hand, but that would be tedious. Instead, in the age before machines, farmers would wait for a windy day and toss the whole mixture straight up into the air. The light, fluffy chaff would be caught by the wind, be forced to accelerate rapidly, and be blown away. On the other hand, the heavy, dense kernels have greater mass and therefore are not blown away. Rather, they fall back downward into a pile, where they can be collected easily.

Threshing Wheat in the Old Days

Threshing wheat in the mountains in Peru.

Modern wheat threshers (called combines) operate on the same principle, but the action is mechanical.

2.8 FORCE AND NET FORCE

A force is defined as any influence that can cause a body to accelerate. Furthermore, we all have an intuitive understanding of force as being a push or a pull. Yet our common experience tells us that we can push or pull something without accelerating it. Try to push a dump truck, your house, or the Rock of Gibraltar—it simply does not move. So while it is true that every acceleration must be produced by a force, it is not true that every force produces an acceleration.

Imagine that two people of equal strength are arm-wrestling as shown in the accompanying photograph. If the person on the left is pushing one way with a force of 300 N, and the person on the right is pushing the other way with a force of 300 N, what happens? There is no movement, because one force balances the other. We say that the total or **net force** on the people's hands is zero. To calculate the acceleration of an object we must add up all the forces acting on it. At this point let us reexamine Newton's Second Law of Motion: "The acceleration of an object is directly proportional to the *net force* acting upon it and inversely proportional to the mass of the object." We emphasize the words *net force* here and ask, what is a net force and how does it differ from a force? A force is any push or pull. The net force is the sum of all the pushes and pulls acting together on a single object. Imagine that a car is perched on top of a hill. If gravity pulls on this car with a force of 15,000 N, and there is a 1000-N frictional drag, the car will accelerate at the same rate as if there were no friction and it had been pulled downward by a 14,000-N force.

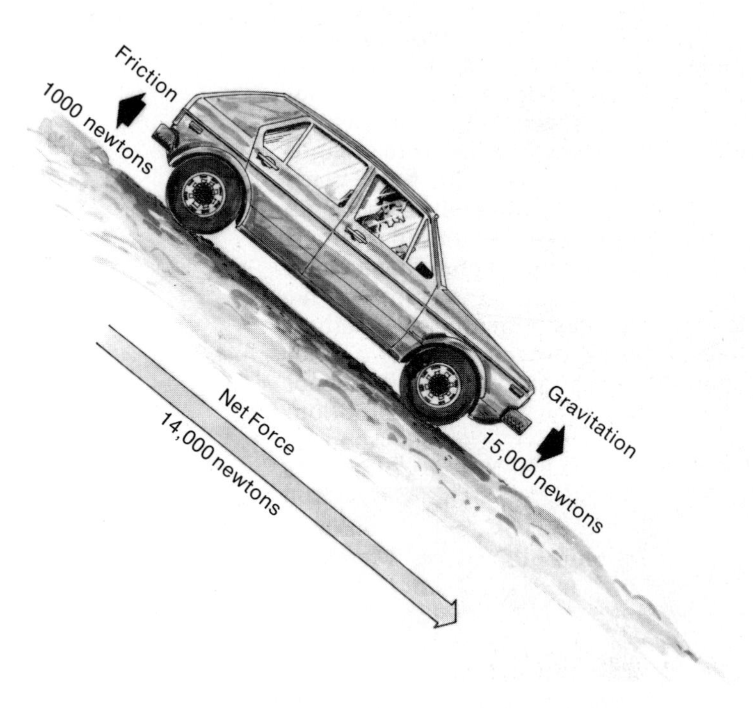

2.9 ACTION AND REACTION—THE THIRD LAW OF MOTION

In discussing motion we have focused our attention on the moving body and have virtually ignored the object that exerted the force and caused the motion. For instance, we were interested in the falling apple but ignored the Earth, which pulled it downward. Now let us widen our vision and study a total system. Imagine that you were a rock climber scaling a steep cliff. You reach up and grab a handhold. Now think about it; in order to

Figure 2–4. Action and reaction. The rock climber pulls down on the rock, and the rock pushes upward on the climber.

stay up, you pull *downward* on that handhold. This downward pull, by itself, doesn't hold you up in the air. But when you pull *down* on the rock, the rock pushes *up* on you with an equal and opposite force. It is this upward force that actually works against gravity so that you don't fall.

Forces always operate in pairs, and Newton's Third Law of Motion states that

For every force there is always an equal and opposite force.

The Third Law is often rephrased to read:

For every action there is always an equal and opposite reaction.

In other words, whenever something pushes or pulls, it is being pulled or pushed in turn. If you pull down on the rock with a force of 700 N, it pushes back on you with an equal force. If the handhold were loose and broke off, the upward force would suddenly be reduced to zero, and you would fall.

The practical reality of Newton's Third Law is forever with us in daily life. If you jump out of a boat, you exert a force on the boat and it moves backward. This occurs because the boat cannot push you forward unless you force it backward. Similarly, when a skier turns (accelerates), the snow must exert a force against the skis to make them turn, but the skis must also exert a force against the snow. Part of the force exerted on the snow by the skis causes a plume of snow to fly into the air.

A car jack, which is used to lift an automobile to change a flat tire, always

For every action there is an equal and opposite reaction.

has a broad base. Why? Because when the car is forced upward, the jack is forced downward. If the downward force is directed over too small an area, the jack will accelerate downward and will bury itself in the ground. A broad base distributes the downward force so that the jack will not sink. The base of a jack is designed to enable it to lift a car above a solid roadway. If you ever get stuck in the mud and have to jack up a car to free a wheel, remember Newton's Third Law and place a broad flat board or rock under the jack to widen its base.

Sometimes it is difficult to appreciate the pairs of forces that must always exist. For instance, if you drop a marble toward the Earth, there is a force directed on the marble by the Earth, and the marble falls down. But there must also be a force exerted on the Earth by the marble, and the Earth is pulled up to the marble. Because of the vast differences in size, the Earth does not accelerate very much—certainly too little to be measured—but we know that it does move!

2.10 ROTATIONAL MOTION

If you are cruising down a straight road in a comfortable car, there are no pushes or pulls acting upon your body, and you can be relaxed and at ease. On the other hand, whenever you turn a corner, there are always various forces acting on the car and on the people in it. If you are driving, you must hold the steering wheel more tightly, and your muscles also tighten somewhat. Perhaps you even lean into the turn a bit or, if you are a passenger, you may reach out and touch the dashboard to

Suppose you were becalmed on a lake in a sailboat and had a large battery-operated fan. Could you aim the fan at the sail and blow yourself home?

Answer:

No, it would not work. In the process of blowing air against the sail, the fan exerts a force against the air itself. But the air pushes backward on the fan simultaneously, so the force of the wind in the sails is balanced by the backward thrust of the air against the fan, and the boat remains stationary. However, you could make the boat go forward by taking down the sail, turning the fan around, and blowing air out of the back of the boat. Then the force of the air on the fan would push the boat forward.

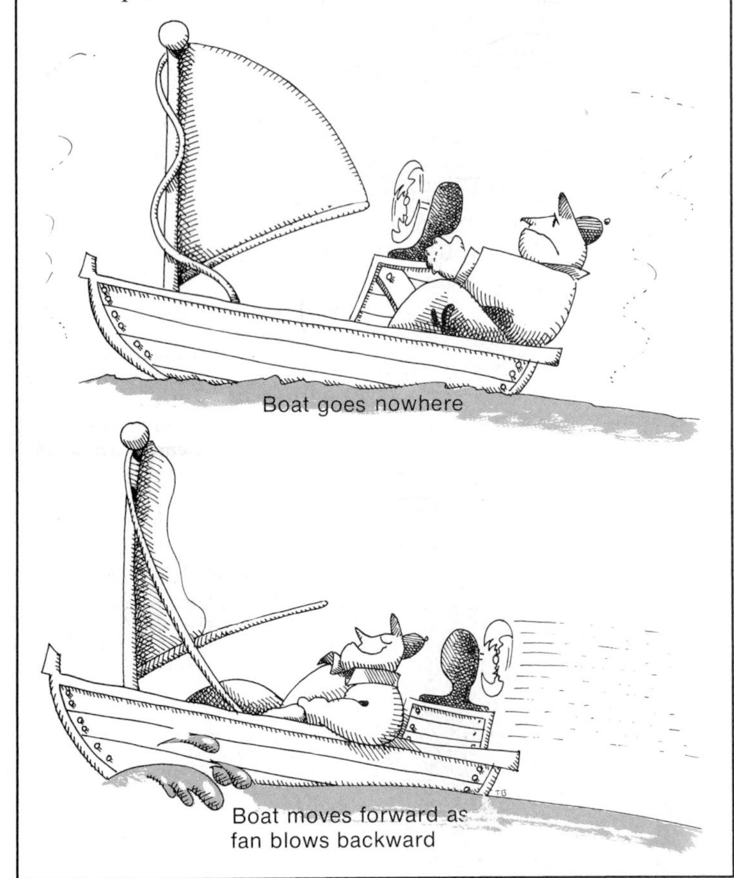

TIGER

keep you from sliding across the seat. These forces arise because any object that is traveling along a curved path has a changing velocity and is therefore accelerating.

A man and his dog are running parallel to each other, separated by a leash, as shown in the accompanying drawing. Suddenly, the man gets tired and stops, but holds on to the leash nevertheless. The dog keeps running, always trying to continue in a forward motion. What happens? Even though the dog keeps running, it can't continue along its straight path, for the leash pulls it inward. As a result, the animal will travel in a circle. The man is exerting a force on the dog causing it to move in a curved path. If the man let go of the leash, the dog could continue to run in a straight line.

As another example, consider a woman whirling a stone attached to a string over her head. In order to hold the stone in a circular path, the woman must continuously exert a force on it. If she let go of the string, the stone would fly off in a straight line, for the inertial tendency of all moving bodies is to continue moving without changing direction.* The inward force that is necessary to keep the object in circular motion is called a **centripetal force.** This force causes the object to change its direction and therefore its velocity. It therefore leads to an inward or **centripetal acceleration.**

Many people find it confusing to think that an object can be accelerating towards the center of a circle yet never get there. To convince yourself that it is really true, think of the dog mentioned before.The man is continuously pulling inward but the dog always remains one leash length away; it does not move inward towards the center.

Let us return now to the whirling stone. The centripetal force causes the stone to curve inward and revolve in a circle. But recall that for every action there must always be an equal and opposite reaction. The string exerts a reaction force on your hand and this is called a **centrifugal force.** Note that the

*We are assuming that the woman is in free space, so gravity is not pulling downward on the stone.

"Centripetal" comes from the Latin roots *centrum* (center) and *petere* (to seek, to rush toward). Think of the word *impetus,* derived from the same root, which means an impulse, a stimulus, a moving force. Thus, *centripetal* refers to a force that causes an acceleration towards the center.

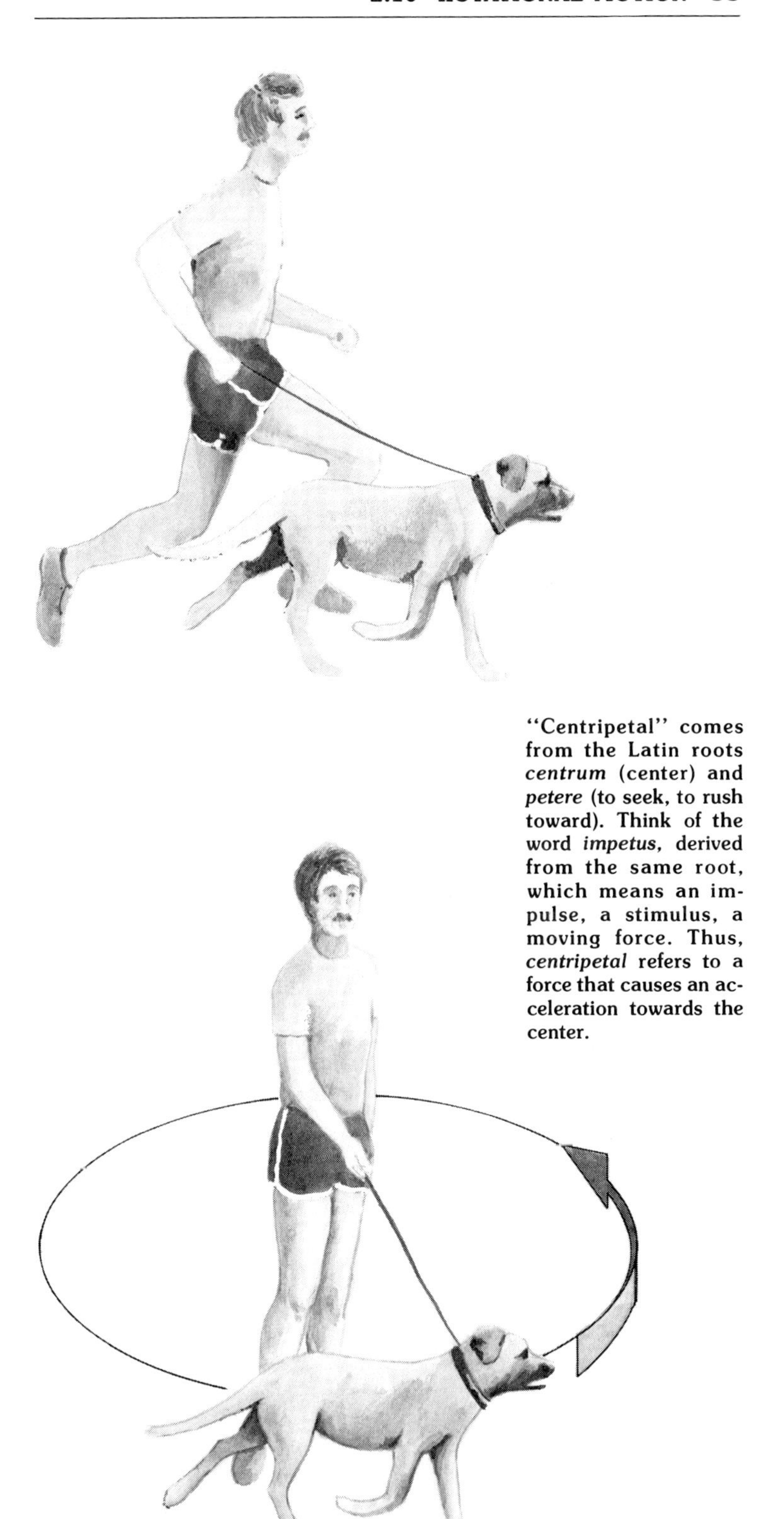

***A*, A man and a dog running together. *B*, The man stops and holds the leash, but the dog keeps running. The dog is now constrained to run in a circle.**

sole force acting on the stone is the centripetal force. It is a common misconception to say that a spinning stone is held out on the end of the string by centrifugal force. The stone is not held out at all. If left to its own inertia, it would fly away. The string holds it in; the center-seeking centripetal force forces the stone to move in a circle.

As one final example, suppose you place a beachball in the back of a flatbed truck that has no sides. If the truck rounds a turn, the ball will continue along its inertial straight path and fly off, as shown in Figure 2–5. Now imagine that we place sideboards on the truck and repeat the experiment. The ball will now be held on the truck; the sideboards exert a centripetal (inward) force on the ball to push it into circular motion and cause it to round the curve. The force exerted *on* the outside of the truck *by* the ball is a centrifugal force.

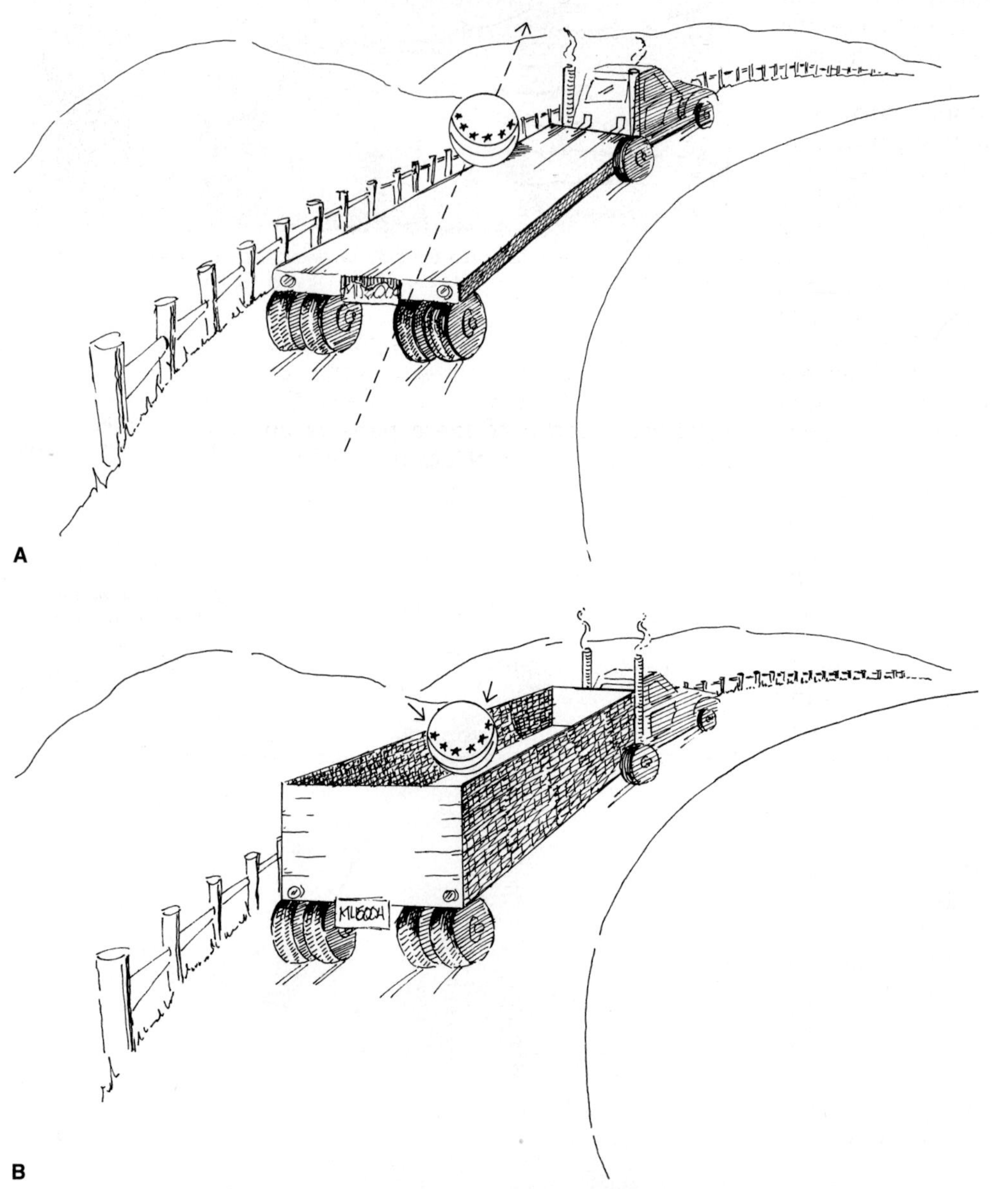

Figure 2–5. ***A***, **If a beachball is on the back of a flatbed truck and the truck rounds a turn, the ball will follow its inertial tendency to go straight and fly off.** ***B***, **The sideboards on this truck exert an inward (centripetal) force on the ball, causing it to round the curve. The force exerted *on* the outside of the truck *by* the ball is a centrifugal force.**

2.11 ROTATIONAL INERTIA

If you turn a bicycle upside down and spin a wheel, the wheel will continue to turn after you take your arm away. Similarly, most power tools such as circular saws, grinders, or food blenders will continue to spin after the power has been disconnected. Thus, just as an object at rest tends to remain at rest and an object in uniform linear motion tends to remain in uniform linear motion, a stationary wheel tends to remain stationary and a rotating wheel tends to continue rotating at a constant speed unless acted on by some outside force. This tendency is known as **rotational inertia.**

The inertia of spinning objects is utilized in a great many applications. For example, a skillful quarterback spins a football on its long axis as it is thrown. Thus the ball is given not only forward velocity but rotational motion as well. Because it has rotational inertia it keeps spinning while it is in free flight. A spinning football is more stable in the air and less easily deflected by small disturbances than is one that does not spin. Therefore, it is more likely to reach its target.

When a quarterback throws a football, he spins it on its axis to give the ball stability in flight. (Photo courtesy of the Denver Broncos.)

Since most machines operate by means of spinning parts such as wheels, shafts, gears, and pulleys, the rotational inertia of these parts is an important consideration in machine

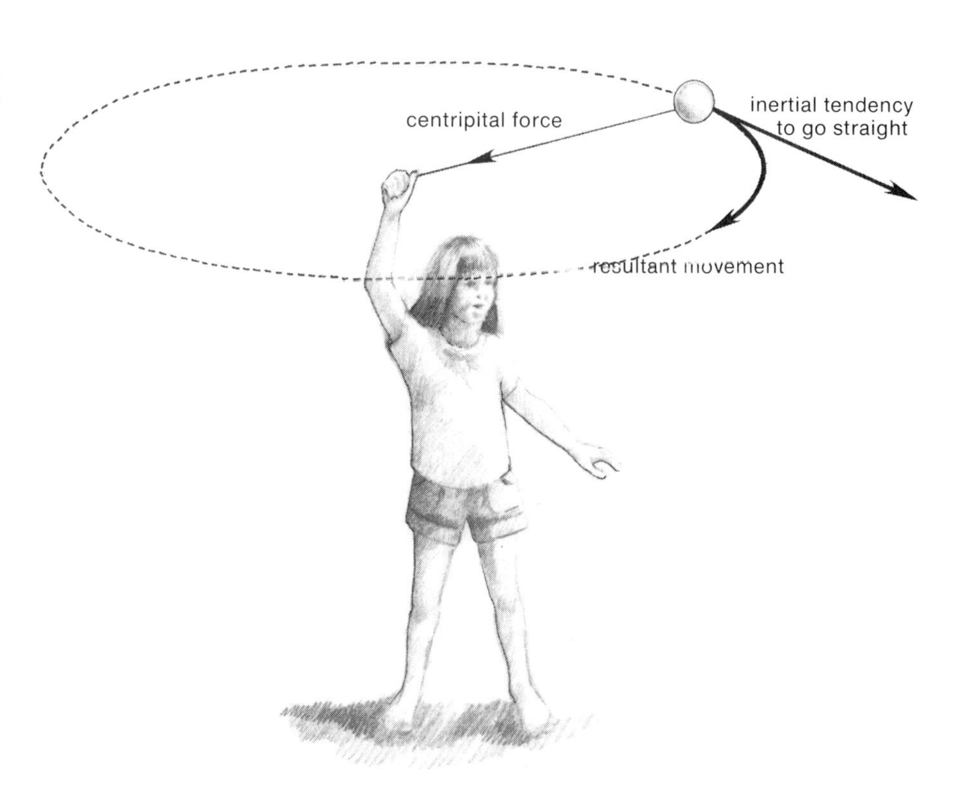

Centripetal force pulls ball inward, causing it to travel in a circle.

design. For example, a potter may spin her potter's wheel by pushing the mechanism with her foot. But it is impossible to push the wheel continuously, so the potter shoves it with her foot, lifts her foot off, and pushes again. Meanwhile the wheel rotates continuously by virtue of its rotational inertia. A good potter's wheel is fairly massive, so that it has a large rotational inertia. Therefore, the wheel rotates smoothly despite the irregularities of the pushes.

Consider some problems in designing an internal combustion machine such as an automobile engine. The energy that makes the engine run is derived from a series of explosions inside each cylinder. But since the explosions are not continuous, power is not generated smoothly but rather in a series of short bursts. The design problem, therefore, is to smooth out the irregularities so that the wheels turn at constant speed. This problem is solved by placing a metal disk, called a **flywheel,** between the engine and the driveshaft. Since the flywheel has rotational inertia, it tends to keep spinning even during the brief periods when the engine is delivering little power, and since the flywheel is connected to the wheels, it smooths out the choppiness of the engine.

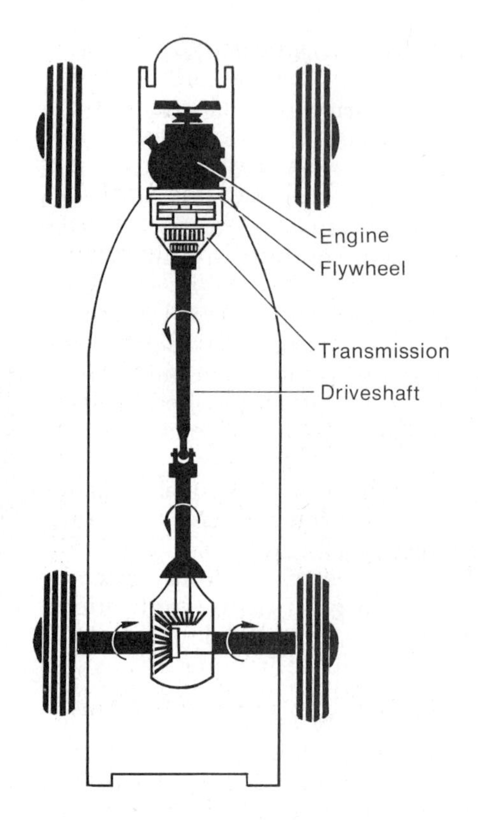

This potter's wheel consists of a heavy flywheel (called a kickwheel) connected by a vertical shaft to the smaller, lighter, working wheel, where the clay is spun. The kickwheel is rotated by foot, leaving the potter both hands free to work the clay. The kickwheel is massive so that the entire assembly will continue to rotate evenly even though the energy from the kicking motion is delivered in bursts.

Now imagine that we were designing two flywheels, one for a racing car and the other for a heavy truck. The racing car must be able to accelerate and decelerate quickly at high engine speeds, whereas the truck must be able to haul heavy loads up long hills at low engine speeds. We would build a light flywheel with a smaller inertia for the racing car, so that the engine parts offer little resistance to acceleration. However, we need a heavier flywheel for the truck, because when it is pulling a load up a hill, the engine is revolving relatively slowly, and in the long intervals between power strokes, a heavy flywheel is needed to maintain smooth, steady power transmission.

2.12 GRAVITATION

In many examples throughout this chapter we have discussed the motion caused by the force of gravitation. We find that we can measure the magnitude of this force, but we really cannot explain its essence. Gravity is a fundamental, inherent property of all matter. Does this mean that you are attracted to this book and the book is attracted to you? Yes! We cannot feel the attraction because it is quite small. It is of the order of 5×10^{-9} N if the book is 1 m away from you. The gravitational force between two objects is proportional to the mass of each object and inversely proportional to the square of the distance between them.

$$\text{Force} \propto \frac{\text{Mass of object 1} \times \text{Mass of object 2}}{(\text{distance between them})^2} \quad [2.7]$$

$$F \propto \frac{m_1 m_2}{d^2}$$

Thus, the force is greatest between massive objects that are close together. If two objects are moved apart, the gravitational force between them will decrease as shown by the equation. If the gravitational force between two objects is 1 N when they are 1 m apart, it will be $^1/_4$ N when they are 2 m apart, and $^1/_9$ N when they are 3 m apart, and so on.

We can now see why astronauts become lighter as they fly skyward, for they travel farther and farther from the center of the Earth. However, if we actually calculate their weight as they are in orbit, a curious fact becomes evident. The *Skylab* spaceship launched by the United States in 1974 orbited approximately 320 km above the surface of the Earth. Since the Earth is 6400 km in diameter, the astronauts were located about 6720 km from the center of the Earth. A person who weighed 650 N (146 lb) on Earth would have weighed 587 N (132 lb) in the orbiting Skylab. But how can that be—television broadcasts

A large flywheel mounted on this old steam engine was necessary to provide smooth power transmission. The engine originally was used to power a sawmill, but it now stands unused in a small town in northern Idaho.

Astronauts demonstrating the effects of zero-g in the Skylab Space Station. The astronauts were weightless within the Skylab environment because the capsule was continuously orbiting the Earth. The force of gravity was not negligible at all, however; a person who weighed 650 newtons (146 lb) on Earth would have been under the influence of a gravitational force of 587 newtons (132 lb) in the orbiting craft. (Photograph courtesy of NASA.)

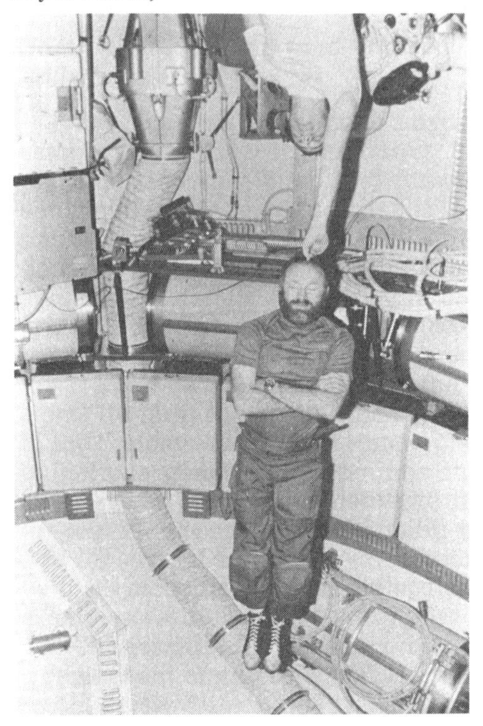

The Skylab Space Station launched by the United States on May 14, 1973, was supposed to stay in orbit for a great many years. But the satellite was just a little low, so that it kept colliding with air molecules in the upper atmosphere. These collisions gradually slowed the craft so that it was pulled into the Earth rather than around it. The Skylab eventually crashed in July, 1979.

from space showed astronauts floating weightlessly about the capsule. To answer this perplexing question, let us set the spaceship question aside for a moment and think about a woman riding in an elevator and carrying a pocketbook (see Figure 2–6). Assume that while this luckless individual is riding upward, the cable suddenly breaks and the elevator starts to fall down the shaft. Just at that moment the scared rider lets go of her pocketbook. There are now three objects (the elevator, the rider, and the pocketbook) falling down the shaft. We learned that the acceleration of gravity is equal for all objects. Thus, assuming that air resistance is negligible, all three will accelerate downward at exactly the same rate. For every meter that the elevator falls, the pocketbook and the woman also fall 1 m. Therefore, if the pocketbook were ½ m above the floor of the elevator initially, it would remain at that height relative to the elevator during the entire descent. If someone photographed the pocketbook it would appear to be suspended, weightless, in the air. Similarly, if the rider had jumped 10 cm in the air just before the cable snapped, she would remain at that height, as if she were weightless.

Now we can describe what happens in an orbiting spacecraft. Rocket action carries the craft aloft until it is, say, 320 km above the Earth, then turns the craft and accelerates it horizontally. Finally, the engines shut off. The motion of the satellite results from two components. The rocket gave it a horizontal velocity. At the same time, the capsule is being pulled downward by gravity and is falling toward the Earth. If the Earth were large and flat, the spaceship would soon crash. But the Earth is spherical, so if the horizontal velocity is just right, the satellite "falls" continuously toward the Earth but never gets there. You see, if the arc of the fall is the same as the arc of the Earth, the satellite orbits. The vehicle is falling freely all the time, and the only reason it does not crash is that the horizontal velocity carries it around at the right speed so that it falls around the Earth and not into it. The astronauts in the capsule are like the rider and suitcase in the falling elevator. They are falling, but since their enclosure is falling at the same rate, they *appear* to be weightless when in fact they are not.

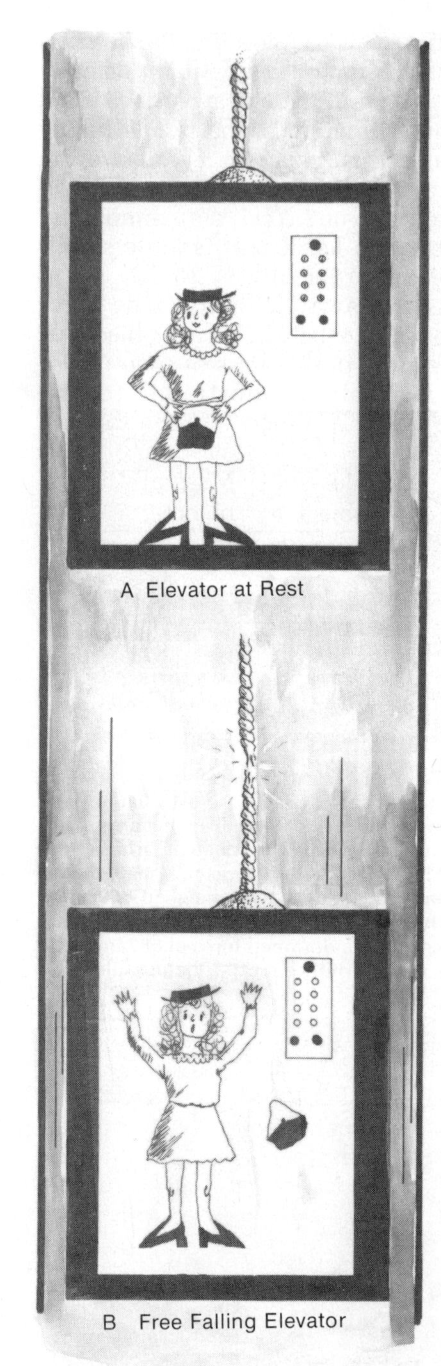

Figure 2–6. Weightlessness in a falling elevator.

To return to Earth, the astronauts fire a retrorocket (Latin *retro* = back-

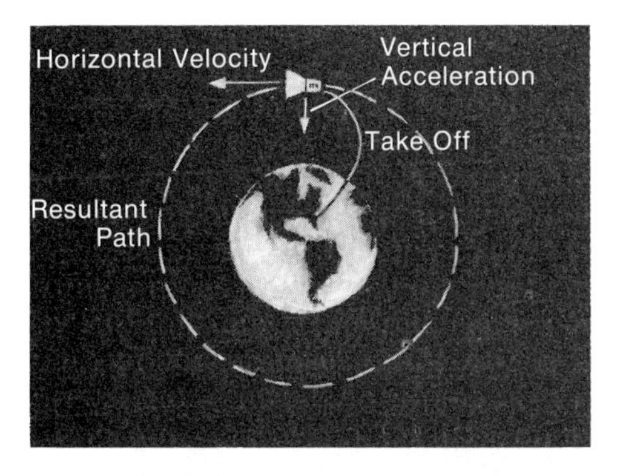

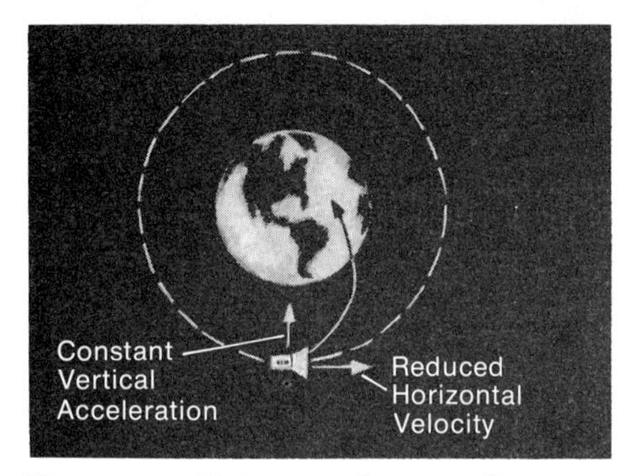

Figure 2–7. Trajectory of spacecraft.

ward), thereby reducing their horizontal velocity. Then suddenly the arc of the fall carries the ship toward the Earth and not around it. Notice that a satellite orbits only because it is given a horizontal velocity. If it were shot straight upward to an altitude of 320 km it would fall straight back down. Also note that in the absence of air resistance, you could orbit a spaceship 1 km above the surface of the Earth, but in practice the resistance of the air would slow it down so fast that it would quickly lose its horizontal velocity and fall.

2.13 EPILOGUE

We must recognize both the power and the limitations of classical physics. On one hand there are a great many problems that cannot be answered intuitively but are easily solved using a few simple mathematical relationships. On the other hand, many seemingly simple practical problems are so genuinely complex that we cannot solve them mathematically and must search for the answers experimentally or intuitively.

Consider, for example, the prediction of avalanches. Avalanches occur when snow that has collected on the sides of mountains breaks loose and slides down the slopes. Avalanches can be incredibly destructive. A large slide fell from the heights of Mount Huascaran in Peru in 1970 and completely buried the town of Yungay. There were no survivors. Many villages in the Swiss Alps have been completely or partially buried by sliding snow, and there have been many deaths. A great many mountaineers and skiers have been caught in avalanches and killed. This author (Jon) was caught in a very small slide in the San Juan mountains of Colorado. I was buried only up to my knees, but the force of the slide compacted the snow sufficiently so that I could not free myself easily and had to dig my feet out with a shovel.

A large avalanche near Loveland Pass, Colorado. It was unintentionally released by skiers crossing near the ridge line. Notice the truck, driving up the pass, that barely missed disaster. (Courtesy of M. Martinelli, Mountain Snow and Avalanche Research, USDA)

One common problem given in many elementary physics classes is to calculate the acceleration of a block of wood down an inclined plane. If you know the angle of the plane, the mass of the wood, and the frictional forces between the wood and the surface, it is a simple matter to calculate whether the block will slide or not, and if so, how fast it will go. Therefore, it might seem possible to calculate the mass of a snow pack, the angle of the mountainside, and the frictional forces between the snow and the soil. Then it would be a simple matter to use these data to calculate when and where avalanches will occur.

However, avalanche prediction is a much more complex problem. Snow is not a cohesive solid like wood. Rather it is a collection of crystals that are held together by forces of different magnitudes. One important factor that determines the binding strength of the snow is the shape and structures of the crystals themselves. There are a great many different types of snow crystals. Sharply pointed crystals, such as the ones shown in Figure 2–8*A*, will bond together more strongly than rounded, smooth ones, as shown in Figure 2–8*B*. The shape of falling snowflakes varies considerably with different weather conditions. To make matters even more complicated, snow crystals change structure after they have fallen. For example, the outside surface layers may melt partially on a warm day and then refreeze into a new shape. Alternatively, on a cold day the surface snow may insulate the lower layers. If the ground is warm, the snow at the bottom may melt partially and then refreeze into a new structure. Wind may compact the snow pack and alter the shape or density of the crystals. When new snow falls on old snow, the layers may or may not bond together strongly.

Physicists attempting to predict avalanche danger try to take all of these factors into account by using complex computer models. They use sensitive ultrasonic sensors to listen to microscopic shifts in the snow. Some of the most successful laboratories report 80 per cent success in forecasting avalanches. Eighty per cent accuracy may be high in forecasting natural disasters, but a skier would be foolish to ski a slope if there were any significant risk of being buried and killed by a slide. Experienced backcountry skiers and mountain climbers study the physics of snow stability and structure, and then use a great deal of judgment and cau-

A

B

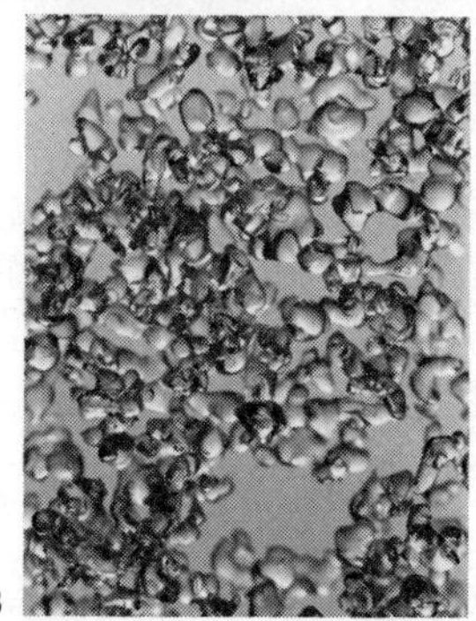

Figure 2–8. ***A*, Newly fallen snow crystals are sharp and pointed and bond to each other strongly. *B*, After snow crystals have melted and refrozen many times they become rounded. These rounded crystals may act like many tiny ball bearings and the snow pack may be likely to slide. (Photos courtesy of Edward R. LaChapelle, Kirkland, Washington.)**

Back country skiiers must use intuition and caution when predicting avalanche conditions. They also carry shovels and radio equipment to help locate and rescue a partner who may be unfortunate enough to make the wrong decision. (Photo by Greg Edmonds)

tion before proceeding over a potentially dangerous slope. We tell this story to emphasize that in solving many practical problems the modern scientist not only must rely on the known laws of classical physics but also must use intuition and trial-and-error experimentation as well. Many seemingly simple problems are much much more complex than they may appear to be at first glance.

CHAPTER OBJECTIVES

Understand speed, velocity, and acceleration, and review vectors and vector notation. Newton's three laws are:

1. A body at rest remains at rest and a body in uniform motion in a straight line remains in such motion, unless acted upon by some outside force.
2. The acceleration of an object is directly proportional to the net force acting upon it and inversely proportional to the mass of the object.
3. For every force there is always an equal and opposite force.

Review:

a. The concept of inertia.
b. The differences between mass and weight.
c. Rotational motion and centripetal and centrifugal force and acceleration.
d. Rotational inertia.
e. Gravitational force and the acceleration of a falling object.

KEY WORDS

Translational motion
Rotational motion
Vibrational motion
Speed
Average speed
Velocity
Vector
Acceleration
Acceleration due to gravity
Force
Friction
Inertia
Mass
Weight
Net force
Centripetal force
Centrifugal force
Rotational inertia
Flywheel

FORMULAS TO KNOW

1. $\text{speed} = \dfrac{\text{distance}}{\text{time}} = \dfrac{d}{t}$

Example 1
What is the average speed of a jet plane that travels 2000 km in 2 hr?

Answer: $\text{speed} = \dfrac{\text{distance}}{\text{time}}$

$$= \frac{2000\ \text{km}}{2\ \text{hr}} = 1000\ \text{km/hr}$$

Example 2
A fox is running up on a sitting duck, and the fox is moving at an average speed of 2 m/sec. If the duck is 100 m from the fox, how much time does he have to detect the fox and fly away?

Answer: $\text{speed} = \dfrac{\text{distance}}{\text{time}}$

We are solving for time, so by simple algebra we rearrange:

$$\text{time} = \frac{\text{distance}}{\text{speed}}$$

or in words, the amount of time the duck has before it must fly away equals the distance between the duck and the fox divided by the speed of the fox.

$$\text{time} = \frac{100\ \text{m}}{2\ \text{m/sec}} = 50\ \text{sec}$$

2. $\overrightarrow{\text{velocity}} = \dfrac{\overrightarrow{\text{distance}}}{\text{time}} = \dfrac{\vec{d}}{t}$

An airplane is flying northward at a rate of 200 km/hr. At the same time the wind is blowing eastward at a velocity of 50 km/hr. (a) Draw a vector diagram showing the two velocity components and the resultant velocity of the aircraft with respect to an observer on the ground. (b) From your diagram, estimate the resultant velocity.

Answer: (a) In drawing a vector diagram, the lengths of the arrows must be *proportional* to the velocities. Therefore the north vector must be drawn as 200 units while the east vector is drawn as 50 units. In other words, the north vector must be four times as long as the east vector.

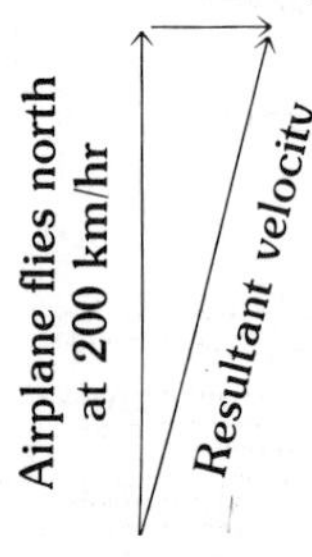

(b) Measuring with a ruler, we see that the velocity is about 206 km/hr, and the direction of travel is approximately north northeast.

3. $\overrightarrow{\text{acceleration}} = \dfrac{\overrightarrow{\text{change in velocity}}}{\text{time}}$

Example 4
A runner accelerates from a standstill to a speed of 12 m/sec in 1.5 sec. What is his rate of acceleration?

Answer:

$$\overrightarrow{\text{acceleration}} = \frac{\overrightarrow{\text{change in velocity}}}{\text{time}}$$

Since the initial velocity is zero and the runner accelerates to 12 m/sec, the change in velocity is 12 m/sec, and,

$$\overrightarrow{\text{acceleration}} = \frac{12\frac{\text{m}}{\text{sec}}}{1.5\text{ sec}} = 8\frac{\text{m}}{\text{sec}^2}$$

4. $\overrightarrow{\text{velocity of a falling object}} = \overrightarrow{\text{acceleration due to gravity}} \times \text{time} = \overrightarrow{g}t$

Example 5
An object on a distant planet is dropped from the top of a tall spacecraft. After 2 sec, the object has reached a velocity of 40 m/sec downward. What is the acceleration due to gravity on this planet?

Answer:

$$\overrightarrow{\text{velocity}} = \overrightarrow{\text{acceleration due to gravity}} \times \text{time}$$

or

$$\overrightarrow{\text{acceleration due to gravity}} = \frac{\overrightarrow{\text{velocity}}}{\text{time}}$$

$$= \frac{40\frac{\text{m}}{\text{sec}}}{2\text{ sec}} = 20\frac{\text{m}}{\text{sec}^2}$$

Thus the acceleration due to gravity on this planet is roughly twice as great as it is on Earth.

5. $\overrightarrow{\text{Force}} = \text{mass} \times \overrightarrow{\text{acceleration}} = \overrightarrow{\text{ma}}$

Example 6
The runner in Example 4 accelerated at a rate of 8 m/sec². If he has a mass of 75 kg, how much force was required to accelerate at this rate?

Answer:

$$\vec{F} = m\vec{a}$$
$$= 75\text{ kg} \times 8\frac{\text{m}}{\text{sec}^2}$$
$$= 600\text{ kg}\frac{\text{m}}{\text{sec}^2}$$
$$= 600\text{ N}$$

TAKE-HOME EXPERIMENTS

1. **Acceleration.** For this experiment you will need to ride in some kind of vehicle. A private automobile would be fine, or if that is not available, a bus or train. Put a marble on the floor of the vehicle and observe what happens to it when you (a) ride at constant velocity on a level roadway; (b) ride at constant velocity on a bumpy roadway; (c) speed up; (d) slow down; (e) turn a corner. Explain your observations.

2. **Acceleration.** Drop a sheet of paper and a pencil at the same time. Which reaches the ground first? Now crumple the paper into a very tight ball and repeat the experiment. Explain your observations again.

3. **Inertia.** Set a glass on a table and place a playing card, or any stiff, smooth piece of paper over the glass, then place a coin on the card or paper. Now flick the card sharply with your finger so as to slide it off the glass. If you do this correctly, the coin will fall into the glass. Explain in terms of Newton's laws. Now replace the playing card with a piece of sandpaper, placed so that the rough side is facing upward. Repeat the experiment. Explain your observations.

4. **Force and motion.** For this experiment you will need a board, a small toy car or truck, and a rubber band.

(a) Take a board that is about 1 m long and 15 cm wide and support it on a slight incline so that it rests on the ground at one end and is raised approximately 15 cm on the other.
(b) Place three nails in the board as shown. The spacing of the nails will vary with the size of the rubber band used, but as a rough approximation, position the forward two so the rubber band just fits over them, and place the third approximately 5 cm behind the others and exactly midway between them.
(c) Position the rubber band over the forward two nails.
(d) Pull the toy car or truck to the third nail with the rubber band. (The third nail is simply a fixed point to be sure you pull the rubber band an equal distance each time.)
(e) Release the vehicle and allow it to roll up the board. Mark the highest point that it reaches. Repeat four times and measure the average distance traveled. Now tape four or five nickels (or an equivalent mass) to the top of the vehicle and repeat the experiment. How far did the car travel this time? Explain your results. Repeat the experiment again with the board lying flat on the ground and explain your results.

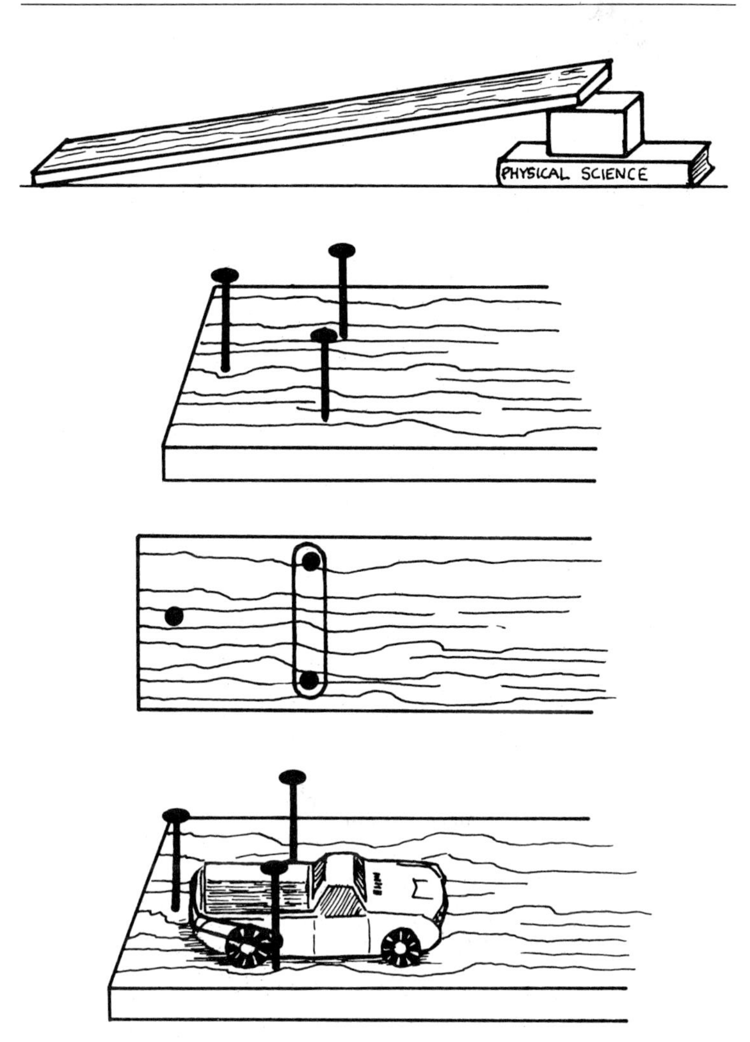

5. **Flywheels.** Investigate two machines with which you are familiar. You may choose an automobile, a sewing machine, a power saw, a blender, or any other similar device. Locate the flywheel on each machine if there is one. (Almost all machines have flywheels.) Discuss the purpose of the flywheel for each particular application.

PROBLEMS

1. **Speed.** (a) When a police officer gives someone a ticket for speeding, is the officer concerned with the driver's average or his instantaneous speed? Explain. (b) On the entrance to many turnpikes, drivers are given a card that indicates the place of entry so the proper toll can be levied at the exit. The time of entry is also noted on the card. At the exit station the toll officer can determine the driver's speed during the journey, since he knows both the elapsed time and the distance traveled. Can the officer determine the driver's instantaneous speed, the average speed, or both? Explain.

2. **Speed.** What is the speed of a horse that travels 20 km in 3 hr?

3. **Speed.** The speed of sound in air is about 340 m/sec. The speed of light is so fast that to a first approximation it seems to travel distances of 100 km or so instantaneously. If you see a flash of lightning and hear thunder 8 sec later, how far away is the lightning storm? Express your answer in meters, and in kilometers.

4. **Average speed.** A person traveling crosscountry drives at a constant speed of 80 km/hr. If he stops for 15 min once every 2 hr for gas and a rest, but otherwise drives steadily, what is his average speed?

5. **Speed and velocity.** Explain what is incomplete about the statement, "The velocity of the automobile was 80 km/hr."

6. **Speed and velocity.** A device on the dashboard of your car is called a speedometer. Why isn't it called a velocity-meter?

7. **Velocity.** (a) A sailor crossing the ocean is sailing at 6 km/hr due east against an ocean current traveling 2 km/hr due west. What is the velocity of the boat over the sea floor? (b) The sailor turns and starts heading south. Draw a vector diagram showing the component velocities and the resultant velocity of the boat. Estimate the new velocity from your diagram.

8. **Velocity.** A child is playing on a train. The train is traveling at a rate of 80 km/hr south and the child is running toward the front of the train at a rate of 3 km/hr. What is the child's velocity with respect to the ground?

9. **Velocity.** As the Earth rotates, all the inhabitants of the surface of the Earth are continuously rotating, too. Are we all moving at constant velocity? Explain.

*10. **Acceleration.** A bicyclist can accelerate from 0 km/hr to 10 km/hr in 2 sec. Similarly, an automobile can accelerate from 80 km/hr to 90 km/hr in 2 sec. Which vehicle is accelerating at a faster rate? Explain.

11. **Inertia.** The word "inertia" is used in many nonscientific applications. Write a physical and a nonphysical definition for "inertia" and show that the spirit of the word is similar in both cases.

*12. **Acceleration.** A driver has to press the accelerator down in order to travel uphill at constant speed. Does the automobile actually accelerate? Explain.

13. **Inertia.** If you placed a marble on the floor of a bus traveling smoothly at constant speed down a straight road, the marble would not roll across the floor. However, if you placed the marble on a merry-go-round traveling smoothly at constant speed around in a circle, the marble would roll. Explain.

14. **Inertia.** Discuss the relationship between inertia and mass and between inertia and weight.

*15. **Inertia.** If you had to push a heavy object across the floor, would there be some advantage to move it all in one steady push, or would you be just as well advised to push and rest alternately?

*16. **Inertia.** An astronaut traveling at steady speed along a straight path from Mars to Jupiter has to go outside the ship to do a repair. While she is working, she lets go of her wrench. Does the wrench fall far behind and get lost in space? Explain. Describe and explain its motion.

*17. **Inertia.** A man has climbed 35 m to the top of the mast of a sailing ship. The ship is traveling east at a rate of 1 m/sec. The man drops a hammer to the deck; the hammer lands after falling for 2.6 sec. How far behind the mast does the hammer strike?

*18. **Inertia.** A chandelier is attached to the ceiling by a weak wire. Another equally weak wire is hanging from the chandelier, as shown in Figure 2–9. If a person on the ground pulls the bottom wire slowly, which wire will break first? If she jerks the wire, which will break first? Explain.

19. **Inertia.** You can remove the dust from a coat by shaking it. Could you shake out the dust in free space in the absence of gravity? Explain.

*20. **Mass.** An astronaut floating in free space is handed two objects and asked to determine which is more massive. Outline a simple procedure for him to follow to get the correct answer.

*21. **Mass and weight.** (a) An object is dropped on a windless day from a tower onto the ground below, and the spot where it lands is noted. The same object is dropped again when the wind is blowing. The force of the wind deflects it as it falls so that it lands at some distance downwind from the point where it has landed on a calm day. The distance between the first and the second landing spots is measured. Does this distance depend on the mass of the object or on its weight? (b) Two objects, X and Y, of the same size are dropped at the same time on a windy day, and object X lands farther downwind than object Y. Underline the correct word in parenthesis in the following sentence: The result tells you that the (mass, weight) of object X is (greater, less) than that of object Y. (c) Would this method of measurement work on other windy planets?

*22. **Mass and weight.** Consider two possible devices for measuring mass: a spring scale and a two-pan balance. In the spring scale, the object to be measured is placed on a spring and the compression of the spring

*Indicates more difficult problem.

ENERGY

3.1 INTRODUCTION

We recognize matter and energy by our senses, but in different ways. You see a book. Is it real, or merely an image, a reflection? You put out your hand, touch it, feel it, determine that it has mass and occupies space. You conclude, correctly, that it is matter. Books, flowers, houses, mosquitos, elephants, and everything else that we can feel and touch, everything that has mass and occupies space consists of matter. Energy, too, can be recognized, but here the interpretation is more subtle. You see a moving freight train, a coiled spring, a rock balanced high on a mountainside, a red-hot bar of iron, and a lump of coal, and somehow you know that they all *have* energy. The reason you know this is that, in every case, you can imagine some *change* occurring in which work is done or heat is transferred.

Energy is the capacity to perform work or to transfer heat. Every time something moves, or has the potential to move, or every time something is heated or cooled, or has the potential to heat or cool, energy transfers or storage are involved.

There are many different forms to the quantity that we call energy. A freight train has energy of motion which is called **kinetic energy.** The coiled spring is not doing anything, but if released, it will suddenly uncoil, and therefore we say that it has **potential energy.** Likewise, the rock perched on the mountain has a potential energy that can be released when it falls. The red-hot bar of iron represents a totally different form of energy—**heat.** The lump of coal again has a potential, this time a potential to produce heat and light when the coal burns. We call this **chemical energy.**

There are many other forms of energy as well. Uranium is said to have **nuclear energy** because the nuclei of its atoms can split apart and produce heat. **Light** is another form of energy. Sunlight can harm your skin or tan it, melt snow, or activate a photoelectric cell to create electricity. **Electrical** and **magnetic energy** are closely related to each other (see Chapter 5) and are familiar in our modern world. An electric current flowing through the filament in a bulb can produce light. Similarly, a magnetic field can lift a piece of metal against the force of gravity. There is also energy in **sound.** We hear noise because the sound waves force the tiny bones in our ears to move. Similarly, an extremely loud noise, such as an explosion, can break windows. In the early 1900's Albert Einstein showed that matter, too, has energy. Matter and energy are different aspects of the same thing. This equivalence cannot be detected in ordinary chemical reactions by ordinary scales and balances, but it has been measured in atomic reactors and high speed accelerators.

Energy can be transferred from one form to another. Sunlight strikes the surface of a leaf, and the energy is used to change chemical bonds and build complex organic molecules. These molecules, like a lump of coal, have chemical potential. If a cow eats the leaf she can utilize the potential to provide the energy to walk about or heat her body.

Energy transformations are basic to

There are many different forms of energy.

A moving freight train has kinetic energy.

This campfire is producing heat energy.

A stone perched high above the floor of the Grand Canyon has potential energy.

This pile of coal can burn to produce heat. It has chemical potential energy.

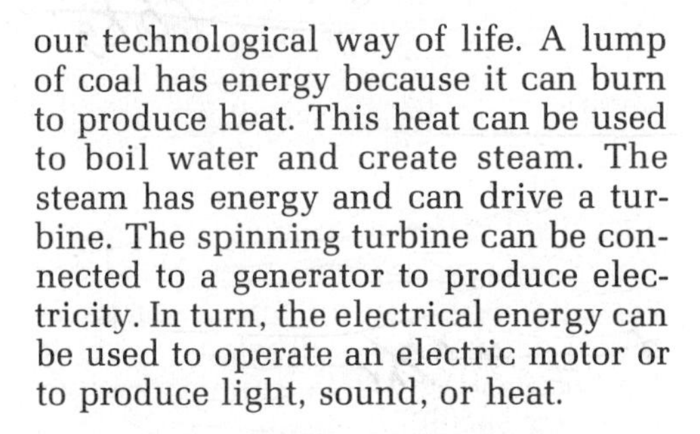

our technological way of life. A lump of coal has energy because it can burn to produce heat. This heat can be used to boil water and create steam. The steam has energy and can drive a turbine. The spinning turbine can be connected to a generator to produce electricity. In turn, the electrical energy can be used to operate an electric motor or to produce light, sound, or heat.

3.2 ENERGY AND WORK

Suppose that there is a certain job to be done; for example, a pile of shingles must be carried up to the roof of a house under construction. We know that energy is needed to lift the shingles. But if someone gave you a can of gasoline and said, "Here's some energy," you could not pour the fuel on the shingles and watch them rise upward. You would have to convert the chemical energy of the fuel into properly directed work. Thus you would first have to find a gasoline engine, then construct a pulley or elevator lift of some kind, find a way to load the shingles onto the lift, and so on. Physicists, chemists, and engineers are concerned with transfer of energy into useful forms.

Work is fundamental to all our lives. In everyday, non-technical conversation the concept is used loosely to describe any physical or mental effort. In physics, however, work is defined simply and precisely.

The horse is doing work by forcing the machine to move.

Work = force × distance
$W = F \times d$
A, The little girl is pulling on the rope, but since she cannot move the car, $d = 0$, and no work is performed. *B,* The little girl can move the toy cart, so she is performing work in this situation.

A

B

$$\text{Work} = \text{force multiplied by distance through which the force acts}$$
$$\text{Work} = \text{force} \times \text{distance}$$
$$W = F \times d$$

or, in more descriptive terms, work is performed when something is forced to move. (The equation $W = F \times d$ applies only when the force is constant and in the same direction as the motion.)

If you push hard all day against the Empire State Building, it will not move at all. Since the distance traveled is zero, the work performed also will be zero. Your muscles get tired because they stretch and contract, thereby performing work within your system, but the work done on the Empire State Building is still zero.

In the metric system, the fundamental unit of work is the **joule.** Notice that the joule is a derived quantity; it is force times a distance,

$$1 \text{ J} = 1 \text{ newton-meter}$$

3.3 KINETIC ENERGY

Work is required to accelerate a stationary object and force it to move. Conversely, any moving object has the capacity to perform work. Thus a person's muscles must work to swing a hammer, and a hammer in the middle of its swing has the ability to force a nail downward into a piece of wood. Similarly, expanding gases perform work inside the engine of a locomotive and the train moves down the track. Once it is in motion, the locomotive has the ability to perform work. Notice that we speak of the *ability* of a moving object to do work. A freight train coasting along a level track is not performing any work at the moment, but it has energy and has the capacity to do work.*

How much energy is possessed by a moving object? We realize intuitively that the amount of energy is related to both the mass and the velocity of the object. A massive, fast-moving body has more energy than a light, slow-moving body. The energy of a moving object is called **kinetic energy,** abbreviated **KE.** The exact relationship between energy and motion is easily derived from Newton's Second Law. The derivation is shown in Appendix D; the final equation is shown below. The work done on an object to bring it to a velocity, v, or the energy of the moving object is equal to $\frac{1}{2} mv^2$:

$$\text{Kinetic energy} = \tfrac{1}{2} \times \text{mass} \times (\text{velocity})^2$$
$$KE = \tfrac{1}{2} mv^2$$

*We assume here that our freight train is operating in an ideal system, where there is no wind resistance or friction. In a real system, work is being performed by the engine to overcome these forces.

3.4 POTENTIAL ENERGY

Gravitational Potential

We understand that a freight train coasting along a level track has energy because it can perform work. However, a book sitting quietly on a desk top can also perform work, because if it is pushed off the edge, it will gain kinetic energy as it falls to the floor. Therefore, the book on the desk top has energy—it has an energy of position, which is called **potential energy.** The magnitude of this potential energy is exactly equal to the work required to lift the book from the floor to the desk top in the first place. If a book is lying on the floor, the

The potential energy of the perched rock is the work it could do by falling into the valley or the work that would have to be done to lift it up again after it had fallen.

force it exerts on the floor is simply its weight. As mentioned in the previous chapter, the weight is equal to mass times the acceleration of gravity. Therefore,

$$\text{Force} = \text{weight} = \text{mass} \times \begin{matrix}\text{acceleration}\\ \text{of gravity}\end{matrix}$$

$$F = mg$$

To lift it to a height h, we need to exert a force equal to mg for a distance of h; the work required is equal to:

$$W = F \times d$$
$$\text{Work} = \text{Force} \times \text{distance}$$
$$\mathbf{PE} = \mathbf{W} = \mathbf{m \times g \times h}$$

Where: PE = potential energy
m = mass of object
g = acceleration due to gravity
h = height of object

Note that $m \times g$ = a force
and h = a distance

So the potential energy $= F \times d$

Note that potential energy depends on some implied process—on a change from the initial state to some assumed final state. Thus, we always speak of the height of an object above some convenient reference point. A woman sits in her office on the fourth story of a building in Denver, Colorado. Denver is 1609 m above sea level, the office on the fourth story is 10 m above the ground, the desk is 0.75 m above the floor of the office. What is the potential energy of a 1-kg mass sitting on the woman's desk? It depends. The object has a potential energy of 7.4 J with respect to the floor of the office, 105 J with respect to the ground, and 15,874 J with respect to sea level. Therefore, any answer is dependent on our reference level.* Since the mass on the desk is likely to fall only as far as the floor, the most reasonable answer would be 7.4 J.

Elastic Potential

A compressed spring, like the book sitting on the desk, has a potential to do work. If allowed to expand, the

*$1\text{ kg} \times 9.8 \dfrac{\text{m}}{\text{sec}^2} \times 0.75\text{ m} = 7.4\text{ J}$

$1\text{ kg} \times 9.8 \dfrac{\text{m}}{\text{sec}^2} \times 10.75\text{ m} = 105\text{ J}$

$1\text{ kg} \times 9.8 \dfrac{\text{m}}{\text{sec}^2} \times 1619.75\text{ m} = 15{,}874\text{ J}$

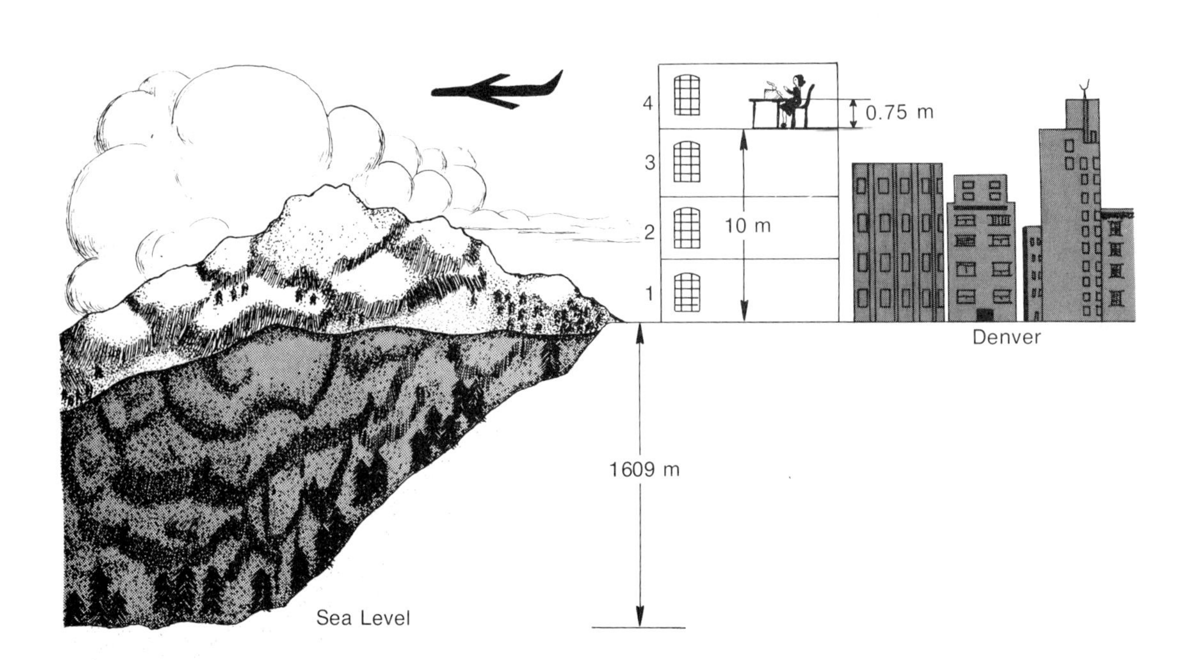

Photo by Dr. Harold Edgerton, MIT, Cambridge, Mass.

spring can force something to move. Conversely, work must be done on the uncoiled spring to force it back to its compressed state.

Although we usually think of springs as being coiled pieces of metal, all materials are elastic and compress or expand in response to outside influence. For example, when a baseball is approaching a batter, it has a certain energy. The batter swings and hits the ball, giving it a kinetic energy in the opposite direction. The ball has done an about-face: first it was headed one way, then it had to stop and reverse directions. What happens just at the point when the bat is connected to the ball and the ball is standing still? What happens to the energy of motion when there is no motion? The bat bends and compresses, and the ball compresses. Both act like springs; the energy is stored as elastic potential energy and released as bat and ball spring back to their original shapes. As another example, see the photo illustrating how golf club and golfball are deformed at the instant when their potential energies are at a maximum.

Chemical Potential

As mentioned previously, many chemical substances also have potential energy. A cold block of wood will produce light and heat if placed in the fireplace and ignited. Chemical potential is another form of stored energy. When a plant traps energy from the Sun to synthesize complex sugars and starches, potential energy is stored in the chemical bonds. This energy can be released later if the plant tissue is consumed by an animal or burned in a furnace.

3.5 HEAT AND TEMPERATURE

In modern times, heat is generally recognized to be a form of energy. During the current energy crisis, for example, there is concern that the available supply of heating oil will not be sufficient to warm our houses. But the relationship between heat and work has not always been obvious. Before the eighteenth century, people did not realize that heat from a fire is really another form of energy and that heat and work are both manifestations of the same phenomenon. This relationship came to be understood only when scientists began to study temperature.

Temperature

A cup of alcohol that has been in the refrigerator feels cold, and a cup of alcohol that has been simmering on the stove feels hot. Our nervous system can detect hotness or coldness and therefore acts as a crude thermometer. Since the degree of hotness of a substance can be sensed easily, and since our sensations are processed by physical and chemical means in our bodies, a substance must undergo some physical or

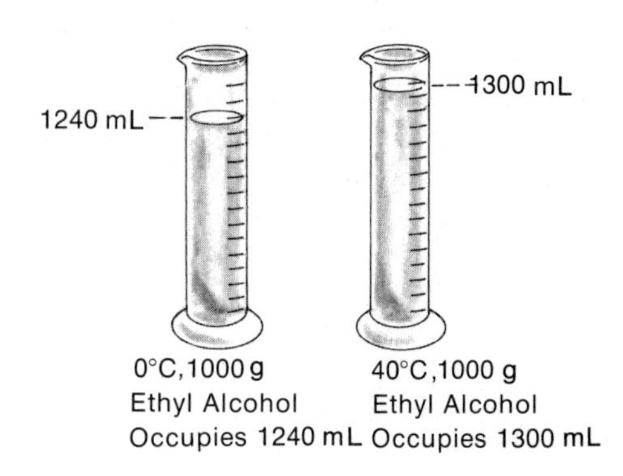

0°C, 1000 g Ethyl Alcohol Occupies 1240 mL
40°C, 1000 g Ethyl Alcohol Occupies 1300 mL

chemical change when it gets hotter or colder. Why not, then, measure this change with a device that is more sensitive than our fingers? Scientists have learned that most materials expand when heated and contract when cooled. Thus, 1 kg of ethyl alcohol occupies 1240 cubic centimeters (cm^3) at 0° C and expands to 1300 cm^3 at 40° C.

A thermometer is a device that measures temperature. One commonly used thermometer contains a column of alcohol (dyed red) encased in glass.* When the thermometer is inserted into a hot medium, the alcohol and the glass both expand, but since the alcohol expands more than the glass, the column of liquid rises in the tube. Conversely, if the thermometer is inserted in a cold medium, the alcohol and the glass both contract, but since alcohol contracts more than glass, the column of liquid drops.

If different observers are to compare their results, they must refer to some accepted standard temperatures. Two standards of the Celsius (formerly Centigrade) scale are melting ice (0° C) and boiling water at sea level (100° C). A Celsius thermometer can be constructed in the following manner: A sealed glass tube with some liquid substance, generally alcohol or mercury, is immersed in a bath of ice water and the liquid level is marked on the glass. The tube is then placed into boiling water and the liquid level is recorded again. The space between the high and the low mark is now divided into 100 equal intervals, and each interval is called 1° C.

People learned how to make thermometers and to measure temperature before they understood how a hot body differs from a cold one. Now we know that all matter is made up of tiny particles called atoms and molecules. (See Chapters 5 and 7.) These particles are constantly moving. Molecules of a gas fly about randomly through space. Atoms in a rigid solid such as iron or diamond are continuously vibrating. When an object is heated, these particles move faster; when it is cooled, they

*Another liquid commonly used in thermometers is mercury.

The British system of measurement uses the Fahrenheit scale to measure temperature. Gabriel Daniel Fahrenheit is said to have invented the first mercury thermometer and the temperature scale that bears his name. He chose 0°F to be the temperature of a mixture of ice and common table salt. This was the coldest temperature that was easily reproducible in the laboratory at that time. He then arbitrarily defined the body temperature of a healthy human to be 96°F. Using this scale, he observed the boiling point of water to be 212°F. However, the bore of his glass thermometer must have been uneven, for body temperature is now recognized to be approximately 98.6°F. Conversion formulas between °F and °C are given in Appendix C.

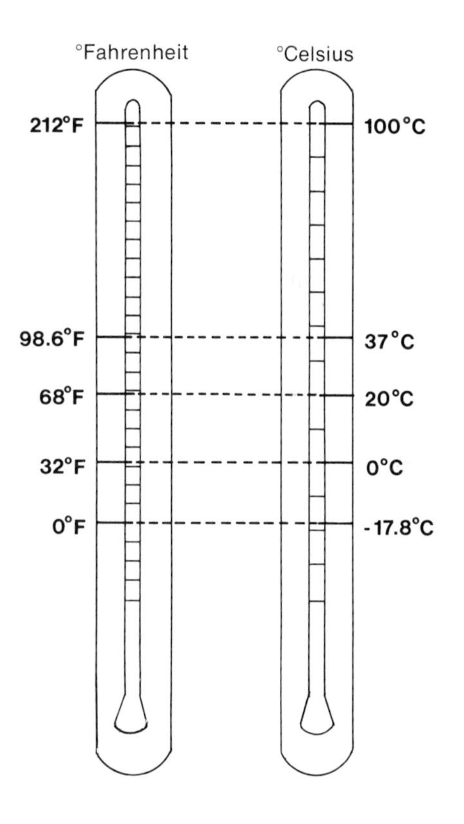

Reference (At Standard Atmospheric Pressure)	°C	°F
Arctic winter	−40	−40
Ordinary winter temperature	−10	14
Melting point of ice	0	32
Brisk autumn temperature	10	50
Normal room temperature	20	68
Summer day	30	86
Body temperature	37	98.6
Boiling point of water	100	212

slow down. Thus, temperature corresponds to the average energy of motion, or the kinetic energy, of the atoms or molecules of a substance.

Heat Energy

If we put a beaker of cold water over a flame, the temperature of the water will rise. Energy from the flame has been transferred to the water. We call this form of energy **heat.** Heat and temperature are not the same, as we shall see shortly. The nature of heat can be best understood by examining the results of a series of heat-temperature experiments.

Experiment 1

A hot block of gold is placed on a cold block of silver. The hot block of gold will get cooler, and the cold block of silver will get hotter. Eventually both will reach the same temperature. This is a law of universal experience: Heat always "flows" from a hot body to a cold body, and the flow stops when the two bodies are at the same temperature.

Experiment 2

For this experiment we need two equal sources of heat, such as identical hot plates plugged into the same source of current. A beaker with 1 kg of water is placed on one of the hot plates, and another beaker filled with 2 kg of water is placed on the other hot plate. The hot plates are turned on, and the temperature rise of the water in each beaker is measured. The temperature of the water in the 2-kg beaker will rise half as fast as the temperature of the water in the 1-kg beaker. If we reversed the process and placed both beakers in a refrigerator, the 2-kg beaker would cool more slowly, for it has more heat within it. *The amount of heat in an object is related to both the temperature and the quantity of matter.*

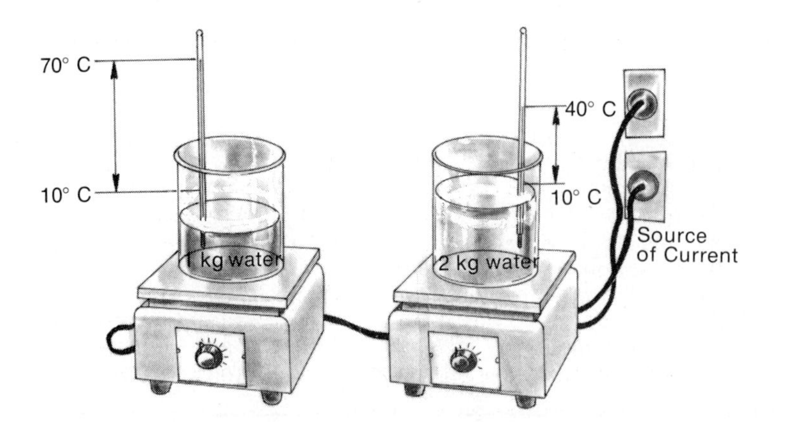

Experiment 3

A beaker with 1 kg of water is placed on one of our two equal hot plates, and a beaker with 1 kg of ethyl alcohol is placed on the other. If both are heated identically, the temperature of the ethyl alcohol will rise about twice as fast as the temperature of the water, even though there were equal amounts of material in each beaker. Therefore, the heat absorbed by an object must be related to the kind of matter as well as to its mass. *The amount of heat in an object is related not only to the temperature and the quantity of matter but also to the type of matter.*

Temperature is a measure of the degree of hotness or coldness of a body and is independent of the quantity or type of matter. Thus, if two objects are in contact with each other, and no heat flows from one to the other, *the two objects must be at the same temperature,* even if one is a 10-ton rock and the other is a copper penny. Heat, on the other hand, is a form of energy. A large sample of material contains more heat than a small sample of the same substance at the same temperature. Thus, there is more heat in a bathtub full of warm water than there is in a teacup full of boiling water. In addition, equal quantities of different substances will generally absorb different quantities of heat for a given temperature rise and release different quantities of heat on cooling. Thus, a bottle full of warm water will contain more heat than the same bottle full of alcohol at the same temperature.

The older unit of heat is called the **calorie.** One calorie represents the amount of heat required to raise the temperature of 1 gram (g) of water by 1° C. Or, just as correctly, a calorie is the amount of heat released when 1 g of water is cooled by 1° C. Although the calorie is still widely used, the official SI unit of energy is the joule (J). One calorie = 4.184 J, or 4.184 J are required to raise the temperature of 1 g of water by 1° C. As we noted in Experiment 3, different substances absorb different amounts of heat per degree temperature rise. You need only 2.4 J to raise the temperature of 1 g of alcohol by one degree; lead takes even less, 0.13 J per g per degree.

The **specific heat** of a substance is defined as the quantity of heat required to change the temperature of 1 g of substance of 1° C. Table 3.1 lists the specific heats of various substances.

If you supply equal amounts of heat to equal masses of different materials, the material with a large specific heat will warm more slowly than a material with a smaller specific heat. However, as we already mentioned, energy is not lost, for both objects will contain the same amount of heat energy. Thus, if you add 4.184 J of heat to 1 g of water, the temperature will rise by 1° C. If you then cool the water by 1 degree, 4.184 J of heat will be released. If you add 4.184 J of heat to 1 g of lead, the temperature of the lead will rise by 32° C,* but then if you cool the gram of lead by 32° C, 4.184 J of heat energy will be released.

* temperature change $= \dfrac{4.184\ \text{J}}{1\ \text{g} \times 0.13\ \text{joule/(g °C)}} = 32°\text{C}$

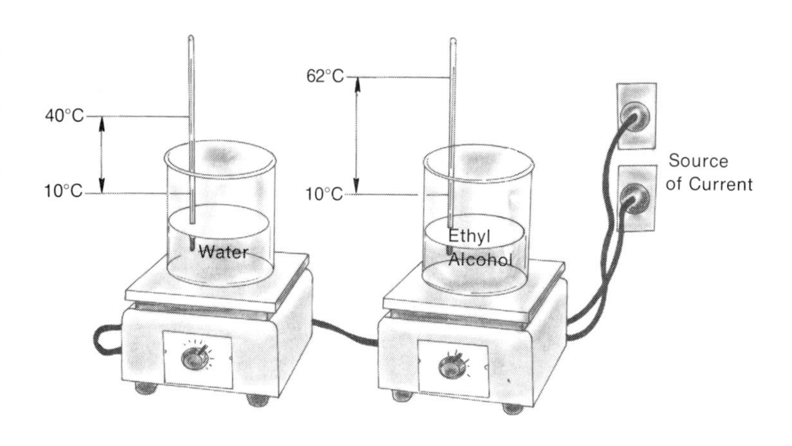

One commonly speaks of heat "flow" to describe its passage from one substance to another. But heat itself is not a substance, although early scientists assumed that it was. Since they could not detect this "substance," they assumed it was an invisible, tasteless, and odorless fluid. This magic material was called "caloric." By the eighteenth century, however, scientists realized that heat is not a material of any kind. It is difficult to define heat exactly; this is why we would rather describe it than define it. One famous thermodynamicist (J. H. Poincaré, as quoted in I. M. Klotz: *Chemical Thermodynamics*. New York, W. A. Benjamin, Inc., 1964) said, "The important thing is to know how to measure heat, not to know what heat really is."

The calorie is a small number to work with, so we often use the kilocalorie, abbreviated kcal, Calorie (capital C), or Cal: 1 kcal = 1000 cal = 1 Calorie. The energy values in food tables are given in Calories. Note also that the definition of calorie in terms of heating water is approximate, because the specific heat of water changes slightly with temperature.

TABLE 3-1. SPECIFIC HEATS OF SOME REPRESENTATIVE SUBSTANCES

Compound	Specific Heat joule/(g °C)
Mercury	0.14
Lead	0.13
Copper	0.38
Iron	0.45
Graphite	0.71
Oxygen gas	0.92
Ethyl alcohol	2.4
Water	4.184
Hydrogen gas	14.3

In a region of space near Jupiter, scientists have recorded temperatures of 300 to 400 million degrees Celsius, much hotter than the core of the Sun. Yet spacecraft passing through this region have not been harmed. The reason is that there is very little matter in these hot spots; they would be considered to be a vacuum in most laboratories on Earth. Therefore, there is very little heat held there, not enough to melt the instruments and electronic circuits of the spacecraft.

TABLE 3-2. DIFFERENT FORMS OF ENERGY

Form of Energy	Example
Kinetic	moving freight train flying cannonball
Gravitational potential	rock on a mountainside water behind a dam
Elastic potential	a stretched rubber band a taut bow
Heat	a warm pot of water a red-hot piece of steel
Chemical	a car battery a piece of coal
Mass	all matter
Nuclear	a piece of uranium
Radiant	a ray of light a laser beam
Electromagnetic	current moving in a wire
Sound	a lover's whisper the noise of an explosion

A Conduction.

Heat Transfer

Heat can be transferred from one body to another by **conduction, convection,** or **radiation.**

If you hold one end of a metal frying pan over a flame, the other end will soon get hot, for heat travels directly through the metal. This type of heat transfer is called conduction. When a substance absorbs heat, its atoms or molecules move more rapidly. When atoms or molecules in a solid are heated, they vibrate with greater energy and collide more frequently and more forcefully with neighboring atoms or molecules. These collisions transfer energy, and the neighboring atoms start to vibrate more rapidly. Thus, the energy from one end of our metal frying pan is passed along by collisions until the other end of the pan gets hot.

Materials differ in their ability to conduct heat. In general, metals and other good conductors of electricity are also good conductors of heat, whereas electrical insulators such as wood, glass, paper, and stone are poor heat conductors and are called thermal insulators.

Liquids and gases conduct heat, but they also permit transfer in other ways. Most liquids and all gases expand when they are heated. Therefore, hot materials are generally less dense than cold ones. A heater sitting on the floor in the corner of a room warms the air around itself. This warm air, being lighter than the air in the rest of the room, rises, displacing colder air downward. The cold air then comes in contact with the heater, becomes hot, and rises in turn. The continuous movement of hot air upward and cold air downward initiates a circulation in the room called a **convection current.** Although heat travels away from the heater by both conduction and convection, convection is a much more rapid process.

The space between the Earth and the Sun is largely empty of matter; it is a vacuum. Heat cannot travel across a vacuum by conduction or convection, because there are no molecules to move. Instead, heat travels from the Sun to us by **radiation,** in the form of electromagnetic waves. As we will learn in Chapter 6, hot objects such as cast-iron radiators or pot-bellied stoves also emit radiant heat, mostly in the infrared region of the spectrum.

3.6 POWER

In many technological applications it is essential to know more than how much work is being done—we must also know how much work is being done *per unit time*. Very simply, if an engineer designs a crane that can lift 4000 kg to a height of 30 m, a practical-minded contractor is apt to say, "Fine, but how fast can it lift the weight; how much material can it lift in an hour, or in a day?" The contractor is interested in power, not just in energy.

We must understand the relationship between energy and power. Briefly, energy is heat or work, while power is the amount of heat or work delivered in a given time interval.

$$\text{Power} = \frac{\text{energy}}{\text{time}}$$

The official SI unit of energy is the watt, abbreviated W.

$$1\ \text{W} = \frac{1\ \text{J}}{1\ \text{sec}}$$

For example, suppose that a strong weightlifter and a weaker child are both asked to carry several 10-kg boxes up a flight of steps. The powerful weightlifter might be able to carry several boxcs per trip and perform the job in a small amount of time, whereas the child could carry only one box at a time and would have to make many more trips. Both people perform the same total amount of work, but the weightlifter, who is more powerful, does the work in less time. Or, as another example, 837 J of energy are needed to heat 10 g of water from 0° C (freezing) to 20° C (room temperature). The correspondence between energy and the temperature rise of a quantity of water is an inherent property of water and is independent of how we do the operation. We could put the water on a hot plate, drop hot rocks in it, concentrate

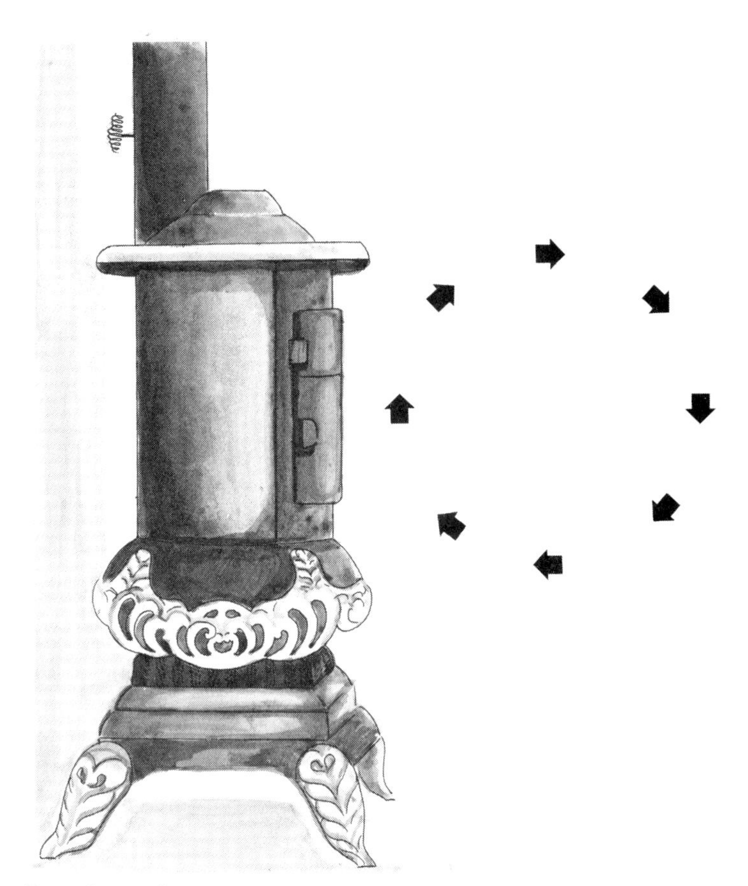

B Convection.

C Radiation.

sunlight on it, beat it vigorously with an egg beater, or do any other conceivable operation involving heat or work. The energy required to heat 10 g of water from 0° C to 20° C would always be 837 J. If we used a hot plate, we could choose to turn the switch to "low" and wait a while, or turn it to "high" and accelerate the process. When turned to "low," the hot plate uses small quantities of energy per unit time, but more time is required to deliver the 837 J. In the "high" position, large quantities of energy per unit time are delivered for a short while. The total energy delivered to the water is the same, but the power delivered in the two operations is different, simply because power is defined as the energy per unit time.

When you buy a light bulb or an appliance, it is generally rated according to the power that it consumes; that is, the amount of energy consumed in a given time interval. Thus, a 100-W heater uses energy at a rate of 100 J every second. But the electric company doesn't charge you for power, they charge for the total energy consumed. It makes no difference to them whether you use 100 J/sec for 1 sec or 10 J/sec for 10 sec; the energy consumed is the same. Electric bills are generally rated in units of kilowatt hours, abbreviated kWh. The units of a kWh are simply power × time. But since

$$\text{Power} = \frac{\text{energy}}{\text{time}}$$

$$\text{Power} \times \text{time} = \text{energy}$$

$$\text{kilowatts} \times \text{hours} = \text{kWh} = \text{energy}$$

The electric company charges for energy.

You can heat water in many different ways: by placing it on a hot plate set for "low" or "high," by focusing sunlight on it, by agitating it with an eggbeater, or by performing any conceivable work or heat operations. But the *energy* required to heat a given quantity of water through a given temperature rise will always be the same.

3.7 IMPULSE AND MOMENTUM

Collisions

Throughout this chapter, we have studied various ways in which energy can be transferred from one form to another or from one object to another. One common form of energy transfer is through collision. To understand collision theory, imagine that you are trying to unfasten a rusted bolt with a wrench. If no amount of pushing or pulling will free the bolt, what do you do? You bang on it, and very often a series of gentle taps, or angry smashes, will move it whereas a long steady pull will not. Similarly, an intruder who wishes to enter someone's house quickly through a locked door does not merely push against it: he rams it or smashes it. How is a sharp blow different from a steady push, and, in general, what is the physics of a collision?

Suppose you are driving along in a car at a constant speed, say, 80 km/hr. If you drive directly into a stone wall, you will stop so suddenly that the vehicle will be destroyed and the passengers injured or killed. On the other hand, if you apply the brakes gradually,

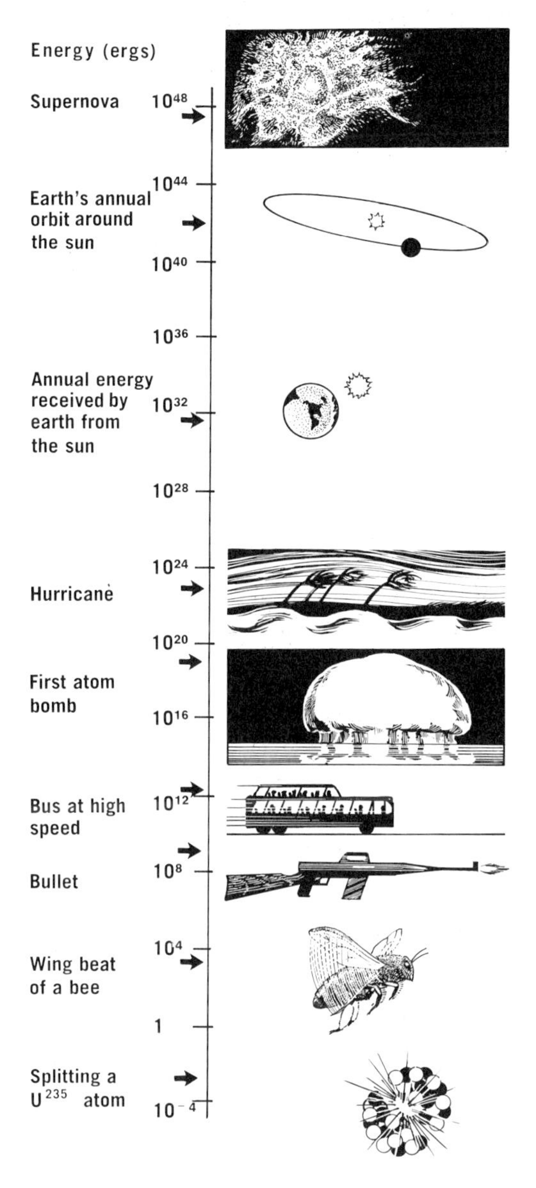

the vehicle will stop smoothly and uneventfully. Why is a sudden stop so much more forceful than a gradual one? When a vehicle is stopping, it is accelerating (remember that acceleration can be positive or negative). If it stops quickly, the magnitude of the acceleration is greater than if it stops gradually. But since

$$\text{force} = \text{mass} \times \text{acceleration}$$

the greater the acceleration, the greater will be the force.

Now we understand why a quick blow is more effective in loosening a jammed bolt than is a steady push. If you tap a wrench sharply, your hammer slows down rapidly, just as a car does when it hits a stone wall, and the rapid acceleration produces a lot of force. If you push down on the wrench slowly, the force delivered at any instant will be small, and the bolt will not budge. We learn the lesson that slow and steady does not always win the race; sometimes fast and jerky is the only solution.

With this background we can easily explain the purpose of bumpers or cushions. If you jump on a concrete floor you will stop quickly; it is like running into a solid wall. But if there is a cushion on the floor, you will decelerate more slowly because the cushion compresses under impact, thereby acting as a gradual brake. Therefore the time span of the collision is longer, and the force exerted is less. An automobile bumper serves the same function. In general, if you want to exert maximum force on an object, you hit it as sharply as possible; if you want to cushion a blow, you try to prolong the time of collision.

Any mechanical device that is likely to be involved in collision is designed with consideration for the force of impact. For example, a sledge hammer has a steel head, but the handle is made of wood. Even though wooden handles break occasionally no manufacturer has tried to sell a steel-handled sledge. When a person swings a sledge hammer against a stone, he wants to maximize the force exerted against the stone and minimize the force exerted against his hand. The head, therefore, is steel. Not only is steel durable but it also delivers a sharp, quick impact. The wooden handle, on the other hand, bends and compresses on impact, thus prolonging the time required to decelerate it and reducing the force exerted on the hand of the operator.

On September 8, 1974, the great motorcycle rider and daredevil Evel Kneivel tried to jump across the Snake River Canyon on a jet-powered motorcycle. The nose cone of his rocket motorcycle was purposely constructed in such a way that it would crumple on impact. The theory behind this design feature was that if the cycle did crash, the nose cone would crumple, thereby prolonging the time span of the collision and reducing the force of the impact. As a matter of fact, his machinery malfunctioned, and Evel crashed to the bottom of the canyon, but emerged unhurt.

Momentum

The momentum of a body is simply its mass times its velocity.

$$\overrightarrow{\text{momentum}} = \text{mass} \times \overrightarrow{\text{velocity}}$$

Since velocity is a vector quantity, momentum, $\overrightarrow{mv}$, is also a vector quantity, and we must therefore describe the mass, speed, and direction of a body in order to describe its momentum.

Evel Kneivel's epic and unsuccessful motorcycle jump across the Snake River Canyon.

Joule in 1849. Joule built a device that consisted of a series of paddle wheels immersed in a container of water and connected through pulleys to a set of weights, as shown schematically in Figure 3–4. The falling weights would rotate the pulleys and turn the paddle wheel. The spinning paddle moved against the frictional resistance of the water. Joule very carefully measured the work of the falling weights and the temperature rise of the water caused by the friction between the water and the paddles. He found that there was a direct relationship between work and heat. Joule then measured the conversion of work to heat by several other processes: by heating water electrically, by compressing gases with falling weights, and by forcing liquids through thin tubes. Each time he found the same relationship between work and heat. Energy never was lost but always was converted quantitatively from one form to another.

We now assume that if we carefully measured thousands or millions of systems, we would always arrive at the same conclusion: the total energy at the beginning of a series of operations always equals the total energy at the end—no more, no less. After many years of research on energy and energy systems, scientists are so sure that energy always will be conserved in any system that they have stated this conviction as a law of nature and called it the First Law of Thermodynamics. This law can be expressed concisely by the statement, *"Energy cannot be created or destroyed."* Or, to put it in other words, *"When mechanical work is converted into heat or heat into work, the amount of work is always equivalent to the quantity of heat."*

Of course, James Joule did not report his findings in joules; the unit was named later in his honor. His results, translated into modern units, were that 1 cal = 4.154 J, which is not bad in comparison with today's accepted value of 4.184.

But the lesson of the First Law is more inclusive and more subtle than is implied by the simple statement, "Energy cannot be created or destroyed." Suppose we take a box and shut it tightly so that no mass can enter or leave it. Such a box is called a **closed system.** Even though we cannot add or remove mass from a closed system, we can alter its internal energy. For example, if we place a flame near our system, it will heat up, or if the system has flexible boundaries like a balloon, we can squeeze it, thereby performing

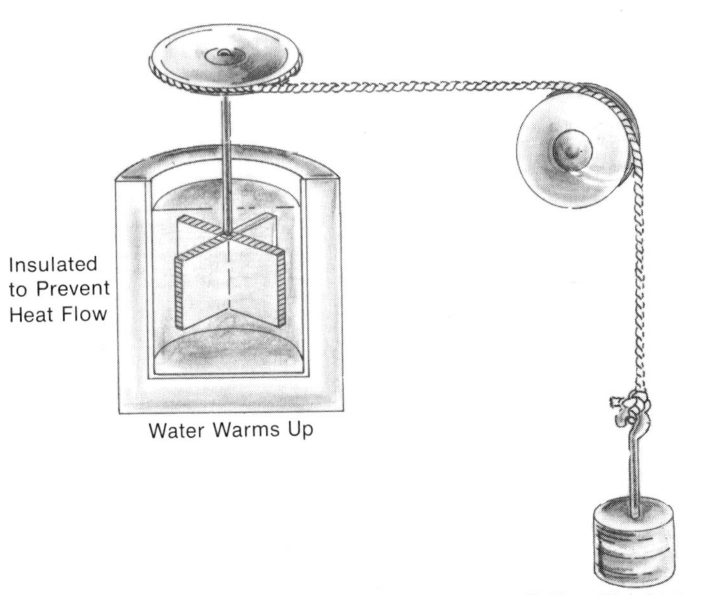

Figure 3–4. Schematic of Joule's experimental apparatus.

work on it without changing its mass.

The First Law states that the change in internal energy of a closed system is equal to the heat absorbed by the system minus the work done by it.

$$\begin{array}{c}\text{the change}\\ \text{of energy}\\ \text{in a system}\end{array} = \begin{array}{c}\text{heat}\\ \text{absorbed}\\ \text{by the}\\ \text{system}\end{array} - \begin{array}{c}\text{work done}\\ \text{by the}\\ \text{system}\end{array}$$

Thus, if a system absorbs 1 J of heat and does 1 J of work, the energy change is

$$\begin{array}{c}\text{Change in energy}\\ \text{of the system}\end{array} = 1\ \text{J} - 1\ \text{J} = 0$$

It will be instructive to follow a closed system through a series of work-heat operations. Since we can invent any closed system we want, we will choose a penny arcade crane as shown in Figure 3–5 and define the system as the volume encased in glass. This consists of a pile of jellybeans and a toy crane. The crane has a motor inside it, which can be operated electrically by a series of controls outside the system. Thus we can add electrical energy to the system without adding mass. Now, imagine that you start to operate the crane. You lift a load of jellybeans, thereby performing work on the system. When you release the jellybeans, they fall. Upon landing, the fallen jellybeans produce heat. So, by lifting and dropping jellybeans, you warm the system slightly. Suppose you raise the temperature from 20.0° C to 20.1° C. You could also raise the temperature of the system the same amount by direct addition of heat, simply by placing a candle under it.

We see that we can change the internal energy of any system from one state to another (from 20.0° C to 20.1° C in our example) by a variety of procedures. According to the First Law, a specific amount of energy (work + heat) is required to effect any change. It does not matter how we go about it; the energy required to change the system from one specific energy state to another is always the same. For exam-

Figure 3–5. Penny arcade crane. (Courtesy of Skip Conner.)

ple, if 1000 J are needed to raise the temperature 0.1° C by dropping jellybeans, 1000 J also will be required to raise the temperature 0.1° C by heating with a candle—no more, no less.

Don't ask for a proof of the First Law. There is none. Its validity, like that of many other basic scientific laws, comes not from a formal proof but from a broad range of experience. For many years, inventors tried to build a machine that operated without outside sources of power. Such a device, called a **perpetual motion machine,** would be able to create energy. All attempts failed. The First Law is simply a concise statement about our experience with energy. If it is impossible to create energy, it is hopeless to try to invent a perpetual motion machine, and we may as well turn to some other method of doing work.

The First Law says that we can never find energy for free. However, it is possible to build machines that operate very efficiently. Many modern devices are highly inefficient and could do the same job using less fuel if clever engineering practices were employed. For example, a subway train must accelerate away from a station and brake to a halt within a few minutes and then repeat the process during the entire operating day. Acceleration requires large amounts of energy. The brakes of a subway train operate by friction; they slow the train by rubbing a brake pad against a wheel. When the brakes are applied, the energy of motion of the train is converted to heat generated in the braking system. Thus most of the energy used to accelerate the train is dissipated as heat. In the summertime the braking mechanism raises the temperature of the cars and creates a need for increased air conditioning. Since the air conditioners also use energy, the whole system is highly inefficient.

An alternative subway system has been proposed, as shown in Figure 3–6. This design employs a large, heavy flywheel mounted under each car. This flywheel is designed so that it can be connected to the wheels of the train or to an electric generator, also mounted under the chassis of each car. Instead of applying conventional friction brakes, the train engineer would pull a lever connecting the wheels of each car to a flywheel. A great deal of energy would be required to set all the flywheels spinning. This energy would come from the kinetic energy of the train. In other words, instead of dissipating the kinetic energy of the train as heat, the engineer could convert the kinetic energy of the train to rotational energy of the flywheel and thereby stop the train. While the subway train rests at the station to pick up and discharge passengers, the flywheels would be spinning rapidly. Now, when power is needed to accelerate the train, the shafts of the flywheels could be connected to their electric generators. The motion of the flywheels would be converted to motion of the generators, electricity could be produced, this electricity would be used to power the train, and the train would speed up while the flywheels would slow down again. The train could produce some of its own

Since the beginning of civilization, people have been faced with the problem of how to lift heavy loads. Buildings have been traditionally built of wood or stone, and engineers have had to move these heavy items from the ground onto the walls and roofs. In the early days, we can imagine that people worked together to lift stones and timbers. Later, clever inventors developed simple machines such as the lever, the wheel, and the inclined plane. A person who can lift 50 kg unaided can lift hundreds of kilograms with a lever and even more with a well-designed system of gears or pulleys. In the early days, engineers believed that machines actually reduced the amount of work required to lift an object. Scientists now understand that such devices do not actually reduce the amount of work. Instead, they spread it out over a longer period of time and smooth out the effort. However, this difference can easily be overlooked, and a device such as a lever can be mistakenly thought of as a "work-saver". Since many "work-savers" had been invented, people reasoned that if you were clever enough you could build a machine that would do all the work for free. They called this imaginary device a **perpetual motion machine.** If you owned a perpetual motion machine you could turn it on and it would lift all the boulders you wanted while you sat and watched. It may be difficult for the modern reader to appreciate that the search for the perpetual motion machine seemed entirely reasonable. Many very clever people looked for a solution. However, all attempts failed. The failures have been so consistent that we are now convinced that the effort is hopeless. We believe that it is a fundamental law of nature that it is impossible to build a perpetual motion machine.

"Waterfall," by M. C. Escher. (Reproduced by permission.)

Figure 3–6. Flywheel-operated subway train.

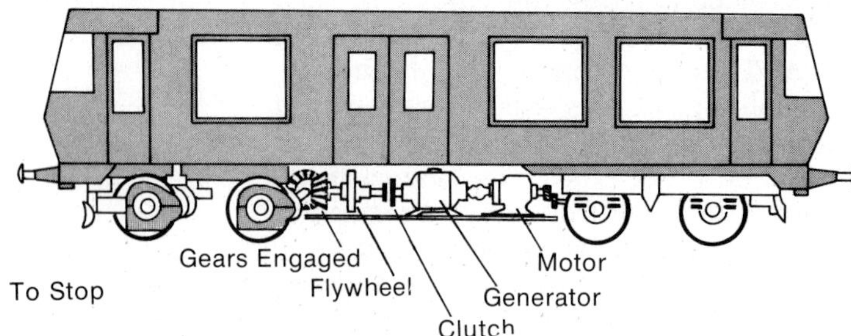

To Stop

When the train is stopping, the kinetic energy of the train is converted to rotational energy of the spinning flywheel. Notice that the clutch is disengaged and there is a gap between the flywheel and the generator. Thus the generator does not spin.

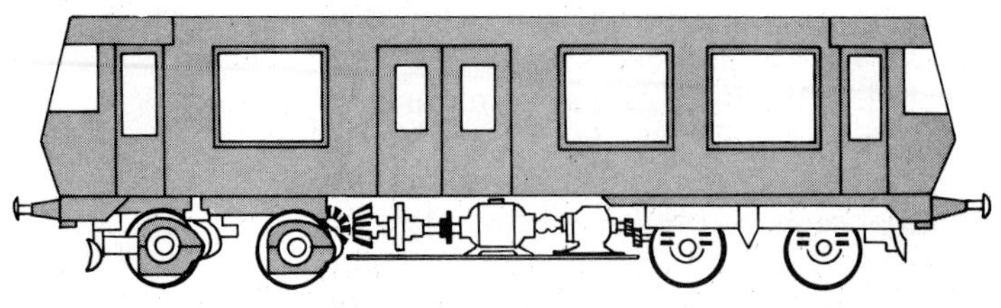

To Start

When the engineer wishes to start the train, the clutch is engaged, connecting the flywheel to the generator. The spinning flywheel forces the generator to turn, thereby producing electricity. This electrical energy drives the motor and helps the train to accelerate.

electric power and in doing so would diminish the need for air conditioning as well.

Naturally, there would be some heat losses in such a system, and outside power would be needed, but much less than is needed at present. This is just one example of how we can conserve energy without curtailing our conveniences. An experimental flywheel car has been built and tested successfully. However, in the 1970's the additional labor required to build, produce, and maintain the cars was more expensive than the cost of the energy saved. In the United States, energy has traditionally been cheap relative to the cost of labor. However, as our resources dwindle and the price of fuels skyrockets, the situation is changing rapidly.

3.10 HEAT ENGINES AND THE SECOND LAW OF THERMODYNAMICS (OR, YOU CAN'T BREAK EVEN)

We have learned that heat is a form of energy and that heat can be converted to work. This concept, obvious to most of us today, was not always easily recognized. In fact, heat engines have been used successfully only during the past 200 years or so. (James Watt developed his steam engine in 1769.) Heat and work are two forms of energy, and it is therefore possible to convert heat into work or work into heat. Thus one can create heat by rubbing two sticks together, and the heat produced is exactly equivalent in energy to the work required to rub the sticks. It is also known that fuels contain potential heat. Thus, a kilogram of coal contains stored energy, which can be released by combustion. But heat is also stored in substances that are not fuels—in such ordinary substances as water. Hot water in a bathtub can heat your body; therefore, the water must *have* energy. Why not, then, use this energy to drive a machine to do work? Such a machine, although seemingly not quite so miraculous as the perpetual motion machine of the first kind, would extract energy from its surroundings (for example, from the air or from the ocean) and convert it into useful work. The air or water would then be cooled by the extraction of energy from it, and could be returned to the environment. Automobiles could then run on air, and the exhaust would be cool air. A power plant located on a river would cool the river while it lighted the city. Such a machine would *not* violate the First Law, because energy would be conserved. The work would come from the energy extracted from the air or water, not from an impossibly profitable creation of energy. Such a device is called a **perpetual motion machine of the second kind;** alas, it too has never been made and never will be.

The formulation of the Second Law, like that of the First, arose out of a long series of observations. If we place a hot iron bar on a cold one, the hot bar always cools while the cold one becomes warmer, until both pieces of metal are at the same temperature. No one has ever observed any other behavior. Similarly, if a small quantity of blue ink is dropped into a glass of water, the ink will disperse until the solution becomes uniformly light blue. The ink does not stay concentrated in one section of the clear water.

Thus there appears to be a natural drive towards sameness or disorder. If we have two blocks of iron at different temperatures in a system, or a spot of ink in a glass of water, there is a differentiation of physical properties. Such differentiation results from some kind of *orderly* arrangement among the individual parts of the system. This is a subtle but important point. In your experience, how is *order* different from *disorder*? The answer is that *order* is characterized by repeated *separations*. Your room is orderly if all the books are separated from your socks; books on the shelves, socks in the drawer. It is disorderly if books and socks are all mixed up in both places. Similarly, if a small spot of blue ink is *separated* from clear water the system is *orderly*. Which system is more natural (that is, more probable)? That's easy—if you neglect your room, does it naturally become more orderly or disorderly? *Disorderly*, of course! The reason is that there are always *more* ways to be disorderly than to be orderly (or, there are more ways to break rules than to follow them). Therefore, any system, if left alone, will tend towards disorder. **Entropy** is a thermodynamic measure of disorder, and it has been observed *that the entropy of an undisturbed system always increases during any spontaneous process;* that is, the degree of disorder always increases. Thus, if you drop a spot of ink in water, the ink will spread out evenly throughout the liquid. It will become disorderly. If you don't clean your room regularly, it will become messy. Similarly, an automobile that extracted heat from the air to run the engine and released cool air as exhaust would cause a separation of hot and cold. This is a more orderly arrangement. Any separation leads to a decrease of entropy of the system, and this is impossible to do without adding energy from some outside source.

Let us return now from the impossible to heat engines that use fuel, where the situation continues to be discouraging. It was learned through experiment that the potential energy inherent in a fuel could never be completely converted into work; some was always lost to the surroundings. We say lost only in the sense that this energy was no longer available to do work; what it did, instead, was warm the environment. Ingenious scientists did try to invent heat engines that would convert *all* the energy of a fuel into work, but they always failed. It was found, instead, that a heat engine could be made to work *only* by the following two sets of processes: (a) Heat must be absorbed by the working parts from some hot source. The hot source is generally provided when some substance such as water or air (called the working substance) is heated by the energy obtained from a fuel, such as wood, coal, oil, or uranium. (b) Waste heat must be rejected to an external reservoir at a lower temperature.

A heat engine cannot work any other way. The original form of this negative statement, as made by Lord Kelvin (1824–1907) is; "It is impossible by means of inanimate material agency to derive mechanical effect from any portion of matter by cooling it below the temperature of the coldest of the surrounding objects." This is an expression of the **Second Law of Thermodynamics.**

The Second Law of Thermodynamics states: Any undisturbed system will naturally tend toward maximum disorder. If a drop of ink is placed in a glass of water, the ink will always disperse until it is evenly distributed.

To gain further insight into this very fundamental concept, imagine a few simple experiments with gases. We observe that when a gas is heated its pressure increases. Thus, if you heat a balloon it will expand; heated steam in a locomotive moves the piston that drives the engine.

Consider a cylinder full of gas with a freely sliding piston in the center (Figure 3–7*A*). Suppose that the system is heated until the gas on the left side of the piston reaches 300° C, while the gas on the right stays at 0° C. The heated gas on the left would expand and force the piston to the right, as shown in Figure 3–7*B*. This, then, is a simple heat engine. Heat is converted to motion of the piston. Now suppose that you

William Thomson (later Lord Kelvin) was a British physicist who proposed the absolute scale of temperature (the Kelvin scale) in 1848. His major contributions to science were in the field of thermodynamics.

Early steam engines operated at about 5 per cent efficiency. That means that only 5 per cent of the potential energy of a fuel was converted to work, and 95 per cent was lost to the environment as heat. It was soon found that higher efficiencies could be obtained by improving the design of the engine, but even today, steam locomotives seldom operate at more than 10 to 15 per cent efficiency.

The author's desk when it is (a) neat and (b) messy. Unless work is performed to clean the desk, it will tend to stay messy, because the entropy of the messy desk is higher than that of the desk when it is orderly.

Steam locomotive.

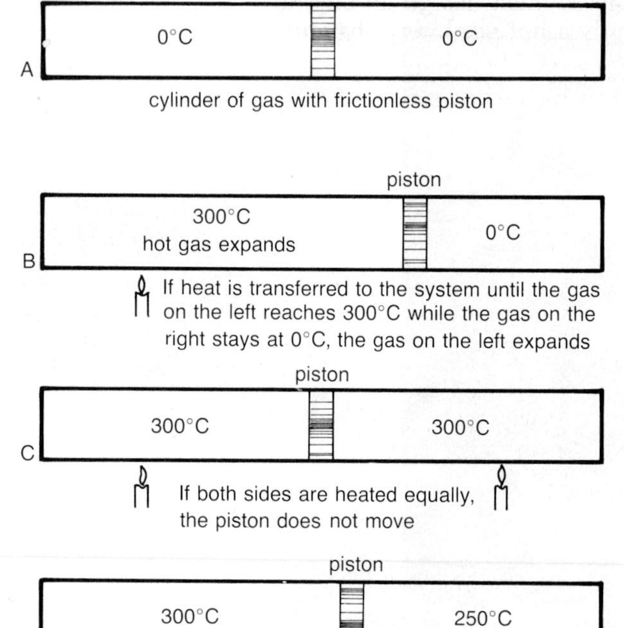

Figure 3–7. A piston moves in response to the temperature difference between the two sides.

started over again with the piston in the center and heated both sides of the cylinder equally (Fig. 3–7C). The gas in the left side would warm and exert a pressure against the piston, but this effect would be equally balanced by the pressure of the hot gas in the right-hand chamber. Since the two pressures would be equal, the piston would not move and the heat would not be converted to work. The piston moves only if the temperature on one side of the cylinder is greater than the temperature on the other. The amount of work performed depends on the *difference* in temperature between the two sides. What does this have to do with heat engines and energy? If one side of the apparatus is heated to 300° C while the other side is maintained at 0° C, the piston will move a large distance, whereas if we heat one side to 300° C and the other to 250° C (Fig. 3–7C), much more heat energy is used but less motion is realized. Since the work performed by the piston is proportional to the distance that it moves, little work is realized in this latter example. We immediately see that the *work performed by a heat engine depends on the temperature difference between the hot reservoir and the cold reservoir.*

Heat energy is useful only if large differences in temperature can be realized. Suppose a mass of coal is burned in a steam locomotive. The heat is converted to useful work and the engine travels from Paris to Amsterdam. When the engine arrived in Amsterdam, the coal would be gone. What happened to the energy? Could you somehow find it, save it, and use it to drive the train back to Paris? The answer is no. The heat from the coal was spread out into the environment. The air between Paris and Amsterdam was warmed lightly. But the locomotive cannot extract enough energy from the warm air to drive back to Paris. Thus, the energy from the coal cannot be recycled. This observation is a general one, and explains why energy, once used, cannot be reused to perform work efficiently. In brief, materials can be recycled but energy cannot.

There are three important practical consequences of the Second Law. The first is that since the efficiency of any heat engine is proportional to the temperature difference between the hot working parts and the cooler surroundings, engineers must design an engine with not only a hot working substance but also an adequate cooling system. The second consequence is that when-

Energy lost to the environment as heat cannot be recycled to drive the locomotive back to Paris.

ever any fuel is used to operate a heat engine, some waste heat is discharged into the environment, and it is therefore impossible to convert all of the potential energy of the fuel to useful work. Finally, as stated above, a fuel can be used only once; after it has been burned and the heat converted to work, the energy cannot be recycled.

3.11 GENERATION OF ELECTRIC POWER

Most of the electricity generated in the world today is produced in steam-driven power plants. Here water is boiled using the heat available from coal, oil, gas, or nuclear fuel. The hot steam is allowed to expand against the blades of a turbine. A turbine is a device that spins when air or water is forced against it. You can think of it as a kind of enclosed windmill. The hot, expanding steam forces the turbine to spin. The spinning turbine then operates a generator which produces electricity. After the steam has passed through the turbine it is cooled, liquefied, and returned to the boiler to be reused. Normally the steam is cooled with river, lake or ocean water. The cooling action of the condenser is essential to the whole generating process.

To understand this important concept, let us return to the discussion on the Second Law of Thermodynamics. Recall that a piston moves when the gases on the two sides of a cylinder are at different temperatures. If both sides are heated equally, there is no movement, and hence no work is performed. Maximum work is realized if one side of the cylinder is hot and the other is cool. A steam turbine operates on this general principle. Hot gases expand against the turbine blades. If the exhaust gases are cooled, then the hot steam has more room to expand into and more work can be performed. Therefore, some provision must be made to cool the steam at one end of the engine.

In practice, cooling is accomplished by circulating water around the condenser. It is obvious that maximum efficiency is reached with very hot

Figure 3–8. Schematic view of an electric generator.

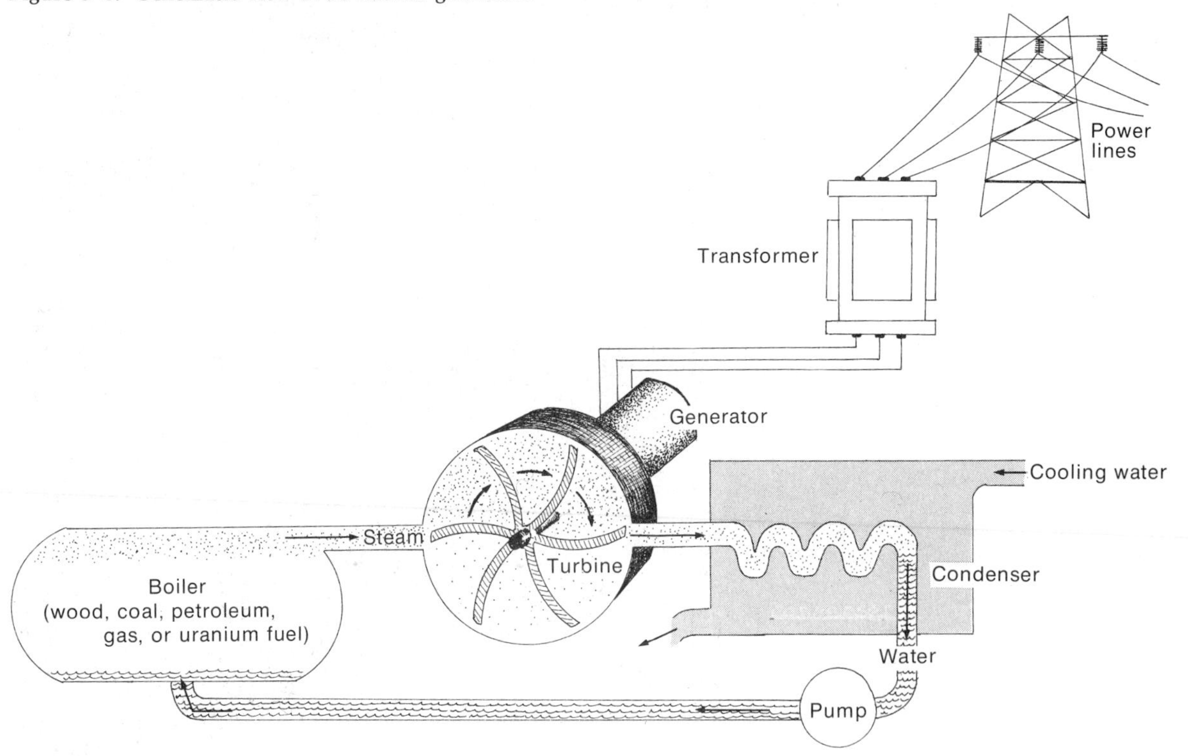

steam and a very cool condenser. In practice, the nature of the metals in the turbine limits the temperature to a maximum of about 540° C. The low temperature is limited by the cheapest coolant, generally water. Within the constraints of these two limits, an efficiency of 60 per cent is theoretically possible, but uncontrollable variations in steam temperature, and miscellaneous heat losses, reduce the efficiency to about 40 per cent, even in the best installations. This level means that for every 100 units of potential energy in the form of fuel, 40 units of electrical energy are available as useful work and 60 units of energy are dissipated to the surroundings as heat.

Nuclear-fueled power plants are less efficient than fossil-fueled units operating at the same cooling temperature. Since the metals that contain the fuel cells must survive radioactive stresses as well as heat stresses, lower operating temperatures are used, and as we have learned from the Second Law of Thermodynamics, the smaller the temperature difference between engine and coolant, the less efficient the engine.

Although a modern electric power plant is only 40 per cent efficient, it is more efficient than other common heat engines. A large diesel is 38 per cent efficient, an automobile is 25 per cent, and a steam locomotive is only 10 per cent efficient. Therefore, electricity is an efficient way to perform work. Less fuel is needed to operate an electric lawn mower or car than gas-powered machines. But electric *heaters* are fundamentally inefficient. The inefficiency arises because heat is first converted to work at the power plant, and 60 per cent of the available energy is lost dur-

A turbine being replaced at TVA's Wheeler Dam. (Courtesy of Tennessee Valley Authority.)

ing the work to heat conversion.* On the other hand, a direct fuel heater, such as a gas stove, delivers the heat directly where it is needed, and there is very little waste.

3.12 THERMAL POLLUTION

Large quantities of heat are released from modern electrical generating stations. For example, a 1000-megawatt facility, running at 40 per cent efficiency, would heat 120 million liters (L) of water by 8.5° C every *hour*. A 1000-megawatt nuclear plant, operating at about 32 per cent efficiency, would require 200 million L of coolant water every hour. In many systems, lake, river, or ocean water is used as a coolant. It is not surprising that such large quantities of heat, added to aquatic systems, cause ecological disruptions. The term **thermal pollution** has been used to describe these heat effects.

What happens when the outflow from a large generating station raises the water temperature of a river or lake? Fish are cold-blooded animals. This means that their body temperature increases or decreases with the temperature of the water. In natural systems, water temperatures are relatively constant. When the temperature is raised, all the body processes of a fish (its metabolism) speed up. As a result, the animal needs more oxygen, just as you need to breathe harder when you speed up your metabolism by running. But hot water holds less dissolved oxygen than cold water. Therefore, cold-water

*An additional 7 per cent of the original energy is lost during transmission, so that a total of 67 per cent of the fuel energy is lost before the electricity is delivered to your home.

"It's not the humidity—It's the thermal pollution." (Am. Sci., Sept.–Oct., 1971.)

fish may suffocate in warm water. In addition, warm water can cause outright death through failure of the nervous system. In general, not only fish but also the entire aquatic ecosystems are rather sensitively affected by temperature changes. For example, many animals lay their eggs and plants disperse seeds in the springtime when the water naturally becomes warm. If a power plant heats the water in midwinter, some organisms may start reproducing. But if the eggs are hatched at this time, the young may not find the food needed to survive.

The careful reader will note an apparent discrepancy here. If an operating efficiency of 40 per cent from a fossil-fuel plant yields 120 million liters of warm water, a nuclear plant at 32 per cent efficiency should warm 135 million liters, not 200 million. The difference is accounted for by the fact that some of the heat from the fossil-fuel plant is not absorbed by water, but instead warms up a lot of *air*, by means of the hot gases discharged from the stacks. This is ecologically less disrupting than the warming of streams and lakes. Therefore, the difference in thermal pollution between the two types of plants is greater than that implied by thermodynamic considerations alone.

3.13 SOLUTIONS TO THE PROBLEM OF THERMAL POLLUTION

The Second Law of Thermodynamics assures us that it is impossible to invent a process to avoid the production of waste heat in steam-fired turbines. It is possible, however, to reduce the amount of heat wasted, to put it to good use, or to dispose of it into the environment with minimal disruption to ecological systems. Some suggestions are described in the following paragraphs.

Use of Waste Steam in Industry (Cogeneration)

Waste steam is too cool to produce work efficiently, but it is hot enough for many other industrial processes. For example, the steam can be used to cook food in a cannery, to heat wood pulp in a paper mill, or to process petroleum in an oil refinery. In the United States most of the waste steam for electric generation is discarded, leading to thermal pollution, but in Europe, much of the waste steam is sold to other industries. Energy is conserved, and pollution problems reduced (see Figure 3–9). Some companies in the United States do utilize their excess heat efficiently. One example is the relationship between the Baywood, New Jersey, refinery of Humble Oil and Refining Company and the Linden, New Jersey, generating station. The Linden power plant is capable of producing electricity at 39 per cent efficiency. For more than a decade and a half, this efficiency has been lowered by less than optimum cooling of the condenser, and some of the waste heat has been sold as steam to Humble. If we consider the two-plant operation as a single energy unit, the overall efficiency of power production has been raised to a level of 54 per cent. The process is beneficial to many: the companies save money, fuel reserves are conserved, and thermal pollution of waterways is reduced.

For many years, the word *pollute* has meant to impair the purity of, either morally* or physically.† The terms *air pollution* and *water pollution* refer to the impairment of the normal compositions of air and water by the addition of foreign matter, such as sufuric acid. Within the past few years two new expressions, *thermal pollution* and *noise pollution*, have become common. Neither of these refers to the impairment of purity by the addition of foreign matter. Thermal pollution is the impairment of the quality of environmental air by raising its temperature. The relative intensity of thermal pollution cannot be assessed with a thermometer, because what is pleasantly warm water for a person can be death to a trout. Thermal pollution must therefore be appraised by observing the effect on an ecosystem of a rise in temperature. Similarly, noise pollution has nothing to do with purity: foul air can be quiet, and pure air can be noisy. Noise pollution (to be discussed in Chapter 11) is the impairment of the environmental quality of air by noise.

*(1857.) Buckle, *Civilization*, 1, viii, p. 526: The clergy . . . urging him to exterminate the heretics, whose presence they thought polluted France.

†(1585.) T. Washington, trans. *Nicholay's Voyage*, IV; ii; p. 115: No drop of the bloud should fall into he water, least the same shuld thereby be polluted.

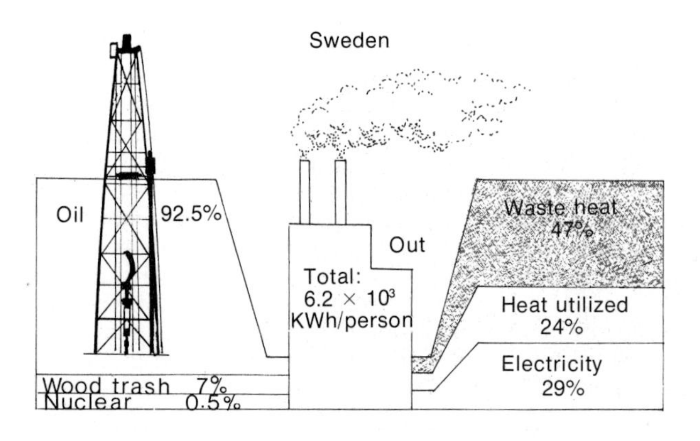

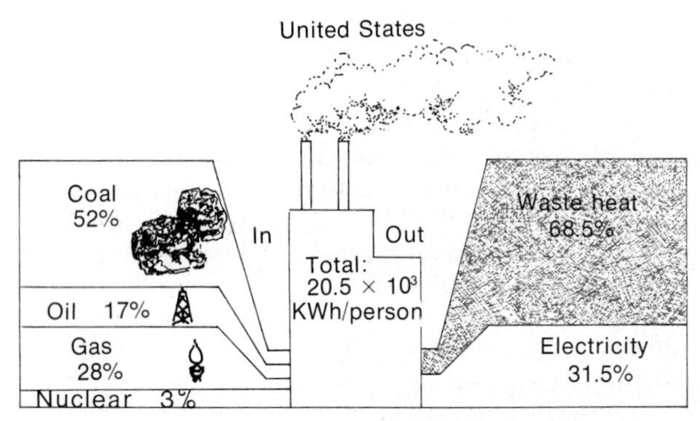

Figure 3–9. Use of fuel to produce electricity in Sweden and the United States. (kWh is an abbreviation for kilowatt hours, a unit of energy.) (From *Science*, Vol. 194, Dec. 1976, p. 1001.)

Other Uses of Waste Heat

Waste steam from electrical generators can be piped directly to home radiators and used for heating. Many European cities have installed piping networks to link power plants to homes and apartment buildings, but the United States has lagged in this area. In the United States, energy has been relatively cheap, whereas labor is expensive. Therefore, conservation programs have not always been immediately economical. However, as fuel costs continue to rise, conservation becomes more and more attractive.

How to Use the Atmosphere as a Sink

Another approach to the problem of thermal insult to our waterways is to dispose of heat into the air. Air has much less capacity per unit volume for absorbing heat than water does, so the direct action of air as the cooling medium in the condenser is not economically feasible. For this reason power plants must still be located near a source of water, the only other available coolant. However, the water can be made to lose some of its heat to the atmosphere and then can be recycled into the condenser. Various devices are available that can effect such a transfer.

The two cheapest techniques are based on the fact that evaporation of water is a cooling process. Many power plants simply maintain their own shallow lakes, called **cooling ponds.** Hot water is pumped into the pond, where evaporation as well as direct contact with the air cools it, and the cool water is drawn into the condenser from some point distant from the discharge pipe.

DOONESBURY by Garry Trudeau

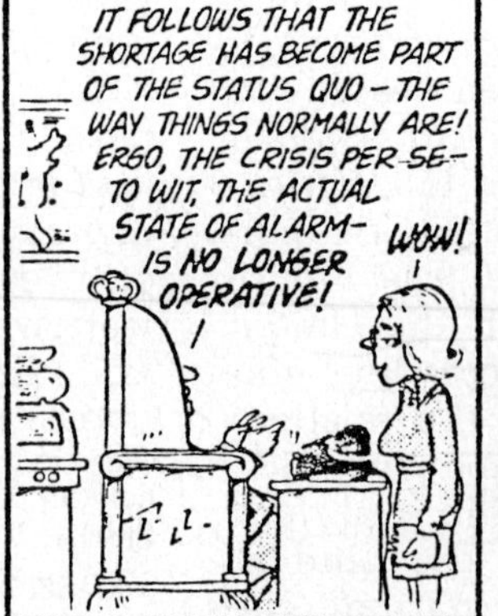

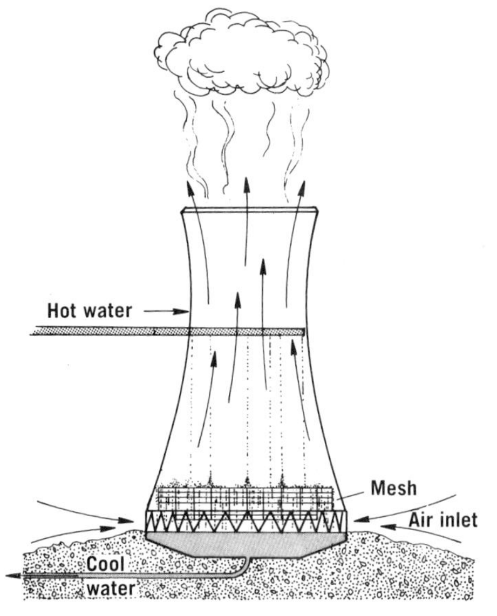

Evaporative cooling tower.

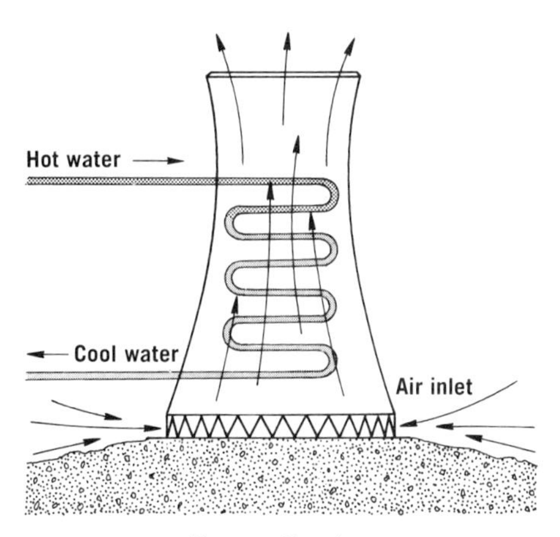

Dry cooling tower.

Water from outside sources must be added periodically to replenish evaporative losses. Cooling ponds are practical where land is cheap, but a 1000-megawatt plant needs 400 to 800 hectares (1000 to 2000 acres) of surface, and the land costs can be prohibitive.

A cooling tower, which can serve as a substitute for a cooling pond, is a large structure, about 180 m in diameter at the base and 150 m high. Hot water is pumped into the tower near the top and sprayed downward onto a mesh. Air is pulled into the tower either by large fans or convection currents and flows through the water mist. Evaporative cooling occurs, and the cool water is collected at the bottom. No hot water is introduced into aquatic ecosystems, but a large cooling tower loses over four million liters of water per day to evaporation. Thus, fogs and mists are common in the vicinity of these units, reducing the sunshine in nearby areas. These fogs and mists are less ecologically disruptive than the thermal pollution of waterways, but they do affect the quality of the environment. Many new electrical generating stations are using cooling towers to dispose of waste heat.

Environmental problems can be re-

This large cooling tower dwarfs the nuclear reactor at a reactor site in southern Washington.

duced even further if dry cooling towers are used instead of evaporative wet ones. A dry tower is nothing more than a huge version of an automobile radiator installed into a tower to promote a speedy flow of air past the cooling pipes. Dry towers are very expensive because of the cost of the prodigious amount of piping required.

CHAPTER OBJECTIVES

Be familiar with the concepts of energy, work, kinetic energy, potential energy, chemical energy, heat, power, collision, and momentum. Understand the two Laws of Thermodynamics, entropy, and the relationship between heat and work. You should be able to explain why the efficiency of an engine such as a steam turbine depends on the difference in temperature between the hot, working parts and the cooler exhaust.

KEY WORDS

Work
Kinetic energy
Potential energy
Gravitation potential energy
Elastic potential energy
Chemical potential energy
Temperature
Celsius scale
Heat conduction
Convection
Radiation
Power
Momentum
First Law of Thermodynamics
Perpetual motion machine
Closed system
Second Law of Thermodynamics
Entropy
Thermal pollution

FORMULAS TO KNOW

1. Work = force × distance
   Work = F × d

2. Kinetic energy = ½ mass × (velocity)^2
   KE = ½ mv^2

Example 1
A man pushes against a stalled car with a force of 400 newtons, thereby moving the vehicle 2 m. How much work has he performed?

Answer:
Work = force × distance
Work = 400 N = 2 m = 800 newton-meters
Recall that
1 newton-meter = 1 J
so the answer is expressed as:
Work = 800 J

Example 2
A little boy in the Netherlands is walking near the seacoast and sees that a stone is about to fall out of the bottom of the dike. He knows that if the stone does fall out, the sea will rush in and flood the land, so the brave boy holds the stone in place against the push of the savage sea. He exerts a force of 100 N, thereby keeping the stone stationary. How much work has he performed on the stone after holding it for 10 hours?

Answer: Work = force × distance
Since the stone is stationary, the distance is zero, and therefore the work performed on the stone by the boy is zero.

Example 3
(a) There are two vehicles, both traveling at the same velocity; but the first vehicle is twice as massive as the second. How much more kinetic energy does the more massive vehicle have? (b) Now imagine that there are two vehicles of equal mass, but the first one is traveling at twice the velocity as the second. How much more kinetic energy does the faster vehicle have?

Answer: (a) KE = ½ mv^2

Since we do not know either the mass or the velocity of either vehicle, it is impossible to calculate the kinetic energy of either; we can only compare the two.

For simplicity we will write the kinetic energy of the first vehicle as KE_1, and the kinetic energy of the second as KE_2. Similarly the mass and velocity of the vehicles will be written as m_1, m_2, v_1, and v_2, respectively. Using these shorthand notations, we write:

$$KE_1 = \tfrac{1}{2} m_1 (v_1)^2$$

$$KE_2 = \tfrac{1}{2} m_2 (v_2)^2$$

According to the rules of algebra, two equations can be divided by each other.

$$\frac{KE_1}{KE_2} = \frac{\frac{1}{2}\, m_1\, (v_1)^2}{\frac{1}{2}\, m_2\, (v_2)^2}$$

But since the number "½" appears in both the numerator and the denominator, this constant can be cancelled. Similarly, the two velocities are equal so they too can be cancelled.

$$\frac{KE_1}{KE_2} = \frac{\cancel{\frac{1}{2}}\, m_1\, (\cancel{v_1})^2}{\cancel{\frac{1}{2}}\, m_2\, (\cancel{v_2})^2}$$

or,

$$\frac{KE_1}{KE_2} = \frac{m_1}{m_2}$$

Since,

$$m_1 = 2\, m_2$$

$$\frac{KE_1}{KE_2} = \frac{2\, m_2}{m_2}$$

or,

$$\frac{KE_1}{KE_2} = \frac{2}{1}$$

or, the first vehicle has twice the kinetic energy as the second vehicle.

(b) Similarly, for question (b):

$$\frac{KE_1}{KE_2} = \frac{\frac{1}{2}\, m_1\, (v_1)^2}{\frac{1}{2}\, m_2\, (v_2)^2}$$

In this case the masses are identical, and

$$v_1 = 2\, v_2$$

so,

$$\frac{KE_1}{KE_2} = \frac{(2\, v_2)^2}{{v_2}^2}$$

$$\frac{KE_1}{KE_2} = \frac{4\, {v_2}^2}{{v_2}^2} = 4$$

or, the first vehicle has four times the kinetic energy of the second vehicle.

3.

$$\text{Gravitational potential} = \text{mass} \times \text{acceleration due to gravity} \times \text{height}$$

$$= mgh$$

Example 4
A rock climber with a mass of 75 kg is 5 m above a ledge and 200 m above the ground. How much potential energy would be released if the climber (a) fell to the ledge? (b) fell all the way to the ground?

Answer
(a) PE = mgh

$$PE = 75\ \text{kg} \times \frac{9.8\ \text{m}}{\text{sec}^2} \times 5\ \text{m}$$

$$= 3675\, \frac{\text{kg m}^2}{\text{sec}^2}$$

but since,

$$1\ \text{J} = 1\, \frac{\text{kg} \times \text{m}^2}{\text{sec}^2},$$ the answer is written as:

$$PE = 3675\ \text{J}$$

(b) $PE = 75\ \text{kg} \times \frac{9.8\ \text{m}}{\text{sec}^2} \times 200\ \text{m} = 147{,}000\ \text{J}.$

4. $\text{Power} = \frac{\text{energy}}{\text{time}}$

Example 5
(a) How much power does an 800-watt heater consume? (b) How much energy does it use in 1 sec; (c) 1 hr; (d) 1 day?

Answer. (a) Watt (W) is a unit of power. Therefore, as stated, the heater uses 800 W.

(b) $\text{Power} = \frac{\text{energy}}{\text{time}}$

rearranging,

$$\text{Energy} = \text{power} \times \text{time}$$

since,

$$1\ \text{W} = \frac{1\ \text{J}}{\text{sec}}$$

the energy in 1 sec is,

$$\text{Energy} = \frac{800\ \text{J}}{\text{sec}} \times 1\ \text{sec} = 800\ \text{J}$$

(c) There are 3600 sec in 1 hr, so, the energy in 1 hr $= \frac{800\ \text{J}}{\text{sec}} \times 3600\ \text{sec} = 2.88 \times 10^6\ \text{J}.$

The answer could also be expressed as,

Energy = 800 W × 1 hr = 800 watt-hours, or 0.8 kWh.

(d) Since there are 8.64×10^4 sec in a day, the energy in 1 day is,

$$\frac{800\ \text{J}}{\text{sec}} \times 8.64 \times 10^4\ \text{sec} = 6.9 \times 10^7\ \text{J}.$$

The answer could also be expressed as,

Energy = 800 W × 24 hr = 19,200 watt-hours, or 19.2 kWh.

5. Momentum before a collision equals momentum after a collision.

$$m_1 v_1 = m_2 v_2$$

Example 6
Suppose an automobile with a mass of 1000 kg were traveling at a rate of 80 km/hr and crashed into a cement truck with a mass of 20,000 kg. If the automobile was stopped completely, how fast would the cement truck travel after the collision?

Answer: momentum of automobile = momentum of cement truck

$$m_1v_1 = m_2v_2$$

$$1000 \text{ kg} \times \frac{80 \text{ km}}{\text{hr}} = 20{,}000 \text{ kg} \times v_2$$

$$v_2 = \frac{1000 \text{ kg} \times \frac{80 \text{ km}}{\text{hr}}}{20{,}000 \text{ kg}}$$

$$v_2 = \frac{4 \text{ km}}{\text{hr}}$$

TAKE-HOME EXPERIMENTS

1. **Work.** Place a box weighing 10 to 25 kg in the center of a smooth floor. Tie a rope around it as shown in the sketch and connect the rope to a spring scale. Pulling evenly on the scale, slide the box a measured distance across the floor. Record the force needed to pull the box. Calculate the work performed. (If a spring scale is unavailable, you can perform the same experiment by using a conventional bathroom scale, setting it behind the box and pushing while you read the force applied, as shown in sketch *b*.

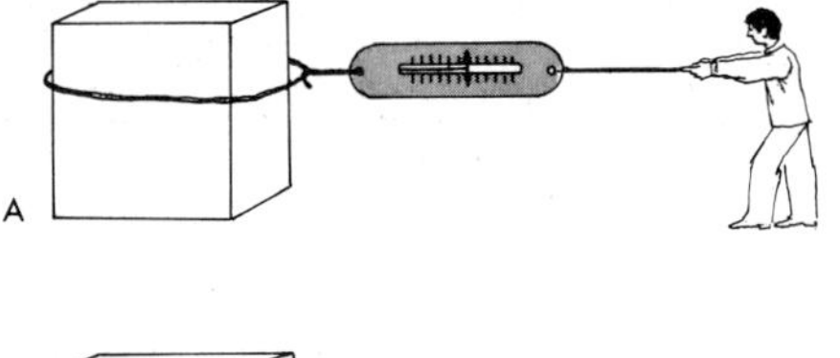

2. **Work and heat.** Place a ¼-inch bit in an electric drill, and drill a hole in a piece of soft pine. Now feel the bit (carefully!) with your fingers. Is it cool, warm, or hot? Next let the drill bit cool to room temperature, and then drill a hole in a piece of metal. What is the temperature of the bit now? Discuss your results. If possible, repeat the experiment, comparing a dull bit with a sharp one and record the results.

3. **Work and heat.** Take a bowl of cold water and record the temperature. Beat the water vigorously with a fork, or if available, an electric egg beater. Record the temperature again. What do you observe? Explain.

4. **Heat.** Turn a hot plate or electric stove heater on to the lowest setting and let it warm up until it reaches a constant temperature. If you have a gas stove, turn on a low flame. Place 250 mL of water in a pan, and record the temperature. Next place the pan on the stove for 5 min, then record the temperature again. Repeat the experiment using 500 mL of water, and again with 250 mL of cooking oil. Record and interpret your results.

5. **Heat.** Heat 250 mL of water and 250 mL of cooking oil in separate pans to 50° C. Place both pans in the refrigerator. Record the temperature in each pan after 5 min, 10 min, and 30 min. Compare your results with those of the previous experiment.

PROBLEMS

1. **Work.** A crane exerts a force of 40,000 N over a distance of 40 m. How much work has it performed?

2. **Work.** A truck with a mass of 5000 kg is rolling along a level road at constant velocity. If there were absolutely no friction or air resistance, how much work would be required to move the truck for a distance of 1 km?

3. **Work.** A horse is pulling a wagon down a hill. As the wagon tends to roll faster than the horse is walking, the animal must hold back the wagon. Does the horse perform work on the wagon as they move downhill? Explain.

4. **Kinetic energy.** A carpenter is trying out hammers of different sizes. The heaviest hammer has a mass of 1 kg but is hard to swing. The carpenter finds that if he uses a 0.5-kg hammer he can swing it twice as fast. With which hammer can he generate more kinetic energy, or will it be the same with both? Explain.

5. **Kinetic energy.** A football player has a mass of 100 kg and can run at a rate of 7.0 m/sec. What is his kinetic energy? If another

player is lighter, having a mass of only 80 kg, how fast must he run to maintain an equal kinetic energy?

6. **Potential energy.** A roller coaster with a mass of 500 kg is sitting on top of the highest incline. The incline is 30 m above the ground and 15 m above the dip in the track below. What is the potential energy of the machine with respect to the ground? with respect to the track below?

7. **Potential energy.** A rock climber scaling a nearly sheer cliff reaches a ledge 500 m above the valley floor. Then he climbs 10 m above the ledge. If he falls from this point, he will land on the ledge. If he has a mass of 75 kg, what is his potential energy with respect to a fall at this point?

8. **Energy.** A woman is bouncing on a trampoline. The drawing shows three different positions she will be in as she bounces. In which position is her kinetic energy greatest, in which is her potential energy greatest, and in which is the elastic potential energy of the trampoline greatest?

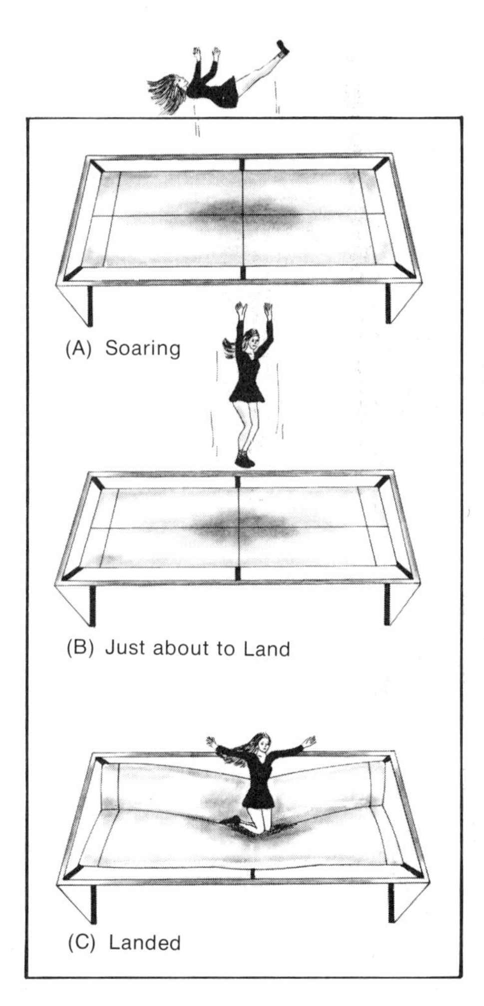

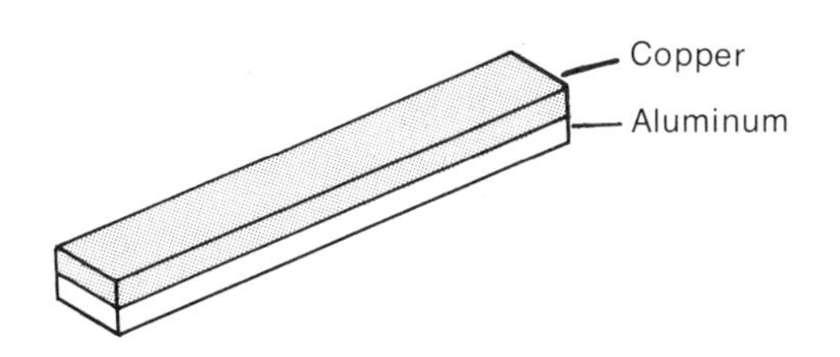

*9. **Bimetallic thermometer.** Aluminum expands more upon heating than does copper. What would happen if you heated a bar that consisted of a sheet of aluminum firmly bonded to a sheet of copper? How could such a bar be used as a thermometer? Can you think of any other use for such a device?

10. **Heat.** How many calories are needed to heat 1000 g of water 40° C? How many kilocalories? How many J? Would you need the same amount of heat to warm 10,000 g of water 4° C?

11. **Heat capacity.** It takes longer to heat a cold room full of furniture than it does to heat an identical empty room. Explain. If the furnace were turned off when both rooms were warm, which one would cool off more quickly?

*12. **Heat capacity.** If a house is built with many large windows facing south, then the sunlight passing through the glass will heat the interior even on cold winter days. Imagine that two houses were built that were identical except that one was constructed of wood, and the other was built of stone and concrete. Both had many south-facing windows. If the furnace were turned off, (a) which one would be warmer during the sunlight hours, and (b) which would be warmer during the evening? Explain. (Hint: The stone and concrete house is much more massive.)

*13. **Heat capacity.** The Sun's rays are most intense at noon, yet the hottest part of the day occurs at about 2 P.M. Explain.

14. **Energy and power.** What is energy? Compare energy with heat, work, power.

15. **Energy and power.** Three farmers are faced with the problem of hauling a ton of hay up a hill. The first makes 20 trips, carrying the hay himself. The second loads a wagon and has his horse pull the hay up in four trips. The third farmer drives a truck

*Indicates more difficult problem.

up in one load. Which process—manpower, animal power, or machine power—has performed more external work? Which device is capable of exerting more power?

16. **Energy and power.** Your electric bill reflects the number of kWh that you have consumed. Are you being charged for power or energy? When we speak of the capacity of a power plant we speak of its wattage. Are we speaking of power or energy? Explain.

17. **Collisions.** Guard rails along roadsides bend and crumple if a car runs into them. Is this an example of shoddy engineering? Would it be advantageous to install stronger, more durable guard rails? Explain.

18. **Collisions.** If you were driving an automobile and discovered that you couldn't avoid a collison, but you could direct the collision a little, would it be better to hit a solid object dead on and get it over with, or to sideswipe it and experience a prolonged impact? Explain.

19. **Momentum.** What is the momentum of a 4000-kg truck traveling at 80 km/hr?

*20. **Momentum.** As a bullet leaves the muzzle of a gun, the gun is propelled backward, and momentum is conserved. What actually forces the gun backward? The bullet? The exploding gases? Describe in detail the forces within the gun barrel as the bullet is being fired.

21. **Momentum.** A bullet with a mass of 0.05 kg is fired out of a gun with a muzzle velocity of 4000 m/sec. If the gun has a mass of 3.5 kg, what will be its velocity after the bullet is fired, assuming that the gun is free to recoil?

22. **First Law of Thermodynamics.** Write four statements of the First Law of Thermodynamics.

23. **First Law.** An engineer designed and built the roller coaster shown in the drawing at the bottom of the page. He was fired. Why?

24. **First Law.** Two bicyclists were coasting down one big hill and up another. Both bicycles were identical except that one cyclist had clipped a few baseball cards to his frame so that the spokes would flick the cards and make noise as the wheels rotated. Which cyclist would coast farther uphill? Explain.

25. **First Law.** Imagine a closed system that consists of a battery and an electric motor connected through pulleys to a set of weights. When the battery is connected to the motor with properly insulated wires, the motor can do 50,000 J of work lifting the weights before the battery runs down. If shoddy wires are used and some partial short circuits develop, the system will spark and sputter, and a fully charged battery will do only 25,000 J work. Does this observation disprove the First Law? Explain.

*26. **First Law.** Figure 3–10 shows a perpetual motion machine based on osmosis. The two identical membranes are permeable to water but not to sugar. Water from the reservoir passes up through membrane 2 to a height that is determined by the osmotic pressure of the solution. Water also permeates membrane 1, falling back to the reservoir and doing work on the way down. Do you think this machine will work? If not, why not?

*27. **First Law.** One of the early pioneers in the science of thermodynamics, Julius

*Indicates more difficult problem.

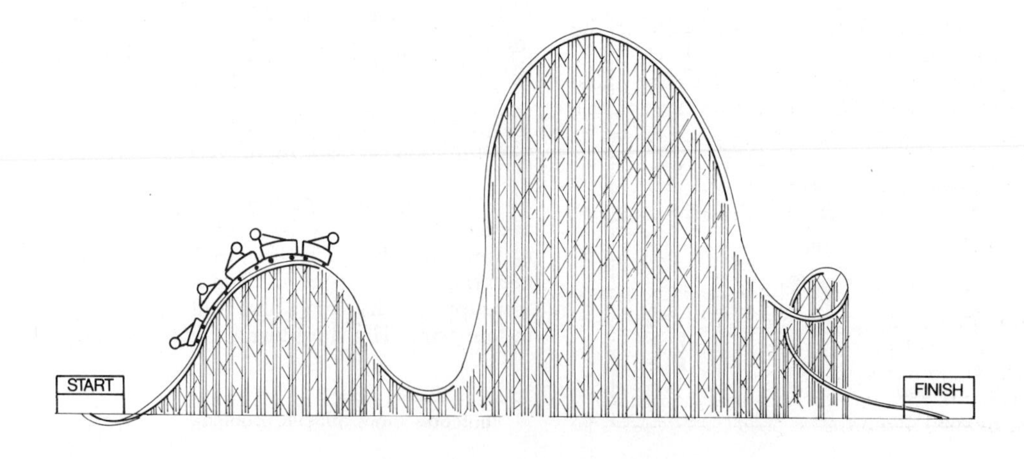

Mayer, started thinking about work and heat while he was a physician on board a trading ship. Dr. Mayer noticed that the sailors ate less when they were in the tropics than they did when they were in colder regions, yet they performed the same amount of work regardless of location. From this observation, Mayer concluded that heat and work must be interchangeable forms of energy. Explain.

*28. **Flywheels.** A car designer has the idea to position large flywheels inside a conventional automobile. He reasons that if the flywheels can be connected to the wheels while the car is coasting downhill, energy can be conserved for the next uphill pull. Do you think that this is a good idea? Explain.

29. **Second Law of Thermodynamics.** Write four statements of the Second Law of Thermodynamics.

*30. **Second Law.** If a room is the same temperature as the surrounding air, and an air conditioner is turned on in the house, the room will get cooler while the outside is heated. Is this a violation of the Second Law? Explain.

31. **Second Law.** Mountain ranges slowly erode and crumble, ultimately weathering down to flat land. Is entropy increasing or decreasing during this process? Explain.

32. **Second Law.** Energy is required to separate a solution of salt water into its individual components. Explain in terms of the Second Law.

33. **Second Law.** Consider two power plants, one that used 500° C steam as its working substance and the other that used 150° C steam. In all other respects both were identical. Both used cooling water at 30° C, and produced the same amount of electricity. Which power plant would add more waste heat to the environment? Explain.

*34. **Second Law.** The surfaces of the tropical oceans are about 15° C to 20° C warmer than the depths. Would it be possible to build a large power plant that utilizes this teperature difference to drive a heat engine to produce electricity? Would such a power plant violate the First Law of Thermodynamics? The Second Law of Thermodynamics? Discuss.

35. **Electric heat.** Why is a steam-fired generator-electric heat system less efficient than a small propane or oil furnace that is installed in a house? Would it be technically feasible to improve the efficiency of an electric heater? Would it be possible to make an electric heater as efficient as a direct fuel heater?

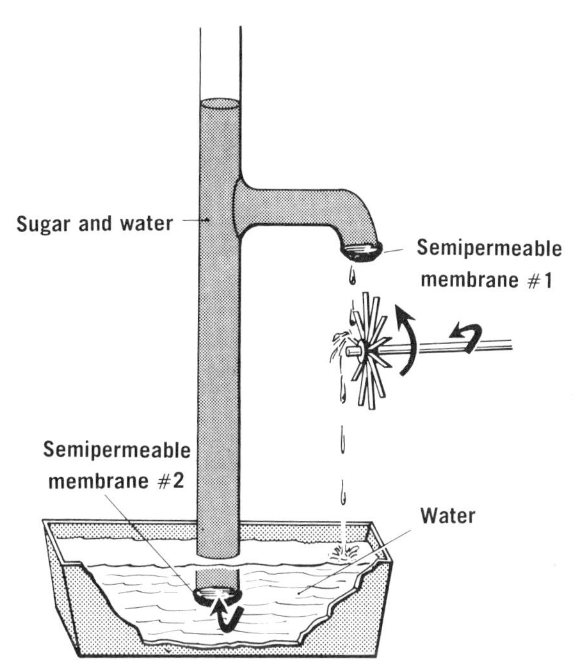

Figure 3–10. Is this a perpetual motion machine?

36. **Electric power generation.** Explain the function of the cooling system in a steam turbine. Is a cooling system needed at a hydroelectric facility?

37. **Efficiency of generation of electricity.** Compare the efficiency of each of the following methods of warming the air in a room: (a) Oil is burned in a home furnace. (b) Oil is burned in a generating plant to make electricity. The electricity is then transmitted to the house to operate an electric heater.

38. **Hydroelectric power.** A hydroelectric power plant can generate electricity efficiently at an operting temperature of about 50° C, whereas steam operating plants must run at temperatures of about 500 to 550° C. Is this a contradiction of the Second Law of Thermodynamics? Explain.

39. **Generation of electricity.** Explain the functions of the boiler, turbine, generator, and condenser of an electric power plant.

40. **Second Law.** Would it be practical to increase the efficiency of a power plant by

*Indicates more difficult problem.

cooling the condenser with a giant refrigerating unit? Explain in terms of the Second Law.

41. **Thermal pollution.** Define thermal pollution. How does it differ in principle from air or water pollution.

42. **Nuclear vs. fossil fuels.** Explain why nuclear-fueled power plants require more cooling water than fossil-fueled plants.

43. **Thermal pollution.** Since marine life is abundant in warm tropical waters, why should the warming of waters in temperate zones pose any threat to the environment?

44. **Thermal pollution.** Warm water carries less oxygen than cold water. This fact is responsible for a series of disturbances harmful to aquatic organisms. Explain.

45. **Hot water.** Describe some difficulties with the use of waste steam for home heating. Describe the potential benefits.

CHAPTER

This chapter opens with a discussion of the magnitude of coal, oil, and gas reserves and then explores some of the environmental problems associated with extraction and refinement of these fuels. A study of these problems reveals that fossil fuels cannot form the basis for a long-term continuation of our technological society. Nuclear fuels may (or may not) become a major source of power in the future. As our problems of energy supply grow increasingly severe, many people are looking towards renewable sources such as solar, hydroelectric, tidal, ocean thermal, geothermal, wind, and plant energies. However, it is expensive and time consuming to switch from one energy base to another. Even if a large scale initiative were started immediately, many years would pass before renewable sources could replace fossil fuels. Therefore, conservation is important as a means of prolonging the life span of our irreplaceable fuel reserves.

ENERGY RESOURCES AND CONSUMPTION

4.1 INTRODUCTION

When European colonizers first arrived on the American hemisphere, they viewed a seemingly boundless land, rich with an overabundance of resources. Loggers cut into the vast forests, and when all the trees were felled from one region, their families simply moved westward. There seemed to be more than enough for everyone. Now we realize that our resources are not boundless. In 1979, fuel prices nearly doubled, gas lines once again became a fact of life, and people were reminded that fossil fuel reserves will not always be available in the quantity that might be desired. The term "energy crisis" became a common household expression.

We are certain that there are no easy answers to the energy crisis. There are no magic formulas, charismatic leaders, or clever scientists capable of producing instant solutions that will satisfy everyone. It is a worldwide problem involving complex technical, social, economic, and political issues.

4.2 OUR FOSSIL FUEL SUPPLY

In 1979, approximately 90 per cent of the total energy used in the United States was derived from fossil fuels—coal, oil, and natural gas. Only 5 per cent was from a renewable supply—mostly power from falling water, plus some wood and solar energy. The remaining 5 per cent was from nuclear fission. The Second Law assures us that someday our reserves will be depleted. How much time do we have? For a realistic estimate of the number of years before we have used all the Earth's energy reserves, we must forecast the rate of growth of the human population, estimate the quantity of the remaining reserves, and predict accurately our future rate of consumption. All such forecasts are subject to large uncertainties.

Natural Gas

It is generally believed that natural gas is our least abundant fossil fuel. Most probably, our peak consumption will occur sometime in the late 1980's. After that, less and less gas will be available every year. Already, gas companies are refusing to supply many new homes and factories because the industry claims it will not have enough fuel for new customers. The scarcity of natural gas is environmentally unfortunate, since it burns more cleanly than any other widely used fuel.

Oil

Petroleum is perhaps the most versatile fossil fuel. Crude oil, as it is pumped from the ground, is a heavy, gooey, viscous, dark liquid. The oil is refined to produce many different materials such as propane, gasoline, jet fuel, heating oil, motor oil, and road tar. Some of the chemicals in the oil are extracted and used for the manufacture of plastics, medicines, and many other products. It is difficult to imagine what would happen to our civilization if the supply of liquid fuels ran out. Automobiles, airplanes, most home furnaces, and many appliances could not operate. Many industries would have to redesign their factories. Yet, reliable estimates indicate that before the year 2000 there will not be enough petroleum to meet worldwide demand. Figure 4–2 shows one projected graph of oil production and demand for the years 1975 to 2025. According to this graph, oil production will continue to increase until about 1997. At that time, many of the richest fields will be de-

Energy consumption by people.

1. Man without fire (2000 kcal/day)

2. Primitive agriculture (12,000 kcal/day)

3. ca. 1860 (70,000 kcal/day)

4. ca. 1980 (230,000 kcal/day)

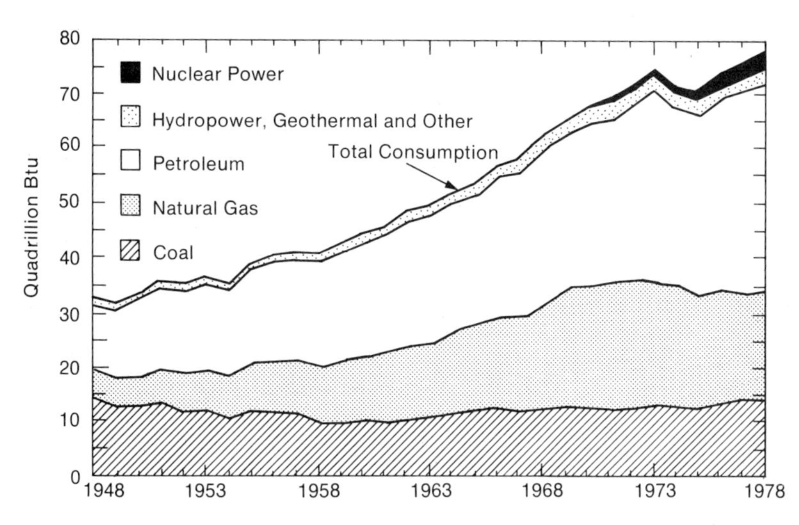

Figure 4–1. Use of various fuels in the United States from 1948 to 1978. (Courtesy of United States Department of Energy.)

pleted and production will slow down. Yet the need for oil will continue to increase. People will want more than is available. Therefore, a real and permanent shortage will result.*

How accurate is Figure 4–2? Of course, no one is sure. Perhaps there is more fuel in the ground than we expect; perhaps there is less. Perhaps demand for fuel will increase more than expected; perhaps it will decrease. Using different estimates of supply and demand, one may draw different graphs. Is it possible that new oil fields may be discovered that will be so large that our oil future may be extended another generation or more? Perhaps. An article in the December 22, 1978, issue of *Science* reports:

> Intensive exploration in Mexico is turning up oil fields so immense that they could overturn the conventional wisdom about world oil supplies and significantly alter the geopolitics of energy.
>
> For the past five years, the conventional wisdom has been that most of the world's major oil fields have already been discovered, that the United States will have to rely more and more heavily on the Middle East for future supplies of oil, and that the giant oil fields around the Persian Gulf are the result of a unique geological occurrence that is unlikely to be matched anywhere else.
>
> Not only does the conventional wisdom appear to be wrong, it appears to be spectacularly wrong. Oil fields apparently equivalent to those in Saudi Arabia have been found only about 1,000 kilometers from the U.S. border.

However, other experts are not nearly so optimistic. Some geologists have reported that although there may be 100 billion barrels of petroleum in Mexican oil fields, the structure of the oil-bearing rock makes extraction difficult and expensive. They say that only five billion barrels are economically recoverable. But economic outlooks change. If the price of oil increases, then petroleum that is now uneconomical to extract might become profitable. Perhaps the technology of oil drilling will improve, and the Mexican fields will produce more than is expected. No

Figure 4–2. One projected estimate of the supply and demand for petroleum through the year 2025. (From Andrew R. Flower, "World Oil Production." Scientific American, March, 1978, p. 42.)

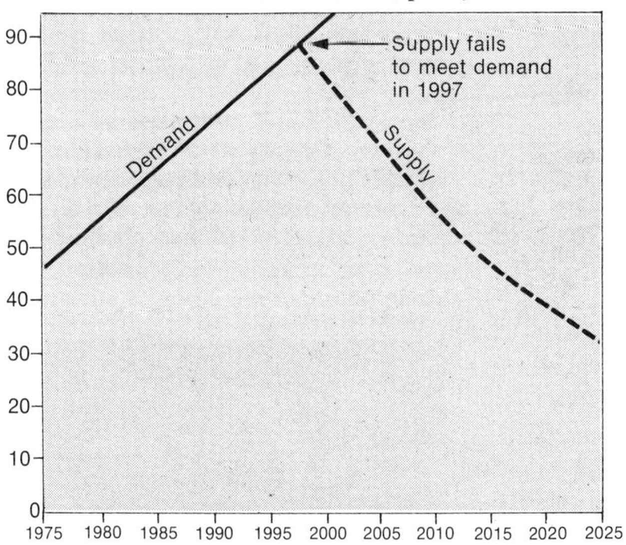

*For a closer look at the assumptions made in Figure 4–2, refer to the reference listed at the top of that figure.

one knows for sure. But we are certain that the fossil fuel supplies are limited and will someday be depleted. Most experts believe that production will not be able to meet demand sometime within the next generation.

What will happen when the petroleum reserves are depleted? Will people all learn to drive teams of horses to town and rediscover the use of wood as a fuel? The answer is almost certainly no. Several stop-gap measures are available, and a few more long-range solutions will probably be found.

The search for oil under the sea.

Coal and Synfuels

Large reserves of coal exist in many parts of the world. As shown in Figure 4–3, we can expect widespread availability of this fuel at least until the year 2200, or perhaps even longer. However, many problems arise. Coal mines deface land surfaces and pollute waterways. More air pollutants are generated when coal is burned than when oil or gas is used. Some of these air pollutants contain trace quantities of radioactive compounds that accumulate in the environment. Another difficulty arises because coal cannot be used directly in conventional automobiles, in most home furnaces, or in many industries. One solution to the problem is to convert coal to liquid or gaseous fuels. The theory of converting solid to liquid fuels is well understood. It has been practiced both in the laboratory and in industry. In fact, conversion of coal was common in the 1920's. During World War II the Germans converted coal to gasoline for military use. By 1979, there were over 50 plants in various parts of the world that produced gaseous or liquid fuels from coal. Most of these were small industrial operations.

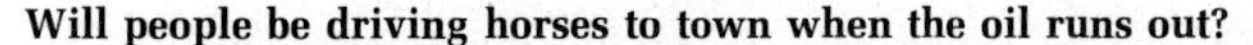

"Coal is cheap, hated, abundant, filthy, needed." Title of an article by Jane Stein, *Smithsonian*, February, 1973.

Will people be driving horses to town when the oil runs out?

In 1979, the only large-scale commercial coal-to-gasoline conversion facility in the world was operating in South Africa. At that time, the plant was producing fuel at a price that was about $3.00 per barrel less than the cost of OPEC oil.* The United States has vast coal reserves, enough to extend our fossil fuel age for several hundred years, and many people have advocated

*OPEC stands for "Organization of Petroleum Exporting Countries."

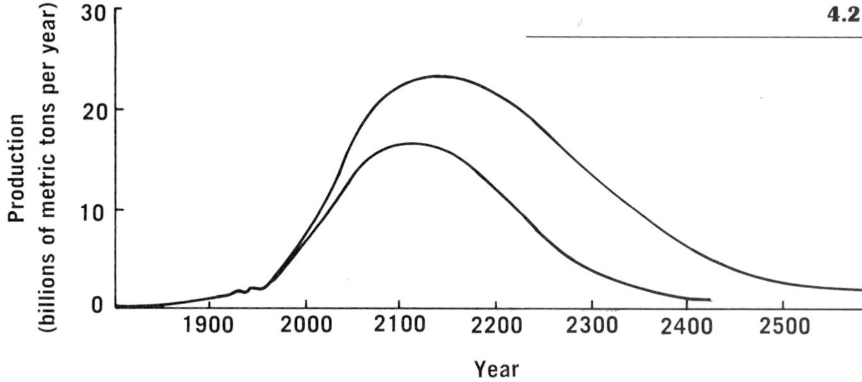

Figure 4–3. Past and predicted world coal production based on two different estimates of initial supply. (From Scientific American, September, 1971, p. 69. Copyright © by Scientific American, Inc. All rights reserved. Adapted from "The Energy Resources of the Earth," by M. King Hubbert.)

Aerial view of a strip mine in southeastern Montana. To the left, piles of rubble are being reclaimed and blended into the terrain. (Courtesy of Bureau of Reclamation, photo by Lyle Axthelm)

a crash program to develop synfuels. However, a great many problems arise:

1. Labor is much more expensive in North America than it is in South Africa. Therefore, the cost of synfuels would be several dollars per barrel higher in this country.

2. The capital investment needed to develop a significant synfuel program is enormous. Best estimates indicate that in the United States it would cost about $85 to $90 billion to construct enough conversion plants to cut the U.S. oil import level by 25 per cent.

3. The engineering difficulties involved are also enormous. As one expert recently wrote,*

> Synfuels plants are very large enterprises—a 50,000 barrel per day coal (liquefaction or gasification) plant would cost, at a minimum, over 2 billion dollars and use several times as much coal as the largest electric generating plant. And no one has ever built even one at this scale. And we are talking about building 20 to 30 of them in the next 10 years. . . . The managers, engineers, and laborers will have to be trained or diverted from other activities, (and) new plants will have to be built to produce the equipment going into the synthetic fuels plants. . . . Some of these steps . . . can be compressed, but, taken together, the prospects for anything like 2.5 million barrels per day by 1990 seem to me slim unless as a nation we decide nothing much else is important.

Decker Coal Mine in Montana. (Courtesy of Bureau of Reclamation, photo by Lyle Axthelm)

---

* *Science*, Vol. 205, Sept. 7, 1979, p. 978.

"Synfuels" is a contraction of "synthetic fuels." They include those fuels made by conversion of other natural sources, such as gasoline from coal, and methane or alcohol by fermentation of agricultural products.

The SASOL (South African Coal, Oil, and Gas Corporation, Ltd.) refinery in South Africa. The plant produces commercial quantities of gasoline, diesel, and heating fuels and many different types of chemicals, using coal as the raw ingredient. (Courtesy of South African Consulate General.)

4. The South African plant is a source of considerable air and water pollution. According to one reporter, "Indeed, smoke often hangs like a gray curtain for days over Sasolburg (where the plant is located)—people are now prepared to accept the air pollution . . ." Many of the by-products of coal gasification are carcinogenic, and radioactive trace elements are released as well. It is certainly possible to build a modern plant that emits less pollution than the South African model, but significant problems would always remain.

5. Coal is composed mainly of carbon, whereas natural gas or gasoline contains compounds of carbon and hydrogen. In order to gasify coal, hydrogen must be added, and the cheapest source of hydrogen is water, H_2O. However, water is scarce in many regions where coal is being mined. Representatives of industry claim that in the southwestern part of the United States there is enough water for production of 500,000 barrels per day of synfuels. However, some environmental experts

A Navajo farmer herding sheep in a coal-rich region of northwest New Mexico. Water is scarce throughout the southwestern United States, and this scarcity poses serious environmental problems to any large-scale coal synfuels program.

disagree and claim that beyond 250,000 barrels per day severe problems would be encountered. In the late 1970's the United States imported about 8.7 million barrels per day of petroleum. If more than 5 to 10 per cent of this import level were to be replaced with synthetic fuels, water priorities would have to be adjusted drastically. It would be necessary to construct new dams and consume water that is now used for agriculture and recreation.

6. Hundreds of thousands of hectares of valuable farm land and scenic regions would be disrupted by a coal mining industry of the scale required for a significant synfuel program. Much of the insult can be reduced by extensive reclamation programs, but even if utmost care is taken, many years would be required for the earth to recover fully.

None of the problems just outlined is totally insurmountable, but we must realize that a synfuel program would be associated with heavy economic and social costs.

Oil Shale and Tar Sands

Until now, most of our petroleum has been pumped directly from underground wells. However, large quantities of oil are also bound within the pores of certain rocks. The fuel can be recovered by mining the ore, then crushing and processing it. Huge deposits of a type of oil-bearing rock called **shale** exist in the United States in Colorado, Wyoming, and Utah. Sand fields laden with oil have been discovered in Africa, the United States, and Canada. We don't know how much oil can be obtained from oil shales and tar sands. A Canadian firm is currently extracting oil from tar sands. The richest deposits of oil shale are believed to add another 25 per cent to the world's usable supply of liquid petroleum. Today it is usually cheaper to import oil than to mine shale. But the situation may change in the near future. As imported

Oil shale country in western Colorado. (Courtesy of Atlantic Richfield Co.)

Mining oil shale in Alberta, Canada. (Courtesy of Suncor, Inc.)

oil becomes more costly, and as the technology for mining shale becomes more highly developed, shale deposits may be used more.

However, economic and environmental problems related to production of fuel from shale are similar in many ways to those involved in the production of synfuels from coal, and these problems are certainly delaying the development of shale resources. Large capital investment would be required, water resources would be strained, land surfaces would be defaced, and other pollution problems would be encountered.

4.3 NUCLEAR FUELS

Oil shale, tar sands, and coal will undoubtedly extend the life of the fossil fuel age. But such stop-gaps cannot be the basis for a long-range survival of our technological society. Instead we must turn either to renewable resources or to nuclear energy.

The use of nuclear energy has sparked one of the most significant debates of our times. As will be discussed in more detail in Chapter 10, there are some people who believe that nuclear reactors are absolutely essential to our society. Others think that these reactors should be banned.

In 1979, only 5 per cent of the energy used in the United States was provided by nuclear fuels. By the year 2000, we may expect this figure to rise to somewhere between 10 per cent and 20 per cent. Several problems arise, however:

1. Nuclear reactors are expensive to build.

2. Many citizen groups oppose construction of the "nukes."

3. The cost of uranium fuels is expected to rise in the near future.

Easily accessible, inexpensive, high-grade uranium ore deposits are being depleted, and the price of nuclear fuels is certain to rise in the near future. However, it is difficult to predict how much the cost of electricity generated from nuclear power plants will be affected by the increase in fuel costs. At the present time, the investment in building and operating a nuclear power plant is large compared to the cost of the fuel, so a significant rise in the price of uranium would result in a much smaller increase in the cost of the electricity produced. Furthermore, advances in the design of conventional reactors have improved their efficiency. Therefore, price increases in the fuel may be temporarily offset by improved technology.

According to one recent prediction,* energy from uranium is expected to be available into the twenty-first century, although its cost will continue to rise.

In recent years **breeder reactors** have been developed (see Chapter 10). Breeders can produce many times more energy per kilogram of uranium than conventional fission reactors can. Some people predict that important environmental problems will be solved and that breeders will therefore extend the life of our nuclear fuel supply for many thousands of years. However, not everyone agrees. In fact, the question is a matter of considerable controversy.

Another possibility can be considered. Scientists may someday harness the hydrogen **fusion** reaction.† The technological problems yet to be solved are so difficult that some authorities

*See Kenneth S. Deffeyes and Ian D. MacGregor, "World uranium resources." *Scientific American*, Jan., 1980, p. 60.

†The development of fission and fusion reactors will be discussed further in Chapter 10.

expect fusion never to be functional. At the other extreme, some optimists predict fusion to be feasible within ten years. However, most members of the scientific community feel that the development of such a power plant is highly unlikely before the year 2000. If fusion is found to be practical, the energy available to us will be enormous.

4.4 RENEWABLE ENERGY RESOURCES—SOLAR ENERGY

One of the most crucial debates of our time is centered on the question: What will the primary energy sources be when the oil runs out early in the twenty-first century? One school of thought argues that: (a) People must learn to conserve energy. *Conservation* will extend the life of our present fossil fuel reserves and provide the time needed to develop new energy systems. (b) The primary fuels of the early twenty-first century will be *coal* and *uranium*. These two fuels will be used to power many new centralized electric generating plants. The electricity will be used to heat homes, drive electric cars and trains, and perform many of the functions now requiring gas and oil. In addition, coal will be converted to petroleum for many uses.

A second school of thought agrees that conservation is vitally important. But these people believe that large-scale centralized power production is not the answer. Future needs should be met by massive use of small domestic power sources. Millions of individual solar collectors and small windmills, coupled with a return to the use of wood and other plant products as fuel, could become a significant power base for the future.

Every 19 minutes the solar energy that falls on our planet is equivalent to human energy needs for a year at the 1980 consumption level. In the *least* sunny portions of the United States (excluding Alaska) an area of only 80 square meters (a square approximately 9 m, or 29 ft, on a side) receives enough sunlight to supply the total energy demands of the average American family. In addition the technology is available *today* to trap and use much of this en-

Mining uranium ore underground near Grants, New Mexico. (Courtesy of Ranchers Exploration and Development Corporation)

ergy. Power can be produced without creating a pollution problem. Yet solar energy is not in common use.

Passive Solar Design

A few years ago, I, Jon, lived in the mountains in a cabin without running water. I set a black plastic pipe in a spring on the hillside above the cabin, and laid the pipe along the sunny surface of the hillside toward the cabin. At the bottom of the pipe I installed a simple faucet. The water would fill the pipe in the morning and then sit in the sun all day. The sun would heat it, so that by evening there was always a plentiful supply of hot water for bathing and washing. You can see, therefore, that a solar hot water heater is not necessarily a complex device. Even a bucket of water sitting in the sun all day will become warm.

An ordinary window admits sunlight. A house without windows would be dull and dreary indeed! Windows may also allow solar heat to enter the house. When the sun shines directly on a window facing south, the radiant en-

Passive solar home near Telluride, Colorado. Sunlight entering through the large, south-facing windows provides a significant heat source. This house is located in the mountains of Colorado, yet in its first year of use, no auxiliary heat was needed until mid-November.

ergy enters the room and warms it. But heat from inside also escapes outside through the glass. During the night, heat escapes and no sunlight enters.

Most homes existing today are poorly planned. They are heated with a furnace and then typically lose 20 per cent of their heat through their windows. But this trend can be reversed through proper planning. If houses were built with large, double pane, south-facing windows and only small windows on the north side, then significant heat gains could be realized. In addition, since heat is lost and none gained through windows during the night, heat can be conserved by installing drapes or insulated shutters for use after the sun goes down.

Many homes, even in such cold climates as in the Rocky Mountains, have been designed so that the windows alone provide a significant portion of the heat needed in the winter. Since the heating efficiency is obtained through the shape of the structure and not through complex mechanical systems, these buildings are said to have a **passive solar design.** If properly planned, a passive solar house is only slightly more expensive to build than an inefficient structure, and the added cost is returned within a few years in the form of reduced fuel bills.

Solar Collectors

Solar heat can be trapped even more efficiently by the use of various types of **solar collectors.** One type of collector consists of a coil of copper pipe welded to a blackened metal base. The whole assembly is covered by a transparent layer of glass or plastic. The operating principle is uncomplicated. Sunlight travels through the glass and is absorbed by the blackened surface. Metal conducts heat readily, so the water in the pipe gets hot. The glass traps the heat within the collector so it does not easily escape back into the atmosphere (Fig. 4–4).

A solar collector of this type can be connected to a home heating system. The hot water produced in the collector is stored in an insulated tank. It can be

(B.C. by permission of Johnny Hart and Field Enterprises, Inc.)

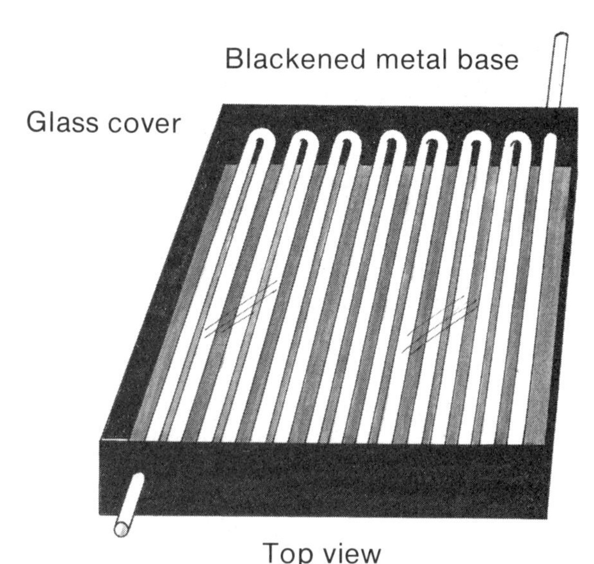

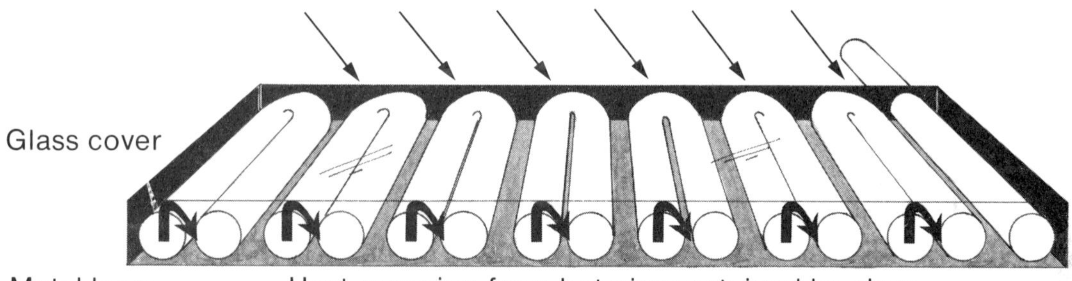

Figure 4–4. Schematic view of a solar collector.

used directly for washing or bathing. Or it can be pumped through radiators to heat the house. Of course, sunshine is not available at night or on cloudy days. Hot water can conveniently be stored to heat a house overnight. But it is expensive to build a system large enough to heat and store enough water to supply heat during several days of cloudy weather. Therefore, most solar systems are installed together with a conventional furnace. The solar collector is used on sunny days and the furnace is used when it is cloudy. Naturally, such a dual system is initially more expensive than a simple furnace. But then large amounts of fuel are saved every year. At the present time, the use of solar collectors for the production of hot water is economical in most places in the world. One of the reasons is that hot water is used in both summer and winter, so the collection system is never idle for long periods of time. Active solar heating sytems haven't been quite as economical, because they are expensive to install and are used only in winter, when the amount of solar energy is lower. However, economic pictures change. In 1979 the price of heating fuel skyrocketed, whereas the cost of installing an active solar system increased only slightly. Thus, economics now favor a well-designed active system in many parts of the country.

Advantages of Using Solar Energy	*Disadvantages of Using Solar Energy*
Limitless supply	Some active systems are slightly more expensive than oil heat in some parts of the country. But if the price of fuels continues to rise, the economic picture is certain to change.
Produces no air pollution	
Produces no water pollution	
Produces no noise	
Produces no thermal pollution	
Produces no harmful wastes	
No possibility of a large-scale explosion or disaster	
Conserves the Earth's resources	
Technology available for immediate widespread use	

Solar Generation of Electricity

When a beam of light is directed onto certain materials, electrons can be energized and the energy can be harnessed for useful production of power. Thus, light energy can be converted directly to electrical energy. A device that produces electricity from sunlight is called a **solar cell.** Solar cells are commonly used today to convert sunlight to electricity in spacecraft. They are quiet and trouble-free. They emit no pollution and appear to have a long life expectancy. Today, it would be entirely possible to build an electric generating station on Earth using solar cells. A 1000-megawatt power plant (equivalent to a large fuel-burning facility) would occupy only 10 square kilometers if it were built in the southwestern American desert. The major problem at the present time is that solar cells are so expensive that a solar plant is uneconomical even though the fuel is free. But the situation may be changing.

Solar collectors on a residential home. (Courtesy of Energy Systems Division of the Grumman Corporation, manufacturers of Sunstream Solar Collectors.)

At the present time only 0.1 per cent of the energy used in the United States is being met by geothermal sources. Even optimistic supporters of the program do not expect a significantly larger portion of our power to be supplied in this manner in the future. There are not enough hot springs at or near the surface of the earth. Continuous exploitation for more than a century or two is expected to exhaust the water or heat content of these wet wells. Geothermal energy is not always free from pollution. Underground steam or hot water is often contaminated with sulfur compounds, which must be removed before they are discharged to the air or to a lake or river.

A large wind turbine generator that has been installed on a mountain top in northwest Carolina. The generator will produce 2 megawatts of electric power in winds of 38 km/hr, enough to supply the annual power needs of 500 average homes. (Photo courtesy of the Department of Energy.)

Energy from the Wind

The power of wind has been used since antiquity to drive ships, pump water, and grind grain. What is its potential in modern society? There is more than enough wind energy available to supply the world's energy needs, and it is technically feasible to build windmills capable of producing electricity. These can be built either as small, home-sized units or as large central generators. At the present time it is slightly more expensive to harness wind power than solar power and therefore it is economically unattractive in most instances. But if windmills were mass produced, then perhaps energy from the wind could be cheaper than energy from nuclear power plants. The "catch-22" of the problem is this: No industrialists want to mass produce windmills because they are not economically attractive, but they are not economically attractive because they are not mass produced. To be economical, a commercial wind turbine must generate electricity at a cost of about 3¢ per kWh (kilowatt hour). In 1974, windmill electricity cost 20¢ per kWh; in 1979 the cost was reduced to 8¢. If the cost can be reduced still further, or if the price of fuel continues to rise, wind turbines will become competitive.

Wind generator.

A century ago most ships were powered by the wind. Today there is some renewed interest in building ocean-going, commercial sailing ships. This space-age "dynaship"—still in the planning stage—would use electric motors to manage sails so that a single person on the bridge could control the entire vessel. (Drawing by Marion Mackay)

Energy from Wood, Plant Matter, Garbage, and Manure

One hundred fifty years ago, the major resource for energy in North America was wood. Today, again, there is interest in renewable plant fuels. In rural regions sales of wood-burning stoves have skyrocketed in recent years, and once again a large number of the people use wood for all or part of their heating requirements.

The feasibility of growing certain types of plants specifically for use as an energy source is now being discussed. Many proposals have been offered. Some of these have centered on energy farms that grow timber, while others advocate high-yield plant products such as various species of swamp grasses. There is also interest in using conventional agricultural products as a source of fuel. For example, if corn is harvested and fermented, alcohol can be extracted. Alcohol is a valuable liquid fuel that can be used in a mixture with gasoline to produce a high-grade automotive fuel called **gasohol.** Gasohol is sold in a few experimental programs in the United States, but there has been only an inconsequential impact on the total national fuel consumption. All plans to use plants as fuel have the same basic problem: The world is facing shortages of food and fiber as well as shortages of gasoline, and agricultural land is limited.

We live in a wasteful society. Half of the household trash in the United States and Canada is paper. Huge piles of bark, wood scraps, and logging wastes rot slowly near many sawmills. If people would collect these wastes and use them as fuel, considerable quantities of energy could be salvaged. In France, there are 20 generators that burn garbage for use as domestic energy sources. A large facility in Paris produces electric power for 130,000 people and 20 per cent of the total steam used for heating in the entire city. In North America a few facilities burn trash for fuel, but in most regions, garbage is simply buried in a landfill.

Fuel can be produced from other waste products as well. Methane gas is released when cow manure decomposes. This gas can easily be collected and utilized. Clearly, extraction of methane from cow manure is not a final answer to the energy problem. But if fuel from cow manure were used in

In many rural regions, people gather wood for use as a fuel to heat homes.

TABLE 4–1. COMPARISON OF VARIOUS ENERGY SOURCES

Energy Source	Current Use	Future Availability of Energy Supply	Current Cost	Environmental Problems
Oil	41%	Shortages by year 2000	Cheap	Considerable
Gas	27%	Shortages by year 1985	Cheap	Cleanest fossil fuel
Coal	19%	Two to three hundred year supply	Cheap	Serious problems
Nuclear	7%	Unknown	More expensive than fossil fuel	Serious problems
Solar	Less than 1%	Excellent	Slightly more expensive than oil	Negligible
Hydroelectric	4%	Small expansion	Cheap	Some problems
Geothermal	Less than 1%	Small expansion	Cheap	Some problems
Waves and tides	Negligible	Excellent	Slightly more expensive than oil	Some problems
Wind	Negligible	Excellent in some regions	Slightly more expensive than fossil fuels	Negligible
Wood, plant matter, and garbage	1%	Small but continuous	Cheap	Some problems
Hydrogen fusion	0	Excellent (if reactors can be built)	Unknown	Serious thermal pollution problems

some areas, and if garbage, wood, and other plant products, as well as solar, thermal, tidal, and wind energies, were all exploited, the total contribution would be very substantial. In fact, these energy sources all together might completely eliminate the need for fossil fuels.

4.6 ENERGY CONSUMPTION AND CONSERVATION—AN OVERVIEW

Up to this point in the chapter we have explored various ways of increasing our energy supply. However, there is another way to relieve the energy crisis: Use less.

As shown in Figure 4–6, in 1978 North Americans used considerably more fuel than the people in any other developed country; over twice as much as the average person in Great Britain, and 1.7 times as much per capita as the West Germans. Yet, by many standards the American life style isn't appreciably better. For example, in West Germany the life expectancy is higher than it is in the United States, the climate is similar, and there are approximately the same number of libraries, schools, universities, doctors, hospitals, televisions, refrigerators, and theaters per capita as in the United States. A great many Europeans own automobiles, and like Americans, flock to ski areas or sunny beaches during their holidays. Yet they do so with far less consumption of energy. Or look at the issue in another way: In 1973, per capita consumption of fuel in the United States

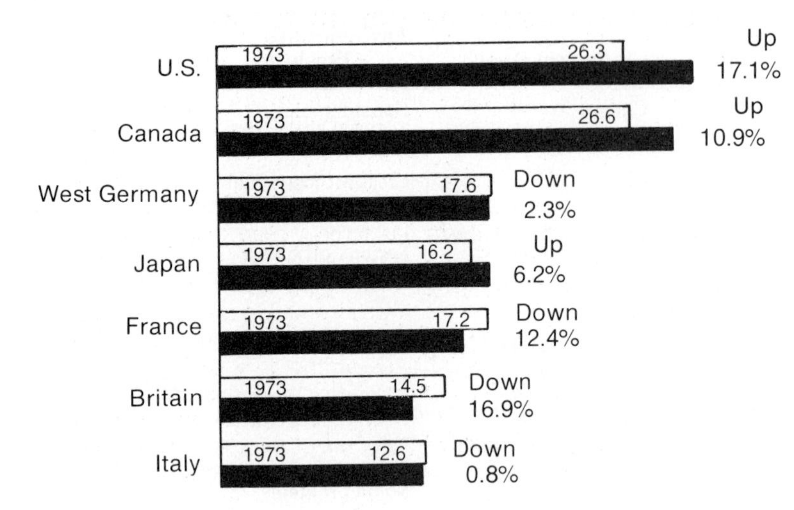

Figure 4–6. Comparison of per capita oil consumption in some selected countries from 1973 to 1978. In each case, the length of the light bar represents fuel consumption in 1973, while the dark bar shows the consumption in 1978.

A section of Hannover, a city in West Germany. The standard of living in West Germany is comparable to that in the United States, but per capita fuel consumption is much lower. (Courtesy of German National Tourist Office.)

was 17.1 per cent less than it was in 1978. Try to remember what you were doing in 1973. Probably you or your family owned at least one car, lived in a warm house, owned a television, and had many of the other amenities of a comfortable existence. Yet, on the average, people used much less fuel. During the summer of 1979, gas shortages became acute in the United States, and fuel consumption declined. Many people across the country added storm windows and extra insulation to their houses, purchased smaller cars, and drove less. Yet there has been no major disruption of living patterns. This trend is encouraging and could very well continue into the 1980's and beyond.

We recognize two basic approaches in the efforts to conserve energy. One approach can be stated as follows: Most major environmental problems are caused by twentieth-century technology. Therefore, the major problems should be solved by technology, and scientific answers must be found.

Another view is expressed in the following terms: People use the products of technology. It is people who drive cars, turn on electric lights, or turn their air conditioners up. Therefore the problems are social and economic and we must search for social remedies to environmental problems.

In order to understand how these arguments apply in a real life example, let us look briefly at automobile use. Remember the mythical magic lamps and their genies? One had only to rub the lamp and speak one's wish, and it was done. The "fully equipped" automobile seems like a modern version of those magic lamps. A touch of the finger, hardly even a push, brings warming, or cooling, or music; it opens or closes windows, locks or unlocks the car doors, or even the garage doors. A touch of the toe brings a surge of acceleration, or a swift stop. Seated within these plush environments, people can move rapidly and comfortably from place to place. Consequently, cars are used by almost everyone who can afford them. But automobiles in the United States consume prodigious quantities of energy. Is it possible to conserve fuel and still transport people from place to place comfortably and rapidly?

ENERGY CONSERVATION AND THE ECONOMY

Energy use is intimately linked with world trade and economic stability. Most nations of North America, Europe, and Asia import some or most of their oil. These imports cost money. A country has an equal **balance of trade** when the total value of all imports equals the total value of all exports. The United States spent more than $170 million *per day* on oil in 1979, and this drain has largely been responsible for a negative balance of trade. More money is spent overseas than is received. This imbalance engenders distrust in the American economic system abroad and is one major factor responsible for the decline of the value of the dollar. The declining value of the dollar means that foreign imports become more expensive. In turn, the rising cost of imports boosts inflation and is a factor that contributes further to the instability of the economy. If less imported oil were needed, the internal and international economic position of the United States would certainly improve.

Technical Solutions

We know that many people enjoy the comfort and convenience of the private automobile. But many of the vehicles in use today are inefficient. Therefore, a technical solution would be to redesign automobile engines without changing interior size or comfort. Ideally, the new engines would emit less pollution and travel further on a gallon of gasoline than our present vehicles do. Technical solutions are appealing because people can conserve fuel without altering their lifestyles. If efficient cars are available, then it is a simple matter to buy one when you would naturally trade in your old car anyway, and you can drive as you please and use less energy. In fact, the fuel economy of automobiles on the market today is much higher than that of automobiles that were on the market a decade ago, so technical solutions are, in fact, being employed.

Social Solutions

Some people believe that reliance on technical solutions alone is not sufficient. They argue that we already have the knowledge to reduce pollution and consumption in many different ways. We need not wait for new technology. For example, many people drive to work alone in their vehicles. If they would share a ride and carpool there would be an immediate and substantial reduction of fuel consumption. There would be no need to wait for new technology or to wait for cars that are now being used to wear out and be discarded. Furthermore, many people argue that carpools would involve very little added inconvenience. True, time is spent picking up riders and dropping them off, but if the number of cars on the highway were reduced, rush hour traffic would move more quickly and people would get to work just as fast.

Other solutions also should be considered. Small compact cars travel two or three times farther on a gallon of gasoline than larger ones do. Mopeds (motorized pedal vehicles) operate at up to 140 miles per gallon of gasoline, and bicycles use no gasoline at all. Buses, trains, and other forms of mass

Transportation by moped uses much less fuel than transportation by automobile. (Courtesy of Columbia Manufacturing.)

transit can operate with low pollution and high efficiency. Since all of these alternatives involve some change in habits and ways of living, many people feel that social solutions are needed to solve transportation problems.

Of course, the most effective conservation program would be to combine both technical and social remedies. Thus, if more efficient engines and mass transit systems were developed, *and* if people used them, fuel consumption would decline drastically.

The bicycle is an energy-efficient means of transportation. (From D. Plowder: *Farewell to Steam.* Brattleboro, Vermont, The Stephen Greene Press, 1966)

4.7 ENERGY CONSUMPTION AND CONSERVATION FOR TRANSPORTATION

The two least efficient modes of transportation, the automobile and the airplane, are the two major transportation industries in the United States.

The automobile, in particular, has modified our lives. Houses are far from places of work and from shopping centers. Many people live in the suburbs and must commute long distances daily. What can be done? No one can reorganize the cities overnight. The system is set in concrete.

People can't easily move existing buildings but they can and are changing transportation patterns. Short-term and long-term solutions can be found. Short-term solutions involve a minimum of capital investment and construction and can be implemented immediately. As mentioned previously, carpooling is an ideal and effective short-term solution. It isn't necessary to buy new automobiles, move houses, stores, or factories, or to build new mass transit systems. If people shared rides, they could reduce fuel consumption by 50 per cent or more overnight. Consider another factor. In the United States, most automobile trips are for distances of less than 5 mi. People drive to the corner market to pick up a newspaper and a quart of milk or to mail a letter. These trips are costly. Large amounts of gasoline are needed to start a cold automobile. As a rough approximation, a car that is capable of operating 25 mi per gallon on long trips operates at 5 mi per gallon on short trips. If people reduced the number of short trips, walked, or rode bicycles, large quantities of fuel would be saved.

Other changes cannot be implemented so quickly, but in future decades they will become increasingly important. For example, a recent trend toward smaller, more efficient automobiles is encouraging, but there is a lag time of several years before most of the older, heavier "gas-hogs" wear out and are discarded.

There have also been some trends toward the redesign of cities and suburbs. Many large offices and manufacturing operations are moving into suburban regions so employees who live in the country don't have to commute to the cities to work. At the same time there has been a renewed interest in centralized downtown shopping centers so people who live in the cities needn't drive to the suburbs to buy groceries and other essentials.

Surface Mass Transit

Surface mass transit—buses, trains, and trolleys—can provide clean, efficient transportation. At the present time, only 3 per cent of urban transport and 4 per cent of inter-city traffic is carried by public ground transportation systems; the remainder is carried by airplanes and automobiles.

As a result, a dangerous situation has evolved. If fuel shortages were to develop quickly, the existing mass transit system could not possibly handle transportation needs. Millions of workers would be stranded—unable to get to work. Cities would be paralyzed. Therefore, it seems vitally important to build public transportation systems now to avert future disaster.

In some cities in North America, bus and train routes have been expanded in an effort to encourage use, but most mass transit systems in the United States and Canada are far behind their European counterparts. Inter-city rail services have been reduced in the United States at the same time that the federal expenditure for new highways has escalated. In many cities a person may have to wait up to 20 minutes for a local bus, while in most European cities bus service is available every five minutes during rush hours. If mass transit systems were properly developed, they could provide an effective alternative to the automobile. At the present time, traffic is often stalled for long periods during rush hours and travel is slow; accidents are common. Moreover, parking spaces are often hard to find; rarely can people drive directly to their destination and park nearby. If quiet, efficient, comfortable mass transit systems were built in most cities, and if road building projects were curtailed, mass transit might become more popular.

FIVE YEARS OF ENERGY PARALYSIS

"Five years ago [1973] the United States received notice that it could not depend indefinitely on obtaining imports of oil. Soon it was also evident that the world would be enduring economic dislocations due to high costs of petroleum and that shortages of oil would be experienced 5 to 15 years from now. Lately, confidence in the dollar has evaporated and the possibility of wild inflation here looms ever larger. On the world scene great changes have occurred in less than a year. In the meantime, the United States plods along with a time-scale for energy development measured in decades and more. During the past five years some constructive development has occurred, but on balance, this country has drifted backward.

The easiest and quickest way to avoid energy shortages is through conservation. In this area, modest progress has been made. Following the recent severe winters, substantial amounts of insulation were installed in homes. Newly constructed buildings are also better protected. Industry now uses 14 percent less energy per unit of product than they did five years ago. But public recycling efforts have largely stopped. Gasoline consumption sets new records.

Unconventional energy sources, though highly touted, have not made much of a contribution. For a time solar heating and cooling caught the attention and interest of the public. Many new companies were formed to meet an eager demand for installations. But in recent months, orders have dropped to 10 percent or less than the peak rates, and many companies have folded.

Domestic reserves and production of oil and natural gas continue to drop. In 1973, crude oil production was 9.3 million barrels per day. It is now about 8.7 million barrels per day. This includes the contribution of 1.2 million barrels per day of Alaskan oil. . . . In the five years there has been a large increase in oil imports and in balance of payments deficits. . . .

Our people have repeatedly given evidence that they will not gladly accept shortages of energy whether natural gas, electricity, or gasoline. Infatuation with the automobile is such that any political party that engineers a shortage of fuel can count on defeat at the polls. . . .

The sad part of the situation is that the technology and resources exist that enable the United States to live smoothly through the transition to more efficient energy use, and to long-term and renewable energy sources. But continuation of present paralysis invites turmoil."

Phillip H. Abelson, *Science*, Sept. 1, 1978.

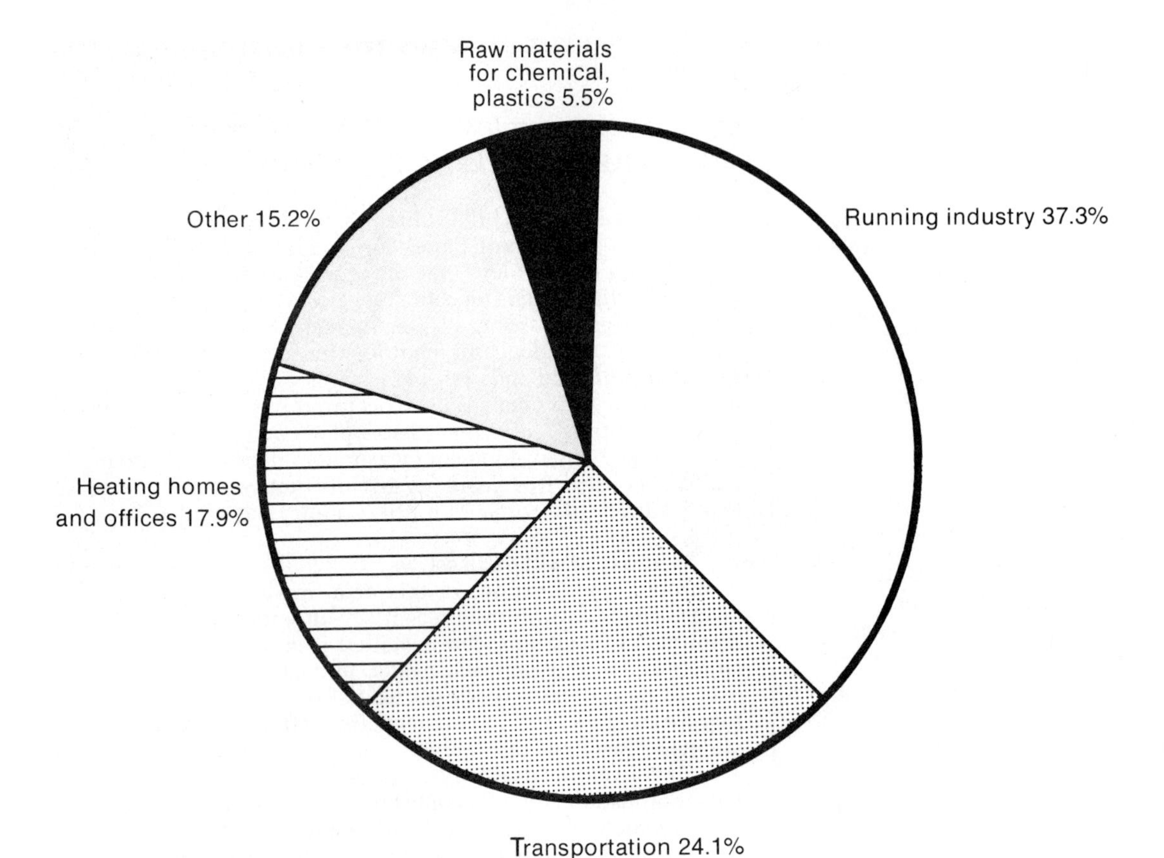

Figure 4–7. Energy consumption in the United States, 1978.

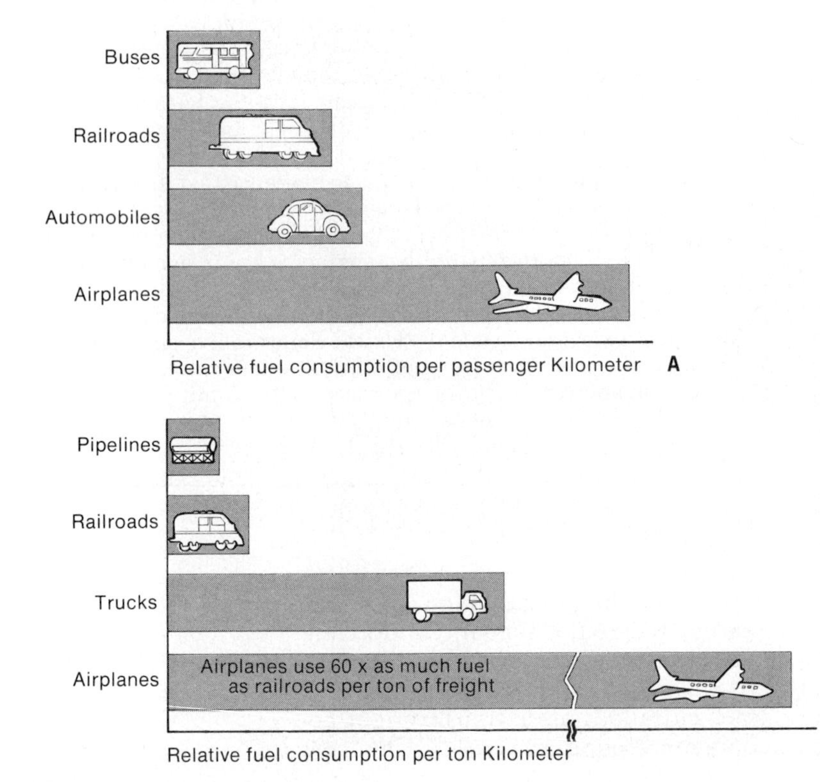

Figure 4–8. Relative fuel consumption of various means of transportation. In each case, estimated average load capacities were used to compute efficiencies. (From "Transportation's Place in the Energy Picture," Association of American Railroads, August, 1979.) *A,* Intercity passenger carriers. *B,* Freight carriers.

BART, a modern mass transit system in San Francisco.

Rush hour traffic in Denver, Colorado.

4.8 ENERGY CONSUMPTION AND CONSERVATION FOR INDUSTRY

In recent years, industries all over the world have responded to the high cost of fuels by modifying their processes to use less energy. For example, in the United States, manufacturing companies have reduced their energy requirement per unit of product by 14 per cent from 1973 to 1978.

However, despite these substantial savings, North American industries are generally more wasteful of fuel than European industries are. One prime example of this waste is the inefficient use of steam. Recall from Section 3.11 that steam is used to drive turbines to produce electricity. After the steam has passed through the turbines it is no longer useful for producing work. But it can be used to provide heat for homes, industry, or a variety of other purposes. In North America, most of this steam is "thrown away." That is to say that the steam is cooled by discharging its heat into the atmosphere or into rivers, lakes, or oceans. If this steam were used for other purposes, large quantities of energy would be saved. Many European electric companies sell their excess steam, thereby saving money and energy.

Another way to reduce industrial energy consumption is to increase recycling of materials. In general, production of manufactured goods from recycled wastes consumes less energy than the production from raw materials. However, total manufacturing *costs* reflect the price of labor, transportation, and capital investment as well as fuel bills. Unfortunately, when the true social costs of depletion of nat-

Large amounts of energy are required for the production of steel. (Courtesy of Bethlehem Steel.)

TABLE 4–2. HOW YOU CAN SAVE FUEL IN TRANSPORTATION

Method	Fuel Savings as Compared to Wasteful Practices
Walk or use a bicycle, stay at home	Saves 100%
Use mass transit	Saves 50% (or more)
Carpool	Saves 50% (or more)
Keep car well tuned	Saves 20%
Drive smoothly (no jerks, fast starts and stops)	Saves 15%
Purchase car without an air conditioner	Saves 10%
Keep tires inflated to proper pressure	Saves 5%

ural resources are not considered, recycling operations often seem more expensive than primary production. Unless industries are offered economic incentives or threatened with penalties, we can expect little significant increase in industrial recycling.

It is also possible to reduce excess industrial energy by consuming less. For example, if appliances were built to last longer, and if people used less paper for packaging, less energy would be needed for production.

4.9 ENERGY CONSUMPTION AND CONSERVATION FOR HOUSEHOLD USE

Perhaps in no other sector of our society can more energy be saved with the need for less social change than in the area of home heating. A well-built, well-insulated home, employing passive and/or active solar heating systems, uses one quarter to one tenth of the energy needed to heat a "conventional" house. Sound design and construction save money, and there would be no need to turn the thermostats down. However, even today, with fuel prices skyrocketing, a great many homes are being built with little consideration for energy conservation, and a great deal of fuel is wasted needlessly. In contrast, recent building laws enacted in Sweden make strict energy conservation practices mandatory in all new construction. As a result, fuel consumption for heating is less per capita in Sweden than it is in the United States, even though the winters are more severe.

Considerable energy savings can be realized in commercial buildings as well. One example of a particularly innovative design is the 20-story office complex built in Toronto, Canada, for Ontario Hydro (Fig. 4–9). This structure uses no fuel at all for space heating during the harsh Canadian winter. Instead, heat from lights, from machinery, and from people's bodies is conserved, stored, and circulated throughout the structure. In addition, double-glazed glass on the southern wall serves as a passive solar collection system. The energy saved every year is enough to supply all the power used by 2500 average homes.

But what about the conventional houses that have already been built? In the long term, it is possible to remodel many so as to retrofit solar design, but these changes are often slow and expensive. Significant savings can be realized through simple and inexpensive conservation practices. If an old, uninsulated house were insulated, storm doors and windows added, and leaky seams caulked, fuel consumption could be cut in half.

TABLE 4–3. HOW YOU CAN SAVE FUEL IN HOME HEATING

Method	Heat Savings Compared to Energy Inefficient House
Have your furnace maintained, cleaned, and tuned properly	Saves 10%–20%
Add extra insulation in ceilings and walls	Saves 30%–50%
Add storm windows	Saves 10%
Caulk leaky windows and doors	Saves 5%–15%
Cover windows with drapes and shades at night	Saves 5%–15%
Close off and do not heat unused rooms.	Variable
Turn thermostat down	Saves 3% per °F

Energy loss from a poorly insulated two story home with an open fireplace.

In modern society, electricity is often used to provide heat. Advertisements advise people to "live better electrically," to buy stoves, toasters, space heaters, and water heaters. But electric heaters are thermodynamically inefficient. As noted in Chapter 3, 67 per cent of the energy is wasted in the generating and distribution system. On the other hand, home furnaces are 65 to 85 per cent efficient. Electricity is essential for many functions, but it is wasteful when used to produce heat. Much energy could be conserved if electricity were used only where it is needed and if fuel were used directly when heat is needed. Despite the obvious waste, electric appliances are encouraged by the utility companies, for electricity becomes cheaper when consumption increases. Thus, in a typical monthly billing system, the first 40 kWh are billed at a rate of 12 cents per kWh, but a person pays only 3.3 cents per kWh on all consumption over 700

Figure 4–9. Ontario Hydro's head office in Toronto, Canada. There is no furnace or heating plant within this building, yet internal temperatures are comfortable throughout both the harsh Canadian winter and the hot summer months. Energy conservation is realized through use of south facing, double-glazed reflective glass, and a system that stores and circulates the heat from lights, people and machinery to supply the heating needs. (Courtesy of Ontario Hydro.)

kWh. In some cases it is cheaper to use electric heat than a furnace.

Until recently, many people in the United States heated their houses to 22° C (72°F) all winter, and cooled them to 20° C (68°F) in the summer. Now, new federal guidelines prohibit heating multiple dwellings over 18.3° C (65°F) in winter, or cooling them below 25.6° C (78°F) in summer. Although many private homes are still heated to 22° C, many people are voluntarily following the federal guidelines. The decision to change the thermostat settings involves a sacrifice; people must adjust to living under what is considered to be less than optimally comfortable conditions. The sacrifice really is not that great, however, and can be largely overcome by changes in dress habits. For example, according to research carried out by The American Society of Ventilating Engineers in 1932, the preferred room temperature during the winter for a majority of subjects was 18.9° C.* Similar research at later dates showed that the comfort range had risen to 19.3° C in 1941 and up to 20° C by 1945. In 1980, many homes were heated to 21° to 22° C. The increase in preferred indoor temperature is due in part to changes in fashion. Fifty years ago people naturally wore sweaters and long underwear indoors. (If one lives through several winters at 18° C, then 21° C seems uncomfortably warm.) Today men wear jackets, ties, and long pants in business offices in summer and then feel the need to turn the air conditioners on to "high." In the winter many women wear dresses and skirts and turn the heaters up. If fashion changed so that men wore short pants and light shirts during hot weather, and women wore wool pants in the winter, we would need less fuel for heating and air conditioning.

The recent rise in the use of energy for air conditioning in particular is a measure of social demand. In 1952, only 1.3 per cent of the houses in the United States had air conditioning; by 1979, over 50 per cent of all homes

*Of course, the temperatures in the 1930's and 1940's were given in °F.

Colorado's Governor, Richard D. Lamm, was asked what was the worst case of waste that he observed in the last year. "That is easy," he said. "It was one day last July when the outside temperature was at 96°F. The state building in Denver had the air conditioner on so cold that one of the secretaries had a heater plugged in alongside her desk."

In some areas of northern Japan, temperatures often fall well below freezing on winter evenings. Yet local residents use very little fuel for heating. After dark, family social life is centered around the dinner table. Tables are low to the floor and people sit on cushions rather than on chairs. A large, heavy tablecloth extends beyond the table and rests on people's laps to serve as a common blanket. The primary source of heat in the dining room comes from a small charcoal brazier located under the table. The heat from the fire is retained by the tablecloth, so the air around people's lower bodies is warm. The remainder of the house is cool, and the people simply wear heavy sweaters to keep their upper bodies comfortable. After dinner and tea, they go to bed and snuggle down under warm quilts.

Figure 4–10. Relative extra fuel consumption for air conditioning to cool an average home to various temperatures *below* 80°F. For example, it takes three times as much extra fuel to cool the average home from 80°F to 77°F as it does to go from 80°F to 79°F.

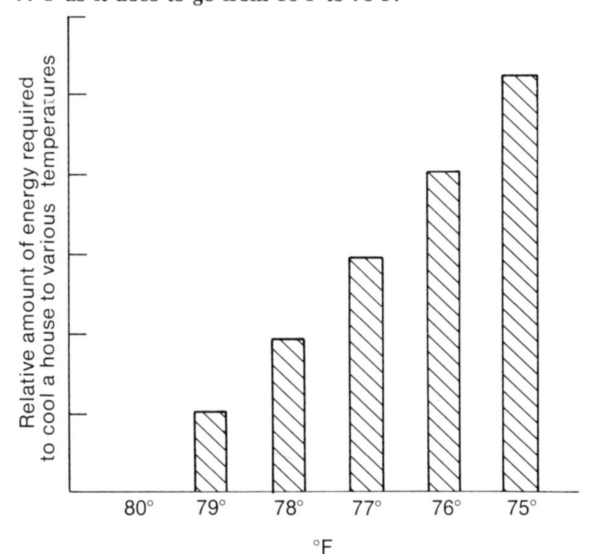

ENERGY-SAVING METHODS THAT DON'T COST MONEY

1. After taking a bath, open the bathroom door and let the water stand in the tub until it cools to room temperature. The heat from the water is enough to heat a small house for an hour.
2. Similarly, after doing the dishes, don't let the kitchen sink water drain out until it cools.
3. Use kitchen and bathroom exhaust fans sparingly, as they blow away a houseful of warm air in 1 hr.
4. Wear sweaters and long underwear in winter, and light clothes in summer. Then adjust the thermostat accordingly.
5. Close off unused rooms, walk-in closets and stairways, and save the fuel that would otherwise be needed to heat them.

were air conditioned. The United States, with a mere 5 per cent of the world's population, uses over 50 per cent of the energy consumed in the world for air conditioning. Houses, cars, shopping malls, and even entire sports arenas are cooled. Any home improvements that conserve fuel in the winter will also save fuel for air conditioning. But even more fuel could be conserved if social norms changed slightly and people turned down their air conditioners, or simply turned them off sometimes and opened their windows.

TABLE 4-4. HOW YOU CAN SAVE FUEL FOR HOME APPLIANCES

Method	Savings (Dollars/ year)*
Place extra insulation around hot water heater	Saves $19/ year
Place insulation around hot water pipes	Saves $20/ year
Hang clothes on line in summer rather than use dryer	Saves $25/ year
Disconnect drying cycle from dishwasher	Saves $25/ year
Put covers on pans when cooking	Saves $5/ year
Use wool or down blankets rather than electric blankets	Saves $8/ year
Use proper size light bulbs, turn lights off when not in use	Variable
Turn off pilot lights on gas stove	Saves $10/ year

*Energy savings here have been calculated using a value of $.05 per kilowatt hour.

Use of Appliances

Modern appliances add comfort and convenience to our daily lives. For example, a sewing machine is truly a work saver. In a minute or less a person using a sewing machine can sew a seam that would take an hour or more by hand. What's more, the machine uses little energy. But much energy is wasted by improper use of appliances. An electric range uses two and one-half times as much energy as a gas range to

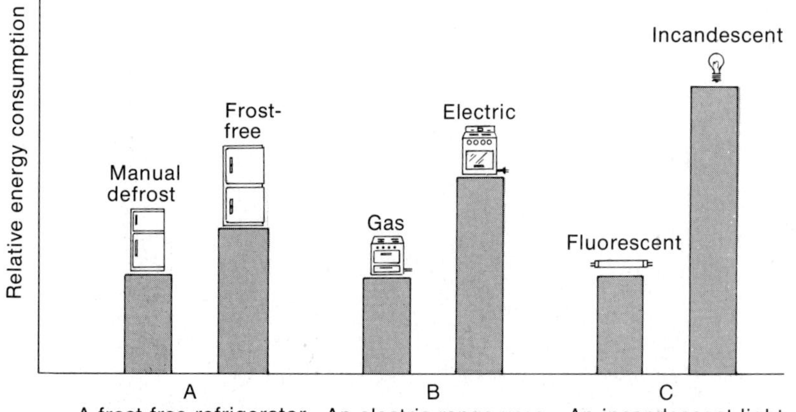

Fuel consumption in the home could be reduced without any loss of comfort if more efficient appliances were used.

do the same job. An automatic dishwasher uses the same amount of energy whether it is full or half empty, and many people run their washers with half a load. Table 4–4 lists some ways that you can save energy used by your home appliances.

From fuel mining to fuel transportation to fuel consumption, the environment always loses when energy is consumed. Early Americans thought that since you could neither damage nor deplete the environment, you may as well take the most convenient route to your goal. Today we know that we can damage and deplete our planet. Old attitudes must, therefore, be reevaluated.

CHAPTER OBJECTIVES

Study the past, present, and projected future availability of natural gas, coal, oil, and nuclear fuels. Understand the problems associated with production of synfuels. Seven types of renewable sources are discussed in the chapter: solar, hydroelectric, tidal, ocean thermal, geothermal, wind, and plant matter. You should know the relative potential quantity of energy available from each source, as well as the economic costs and environmental problems associated with development of each.

Recognize the differences between technical and social approaches to conservation, and review some conservation procedures and their possible impact on transportation, industry, and household uses.

KEY WORDS

Synfuels
Oil shale
Tar sands
Passive solar design
Solar collector
Solar cell
Hydroelectric energy
Tidal power
Ocean thermal power
Geothermal energy
Gasohol
Mass transit

TAKE-HOME EXPERIMENTS

1. **Efficiency of electrical consumption.** Look at your last month's electric bill and record the number of kilowatt hours of electricity used at that time. Now initiate an energy conservation program in your home. Report on the conservation measures used. Look at the electric bill one month later, and record the amount of electricity saved. (Caution—if your house is heated or cooled electrically, there may be a large monthly variation in electric bills due to change of seasons. For example, less heat is needed in March than in February. If the records are available, compare electric consumption for a month this year with the consumption for the same month last year.) Did your program save money? Discuss any inconveniences raised by the conservation practices.

2. **Solar collectors.** Remove the inner dividers from each of four identical ice cube trays. Fill each tray with the same amount of water, until it is about ⅔ full. (Between 1½ and 2 cups will do for the average-size tray. Use a measuring cup.) Set all four trays in the freezer compartment of a refrigerator until the water is frozen. Cover two of the trays with clear plastic wrap, sealed around the edges with tape or a large rubber band. Replace the trays in the freezer and let them stay overnight. Next day, about midmorning, prop the four trays on a small box on a waterproof surface outdoors. Let two of them (a covered one and an open one) slope toward the north and the other two slope south. Let them sit in the sun and note the rate at which they melt. Which design was the most efficient collector of solar energy? Explain your results.

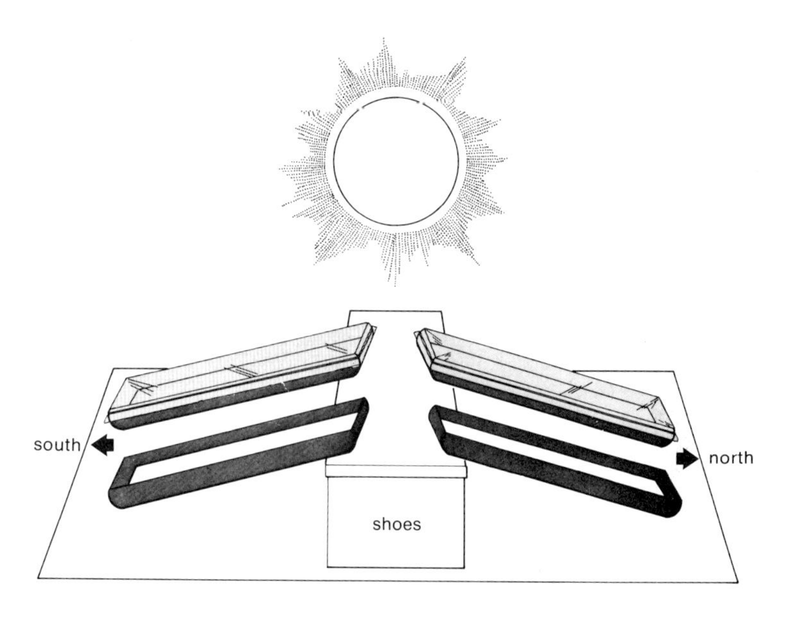

3. **Efficiency of transportation.** Obtain a map of your local community. Mark the locations of your residence, your school, the grocery store, post office, bank, and the five other stores that you visit most frequently. Measure the distance from your home to each of these locations. What type of transportation do you usually use to travel from one to another? Discuss the efficiency in terms of fuel consumption, time, and cost of the transportation system you use. Would it be difficult to improve the fuel efficiency of this system?

4. **Fuel for cooking.** Turn on your stove and wait until the burner reaches constant heat output. Pour 1 cup of cold water in a pan, cover it, and measure the time needed for the water to boil. Cool the pan, pour another cup of cold water in it, and measure the time needed for the water to boil with no cover on it. Compare your results.

PROBLEMS

1. **Fossil fuel resrves.** Discuss the prospects for the availability of petroleum in the next 10, 20, and 40 years. What types of uncertainties are inherent in these predictions?

2. **Fossil fuel reserves.** Discuss the prospects for the availability of coal in the next 10, 40, 100, and 200 years. What types of uncertainties are inherent in these predictions?

3. **Synfuels.** The United States imported approximately 8.7 million barrels of oil per day in 1979. Discuss some problems involved with replacing half of the oil with synfuels. Compare some of the social costs of synfuel production to the social costs of conservation.

4. **Uranium reserves.** Describe the availability of uranium reserves and the possible impact on future development of nuclear power plants.

5. **Home heating.** Describe the design of a passive solar house. How does it differ from the design of a conventional house? of a house equipped with solar collectors?

6. **Solar collectors.** Describe the design of (a) solar hot water systems; (b) solar space heating systems.

7. **Hydroelectric power.** How does the design and operation of a hydroelectric power generator differ from a fossil fuel—powered one? Compare the two with respect to availability of energy supply and environmental impact.

8. **Tidal power.** The strength of tidal currents fluctuates on a 6-hour basis. Tidal currents are strongest midway between high and low tides, and stop altogether just at high and at low tides. How would these fluctuations affect the use of tidal power for the generation of electricity? Suggest some possible solutions to the problem.

9. **Ocean thermal power.** Explain why ocean thermal power plants are inherently inefficient. Why are they being developed nevertheless?

10. **Wood heat.** Increased use of wood heat has led to significant air pollution problems in many small towns. Discuss some of the environmental trade-offs inherent in the use of wood heat.

11. **Wood heat.** Loggers in New England have traditionally sold low- or medium-quality logs to pulp mills for the production of paper. During the 1979 season, it was often more profitable to sell logs as firewood. Using these data as an example, discuss how the energy crisis could affect the price of various agricultural products.

12. **Burning of garbage.** Discuss the environmental impact of burning garbage as a fuel.

13. **Conservation.** Which of the following conservation procedures involve primarily technical solutions; which would involve social readjustment; and which involve a combination of both: (a) Carpooling; (b) use of small cars; (c) addition of storm windows on houses; (d) turning the thermostat down to 65° in winter; (e) use of gas stoves rather than electric ranges.

14. **Transportation.** Give some reasons why it is often difficult to alter patterns of surface transportation.

15. **Transportation.** It takes a few hours to fly across the United States. A comparable journey by train takes several days. Yet the cost to the passenger is more by train. Discuss the impact of this economic structure on world fuel reserves.

16. **Transportation.** Discuss present transportation patterns in the United States. How could they be made more efficient?

17. **Energy of transportation.** Compare the relative fuel consumption of: (a) a single person driving in a heavy, luxury car; (b) four people riding in a heavy, luxury car; (c) one person driving in a small sub-compact car; (d) four people riding in a small sub-compact car; (e) travel by bus; (f) travel by bicycle.

*18. **Transportation.** In 1975, 97 per cent of urban traffic was carried by the automobile, and only 3 per cent was carried by mass transit systems. Thus, even if mass transit systems were to double the number of passengers they carry, there would be relatively little impact on overall fuel consumption rates. Should these figures be used as an argument against building new mass transit systems? Defend your answer.

19. **Energy consumption for industry.** Compare the use of waste steam in North America with its use in Europe.

20. **Energy conservation for industry.** Discuss some factors that might make recycling economically attractive.

21. **Home heating.** Why is a furnace more efficient than an electric heater?

22. **Home heating.** List five ways that you could reduce heat loss in your present home. If possible, list the approximate cost of each type of improvement. Comment on the feasibility of altering your living space to use less fuel.

23. **Conservation of electricity.** How do clothing styles affect energy consumption in the United States?

24. **Conservation of energy.** Name the three appliances in your home or apartment that consume the largest amounts of electricity. Can you think of ways to conserve some of the energy used by these devices? Do your suggestions involve personal sacrifice or technological improvements?

25. **Conservation of energy.** Certain fuels, such as gasoline, are now taxed. Some people have suggested that higher taxes be placed on all fuels. Discuss the relative advantages and disadvantages of high fuel taxes. How would these taxes affect (a) electric heating systems, (b) solar heating systems, (c) fashions? Discuss with your classmates.

---

*Indicates more difficult problem.

CHAPTER 5

During the past decade and a half, some of the most rapid technical advancements have been made in the field of electronics. Pocket calculators were virtually unavailable in 1970, available but expensive in 1972, and selling for under $10.00 by 1975. Computer-operated control devices are now used routinely to monitor industrial processes to save time and energy, and increasingly sophisticated communication systems link businesses around the world.

This chapter introduces the concepts of electrical force and current and discusses the basic elements of some simple electric circuits. In the early 1800's, scientists discovered that electricity and magnetism were closely related. The chapter describes how an understanding of electromagnetic interactions has led to the development of electromagnets, motors, generators, and transformers.

ELECTRICITY AND MAGNETISM

5.1 INTRODUCTION

If a primitive person were shown a horseshoe magnet, an electromagnet, an electric motor, a compass, a television set, a light bulb, and a pocket calculator, it would be unlikely that he would realize that all these various devices and phenomena could be embraced by one *single* physical concept. The concept that we are referring to is electromagnetism.

Most of the motion that we observe on Earth, except that of falling bodies, involves electromagnetic forces. Any type of fire or explosion (excluding nuclear explosions), such as the combustion that operates heat engines, boils water, heats your house, or destroys a forest, is a chemical reaction. But since atoms are bonded to each other by electrical forces, the chemical reactions in a fire are caused by a series of electromagnetic interactions. Similarly, muscle action arises from electrical interactions within living cells. Light and heat from the Sun come to us as electromagnetic waves. The Sun's energy warms the Earth unevenly, causing the atmosphere to expand unevenly and to move about. Therefore, the seemingly eternal winds that blow across the globe arise originally out of electrical forces. Thus we can easily appreciate how important electricity and magnetism are.

We can measure electrical forces, we can predict what will happen when charged bodies are brought in contact with one another, we can generate electrical fields, we can utilize electricity for our own benefit, but we really cannot explain what electromagnetism is. Electromagnetism, like gravitation, is an inherent property of matter.

5.2 ELECTROSTATIC FORCES

If you rub a balloon against your hair and then place it against the wall, it will stick. On the other hand, if you rub two balloons against your hair and place them close together, they will repel each other. From experiments of

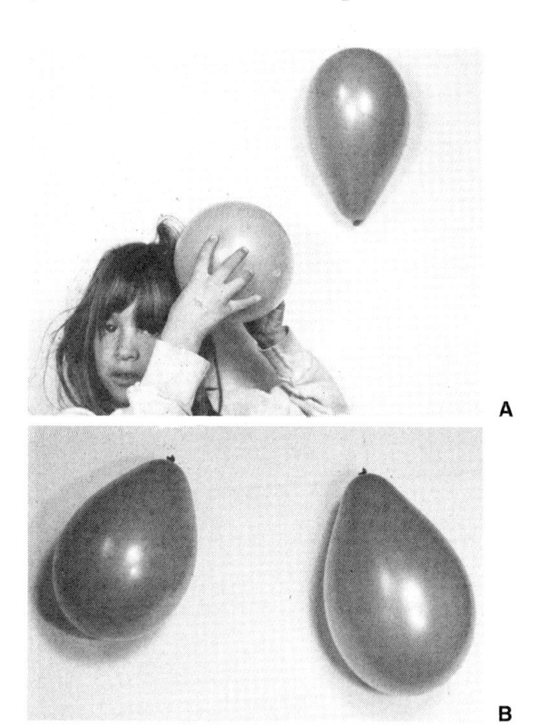

Figure 5–1. *A,* **Balloons stick to the wall after being charged by rubbing against a person's hair.** *B,* **If two balloons are charged and suspended (away from the wall) by light threads, they will repel each other and swing apart. The repulsion is due to the fact that each balloon carries a net negative charge.**

this type, scientists learned that somehow the act of rubbing a balloon changes its physical properties; it has been given an **electrical charge.** There are two types of electrical charges, +, positive, and −, negative. Like charges (− −) or (+ +) repel each other, and unlike charges (+ −) or (− +) attract. Recall that gravitational force is only attractive, but electrical forces can be attractive or repulsive.

Electrical forces are strong. A balloon hanging on the wall is being pulled downward by the gravitational force of the whole Earth, but the small electrical charge it gained when it was rubbed against your hair produces an even stronger force.

In general, a charged body will affect any other charged body. We say that there is a **field of force** surrounding the charged body. This field extends outward through space. It cannot be seen or held, yet it can be measured and objects are affected by it. The nature of space itself is affected by electrical charges. It is convenient to illustrate the presence of fields of force by drawing lines to represent their intensity and their distribution in space. In these pictures the distance between lines is a measure of the intensity of the fields. When lines are close together, the field is intense; when lines are far apart, the field is weak. Consider a very small charged body, which we imagine to be no larger than a point. The electrical force is then greatest at the point of the charge and diminishes as we move away from it. Therefore the fields of force are drawn as shown in Figure 5–2*A*. If two point charges of opposite sign are close together, the fields of force attract each other as shown in Figure 5–2*B*. It is important to remember that any charged particle, whether it is moving or stationary, generates a field of force.

Interestingly, the equation that describes the strength of an electrical field has the same form as the equation that describes the strength of a gravitational field. The force of gravitation is equal to:

$$\text{Force of gravitation} = \text{a constant} \times \frac{\text{mass of object A} \times \text{mass of object B}}{(\text{distance between the objects})^2}$$

$$F_{grav} = G\frac{m_A\, m_B}{d^2} \qquad [5.1]$$

whereas the force between two electrically charged bodies is equal to:

$$\text{Electrical force} = \text{a constant} \times \frac{\text{charge on object A} \times \text{charge on object B}}{(\text{distance between the objects})^2}$$

$$F_{elec} = k\frac{q_A\, q_B}{d^2} \qquad [5.2]$$

The standard unit of electric charge is called the **coulomb.** We know from Equation 5.2 that electrical forces vary *inversely* with the square of the distance between the charged objects. Thus, the force *decreases* rapidly as the two bodies move away from each other.

The constants G and k in the equations tell us about the magnitude of electrical and gravitational forces.

For gravitation: $G = 6.67 \times 10^{-11}\ \text{Nm}^2/\text{kg}^2$
For electrical: $k = 8.99 \times 10^{9}\ \text{Nm}^2/\text{coulomb}^2$

Substituting the values of the constants in Equations 5–1 and 5–2 we see that the force of gravitation between two bodies, each with a mass of one kilogram resting one meter apart, is 6.67×10^{-11} newtons, whereas the electrical force between two bodies, each with a charge of one coulomb resting one meter apart, is 8.99×10^{9} newtons.

5.3 ELECTRICITY AND ATOMIC STRUCTURE

Scientists have learned that all matter is made up of a collection of fundamental units called **atoms.** An atom consists of a small, dense, positively charged center called a **nucleus.** The nucleus is surrounded by a diffuse cloud of negatively charged particles called **electrons.** The nucleus is composed of two types of particles, positively charged **protons** and electrically

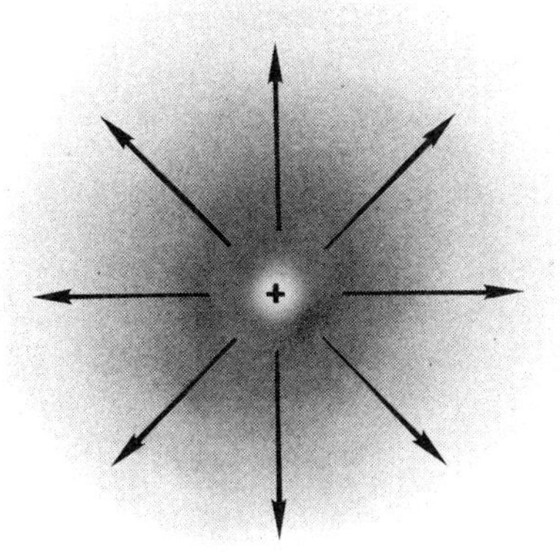
A Isolated Positive Charge

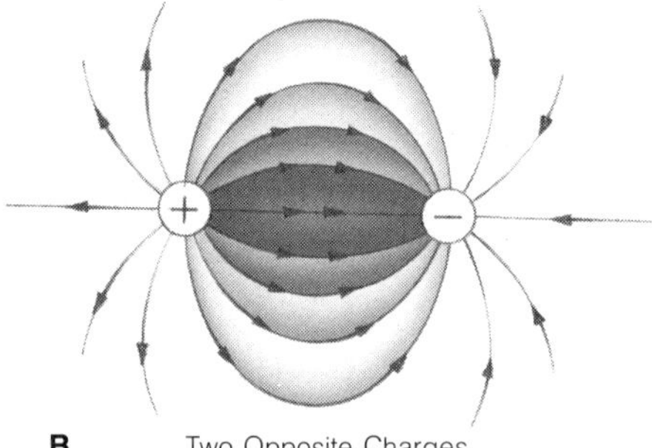
B Two Opposite Charges

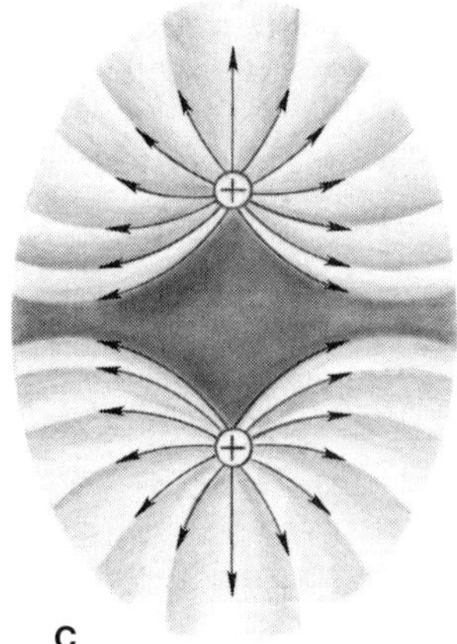
C Two Like Charges

Figure 5–2. Fields of force.

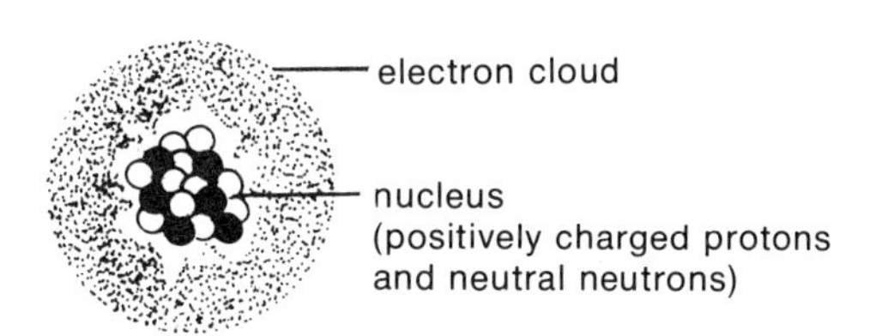

Figure 5–3. A simple picture of an atom.

neutral particles called **neutrons.** Practically all of the mass of the atom is contained in the nucleus. All neutral atoms have the same number of protons as electrons. Therefore, a neutral atom has an equal quantity of positive and negative charge, so that its net charge is zero. Atomic structure is discussed further in Chapter 7.

The negatively charged electrons are attracted to the positive nucleus by electrical force. However, it is possible to remove electrons from an atom, just as it is possible to launch a spacecraft against the force of the Earth's gravity. When a person rubs a balloon against his hair, electrons are pulled from the surface of the hair and are attracted to the atoms in the rubber. The hair becomes positively charged (it loses electrons) while the balloon gains an equal negative charge (it acquires the electrons that the hair lost). The balloon will then be attracted to other positively charged objects and repelled by other negatively charged objects, such as other charged balloons.

> Only a very small percentage of the electrons are exchanged. Electrical forces are extremely strong. If a balloon were one quarter of a meter from your head, and the balloon had one per cent more electrons than protons, and your hair carried an equivalent positive charge, the attractive force between the two would be great enough to lift a "weight" equal to that of the entire Earth.

5.4 THE MOTION OF ELECTRICAL CHARGES (I)

Imagine a large box that was completely evacuated—absolutely empty. Then we dropped two electrons into the center of this box and shut the lid. What would happen? Since the electrons repel each other, they would move as far away from each other as possible, as shown in Figure 5–4. That's simple enough: charged particles move in response to the net force acting upon them, and in this case there is a net repulsion.

This experiment and the one described in the next paragraph are "thought experiments." They could never be performed because we cannot handle atomic particles so precisely.

Now, how do electrons move in a solid such as a balloon, a wall, or a piece of wire? Recall that a solid is a coherent collection of protons, neutrons, and electrons, bound together in

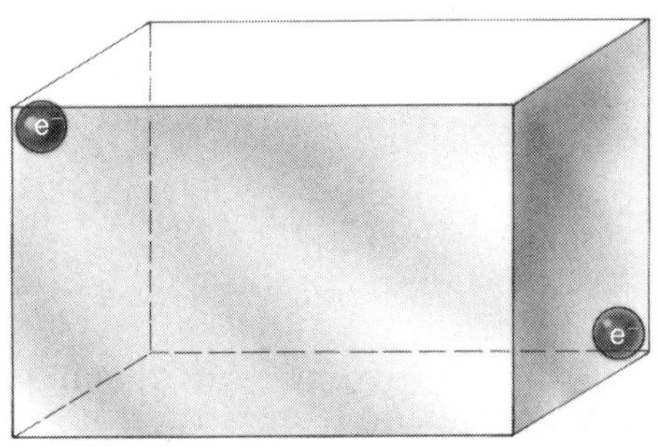

Figure 5–4. Two electrons in an empty box would move as far away from each other as possible.

some regular array. Let us say that we had two electrons and that we placed them in the middle of a solid just as we placed two electrons in an empty box. What would happen? The answer to this question is not simple at all. The two electrons are mutually repelled by each other, as before, but they are also repelled by all the billions and billions of other electrons all around them. At the same time, they are attracted by all the billions and billions of protons in the vicinity. To calculate whether or not the added electrons would move, we would have to calculate the net force resulting from the sum of all these attractions and repulsions.

An approximate mathematical solution of the problem is extremely difficult, and an exact solution is entirely beyond our capabilities, but we can learn a lot by performing a few simple experiments. If you rub a balloon on your hair, it becomes negatively charged. If it is then placed against a wall, the negative charges are attracted to the positive nuclei on the surface of the wall, and therefore the balloon sticks. On a dry day, the balloon may hold fast for several hours. The electrons on the surface of the balloon must stay in place; they do not move through the rubber very easily. Rubber is an **insulator,** and insulators resist the movement of charge through them. Now touch a metal wire to the balloon just at the point where it touches the wall. The balloon falls down immediately. Why? The excess electrons on the surface of the balloon travel easily through the metal, and the balloon loses its charge. All metals are electrical **conductors** and permit the passage of electrons through them.

The conductivity of a material is a measure of its ability to carry electrical current. Conductivities vary quite widely; it takes about 10^{21} times more force to push an electron through a mass of rubber than through an identically sized mass of pure copper. Glass, rubber, many plastics, wood, mica, and slate are other good insulators, whereas all metals are good electrical conductors. It is convenient for us that there is such a large range of electrical conductivities. Thus it is easier for an electric current to pass through thousands of kilometers of wire in overhead transmission lines than through the few centimeters of insulating matter that stand between the wire and its supporting tower (Fig. 5–5).

There is no known material that is a perfect insulator, nor is there any perfect conductor under ordinary conditions. Electric currents can be pushed through even the best insulators, and similarly, even the best conductors offer some resistance at all but the very lowest temperatures.

Let us look more closely at the movement of electrons through a metal.

Figure 5–5. Current can flow more easily through thousands of kilometers of transmission wire than through a few centimeters of insulators.

Think of a battery that continuously pushes electrons out of one terminal and pulls them in at the other. We then connect a wire between the two terminals to provide a path for the flow of electrons. Imagine a single electron entering the metal wire from the battery. It doesn't race off through the wire without interruption. Rather, it travels a short distance (less than a millionth of a centimeter) until it comes close to another electron situated in the wire. At this point the incoming electron repels its neighbor and pushes it a short distance until it, in turn, repels the next electron it meets. This sequence of events continues on and on through the wire. It is essential to understand that the electrons move rather slowly, while the energy resulting from the series of pushes, called the **electric field,** moves

> While it is theoretically possible to move current through any substance, it would require so much work to push a substantial current through, say, a rubber band that the rubber would quickly heat up, start to melt and smoke before it carried a significant amount of current.

Figure 5–6

***A,* Direct current in a wire.**

***B,* Analogy of people pushing to view quickly. The force of a push is transmitted quickly, although the people move slowly.**

much more rapidly. Specifically, the electric field travels at nearly the speed of light, 3×10^{10} cm/sec, while the electrons themselves travel at about 0.02 cm/sec. Such one-directional movement is called **direct current,** abbreviated **dc.**

To visualize the movement of electrons in a wire, imagine a group of people lining up to view the Grand Canyon. When a new person arrives, he or she pushes against the back of the line in an effort to move forward. The force of the push is transmitted down the line quickly, and the unfortunate person near the rim is shoved off. Then the line moves forward slightly. Thus the new person initiated a rapid transmission of force by means of a slow movement of people, just as an electric field moves much more rapidly through a wire than does an electron itself.

A battery utilizes chemical action to push electrons through a wire. The electrons go in one direction, producing a direct current. However, the electricity coming into your house from the electric company is produced in large generators, not batteries. As will be explained later, the generators used in conventional power production do not produce a direct current. Rather they generate an alternating field, which pushes the electrons a fraction of a centimeter in one direction then pulls them back in the opposite direction, and continues to force them to oscillate back and forth. If an electron starts at a given point, it moves one way a small distance, less than 10^{-8} cm, comes back to the center, moves the other way, back to center, etc. This is called **alternating current,** abbreviated **ac.** In a household circuit each electron makes 60 cycles every second, and we say that this circuit operates at 60 cycles per second. Thus, you do not buy electrons from the power company; you buy the energy needed to push them around.

We have seen how an electric current in a wire consists of moving electrons. However, electric currents can also flow through liquids that do not have free mobile electrons. In these situations, moving **ions** constitute the current. An ion is an atom or molecule with an unbalanced charge.* If there is an excess of electrons, the ion is negative; if there are fewer electrons than protons, the ion is positive. Any flow of charged particles, whether electrons or ions, is an electrical current.

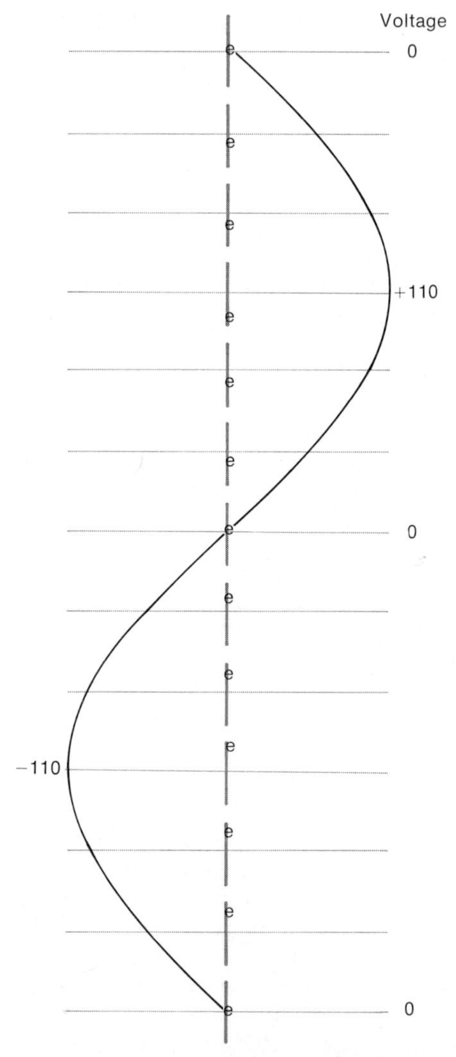

Figure 5–7. Alternating current (ac). The 13 short vertical lines represent a wire in which an electron, *e*, moves up and down. The first vertical line shows the electron in the center of the wire, representing zero voltage. As the voltage, represented by the curved line, alternates back and forth, the electron periodically changes its direction, thus producing an alternating current.

*A molecule is a collection of atoms held together by chemical bonds. Molecules will be discussed further in Chapter 7.

5.5 THE MOTION OF ELECTRICAL CHARGES (II)

Voltage

It is fine fun to rub balloons on your hair and then to stick them onto walls, but if that were the extent of our use of electricity, it would be merely a curiosity. In today's society, people use electricity to transmit energy to produce light and heat, to perform mechanical work, and to transmit information.

As we study practical electrical currents we are reminded of many mechanical analogies. Think of a water wheel connected to a shaft. A rope is tied to the shaft and connected to a weight as shown in Figure 5–8*A*. When the wheel rotates, it turns the shaft and lifts the weight. In order to activate the system, water is pumped up through a hose and allowed to drop onto the water wheel. The falling water turns the wheel, lifts the weight, and is then collected into another hose and returned to the pump. In this system the mechanical energy of the pump forces water upward to the top of the hose. The water now has a certain amount of potential energy. When the water falls onto the water wheel, this potential is reconverted to work, and the weight is lifted. Suppose that instead of this mechanical system we had a simple electrical system consisting of an electric generator, some wire, and an electric motor, as shown in Figure 5–8*B*. The generator is analogous to the pump, the wire to the hose, and the motor to the water wheel. If someone cranks the generator, an electric field travels through the wire. This moving electric field can perform work. As the field moves through the motor, mechanical work is done and a weight is lifted.

Electrical potential is measured in **volts.** One *must* remember that a volt is a potential and as such must be measured with respect to some other point. Thus, the potential energy of a drop of water is measured with respect to its height above the ground, and the potential energy in an electric circuit is measured with respect to another point on the circuit.

If water is sitting in a tank, the total energy available is proportional to the height of the water above ground × the amount of water available. Similarly, the energy of an electrical circuit is proportional to the electrical potential (volts) × the amount of charge (coulombs).

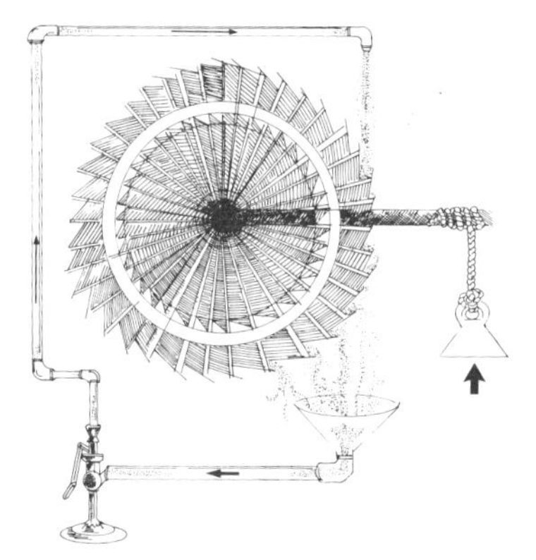

A Mechanical pump, water wheel analogy

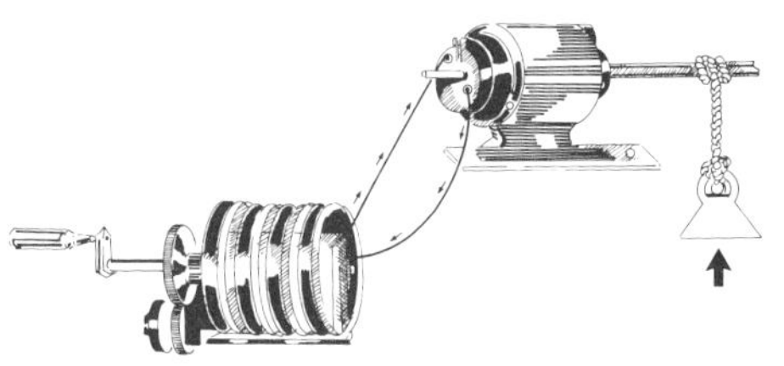

B Electrical system

Figure 5–8. Electrical energy.

$$\text{Energy} = \frac{\text{electrical}}{\text{potential}} \times \text{charge} \qquad [5.3]$$

$$1 \text{ joule} = 1 \text{ volt} \times 1 \text{ coulomb}$$

Or, in words, if 1 coulomb of charge travels through 1 volt of potential difference, the work performed is equal to 1 joule (J).

The most convenient reference for measuring voltage in many applications is the Earth itself. Thus, the state-

> If a coulomb is the standard unit of electric charge and an electron is the smallest electrically charged particle, then there must be a relationship between the two. There is; and the coulomb is a *much* larger amount of charge than that carried by one electron. In fact, 1 coulomb is equal to the charge carried by 6.24×10^{18} electrons.

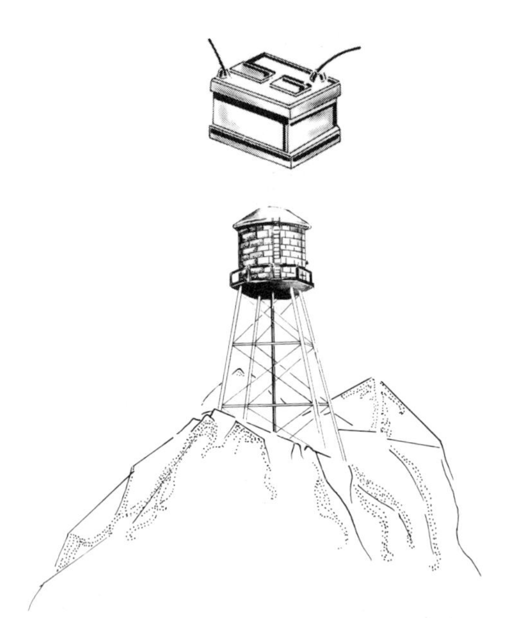

Figure 5–9. There is potential energy in the battery and the water tank, but no work is performed unless current or water is allowed to flow.

ment that the "hot" wire of a house circuit has a potential of 110 volts means that if a convenient path is provided, 1 coulomb of charge moving from the wire to the Earth can perform 110 J of work. Of course, not all measurements of height are made with respect to sea level, nor are all voltage measurements made with respect to the Earth's potential. Thus one part of a certain instrument is held at +3000 volts above ground potential, and a nearby point is held at +3070 volts. The potential difference between these two points is simply 70 volts.

Actually, charge leaks out of a battery slowly, because air is not a perfect insulator. The rate of flow is extremely small, and a battery can sit in a dry place for years without losing all its charge. The insulators within the circuitry of a car generally allow charge to pass through faster than the air does, so if you ever plan to park your car for several months, it is a good idea to disconnect the battery cables.

Another fact to remember about voltage is that its magnitude does not tell us anything about the movement of current. A charge can have a high potential and not move at all. Think of a car battery, for example. There is always a potential of 12 volts between the positive and negative terminals. But if the battery is just sitting somewhere, with no wires attached to it, no current will flow despite the 12-volt potential between the terminals. We are reminded of a tank of water perched on a hilltop. If all valves are closed, the water may sit for a thousand years without flowing, even though the potential to flow is always there. Voltage is a description of the electrical potential of a system.

Electric Circuits; Current

We already noted that some materials conduct electricity better than others. Copper wire is a good conductor; air is a poor one. Let us say that we had a simple circuit consisting of a light bulb wired to a small battery, as shown in Figure 5–10. Under normal operating conditions the electric current moves through the wire to the bulb, and the bulb lights up. If a small piece of wire is cut out of the circuit, leaving a gap, the electric current cannot cross the air space, and the bulb will not glow. Very simply, there must be a path, a circuit, to conduct the flow of charge.

Figure 5–10. *A,* Bulb glows if there is a complete circuit. *B,* Bulb does not glow if the switch is opened.

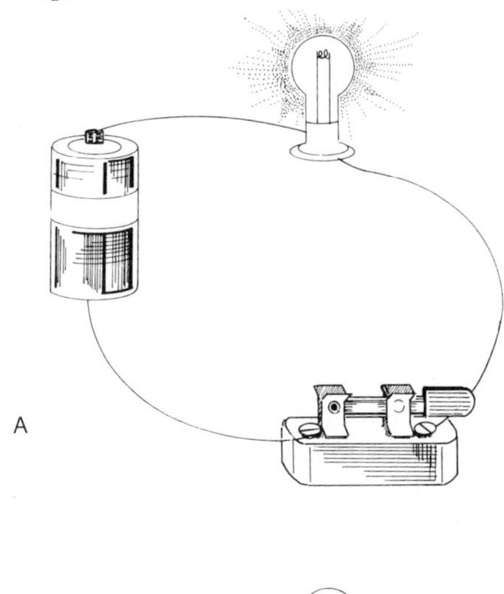

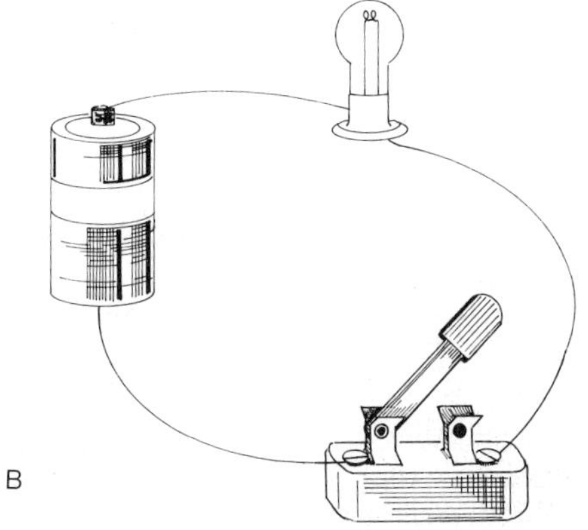

An electric current in a metal wire is a concerted movement of electrons. The magnitude of the current is proportional to the number of electrons that move along the wire within a given period of time. Current is commonly measured in **amperes** (amp). One amp is equal to the movement of 1 coulomb of charge past a given point in a wire in 1 sec.

$$1 \text{ amp} = 1 \text{ coulomb/sec} = 6.24 \times 10^{18} \text{ electrons/sec}$$

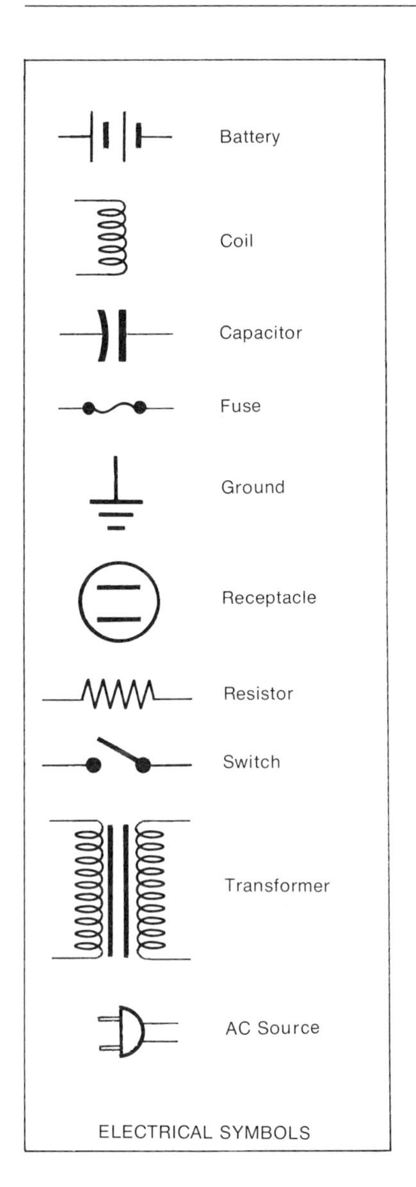

ELECTRICAL SYMBOLS

Resistance; Ohm's Law

Just as it is harder to pump water through some types of pipes than others, it is harder to push electricity through some types of materials than it is through others. There is some frictional drag between flowing water (or any other fluid) and even the smoothest pipe, and therefore energy is needed to force water through even a level pipe. If a pipe were filled with sand, however, more energy would be required to push water through it. This energy is not lost but rather is converted to heat by the friction between the water and the sand. Electrical resistors can be considered to be analogous to sand-filled pipes, and good conductors can be compared to smooth pipes. Thus it takes energy to push current through any material at room temperature (even copper or silver wire), but it takes much more energy to push current through materials with a high resistance than through those with a low resistance. This energy is converted to heat. The resistance of a material is a measure of the difficulty encountered in passing current through it. Resistance is generally expressed in ohms, symbolized by the Greek letter omega, Ω. In a circuit diagram, a material with a relatively high resistance is marked by the symbol ⩘⩘.

The resistance of metals has interested scientists for a long time. It is believed that when nuclei jiggle about because of thermal motion, they occasionally impede the progress of moving electrons. When metals are cooled to extremely low temperatures (about −270° C), the thermal motion slows down, the resistance drops toward zero, and the metals become **superconducting.** The resistance of a typical metal as a function of temperature is shown in Figure 5–11. When electricity is sent through high-tension transmission wires from major power plants to cities, the resistance of the wires becomes a problem. It takes energy to push currrent past the resistance, and this energy loss becomes significant when large quantities of electricity travel long distances. If the wires could be cooled to become superconducting, most of this lost electrical energy could be saved. However, refrigeration con-

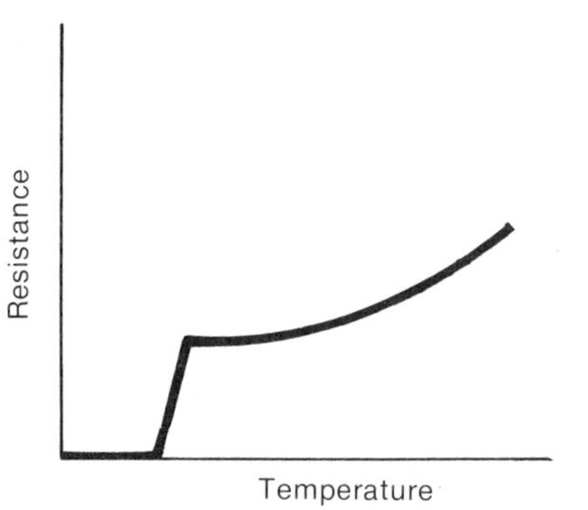

Figure 5–11. Resistance of a superconducting metal.

sumes energy, so a trade-off problem arises. Is it more economical to leave wires at open-air temperatures and suffer the energy loss from the resistance, or to pay the price to refrigerate the lines and then benefit from the effects of high conductivity? At present, refrigeration is more expensive, but success in any of several areas of research may shift the balance. Scientists are looking for alloys that become superconducting at higher temperatures; even a few degrees would reduce refrigeration costs significantly. The development of new types of thermal insulation and more efficient cooling devices may also ultimately shift the balance in favor of low-temperature power transmission.

When a current passes through a resistor its electrical energy is diminished. The energy itself does not disappear; instead the resistor gets hot. In fact, resistors are commonly used as heating elements. Electric stoves, toasters, and space heaters are all simple resistors designed to be connected to household circuits. Whenever electrons pass through a resistor, electrical energy is dissipated as heat, and the potential energy of the electrons decreases. Thus, the voltage on one side of the resistor is higher than that on the other side. The magnitude of the voltage drop across a resistor is given by the simple relationship known as **Ohm's law.**

Voltage drop across a resistor = current × resistance

$$V = IR \qquad [5.4]$$

where V = volts
I = current (in amperes)
R = resistance (in ohms)

Ohm's law is extremely useful in analyzing any circuit. Suppose we have a simple circuit consisting of a 12-volt battery and a 100-ohm resistor (Fig. 5–12). Assume for simplicity that the resistance of the wire is negligible. Electrons leaving the negative terminal of the battery have a potential of 12 volts with respect to the positive terminal. Thus the voltage between points A and D in Figure 5–12 is 12 volts. Since there is only one resistor in the circuit, the potential drop across this resistor must also be 12 volts. Knowing that there is a 12-volt potential drop across a 100-ohm resistor, it is possible to calculate the current in the circuit.

Figure 5–12. A simple circuit.

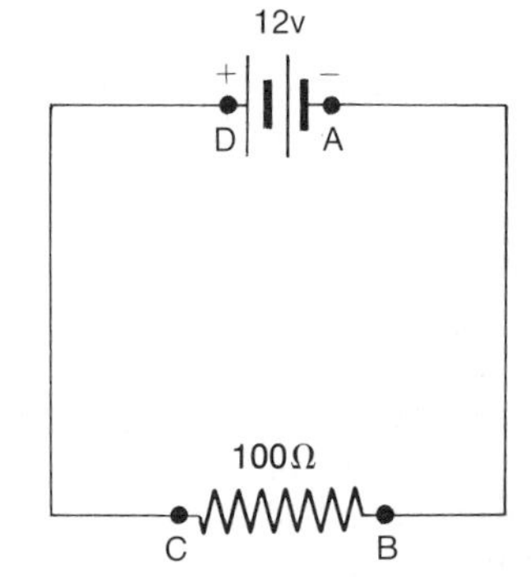

Voltage between points A and D, V_{AD} = 12 V

Voltage between points A and B, V_{AB} = 0 V

Voltage between points B and C, V_{BC} = 12 V

Voltage between points C and D, V_{CD} = 0 V

When a substance is cooled, the motion of its atoms and molecules slows down. No substance can be cooled below −273.15° C. This temperature is therefore called **absolute zero.** An absolute temperature scale, called the Kelvin scale, has been established. The Kelvin scale starts at absolute zero, and the magnitude of one kelvin is equal to the magnitude of one degree on the Celsius scale. Therefore, 0° C = +273.15 K. To convert from K to °C, use the formula

$$K = °C + 273.15$$

This subject is discussed further in Section 7.5.

$$\text{Voltage} = \text{current} \times \text{resistance}$$
$$\text{Current} = \frac{\text{voltage}}{\text{resistance}}$$
$$\text{Current} = \frac{12 \text{ volts}}{100 \text{ ohms}} = 0.12 \text{ amp}$$

Thus we see that the current is determined by the voltage and the resistance. Using Ohm's law, we could also calculate the resistance of a circuit if we knew the voltage and the current, or we could calculate the voltage with knowledge of the current and the resistance.

Example 1.

Imagine that your car won't start when you turn the ignition on. You check the battery and find that it is fully charged and there is a 12-volt potential between the two terminals. When you turn the ignition key, almost zero current flows through the ignition wires. Speculate on the nature of the problem.

Answer: **Since the current through the wires is virtually zero, there must be an extremely high resistance in the circuit somewhere. This problem commonly occurs when corrosion builds up between the battery terminals and the wires connected to them. The corrosion has a high resistance and retards the flow of current. As a practical matter, clean the terminals and try to start the car. If this fails, there is probably a disconnected wire somewhere in the system. (Perhaps your starter motor is burned out.)**

Power

Both electrical and mechanical energy can be converted to heat or work. Referring once again to our water system, the potential energy of water stored in an elevated pipe could be converted to work if the flow were directed against the blades of a water wheel. Or it could be converted to heat if the water were allowed to flow down through a sand-filled pipe. Heat is generated when electrical current is passed through a resistor, and mechanical work is generated when an electric current is passed through the coils of an electric motor. We are interested in the rate at which heat or work is produced by an electric current. Recall from Section 3.6 that power is defined as the rate of energy transferred, or energy per unit time. Power is commonly expressed in watts (abbreviated W) in both mechanical and electrical applications. One watt equals 1 joule per sec. Therefore,

$$\text{Power} = \frac{\text{energy}}{\text{time}} \qquad [5.5]$$

$$1 \text{ watt} = 1 \frac{\text{joule}}{\text{sec}}$$

A 100-W light bulb uses twice as much power as a 50-W bulb or a 50-W record player. In any one interval of time, the 100-W appliance uses twice as much energy as any 50-W appliance.

Electrical power equals the push (volts) times the amount that is being pushed per sec (current).

$$\text{Power} = \text{current} \times \text{voltage} \qquad [5.6]$$
$$P = IV$$

Looking at Figure 5–12 again, the power consumed as current passes through the resistor is equal to:

$$\text{Power} = \text{current} \times \text{voltage}$$
$$P = IV$$
$$\text{Power} = 0.12 \text{ amp} \times 12 \text{ volts}$$
$$= 1.44 \text{ W}$$

There is a power loss in a circuit only when there is a current moving across a voltage drop.

It is important to understand the interrelationships among voltage, current, resistance, and power. For reference during this discussion, two important equations are repeated below:

(1) $$\underset{\text{(volt)}}{\text{Voltage}} = \underset{\text{(amp)}}{\text{current}} \times \underset{\text{(ohm)}}{\text{resistance}} \qquad \text{(Ohm's law)}$$
$$V = IR$$

(2) $$\underset{\text{(W)}}{\text{Power}} = \underset{\text{(amp)}}{\text{current}} \times \underset{\text{(volt)}}{\text{voltage}}$$
$$P = IV$$

From Ohm's law we see that at constant voltage, a circuit with low resistance carries more current than does a circuit with high resistance. This conclusion is reasonable. Returning to our water-pipe analogy, it is obvious that a given pump will push a large flow of water through an empty pipe (low resistance). The same pump will push less water through a sand-filled pipe (high resistance).

Equation 5.6 tells us that the power output of a section of a circuit is equal to the current times the voltage drop. Again referring to our water-pipe analogy, the power directed against a water wheel is proportional to the rate of flow of water (also called the water current, just like an electrical current) times the distance that the water falls (analogous to voltage).

Following this logic, a circuit will produce the most heat if there is only low-resistance copper wire or other conductor throughout the current loop. Thus if you were to take an ordinary car battery and bridge the two terminals with a metal bar of low resistance, the bar will glow bright red and the battery will discharge quickly. (Don't do it!) The low resistance of the bar allows a great deal of current to flow, which produces a large amount of heat in a short period of time. Thus, the heating element in a stove has a much lower resistance than the circuitry of a radio, and the stove gets much hotter than the radio. Similarly, a great deal of heat will be produced if a copper wire is connected directly across the two terminals of a household outlet. The resistance of the circuit would then be simply the resistance of the wire, which is low—of the order of 10^{-4} ohms. Such low resistance would allow a very high flow of current. This type of situation is called a **short circuit.**

> *Don't ever create a short circuit as an experiment!* If you are working with battery circuits, you will burn out the battery. In household circuits you will burn out fuses, trip circuit breakers, perhaps start a fire, or electrocute yourself in the attempt.

5.6 HOUSEHOLD WIRING

Generally three wires go from the outside power pole to every house. Two of them are called "hot" wires. The voltage of these hot wires alternates, and the average potential is maintained at 110 volts with respect to the ground. The third wire, called the **ground wire,** is maintained at zero volts with respect to the ground by connecting one section of it to a copper rod that is literally pounded into the earth. Most wall sockets operate at 110 volts and are wired to one hot lead and the ground. Stoves, clothes driers, large

Figure 5–13. Household wiring.

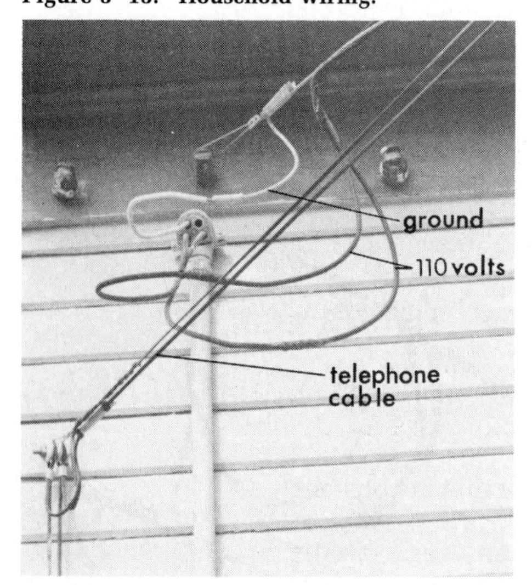

***A,* Wires entering a house. The two upper black wires are each held at 110 V. The upper white wire is a ground wire. The lower cables are for telephone.**

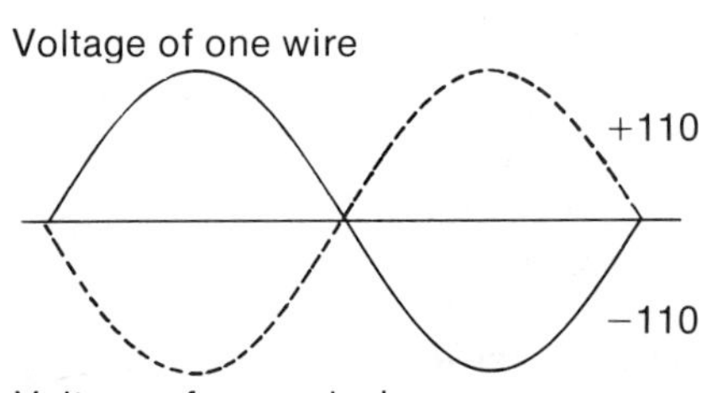

***B,* The voltage of the two 110 volt wires in a household circuit are out of phase with each other, so the potential difference between them is 220 volts.**

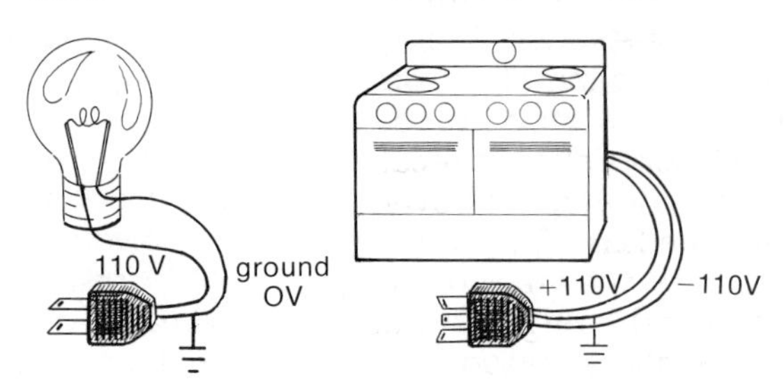

***C,* Wiring of 110 volt and 220 volt appliances.**

heaters, and other pieces of equipment that need a lot of power draw their electrical energy from both hot leads and operate at a potential of 220 volts.

A typical house is wired in many separate complete circuits. There may be a circuit for the downstairs lighting, another for the outlets in the kitchen, a third for the electric range, a fourth for the outlets in the bedrooms, and so on. Each circuit is wired independently so that a blown fuse, a short circuit, or a broken wire in one region will not affect all areas of the house.

Parallel Versus Series Circuits

If we have a collection of appliances and wish to wire them all into a single circuit, we can connect them either in **series,** as shown in Figure 5–14*A* or in **parallel,** as shown in Figure 5–14*B*. Notice that the schematic diagram does not specify the type of appliance; it just records its electrical characteristics. Thus a 100-ohm heater is noted by the symbol 100 Ω, just as a 100 ohm light bulb is drawn as 100 Ω.

The characteristics of parallel and series circuits are very different from one another. In a great many applications, such as the design of amplifiers or computers, it is essential to wire resistors in series. However, many other situations require parallel wiring. For common household wiring, parallel circuitry has a great many advantages. First of all, consider the fate of the toasters (the last outlets on the line) in Figure 5–14*A* and *B*. In the parallel circuit (Fig. 5–14*B*), there is always an unbroken wire leading to and from this outlet, and one can plug into it while leaving the other outlets vacant. In other words, if we plug our electric toaster into the third outlet and unplug the rest of the appliances, the resultant circuit looks like the one shown in Figure 5–15*B*. This is a workable situation. Electric energy is available to the toaster, and if you insert a slice of bread it will turn warm and brown. However, if any outlet along the line of the series circuit is unused, there is a break in the wire, and the electrical energy cannot pass. Figure 5–15*A* shows what happens to a series circuit in this situation.

There are additional advantages to the parallel circuit over the series circuit in household wiring. Let us study each system in turn. Imagine that each circuit includes three appliances—a light bulb with a resistance of 100 ohms, a record player with a resistance of 300 ohms, and a toaster with a resistance of 20 ohms. In a series circuit there is only one path for electrons to follow; therefore, the current in all parts of the wire must be the same. This

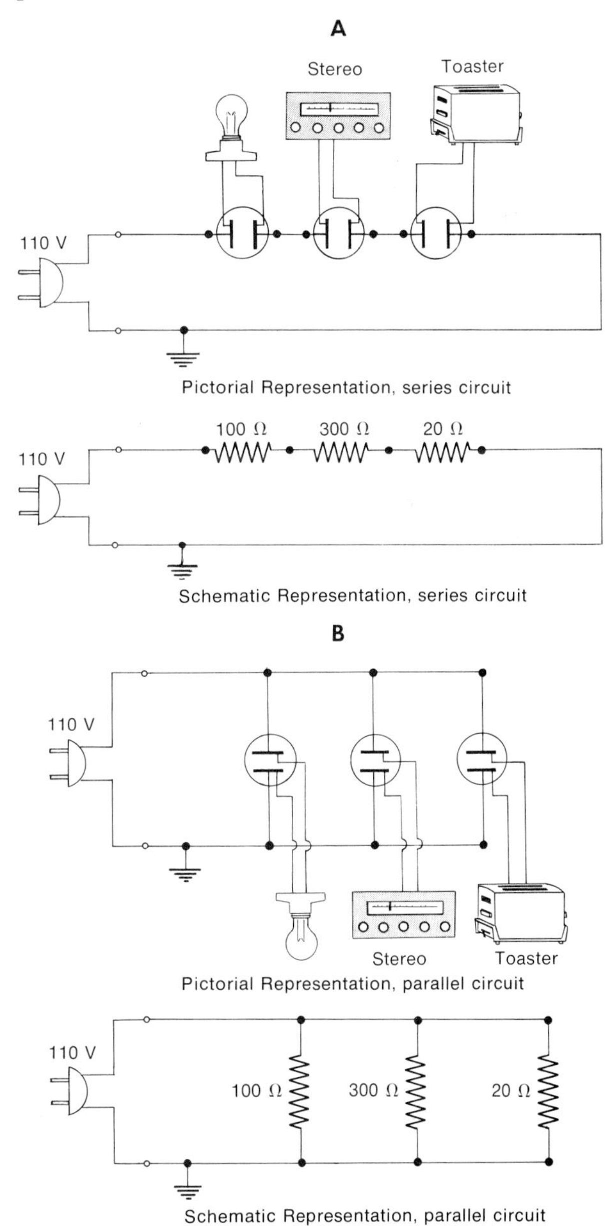

Figure 5–14. ***A,*** **A series circuit.** ***B,*** **A parallel circuit.**

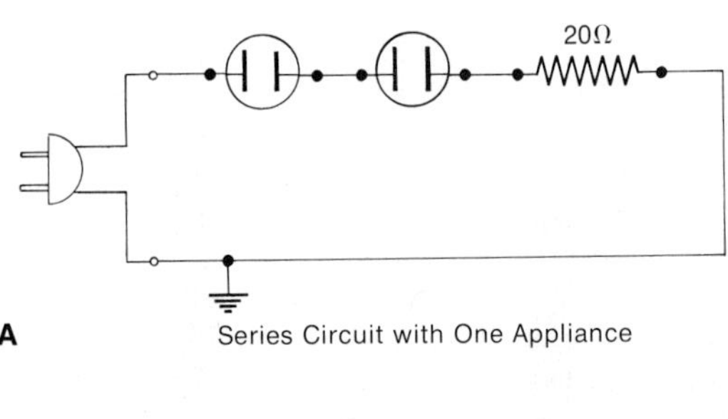

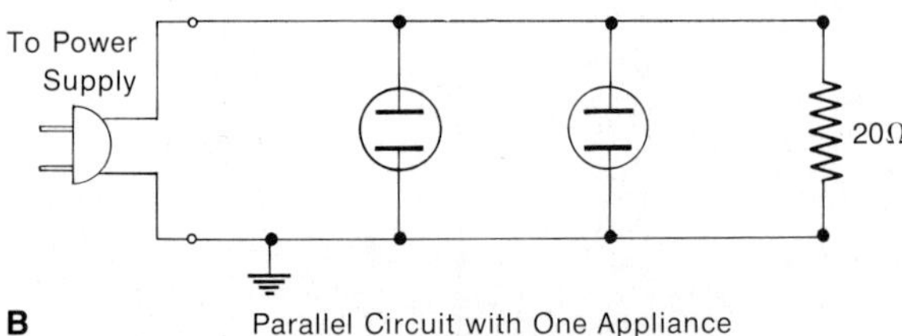

Figure 5–15. Circuits with one appliance.

current must overcome the first resistance, then the second, and finally the third. Therefore the total resistance is equal to the sum of all the resistances. In the example of Figure 5–15*A*, the circuit resistance is equal to 100 ohms + 300 ohms + 20 ohms = 420 ohms. The total current in the circuit can be calculated by Ohms's law and is equal to the voltage divided by the total resistance. In the example,

$$\text{Current} = \frac{\text{voltage}}{\text{resistance}}$$

$$I = \frac{V}{R} = \frac{110 \text{ volts}}{420 \text{ ohms}} = 0.26 \text{ amp}$$

Thus, as we plug in more appliances in a series circuit, the total resistance of the circuit goes up and the total current goes down. Since the power available to each appliance is equal to current × voltage, the power also decreases. Moreover, since the current through each appliance is identical, those devices with the highest resistance receive the most power.

We immediately see how unsuitable this type of wiring is for household use. If there is a single 100-ohm light bulb in a series circuit, the power available is greater than if the light bulb is in series with a record player and a toaster. Thus, the light would dim as other appliances were plugged in. In a series circuit, the power output of any appliance depends on the other resistors in the line and changes drastically with the total resistance of the circuit.

This problem is avoided in a parallel circuit. Since each resistance forms a bridge from the 110-volt line to ground, the potential drop across each resistance is identical: 110 volts. Thus the current through any resistor depends *only* on the magnitude of its resistance and not on the values of the other resistors in the rest of the circuit. It does not matter whether that light bulb is alone in the circuit or if there are 20 other appliances; the power to it is always the same.

We see that as we add more resistors to a *series* circuit, the total current *decreases*, but as we add more resistors to a *parallel* circuit, the total current *increases*. This process occurs because in a parallel circuit we are adding new pathways for current flow while in a series circuit we are restricting the flow in a single pathway.

Example 2

Calculate (a) the power available to a 100-ohm light bulb if it is alone in a circuit; (b) the power available to a 100-ohm light bulb if it is wired in series with a 300-ohm record player and a 20-ohm toaster; (c) the power available to a 100-ohm light bulb if it is wired in parallel with a 300-ohm record player and a 20-ohm toaster.

Answer:

(a)

$$\text{Voltage} = \text{current} \times \text{resistance}$$

$$V = IR$$

$$I = \frac{V}{R}$$

$$= \frac{110 \text{ volts}}{100 \text{ ohms}} = 1.1 \text{ amp}$$

$$\text{Power} = \text{current} \times \text{voltage}$$

$$P = IV$$

$$= 1.1 \text{ amp} \times 110 \text{ volts}$$

$$= 121 \text{ W}$$

(b) If the light bulb is in series with a record player and a toaster, the total resistance in the circuit is 100 ohm + 300 ohm + 20 ohm = 420 ohm. Therefore

$$I = \frac{V}{R} = \frac{110 \text{ volts}}{420 \text{ ohms}} = 0.26 \text{ amp}$$

$$\text{Power} = \text{current} \times \text{voltage}$$

$$P = IV$$

$$= 0.26 \text{ amp} \times 110 \text{ volts}$$
$$= 29 \text{ W}$$

Note that the power to the light bulb is much less when other appliances are wired in series with it than when it is alone in the circuit.

(c) When the light bulb is in parallel with other appliances, each appliance makes its own bridge between the 110-volt line and ground, so the light bulb draws the same current as if it were alone in the circuit.

$$\text{Current} = \frac{\text{voltage}}{\text{resistance}} = \frac{V}{R}$$
$$= \frac{110 \text{ volts}}{110 \text{ ohms}} = 1.1 \text{ amp}$$
$$\text{Power} = \text{current} \times \text{voltage}$$
$$P = IV$$
$$= 1.1 \text{ amp} \times 110 \text{ volts}$$
$$= 121 \text{ W}$$

What would happen if we kept plugging more and more light bulbs into a parallel circuit? We would keep drawing more and more power with each succeeding bulb. Can we keep doing this forever? The answer is no. Recall that when a large amount of current passes through a copper wire, the copper gets hot. Eventually it could get so hot that it would melt the insulation and perhaps ignite the wooden framework of a house. To protect against this possibility, fuses or circuit breakers are always placed in a 110-volt household line. A fuse is a device with a metal strip making an electrical connection between two points in a wire. This metal strip melts at a low temperature so that when too much current passes and the wire heats up, the fuse will melt, thus breaking the connection and "turning off the power" before the wire can become hot enough to cause a fire. A circuit breaker serves the same purpose, only it is a switch activated by current.

Example 3

A person had an automobile that ran well, but when the car was left standing overnight (even with the ignition off) the battery would go dead by morning. (a) Speculate on the general nature of the problem, and (b) if the person drove home one night and wanted to be sure

A modern steam-fired power plant.

that the car started the next morning, but didn't have time to fix it, what could be done?

Answer: A battery will go dead only if current is being drawn. If the key is turned off but current is still flowing, there must be some pathway for current to flow; a faulty connection, a switch that doesn't turn off even when in the "off" position, a light that remained on even when the ignition is off, or a partial leak to the ground that provides a pathway for a current drain. The owner should check to be sure that all lights or electrical devices are off, and if the battery still wears down, it should be disconnected at night by removing the battery cable. This would isolate the battery from the electrical system of the car so it would not be discharged.

Example 4

Explain why a bird can perch on a 10,000-volt power line without being killed.

Answer: If you cannot answer this question, try a simpler one: why doesn't a person stepping off a curb in Denver, Colorado, elevation 1.6 km, get hurt? That's simple—even though Denver lies

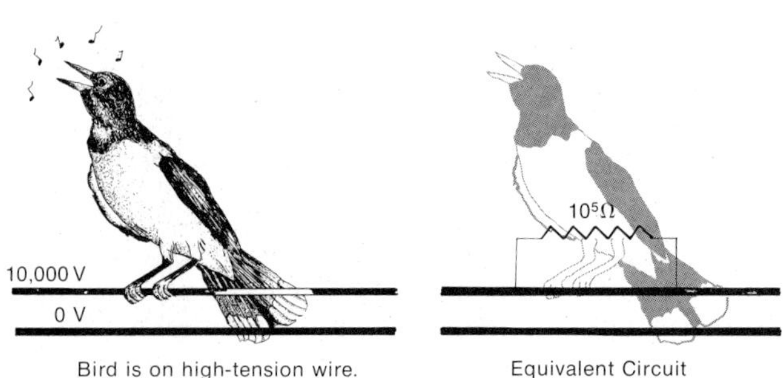

Bird is on high-tension wire. Voltage difference between feet is small. Bird is happy.

Equivalent Circuit

Bird is straddling two high-tension wires. Voltage difference between feet is large. Bird is electrocuted.

Equivalent Circuit

far above sea level, there is no way to fall that distance, and a person stepping off the curb falls only a few centimeters, which is hardly lethal. Just as height, *per se*, is not dangerous, but only differences in height are, so high voltage is not dangerous, only differences in voltage are. What is of concern to the bird is not the absolute potential of the line, but the potential difference between its two feet—the voltage directed across its body. The resistance of copper wire is quite low: a few centimeters of heavy wire has a resistance of about one millionth of an ohm. If the power line is carrying 1 amp of current, the voltage difference between the bird's feet is simply:

Volt = current × resistance
Volt = 1 amp × 10^{-6} ohm = 10^{-6} volt,

one millionth of a volt. The bird is safe because there is little voltage drop across its body.

If, on the other hand, the bird straddled two wires, one at 10,000 volts and the other at 0 volts, the potential difference between its feet would be the full 10,000 volts, and the bird would die instantly. Therefore, if the bird, or a human for that matter, touched one foot to the high-voltage line and the other foot to the ground, the resultant shock would be lethal.

The Importance of Grounding

Any good power tool, such as an electric drill or a circular saw, has three wires leading from it, even though it is connected to a 110-volt source. Why are there three wires from the tool but only two wires leading from a lamp or an electric heater? Two of the wires plug into the 100-volt leads of the outlet, and under normal conditions they carry all of the current (see Figure 5–16). The third is generally connected to a round post on the plug and is called a *system ground*. Under normal situations, this wire carries no current. But suppose that the tool gets old and worn, and through some accident the hot wire inside the motor jiggles loose and touches the inside of the metal motor case. If there were no system ground and you were holding the tool, a 100-volt potential would exist between you and the Earth. The resultant shock could have any effect from being simply scary to being lethal. The system ground wire connects from the case of the tool directly to ground so that if there is a short circuit, most of the electricity will pass to ground through the low-resistance copper

Figure 5–16. A three-pronged plug commonly used with small electric motors such as found in vacuum cleaners or in portable electric drills and saws.

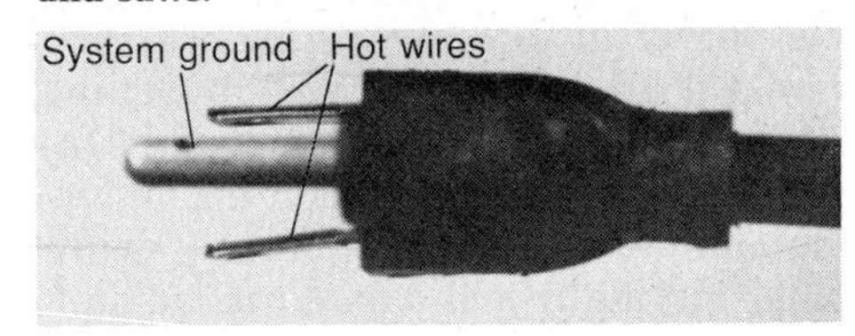

A, **Drill in good condition; no short.**

The outcome of an electric shock depends on two factors. One is the resistance from your hand through your body to the ground. Dry skin is a good resistor, so if your hands and feet are dry, your body resistance will be high, and little current can flow. On the other hand, any moisture on your hands and feet will absorb salts from the body and provide a good conducting path, so that lots of current can flow. Even a small current at 110 volts may kill you. However, if you are wearing rubber-soled shoes or are standing on a good insulator, the resistance from the hand to ground will be high and you will receive little shock. The other factor is related to your own personal resistance to electrical shock. Owing to unknown series of factors, some people are more able to withstand shock than others.

It is important to know that electric shock sometimes looks fatal but need not be if immediate and *prolonged* artificial respiration is provided and competent professional assistance is summoned as soon as possible. A shocked person should be given this treatment even if he or she looks dead. Some medical experts have said that many people have died needlessly from electric shock.

B, **Hot wire shorted to metal case; current flows through operator to ground.**

C, **Hot wire shorted to metal case but system ground connected; current flows through wire to ground. The operator is unhurt.**

wire. If the tool shorts out but the system ground is connected, there are two parallel resistors leading to ground—you and the copper wire. Since the wire has a much lower resistance, most of the current will pass that way and you will not be shocked. In the absence of this extra wire, all the current passes through you.

5.7 ELECTRONIC AMPLIFIERS

Electrical equipment can perform many diverse tasks besides simply powering a light bulb, a heater, or an electric motor. We can now send electrical waves across great distances (see Chapter 6) and thereby transmit information for radio, television, radar, and other communication and detecting systems. In addition, thousands of devices such as record players, tape recorders, telephones, some watches and clocks, a great many scientific instruments, and computers are all electrically powered. Electronic circuits are used in counting, switching, sensing, and amplifying devices. In this section we will consider a simple electronic amplifier.

Signals from most electric sensors such as a record-player cartridge, a microphone, a television receiver, or a radio antenna are quite small and carry little power—far too little power to drive a speaker and fill a room with sound or illuminate the screen of a television set. Yet these weak signals are valuable because they carry *information*. For example, consider the radio transmission of a Morse code message. In Morse code, letters are translated into dots and dashes, which can then be transmitted electrically as a series of pulses. For instance, the message, "hello" is written as ".... . .-.. .-.. ---" in Morse code. When this word is transmitted electrically, each dot is translated as a short burst of energy and each dash as a longer burst of energy. If we plotted energy (or voltage) as a function of time, the message would appear as follows.

Unamplified Signal

Now suppose that one radio station transmits the preceding signal and another station many miles away receives the information. That radio receiver picks up only a tiny amount of energy, and if the message is to be converted to sound, the signal must be amplified.

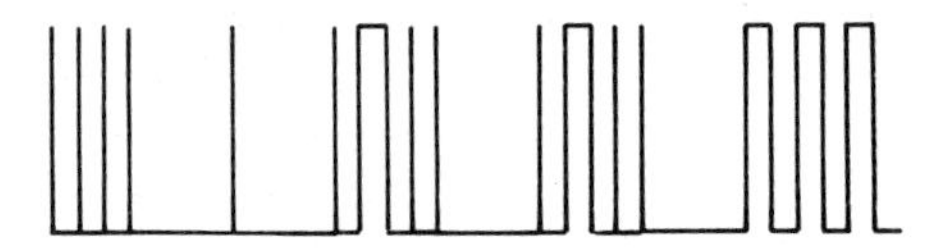

Amplified Signal

During amplification we wish to retain the shape and form of our electrical signal while we increase its energy. To do this we must add energy, because electrical energy, like mechanical energy, cannot grow spontaneously. The trick to an amplifier is to build an energy-producing circuit with a conventional energy source such as a battery or your household electrical supply and then to vary this current to match the weak signal from the receiver. Thus the energy comes from the battery or from the electric company whereas the information comes from the input signal.

In order to understand amplifier design, consider the following analogy. Suppose there is a water tank positioned above a water fountain as shown in Figure 5–17*A*. If a child opens the valve in the fountain, the water will flow evenly and smoothly. If the valve is closed, no water will flow. You see that a skillful valve operator could, by opening and closing the valve quickly, send a Morse code signal as alternating short and long bursts of water. The person operating the valve does very little work. He does not have to pump the water. The primary energy of the system comes from the potential energy of the water in the tank, while the information is delivered by the person operating the valve.

An electrical amplifier works on the same general concept. Amplification can be accomplished through the use of either **vacuum tubes** or **transistors.** Transistors are built of pieces of specially constructed semiconductor metals. As the name implies, a semiconductor is a material that is neither a good conductor nor a good insulator. Two basically different types of semiconductor materials can be constructed, and each behaves differently in an electric field. These two types of materials are called type N (N for negative) and P (P for positive).

A transistor is made by sandwiching slices of N and P semiconductors together, as shown in Figure 5–18.

Now look at the simplified electronic amplifier circuit shown in Figure 5–17*B*. Imagine that the amplifier is installed with a portable microphone. The battery establishes a current in the power circuit (shown in circuit 1 in the diagram). If you turn on the amplifier but not the microphone, you can hear a faint hum in the speaker but no music. No information is being fed to the power circuit. When a person sings into the microphone, a small but varying voltage is relayed across the transistor. This small input voltage causes the voltage and current in the power circuit to vary, just as in the fountain analogy. When this varying electric field is fed into a speaker, music is produced.

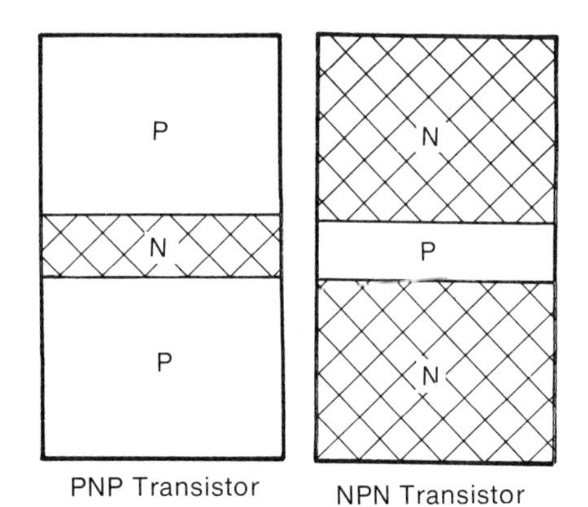

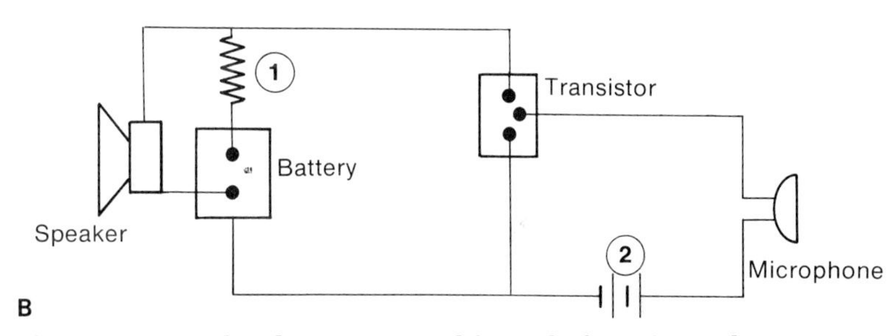

Figure 5–17. Analogy between an amplifier and a fountain. ***A,*** **The person opening the valve does very little work. The water pressure is derived from the potential energy of the water in the tank.** ***B,*** **The microphone transmits very little power. The battery provides most of the energy needed to drive the speaker.**

> Amplifiers are enormously more complicated than is indicated here. Even simple ones have five to eight amplifier stages, and a great many electrical devices to insure clear, audible tones.

5.8 ELECTRICITY IN OUR MODERN AGE

Twenty years ago, radios, televisions, and many other electrical appliances were built with vacuum tubes in the amplifier circuits. Today, most electronic equipment and almost all low-power amplifiers are built with transistors. Transistors are smaller than tubes; they use less power and therefore are more adaptable to battery-operated portables. They are more rugged, last longer, and are cheaper to build and install. Moreover, new technologies have led to the development of devices that can be used to build an entire amplifier or switching circuit to fit into an incredibly small volume (see Figure 5–19). Without transistors, modern computers would be almost impossible to build, much of the space program probably would have been impossible, and many modern conveniences, such as portable radios and pocket-sized calculators, could never have been developed. A few of the more amazing electronic advancements are described briefly below.

The telephone industry has developed microwave conduits that can carry 230,000 telephone conversations simultaneously. Incredibly, nearly a quarter of a million conversations can be fed into a single pipe and then the signals can be unscrambled and routed to the proper telephones at the other end of the line.

Some portable calculators, complete with batteries, are so compact that they fit into the back of a checkbook. Others, no larger than the palm of a person's hand, not only can add, subtract, multiply, and divide but also can calculate logarithms, reciprocals, exponents, and trigonometric functions and store data for later use. Even more versatile little computers can accept punch cards with information for multistep programs.

The United States Department of Defense has developed a special automatic-pilot device for low-flying aircraft. When attack planes approach a target at low altitudes, the pilot's reactions are not fast enough to maneuver the planes at treetop level and compensate for hills, tall towers or other obstructions. So a computerized radar device flies the plane. The radar antenna senses objects in the plane's flight path and receives information concerning the size and shape of the obstruction. The computer then calculates the best way to avoid a collision while maintaining speed and course, and the output from this device controls the flight of the craft. All this happens while pilot and machine are moving along at over 1500 km/hr!

The aerospace industry has developed many fantastic devices. The Earth travels at a rate of about 160,000 km/hr

Figure 5–19. Left, a vacuum tube. This tube can perform a single function in an electronic circuit. On the right is a solid-state integrated circuit. This device is a complete switching and counting circuit and can replace several tubes and their connecting circuitry.

around the Sun and is simultaneously rotating about its axis. The Voyager 1 space probe was launched from this moving Earthly platform to travel nearly 640 million km to meet with the planet Jupiter, which itself moves along at about 34,000 km/hr. The complexity of the navigation needed to perform this task is staggering. But the navigation was only part of the technological marvels of Voyager. Spacecraft cannot use conventional cameras, for there is no way to return the negatives to Earth. Instead, they use photoelectric sensing devices. Light activates a photosensitive surface, and the light energy is converted to electrical potential, which is registered as a change of voltage. If the voltages of various regions of the photosensitive surface are transmitted in the proper sequence, they can be converted to a visual image in laboratories on Earth. In 1965, the Mariner 4 spacecraft recorded 22 photographs as it flew close to the planet Mars. It took 8½ hours to transmit each complete picture to Earth. In 1979, Voyager I was transmitting photographs at a rate of one every 48 seconds. The signal energy reaching Earth was less than 10^{-18} W/m^2. This amount of energy is so small that if a 1-m^2 antenna could collect and store a signal of this magnitude for 20 billion years,

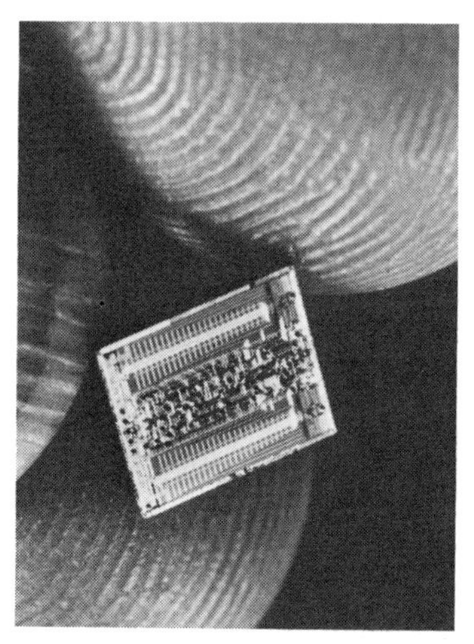

This tiny, solid state memory chip, used in modern computers, can hold up to 64,000 individual pieces of information, enough to store the information for 1000 eight-letter words. (Courtesy of IBM.)

The Bell System's Millimeter Waveguide System, WT-4, is under construction in New Jersey. WT-4 will be able to transmit 230,000 two-way telephone calls simultaneously. (Courtesy of American Telephone and Telegraph.)

Spacecraft like this lunar lander are filled with sophisticated electronic devices. Our modern space program would be impossible without the use of transistors and solid-state circuitry. Solid-state circuits are much smaller, lighter, and more rugged than vacuum-tube circuits. (Courtesy of NASA.)

This calculator, complete with batteries, is not much longer than a pen. Not only can it do arithmetic and perform many simple functions but also it can accept multistep computer programs. (Courtesy of Hewlett-Packard.)

there would be enough energy to light a Christmas tree bulb for 1 sec! Yet the data from Voyager were received, amplified, and processed, and sharp photographs were produced. Devices have also been built that can reach out of an unmanned spacecraft resting on a foreign planet, grab some rock or dust, vaporize it, ionize the molecules of the sample, systematically record some characteristics of the ions, and relay enough information to Earth so scientists here can determine whether or not the sample contains organic matter. In this way, electronic devices operated by remote control search for evidence of life.

Sailors have traditionally used compasses to determine direction at sea. (Courtesy of Aluminum Corporation of America.)

5.9 MAGNETISM AND MAGNETIC FIELDS

Ancient navigators learned that if certain natural materials, known as lodestones, were mounted to rotate freely, one end would always point towards the north. We now know that these materials are permanent magnets and that they are attracted by the magnetic field of the Earth. The device that points toward the north is known as a **compass,** and it has obvious uses in navigation, for a person can determine direction even on a cloudy day or night, when the Sun and stars are invisible.

Experiments with lodestones and other types of permanent magnets showed that every magnet has two poles, called a **north pole** and a **south pole.** Like poles repel each other and unlike poles attract. Thus, the south pole of a lodestone is attracted to the north pole of the Earth's magnetic field. Similarly, two bar magnets will attract each other if they are aligned north to south or south to north and will repel each other if they are aligned north to north or south to south. A magnet creates a magnetic field around itself. Magnets, like electric charges, alter the nature of space in their vicinity. The magnetic fields about bar magnets are shown in Figure 5–20.

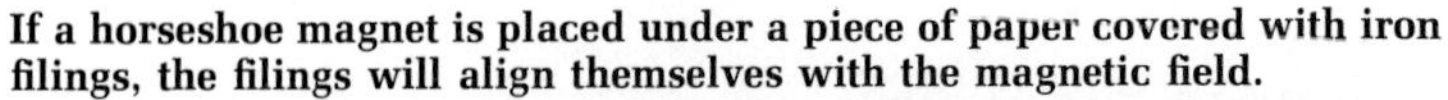

If a horseshoe magnet is placed under a piece of paper covered with iron filings, the filings will align themselves with the magnetic field.

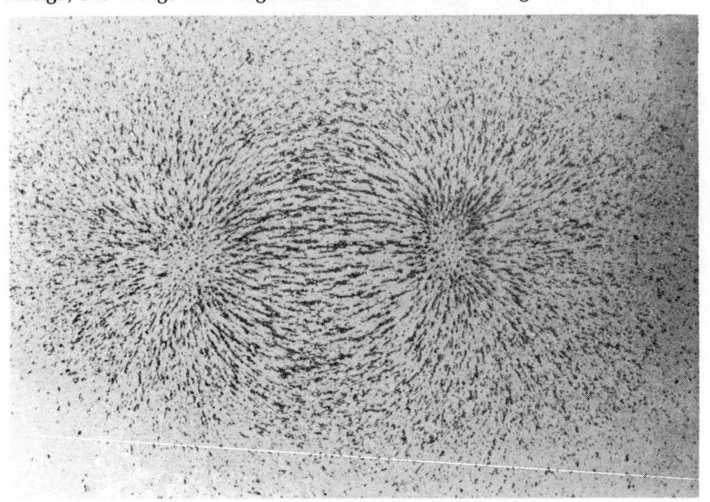

5.10 INTERACTIONS BETWEEN ELECTRICITY AND MAGNETISM

Early scientists did not recognize a close association between electricity and magnetism. Magnetic compasses were used by navigators probably more than 2000 years ago, and scientists have experimented with electric currents for several hundreds of years, but the first investigation of the interrelationship between the two phenomena was conducted by Hans Christian Oersted in 1820. Oersted's simple experiment was to hold a magnetic compass needle under a wire carrying a direct current. He noticed that the needle of the compass always swung so that it was at right angles to the wire. If Oersted moved the compass so that it rested directly above the wire, the needle swung completely around (180 degrees), as shown in Figure 5–21. The

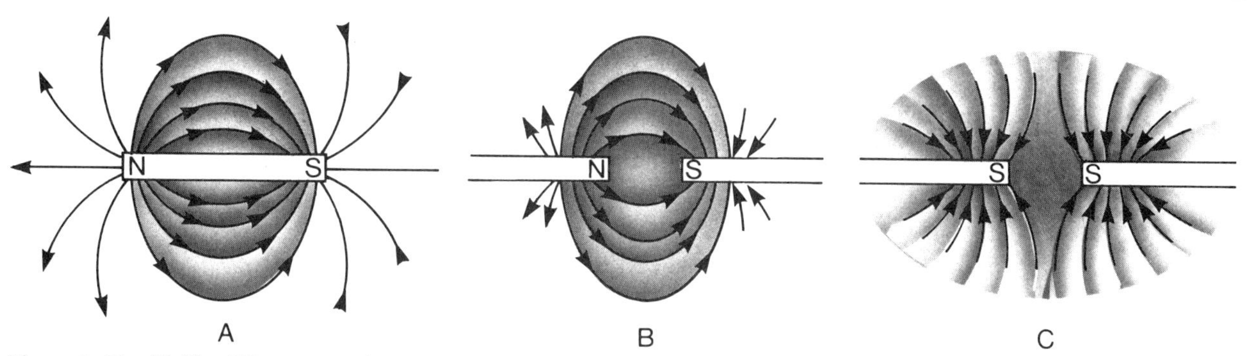

Figure 5–20. Fields of force around magnets. *A,* Single bar magnet. *B,* Two bar magnets with opposite poles near each other. *C,* Two bar magnets with like poles near each other.

Figure 5–21. Oersted's experiments.

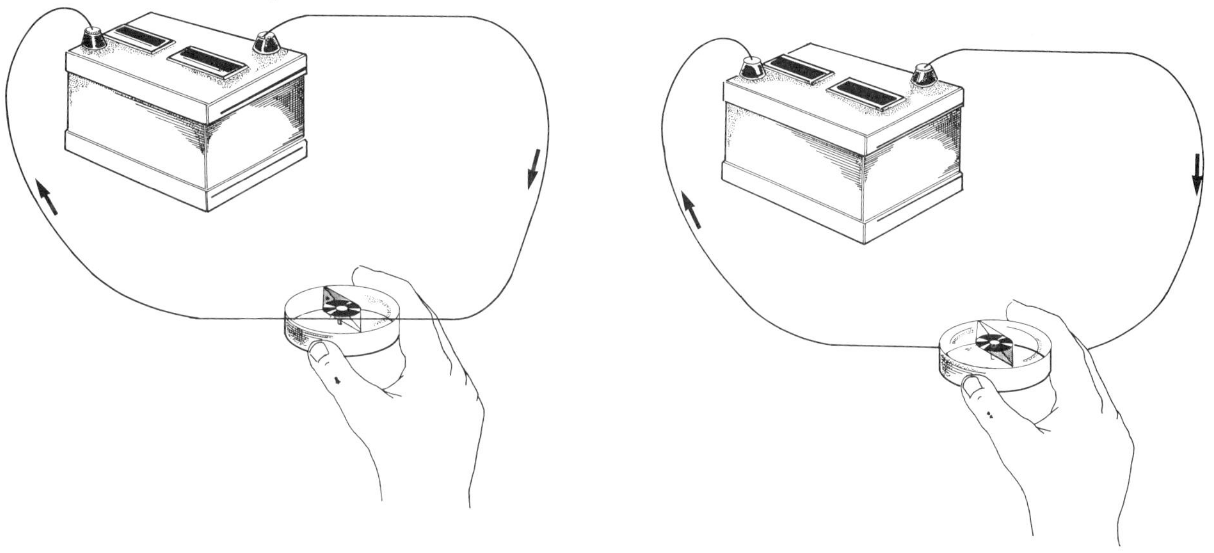

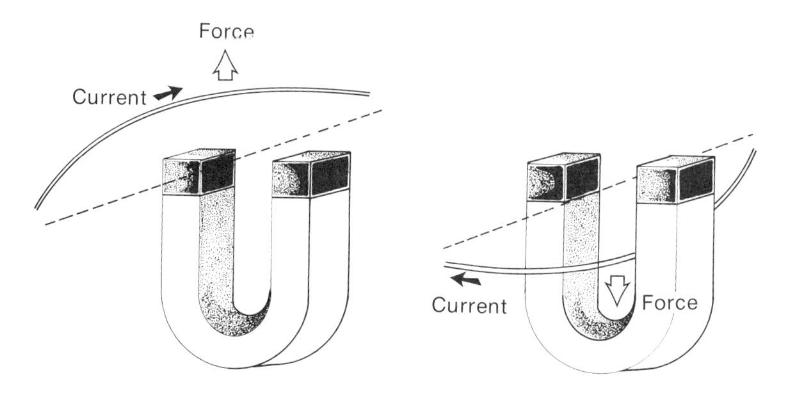

compass would point north only if a switch were opened and no current flowed through the wire. In a second experiment, Oersted had a flexible wire running through the poles of a rigid magnet. When a current passed through the wire, the wire bent upward or downward, depending on the direction of the current flow. If the wire were held in line with the magnetic field lines, no effect was observed. From these and a few other simple experiments Oersted learned several important facts:

1. Whenever an electric current flows, a magnetic field is generated. The lines of this magnetic field form concentric circles about the wire. The *direction* of this magnetic field is determined by the direction of the electron flow (Fig. 5–22).

2. If a magnet is held near a wire that is carrying current, the field of the magnet will interact with the field generated by the current. The resultant force can cause either the wire or the magnet to move, thereby converting electrical energy into mechanical energy. Thus Oersted's discovery led directly to the development of the electric motor.

3. A stationary electric charge does not interact with a stationary magnetic field. Likewise, no force is generated if electrons move *in line* with a magnetic field. An electromagnetic force is generated only if a charged particle moves *across* a magnetic field.

4. The magnitude of the electromagnetic force is proportional to the strength of the magnetic field and the amount of current passing through this field.

Shortly after Oersted's experiments, people began to speculate that since a moving current produces a magnetic field, perhaps a moving mag-

Figure 5–22. Magnetic fields around electric currents.

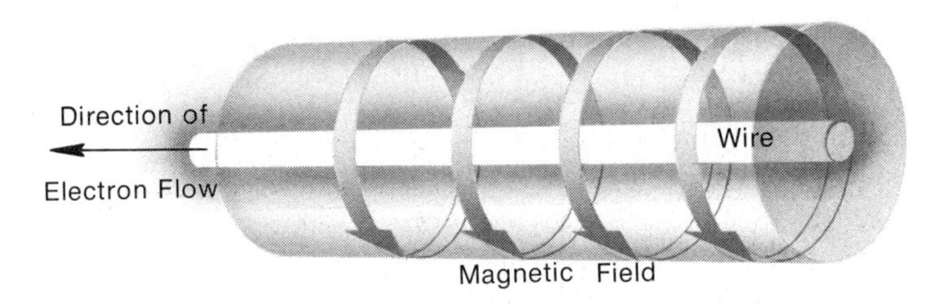

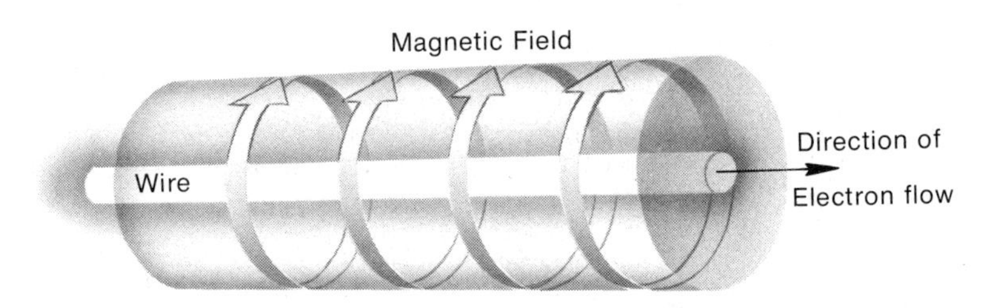

A Magnetic Field around Current-Carrying Wires

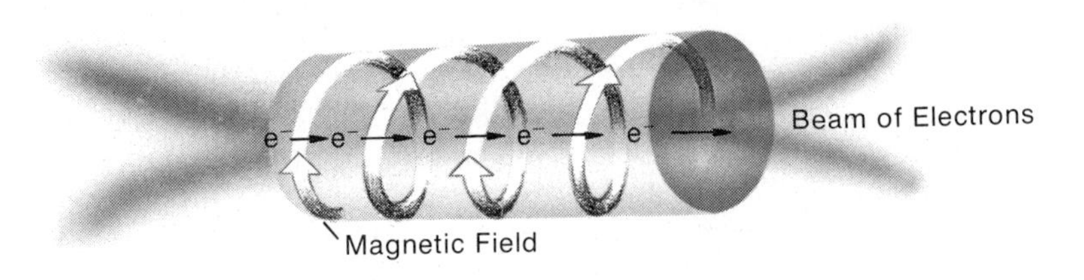

B Beam of Electrons Moving through Space

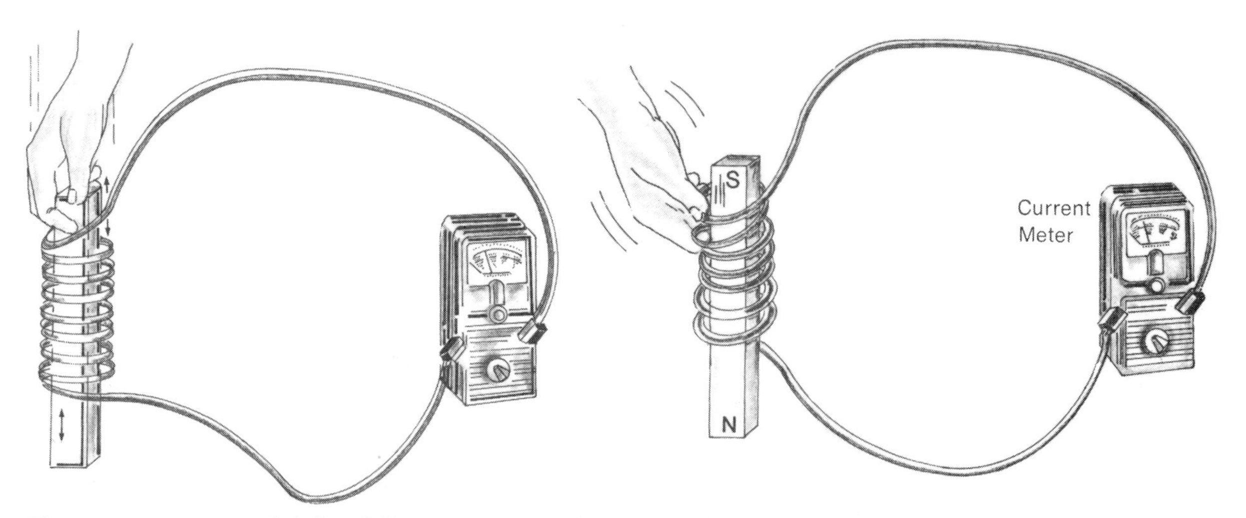

Figure 5–23. A current is induced if a magnet is moved perpendicular to a coil of wire or if a wire is moved perpendicular to a magnet.

net would produce an electric current. Eleven years after Oersted's experiment, Joseph Henry of the United States and Michael Faraday of England independently tried to produce an electric current by moving a magnet up and down through a coil of wire (Fig. 5–23). Both men were successful. They learned that electric current can be induced either if a magnet is moved past a coil of wire or if a coil of wire is passed past a magnet. Further studies showed that whenever a magnetic field that is perpendicular to a wire is varied in any way, a current is generated. This phenomenon is called **electromagnetic induction.**

More current is generated if the magnet passes through many coils of wire than if it passes through only a few. In addition, a rapid motion produces more current than a slow motion. Therefore, significant amounts of electric current can be generated if a magnet is moved rapidly past many coils of wire or, alternatively, if many coils of wire are moved rapidly past a magnet.

Think of the simplicity of these experiments and their significance in world history. Thus Oersted had discovered that electrical energy can be converted to mechanical work, and Henry and Faraday discovered that mechanical energy can induce an electric current. The way was paved for the development of electric motors, generators, and the entire electric age.

5.11 ELECTROMAGNETS

Permanent magnets are rarely used to generate the intense magnetic fields needed for many industrial applica-

A large electromagnet is used to carry blocks of scrap iron to be recycled. When the current is turned off, the iron drops into the furnace. (Courtesy of Bethlehem Steel.)

tions. Instead, the preferred devices are **electromagnets,** which generate magnetic fields from electric currents. Recall Oersted's discovery that any current moving through a wire establishes a magnetic field. The field around any long straight wire is circular. However, if we coil the wire in loops, we get a field that has the same shape as the field of a bar magnet (Fig. 5–24). The strength of this field is directly proportional to the current; the more current, the stronger the field. The easiest way to produce a loop with a lot of current is simply to coil wire around and around and around. The current through each coil produces a magnetic field, and these fields add to each other. Thus, if the field produced by one current loop is B, the field produced by two loops is B + B, or 2B, and the field of a coil of *n* loops is *n*B. If you place an iron bar inside a current loop, the magnetic field generated by the wire will temporarily magnetize the bar, and the two fields will reinforce each other. Therefore, an electromagnet is constructed by simply coiling wire around a piece of iron and connecting the ends of the wire coils to a dc power source.

Electromagnets are much more versatile than permanent magnets for many applications. They can be turned on and off, or the field intensity can be changed by altering the amount of current in the coil. Cranes that move scrap iron often use electromagnets. The iron can be lifted by turning on the current and dropped simply by turning it off.

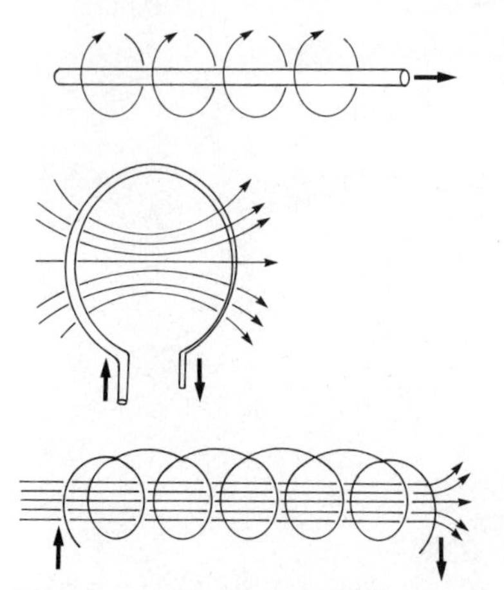

Figure 5–24. Magnetic field around a straight wire and a wire loop. (Short, dark arrows indicate the direction of electron flow; the lighter lines indicate the magnetic field.)

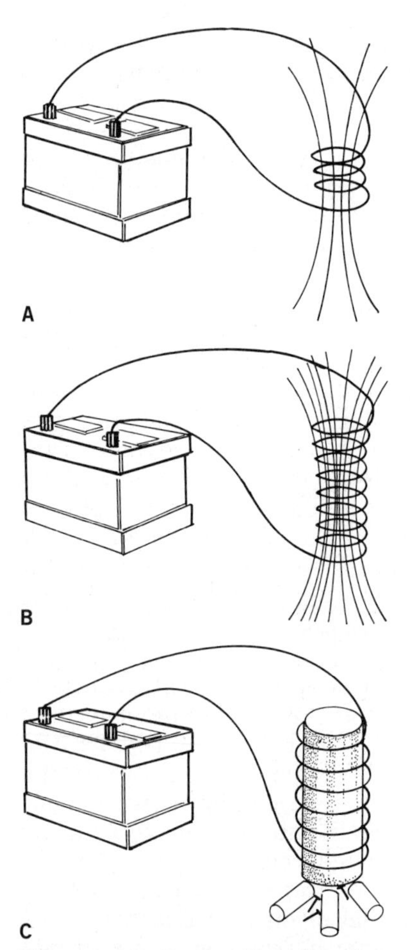

Figure 5–25. Construction of an electromagnet. ***A,*** **A weak magnetic field can be generated if a few loops of wire are connected to a dc power source.** ***B,*** **A much stronger field is generated if many loops of wire are used.** ***C,*** **A practical electromagnet is made by wrapping many loops of wire around a solid iron core.**

5.12 ELECTRIC MOTORS AND GENERATORS

The first conversion of electrical energy to mechanical energy was performed by Oersted when he held his compass near an electric current. The magnetic field produced by the wire interacted with the field of the permanent magnet of the compass and caused the compass to turn. Electrical energy was converted to mechanical energy of motion. However, this was not a very useful or efficient motor, for once the needle turned so that it was perpendicular to the wire, it stopped and was held in a fixed position by the field. If an electric drill were constructed in this manner, it would turn only half a revolution and then stop. In order to keep a motor running, some way must be found to alternate the current flow, so the shaft of the motor is forced to move continuously. To understand this concept, refer back to Oersted's original experiment, redrawn in Figure 5–26. When electrons in the wire flow in one direction, the compass needle moves perpendicular to the wire, and then stops. But if the ends of the wires connected to the battery are switched, the electric field will be reversed and the needle will no longer remain stationary but will rotate 180° as shown. If the wires are switched back again, the needle will move to its original position. The needle will rotate continuously if some way can be found to switch the wires rapidly and in synchronization with the compass.

An electric motor operates on the principle that whenever an electric current moves perpendicularly to a magnetic field, a sideways force is generated. A **generator** works on the reverse principle, namely, that whenever a wire moves perpendicularly to a magnetic field, an electric current is induced. A simple generator, therefore, looks very much like a simple motor. The two are depicted in Figure 5–28. In the motor, an external current source is supplied to a wire loop, the loop turns,

Figure 5–26. Demonstration of the principle behind construction of a simple electric motor. *A,* Oersted showed that a compass needle will align itself perpendicular to an electric current. *B,* If the wires are switched and the direction of current is reversed, the needle will rotate 180°. *C,* The needle will continue to rotate if the wires are switched again. In a real electric motor, the direction of current is switched rapidly in time with the movement of the motor shaft.

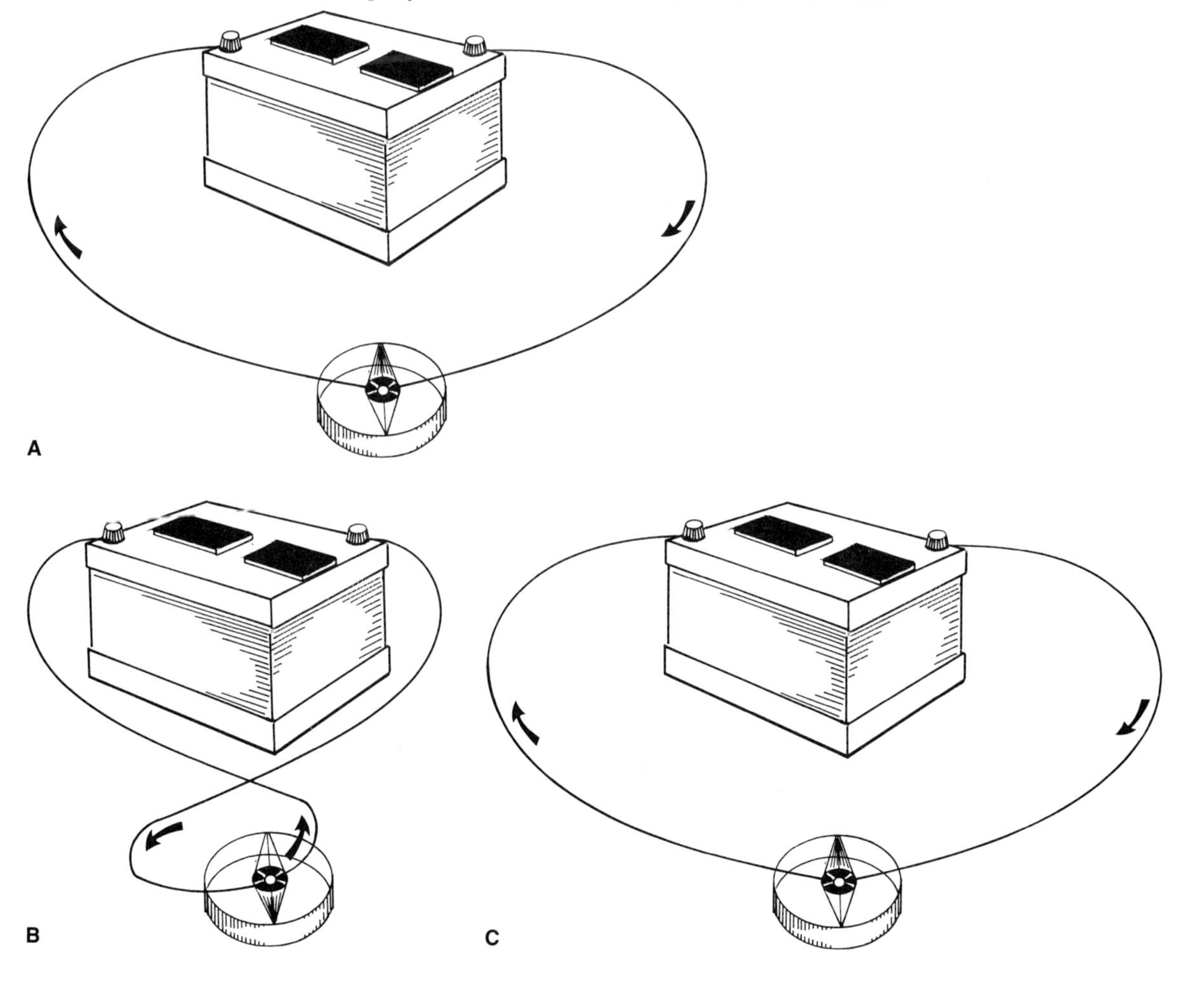

and mechanical work is performed. In a generator, mechanical work is supplied to turn a wire loop, and electricity is induced.

As mentioned previously, most of the commercial electric generators are powered by steam turbines. (A few per cent of the electric generators in North America are powered by falling water.) The generators themselves are highly efficient and convert about 99 per cent of the mechanical energy of the turbine into electricity. It is the turbines that are inefficient, for 60 per cent of the heat energy of the fuels is lost during

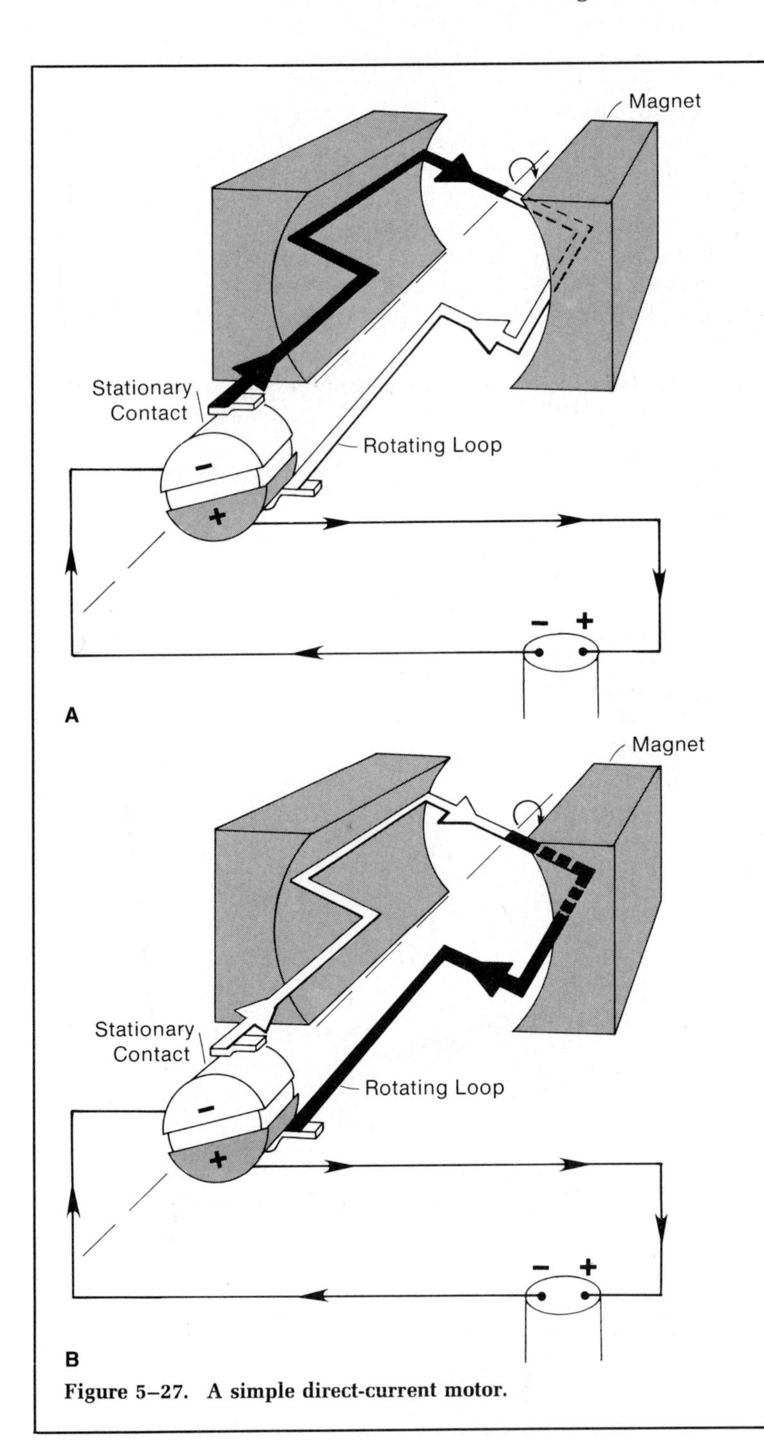

Figure 5–27. A simple direct-current motor.

A simple, practical, direct-current motor is shown in Figure 5–27. A permanent magnet is held stationary, and a wire loop is mounted between the poles so that it is free to spin. The wires from the battery are not connected directly to the wire loop but to two stationary contacts so that the upper contact is always negative and the lower one is always positive. Imagine that the motor is initially resting in the position of Figure 5–27*A*, and that we close the switch and allow electrons to flow through the wire as shown. Electrons from the darker half of the loop are crossing the magnetic field from left to right, forcing the loop to turn clockwise. At the same time, electrons from the lighter half of the loop are crossing the same field from right to left, which also helps to turn the loop clockwise. Since one part of the loop is pushed one way and the other is pushed in an opposite direction, the wire rotates 180°. Now remember that although the wire loop is rotated, the electric contacts are stationary. The dark half, originally in touch with the negative terminal, is now in touch with the positive one, and the other end of the wire is now in touch with the negative terminal. The current flow through each section of wire is reversed, as shown in Figure 5–27*B*. Since the current alternates, the loop does not come to a stop after a 180° rotation. In the new position, the wire has rotated, but the current flow still crosses the magnetic field so as to produce a force that causes the wire to continue rotating. After the wire coil has moved 360°, it is in its original position, and thus the motor still continues to rotate in a single direction.

the conversion to mechanical energy.

We now come to an interesting question. Why does a motor consume electric power? If a current is passed through a coil of wire that is not under the influence of a magnetic field, there is very little resistance in the wire, and little power is required to push electrons through it. But a considerable amount of power is required to push current through a coil of wire that lies in a magnetic field. This electric power is not lost; it is converted to mechanical energy of the rotating shaft, but what kind of force resists the flow of elec-

An antique industrial generator found rusting in the ruins of a hydroelectric facility that had been abandoned several decades ago.

The motor shown in Figure 5–27 is not likely to be very powerful. Recall that the magnitude of the established force is proportional to the strength of the magnetic field and the quantity of the current passing through it. A practical motor, then, differs from the simple one pictured here in two important respects. First, one loop of wire as shown in the diagram will carry only a small amount of current through the magnetic field, so the core of any useful electric motor must have many loops of wire. Since the current moving through the magnetic field is equal to the current carried by any one loop times the number of loops, a large motor will have many coils of heavy wire, each capable of carrying a lot of current. Second, a permanent magnet is not really suitable for a rugged, long-lasting motor. Permanent magnets are heavy and liable to lose their strength. Therefore, the magnetic field is provided by an electromagnet.

Notice how simple an electric motor really is. There is only one moving part, a central shaft containing the wire coils. The rotating loop rubs against the stationary contacts, and so the rubbing parts, called the **brushes,** wear out after a while and must be replaced. Otherwise there is little to wear out or go wrong. Therefore electric motors have a long life span and generally require little repair. The most common way in which an electric motor is ruined is through misuse, not through ordinary wear and tear.

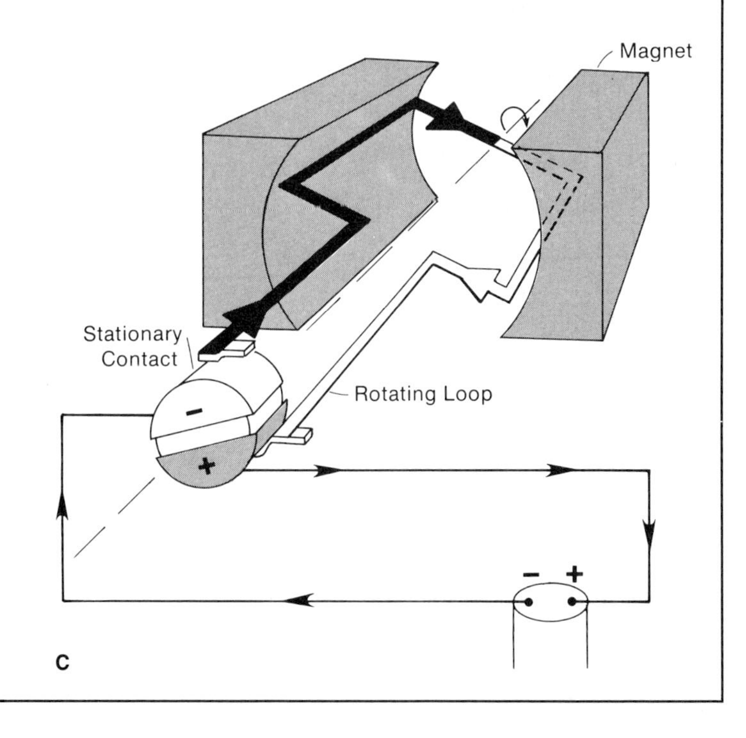

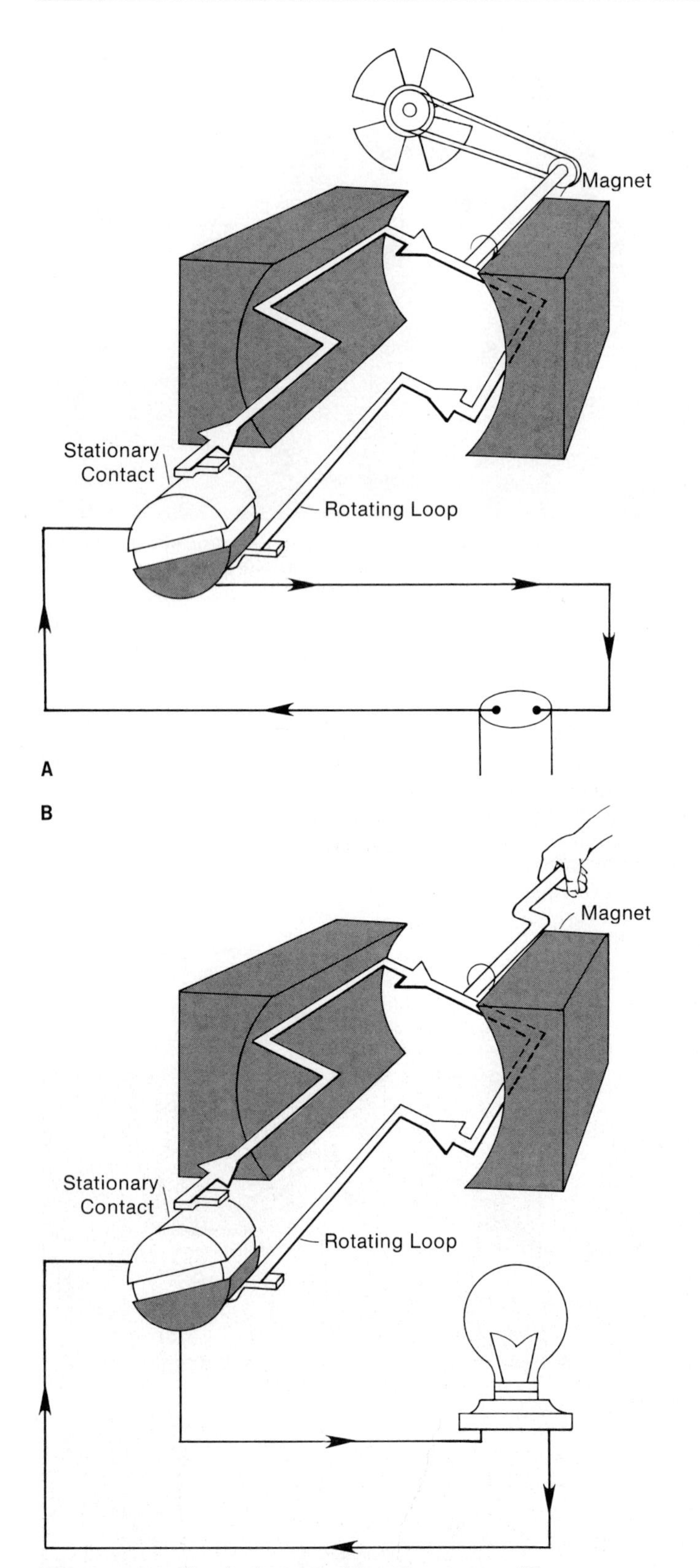

Figure 5–28. Simple dc motor (A) and generator (B).

trons? Where does the electrical resistance come from?

To answer these questions we must think about the similarities between a motor and a generator. Both devices are essentially the same, each consisting of a coil of wire rotating inside a magnetic field. When we start an electric motor, the spinning coil not only does mechanical work but also generates electricity. So every motor is also a generator. The spinning motor generates an electric field that opposes the electric field applied by the outside power source. This opposing field establishes an **electromotive force** (emf), which is a voltage that resists the flow of electrons into the motor. The energy required by the motor is simply the energy required to push a current against the opposing emf.

Now that we understand why a motor consumes electric power, we can easily see why work is required to operate a generator. If a well-balanced coil of wire is spun while it is not under the influence of a magnetic field, there is little resistance to motion, and the coil can be spun with little expenditure of work. But considerable work is required to spin the coil in a generator. When the coils of a generator are turned mechanically, a current is produced. This current, traveling through a magnetic field, tends to force the coil of wire to rotate, just as a current in a motor causes it to spin. The **"motor effect"** force in a generator *opposes the applied mechanical force.* Whenever we generate electricity, we construct a motor that works against us. It is a fundamental law of nature—nothing less than the First Law of Thermodynamics in another guise. Alas, electric power can be produced only at the expense of mechanical power; we cannot produce electricity without working for it.

5.13 TRANSFORMERS AND TRANSMISSION OF ELECTRICITY

Most of the electricity available today is generated in large centralized power plants. As mentioned in the previous chapter, most power plants use fossil or nuclear fuels to drive a steam

Large transformer centers near every big city step down the 120,000 volts to about 2200 volts for transmission along conventional "telephone poles" to residential and commercial buildings. The 2200-volt lines carry about 55 times as much current as the large transmission lines. The 2200-volt service potential must be stepped down again before electricity is brought into a house or a business. Therefore, another transformer is placed just before the fuse box leading into each house. This transformer steps down the voltage again, this time from 2200 volts to 110 volts.

Now we can understand why electrical power is supplied to us as alternating current. Generators can easily be built with a direct current output; in fact, the first electric generators supplied direct current to local consumers. However, the direct-current voltage cannot be altered in a transformer, so the power-saving trick of sending high voltage and then transforming it to low voltage could not be used. Today, nearly all electric generators produce alternating current.

CHAPTER OBJECTIVES

Understand the following:

- Electrostatic forces
- Atomic structure and the electric charges on protons and electrons
- Electric current (ac and dc)
- The interrelationships among voltage, current, and resistance in an electric circuit
- Electric power
- Household wiring and the differences between series and parallel circuits
- The fundamental theory of amplifier design
- Magnets and magnetic fields
- Electromagnetic interactions, electromagnets, motors, and generators
- Transformers and transmission of electricity

KEY WORDS

Electrical charge
Electrical force
Field of force
Coulomb
Electron
Resistor
Insulator
Conductor
Electrical field
Direct current
Alternating current
Ion
Volt
Ampere
Ohm
Ohm's Law
Parallel circuit
Series circuit
System ground
Transistor
Magnetism
North pole
South pole
Electromagnetic induction
Electromagnet
Electric motor
Electric generator
Electromotive force
Motor effect
Transformer

FORMULAS TO KNOW

$$\text{Electrical force} = k \frac{q_a q_b}{d^2}$$

Example 5
If two charged bodies are attracted to each other with a force of 1 N when they are 1 m apart, what is the force of attraction when they are 2 m apart?

Answer: The solution to this problem is similar to the solution to Example 3 in Chapter 3. It is impossible to calculate absolute answers, because there are not enough data available. It is only possible to compare the two situations.

$$\text{Electrical force}_2 = k \frac{q_a q_b}{(2\text{m})^2}$$

and,

$$\text{Electrical force}_1 = k \frac{q_a q_b}{(1\text{m})^2} = 1\text{ N}$$

dividing one equation by the other, and cancelling out the k's and q's

$$\frac{\text{electrical force}_2}{\text{electrical force}_1} = \frac{\cancel{k} \dfrac{\cancel{q_a} \cancel{q_b}}{(2\text{m})^2}}{\cancel{k} \dfrac{\cancel{q_a} \cancel{q_b}}{(1\text{m})^2}}$$

$$\frac{\text{electrical force}_2}{1\text{ N}} = \frac{\frac{1}{(2\text{m})^2}}{\frac{1}{(1\text{m})^2}} = \frac{1\text{m}^2}{(2\text{m})^2}$$

$$= \frac{1\text{m}^2}{4\text{m}^2}$$

$$\text{electrical force}_2 = \tfrac{1}{4}\text{ N}$$

Example 6
(a) Calculate the current in a circuit if a 12-volt battery is wired to a 24-ohm resistor. (b) Calculate the resistance of a simple circuit in which a 110-volt potential causes 10 amperes of current to flow.

Answer: (a) This problem can be solved using Ohm's law.

$$\text{Voltage} = \text{current} \times \text{resistance, or}$$

$$\text{Current} = \frac{\text{voltage}}{\text{resistance}}$$

$$= \frac{12\text{ volts}}{24\text{ ohms}} = 0.5\text{ amp}$$

(b) $\text{Voltage} = \text{current} \times \text{resistance, or}$

$$\text{Resistance} = \frac{\text{voltage}}{\text{current}}$$

$$= \frac{110\text{ volts}}{10\text{ amp}} = 11\text{ ohms}$$

Example 7
Calculate the internal resistance of an 11-W clock and an 1100-W space heater, assuming both are designed to operate at 110 volts.

Answer: Power = current × voltage, or

$$\text{Current} = \frac{\text{power}}{\text{voltage}}$$

$$\text{Current through the clock} = \frac{11\text{ W}}{110\text{ volts}} = 0.1\text{ amp}$$

Now using this value in the Ohm's law equation,

$$\text{Voltage} = \text{current} \times \text{resistance}$$

$$\text{Resistance} = \frac{\text{voltage}}{\text{current}}$$

$$\text{Resistance of clock} = \frac{110\text{ volts}}{0.1\text{ amp}} = 1100\text{ ohms}$$

Similarly, for the space heater:

$$\text{Current through the space heater} = \frac{1100\text{ W}}{110\text{ volt}} = 10\text{ amp}$$

$$\text{Resistance of the space heater} = \frac{110\text{ volts}}{10\text{ amp}} = 11\text{ ohms}$$

Notice that the appliance with the least resistance draws the most current and uses the most power.

TAKE-HOME EXPERIMENTS

1. **Electric circuits.** For this experiment you will need a flashlight and two pieces of wire. Remove the bulb and the batteries from the flashlight. Examine the inside of the bulb carefully without breaking it. Draw a picture of what you see. How many wires are there inside the bulb? Are these wires attached to metal conductors on the outside? How is electricity conducted from an outside power source to the inside of the bulb? Using rubber bands or tape to hold the wires in position, connect the battery to the bulb so that the bulb lights up. Replace one of the wires with a piece of wood and record your observations. Explain the results. (A flashlight "battery" is more properly called a "cell," because it has only one pair of electrodes. A "battery" consists of a series of cells, as in an automobile battery.)

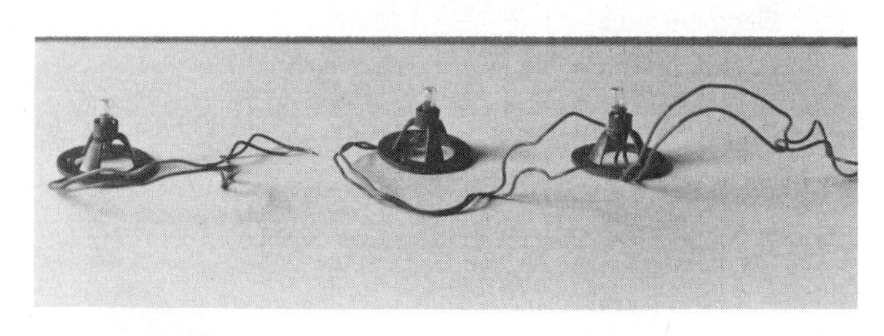

2. **Electric circuits.** For this experiment you will need three small light sockets with bulbs such as the ones shown in the photograph. The sockets shown here are available from hardware or hobby stores. You will also need a 1.5-volt battery. Connect the three lights to the battery in series. Observe how much light is given off by each bulb. Now remove one bulb and record what happens. Next, rewire the bulbs in a parallel circuit. Observe how much light is given off by each bulb. Remove one of the bulbs and record again what happens. Draw a picture of both circuits. In which circuit did the bulbs glow more brightly? Explain.

3. **Electric meter.** Find the electric meter in your house or apartment. If you live in a private house, the meter is probably located on the outside wall, whereas if you live in an

A household electric meter.

apartment, it is probably in the basement. As shown in the photograph, a meter has several small dials and a horizontal disc. This disc spins when electric energy is being used, and the rate of spinning is proportional to the amount of electricity consumed. Thus, if many appliances are plugged in, the disc will spin rapidly, and if little electricity is being used in the house, the disc will barely move. Turn off all the electrical appliances in your house, and unplug the refrigerator and freezer. The disc should now be stationary. Plug in one 100-W light bulb. How many seconds are required for the disc to make one complete revolution? Plug in a 50-watt light bulb and measure the time required for one revolution. Now plug in an appliance whose power requirement you do not know. Record the time required for one revolution of the disc. How much power is consumed by the unknown appliance? When you are finished with the experiment, remember to reconnect all your appliances.

4. **Magnetism.** Magnetize a needle by stroking it many times on a strong magnet. Now run the needle through a small piece of cork until the cork is halfway along the needle, and float it in a plastic pan of water. Does it behave as a compass?

5. **Magnetism.** Wrap about 50 loops of thin, insulated wire around a screwdriver or large nail. Connect the ends of the wire to a battery. Will this device pick up a staple or a small paper clip? Explain. Hold your nail near a small compass. What do you observe? Explain. (Do not hold the wires on to the terminals of your battery for very long, as your battery will soon wear out.)

PROBLEMS

1. **Electrical force.** Define electrical force. Compare electrical force with mechanical force. Can electrical force, like mechanical force, cause bodies to accelerate?

2. **Electric fields.** What is an electric field? Draw a diagram showing the field that exists about an electron in space. Where is the field most intense; weakest? Are electric fields present in air; in free space?

*3. **Movement of electricity.** A student living near the seashore, where salt spray is in the air, tried to stick balloons on the wall after rubbing them in his hair. The balloons didn't stick. Explain.

4. **Movement of electricity.** Could you cause a thin metal ball to stick on a wall by first rubbing it against your hair? Explain.

5. **Movement of electricity.** Could you cause a balloon to stick to a water pipe by first rubbing the balloon against your hair? Explain.

6. **Electric current.** How do alternating currents, direct currents, and currents that are carried by ions differ from one another? How are they similar? Explain.

7. **Volts.** A high-tension transmission wire is at a potential of 120,000 volts, local power lines are at a potential of 2200 volts, and household wiring is at 110 volts. What is the potential difference between (a) the high-tension line and the local power line; (b) the local power line and the ground; (c) the high-tension line and household wiring?

8. **Electric circuits.** Draw a diagram showing how to connect a light bulb to a flashlight battery.

9. **Electric circuits.** Explain why there must be a complete circuit of conducting materials in order for current to flow.

*Indicates more difficult problem.

*10. **Electric circuits.**

(a) Explain why there must be always two wires leading to an electric light bulb if it is to draw current and light up.

(b) In an automobile, the wire from one terminal of the battery (the "ground") generally is connected directly to the metal chassis. The other terminal is said to be "hot." Therefore any electrical device, such as a light bulb, can be energized by first bolting one of its wires to the chassis and running the other wire to the battery. Explain. From which terminal, the ground terminal or the "hot" terminal, should the wire be run? Which terminal, the positive or the negative, should be grounded, or does it matter? Compare the wiring of an automobile to that of a household circuit as discussed in (a).

11. **Resistance.**

(a) Calculate the resistance of a simple circuit in which a 40-volt power supply causes 4 amp of current to flow.

(b) Calculate the voltage of a battery if it can push 1.5 amp through a 8-ohm resistor.

12. **Power.** Define electrical power. Compare this definition with a definition of mechanical power.

13. **Power.** Calculate the internal resistances of a 25-W light bulb, a 50-W light bulb, a 50-W stereo amplifier, a 100-W light bulb, a 250-W toaster, and an 800-W space heater, assuming all are designed to operate at 110 volts.

*14. **Power.** During a "brown-out" in a big city, fuel shortages forced a power company to supply 90-volt potential instead of the usual 110-volt potential. If a 250-W toaster is plugged in during a brown-out, how much power will it deliver?

*15. **Power.** Farmers today frequently use electric fences, which deliver a shock to animals if they rub against the wires. The fence wire is maintained at high voltage, but under normal conditions, almost no current is carried by the fence. (a) Would it be important to use expensive low-resistance wire for an electric fence? Explain. (b) Would it be expensive to operate an electric fence continuously? Explain.

*16. **Power.** If two different heaters are compared, the one with the lower resistance uses the most power. Since pure copper wire has a lower resistance than heater elements, why doesn't the wiring in your house or the wire in an extension cord get hot when it is drawing current?

*17. **Electric circuits.** A customer brought her new portable radio into the repair shop, complaining that although the radio operated well, a set of batteries lasted only a short time before running down. Speculate in a general way on the nature of the problem. Would you think the radio was drawing excess voltage, or excess current? Discuss the reasons for your answer.

18. **Voltage and power.** A stream dropping over a waterfall has the ability to turn a water wheel and produce mechanical power. Show that the amount of power produced is dependent on both the height of the waterfall and the volume of water in the stream. Draw an analogy between the waterfall and an electric current. Compare voltage, current, and electric power with the different characteristics of the stream-water-wheel system.

19. **ac and dc.** Discuss the motion of both the electron and the electric field in wires carrying ac and dc.

20. **Current.** Define electric current.

21. **Current.** In the text, electric current was compared to the flow of water in a pipe. Although electricity and water act in much the same manner, the movement of molecules in a flowing stream of water is much different from the movement of electrons in a wire. Discuss the movement of electrons in both ac and dc circuits, and show how in each case electric current flow differs from water flow.

22. **Series and parallel circuits.** Draw diagrams showing how to wire two light bulbs together in series and in parallel.

23. **Series and parallel circuits.** Explain why Christmas tree lights are generally wired in parallel. If they were strung together in series and one bulb blew out, would it be hard or easy to find that bulb? Explain.

24. **Series and parallel circuits.** Give two reasons why series circuits would be unacceptable for household wiring.

---

*Indicates more difficult problem.

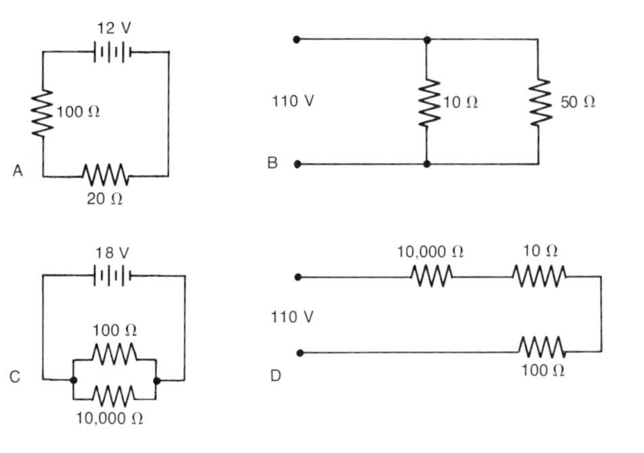

25. **Series and parallel circuits.** Calculate the current in the wire and the power delivered to each resistor in each of the above circuits.

*26. **Circuit design.** Assume that you have a 12-volt battery and a small appliance with a resistance of 6 ohms. The appliance manufacturer states that the appliance will burn out if more than 15 W are drawn. Can the appliance be safely connected to the battery? If not, design a circuit using the 12-volt battery that will operate in such a manner as to supply 15 W to the appliance.

27. **Fuses.** What is a fuse? Why are fuses used? Why is it unsafe to put a penny in a fusebox?

*28. **Fuses.** Fuses are always placed in series with a 110-volt wire and never in the ground wire. Explain why circuits are wired in this way. What would happen if a fuse were placed in the ground wire and the hot wire was shorted against a water pipe?

29. **Fuses.** Fuses are generally placed in automobile circuits. What would happen if an automobile were wired without fuses and a short circuit developed?

*30. **Grounding.** Suppose that you own an old refrigerator, and every time you open the door you receive a small electric shock. What can you do if you are unable to repair the refrigerator but wish to make it safe until the electrician arrives?

31. **Amplifiers.** Look up four definitions of "amplify" in a good dictionary. Show that, although in each case something has indeed been "made bigger," the First Law of Thermodynamics is always obeyed.

32. **Amplifiers.** Where does most of the electric energy used to drive a speaker originate from?

33. **Magnetic fields.** Compare and contrast magnetic field interactions with electric and gravitational field interactions.

*34. **Magnetism.** The nucleus of every hydrogen atom contains one proton. This proton spins on its axis at all times. Do you think that this spinning proton would produce a magnetic field? Do you think that the lone electron orbiting around the hydrogen nucleus would establish a magnetic field? Explain.

*35. **Compass.** Modern ships and airplanes use both conventional compasses and sophisticated electronic equipment for navigation. Would it be possible for the electronic equipment to damage the effectiveness of the compass? Do you feel that precautions would be needed to shield the compass from the ship's electronics? Explain.

36. **Electromagnetic interactions.** If you rubbed a balloon on your hair to charge it and then placed the charged balloon near a compass, would the compass needle deviate from pointing northward?

37. **Electromagnetic interactions.** How do you build an electromagnet? List two situations in which an electromagnet would be more useful than a permanent magnet. List two situations in which a permanent magnet would be more useful.

38. **Electromagnetic interactions.** If a powerful electromagnet were suspended by a long cable and held stationary over a coil of wire, would a current be induced in the wire? If a wind came up and the magnet swayed in the breeze, would it induce a current in the wire? Explain.

39. **Electromagnetic interactions.** Imagine that you are a space explorer who discovered a rain of high-energy, fast-moving, glowing particles in the atmosphere of some faraway planet. Design a simple experiment to determine whether or not these particles are charged.

40. **Electromagnets.** Explain why an electromagnet made with 10 loops of wire would be stronger than one with 5 loops of wire. How much stronger would it be?

---

*Indicates more difficult problem.

41. **Electromagnets.** If you were building an electromagnet to lift scrap iron, would you use alternating current or direct current, or would it make any difference? Explain.

*42. **Electromagnets.** If scientists are ever to harness the power of a hydrogen bomb for peaceful purposes, they must build some kind of a "bottle" that will hold charged particles even when heated to 40 million degrees Celsius. Since no material can remain solid at these temperatures, physicists are building magnetic "bottles" to hold the charged particles. Explain briefly how a magnetic bottle might work. Would this device hold neutrons?

43. **Electric motors.** Describe, in your own words, how an electric motor works.

44. **Electric motors.** Electric motors can be constructed to operate from a direct or an alternating power source, but inside the motor itself there must always be alternating current. Explain.

45. **Electric motors.** As the price of copper wire continues to increase, do you think that small portable electric motors might someday be built with permanent magnets rather than with electromagnets? Defend your answer.

*46. **Electric motors.** The motor described in the text and illustrated in Figure 5-57 has a loop of wire spinning in a magnetic field. Would it be possible to build a motor in which a permanent magnet rotated in an alternating electric field? Explain.

*47. **Electric motors.** When you turn on an electric motor, there is an initial rapid surge of current, followed by a rapid approach to constant current flow. Explain why this current surge occurs. Is the surge harmful to the motor?

48. **Electric generators.** Compare an electric generator with an electric motor.

49. **Electric motors.** Explain why more power is required to move current through a coil of wire when it is within a magnetic field than when it is not. Does this observation contradict the First Law of Thermodynamics? Explain.

50. **Transformers.** What is a transformer? What does it do?

51. **Transformers.** If the primary coil of a transformer had 100 loops of wire carrying 10 amps at 2000 volts, how many loops are needed in the secondary to produce 4000 volts. What about 200 volts? 2000 volts? What would the current be in each case?

52. **Transformers.** A transformer can be built to step up the potential of a line from 50 volts to 500 volts. Is this a violation of the First Law of Thermodynamics? Explain.

53. **Transformers.** Slot cars and electric trains operate at about 10 to 15 volts. The 110-volt household current is stepped down to lower voltage in a transformer. The speed of the toys can be changed by changing the voltage applied to them. Draw a labeled diagram of a transformer that can supply a variable output voltage.

54. **Power transmission.** Explain why direct current is not generally supplied to household circuits.

---

*Indicates more difficult problem.

CHAPTER

Galileo and Newton pioneered the study of classical physics during the sixteenth and seventeenth centuries. These scientists observed the motion of astronomical bodies, such as planets and moons, and experimented with objects that they could handle, such as balls and blocks of wood. They understood virtually nothing about small particles such as atoms, however, and although Newton was renowned for his work in optics, his understanding of the nature of light was rudimentary. Seventy-five years after Newton's death, Thomas Young showed that light exhibited wave properties, and nearly 100 years later, in 1899, physicists showed that light also acts like a stream of particles. Further studies showed that light energy is delivered in packets, called quanta. In this chapter, the concept of the combined particle and wave nature of light is used to explain absorption and emission. Refraction and reflection are discussed, and then the chapter proceeds to examine the components of the electromagnetic spectrum.

ELECTRO-MAGNETIC WAVES

6.1 INTRODUCTION

If one fundamental goal of philosophers is to understand the structure and harmony of the universe, the great discoveries of physics have certainly had immense philosophical impact. Think about the discoveries of James Clerk Maxwell. In the mid-1800's, Maxwell was studying the nature of the magnetic fields generated by an alternating current carried in a wire. The problem at hand was this: If a wire carries no current, there is no magnetic field around it. When the current starts in the wire, a changing magnetic field is produced. The varying magnetic field then generates a varying electric field, as shown in Figure 6–1. The combined electric and magnetic fields are called an **electromagnetic field.** It would seem reasonable to assume that the electromagnetic field appears first close to the wire that carries the current, then spreads outward. What, then, is the speed at which the field travels? When Maxwell solved the problem and arrived at a value for the speed of a traveling field, he discovered that this value had a special significance. *The speed of propagation of an electromagnetic disturbance is the same as the speed of light.* It was starting from this insight that he learned that light is an electromagnetic disturbance very similar to the field generated by an accelerating current in a wire.

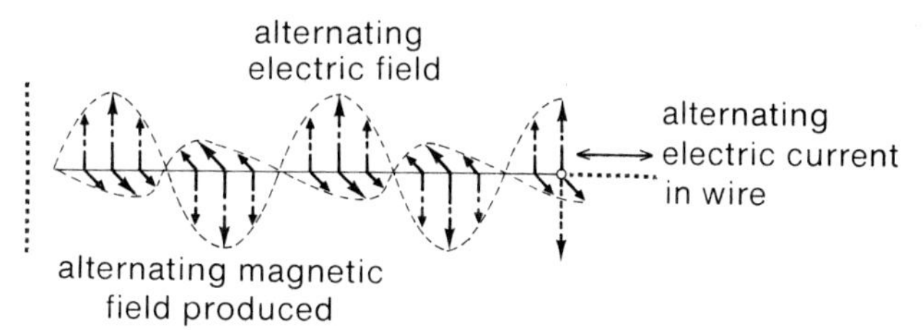

Figure 6–1. Electromagnetic waves produced when an alternating current passes through a wire.

The great scientists have shown us how wonderfully simple yet how astonishingly complex our universe really is. On the one hand, there are only four forces and a relatively few types of subatomic particles. From that point of view, our universe is simple. On the other hand, these four forces and a handful of types of particles combine to create such diverse and complex objects as the human body, an ant, a star, and a spiral nebula.

Maxwell showed that any time an electric current oscillates in a wire or in space, it generates an electromagnetic wave that travels outward at 3×10^8 m/sec. Earlier workers had measured the speed of light and found it also to be 3×10^8 m/sec. The close agreement led to the obvious conclusion that light is an electromagnetic wave. Thus light waves are generated originally by oscillating electric charges, just as all other electromagnetic waves are.

How is something as fast as the speed of light measured? Galileo attempted to measure it by positioning two people, one on each of two hilltops about 1.5 km apart. Both experimenters carried covered lanterns. One person quickly removed the cover from his lantern, while his partner was instructed to uncover the second lantern as soon as he saw the light from the first. The speed of light would then be calculated simply by measuring the

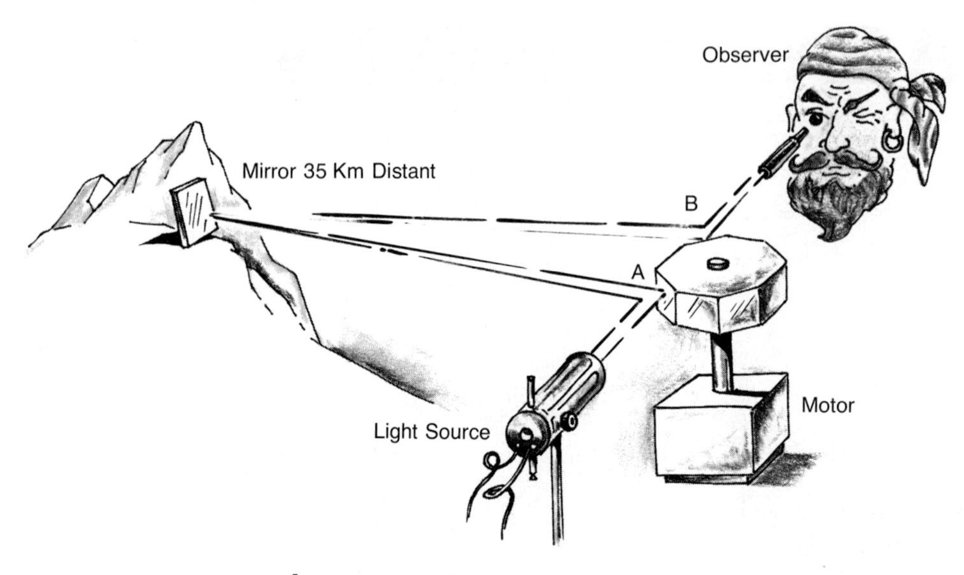

A Focusing while mirror is at rest

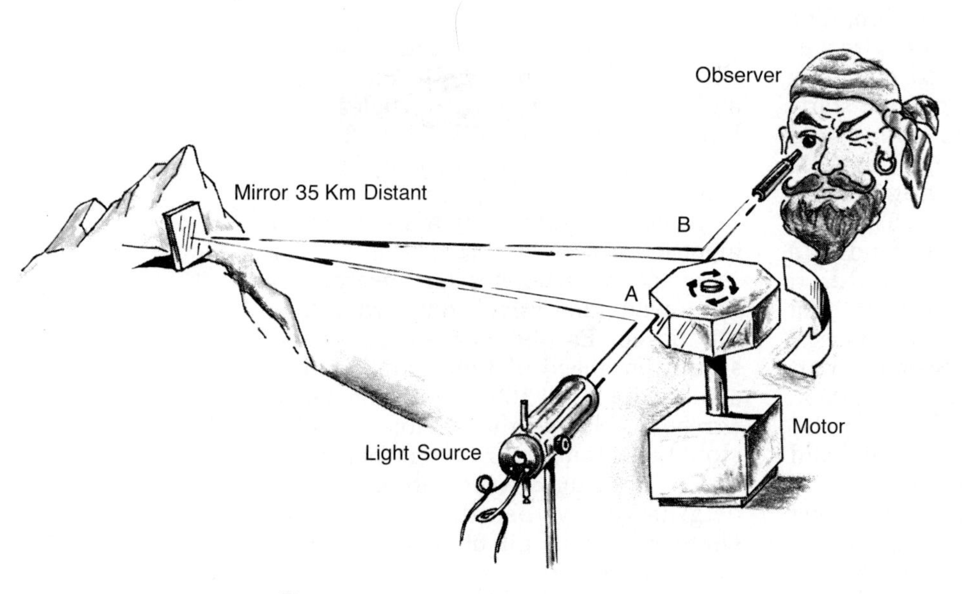

B Mirror rotates at correct speed

Figure 6–2. Measurement of the speed of light by Michelson's method.

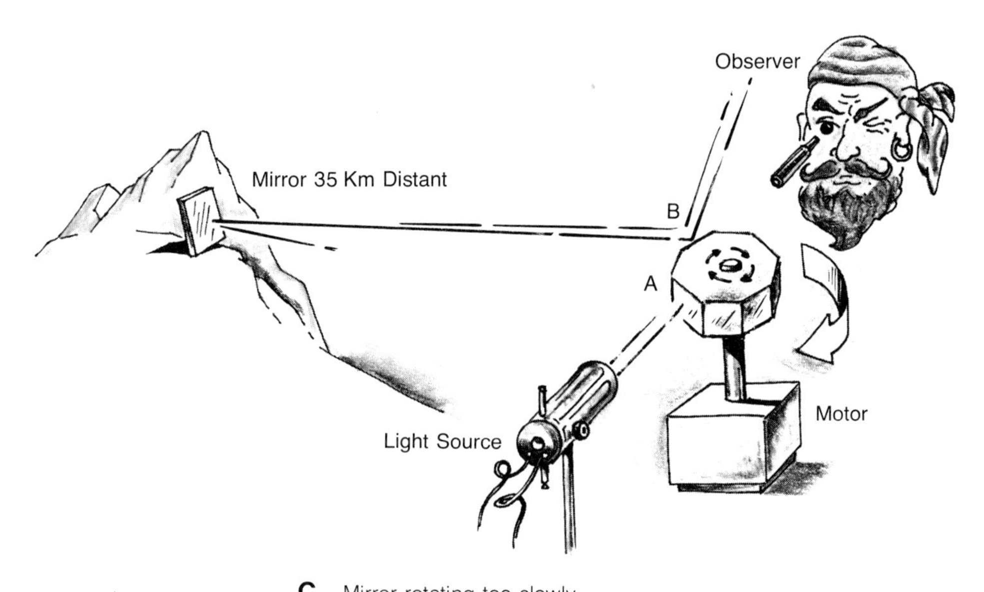

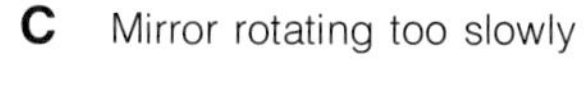

C Mirror rotating too slowly

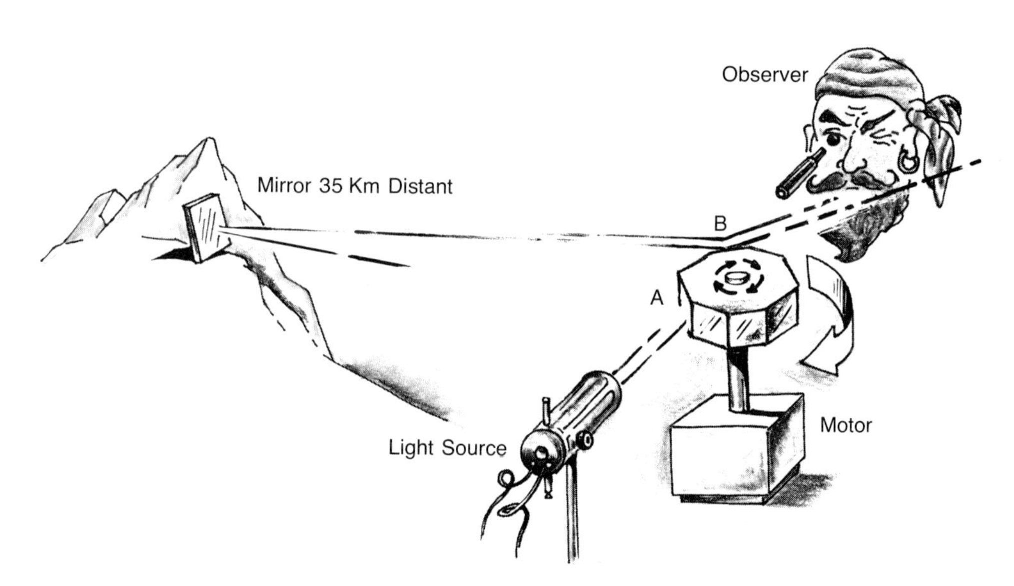

D Mirror rotating too fast

time required for the light to make the round trip. But Galileo learned that human reaction time was so slow compared to the speed of light, that all he was really able to measure was the time required to uncover a lantern. As far as he could tell, the light made the round trip instantaneously, or at least with an unmeasurable speed.

Several techniques have been used to measure the speed of light here on Earth. Since it is impossible to turn switches on and off fast enough to time the speed of a light ray as one would time the speed of, say, a human runner, all terrestrial measurements have been performed with the aid of some continuously moving device. The most famous such experiment was performed by Albert Michelson in 1880. His apparatus, shown in Figure 6–2, consisted of a rotating octagonal mirror, an intense light source, a flat mirror located approximately 35 km from the rotating one, and an observer with an eyepiece located as shown. With the mirror originally at rest, the light source and eyepiece were aligned so that the light would shine on one octagonal face, reflect to the distant mirror, bounce back to another octagonal face, and enter the eyepiece (Fig. 6–2*A*). Then the mirror was rotated at a rapid and constant speed. Light is reflected from the distant stationary mirror only when the octagonal mirror is properly aligned. Thus the continuous light source is chopped up, and only discrete bursts of light reach the distant mirror. Let us follow the path of one of these bursts. As light hits point A, it takes off for a 70-km round trip to the distant mirror. Now, if in the time required to make this trip, the octagonal mirror has rotated exactly one eighth of a revolution, light will be reflected directly through the eyepiece (Fig. 6–2*B*). If the rotating mirror is traveling too slowly, the light will be deflected as shown in Figure 6–2*C*; if it is revolving too fast, it will be reflected as shown in Figure 6–2*D*. Thus, by accurately measuring the distance between the source and the distant mirror, and by accurately adjusting the speed of rotation of the mirror until the light was focused on the eyepiece, Michelson was able to calculate the speed of light. His experimental value was 2.9992×10^8 m/sec. In this book we will round off this figure to 3.0×10^8 m/sec, or about 300,000 km/sec.

The speed of an electromagnetic wave, 3×10^8 m/sec, is a universal constant and is often abbreviated by the symbol *c*.

c = speed of electromagnetic radiation in a vacuum = 3×10^8 m/sec.

We now know that the speed of light in a vacuum is a universal constant. Any time, any place we choose to measure it, light travels at a rate of 3×10^8 m/sec; never faster and never slower.

In terrestrial terms, 300,000 km/sec sounds mighty fast. A light ray travels 1 km in about 0.000003 sec (3×10^{-6} sec) and could travel around the Earth at the Equator 7.5 times in a single second. If a beam of light were to travel in an uninterrupted path for an entire year, it would cover a distance of 9.5 trillion km (9.5×10^{12} km). This distance is called 1 **light year.** But numbers can be misleading: On an astronomical scale, the speed of light no longer seems so great. For example, the closest star to our Solar System is 38×10^{12} (38 trillion) km away. A light ray leaving that star for Earth must travel for 4 years before it reaches us. If we move our focus of interest farther out into space, even a distance of 4 light years can seem small. The Andromeda Galaxy has a diameter of 100,000 light

Accurate measurements now place the value of the speed of light at 2.997925×10^8 m/sec, but in this book we round it off to 3.0×10^8 m/sec.

"Its top speed is 186 m.p.h.—that's 1/3,600,000 the speed of light."

years! That means that light traveling at 300,000 km/sec takes 100,000 years just to travel across that galaxy. The most distant galaxies are up to 10 billion light years from Earth. That means that if one of these galaxies had exploded nine billion years ago, we still wouldn't know about it for another billion years to come.

6.2 THE NATURE OF LIGHT

By 1900 scientists knew that light is one type of electromagnetic disturbance and that all electromagnetic disturbances travel at the same speed—about 3.0×10^8 m/sec. But what is the nature of this disturbance? How does a ray of light or an electromagnetic wave leaving a wire behave?

Two conflicting theories of light were proposed in the late 1600's and early 1700's. Robert Hooke and Christian Huygens argued that light travels in waves, while Isaac Newton postulated that light rays consist of streams of particles—so-called packets of light. None of these scientists had any sound experimental proof to substantiate his theory. The disagreement was ultimately resolved in a happy manner. Hooke and Huygens were correct—light exhibits wave behavior; and Newton was also right—light acts as if it were composed of a stream of particles. But how can light be two things at the same time—both a wave and a particle? Well, in a sense this question isn't a fair one to ask. Light is light and it happens to exhibit the properties of both waves and particles. It is unique, and there is no fundamental reason why it should be "like" ocean waves or speeding bullets.

6.3 WAVE BEHAVIOR

In Chapter 3 we learned about how particles interact. Now we will learn about how waves interact. As you read this section, remember that although we are focusing attention on electromagnetic waves and in some places particularly on visible light waves, the phenomena that we are discussing are common to all wave motion.

We can conveniently visualize wave motion as water waves, especially ocean waves striking a beach or ripples in a pond or swimming pool. Water that is still ("quiet" water) has a smooth, level surface. Water waves are disturbances; they alter the normal level so as to make it higher in some places and lower in others. The highest places are called **crests;** the lowest,

Water waves

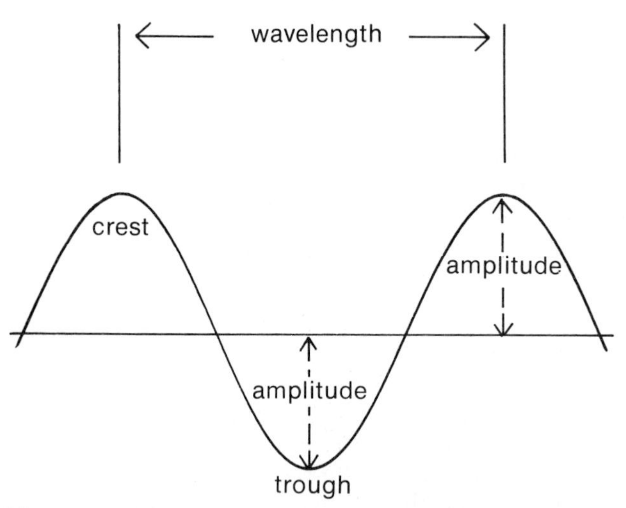

Figure 6–3. Waves.

troughs. The distance between successive disturbances of the same type, such as between neighboring crests, is called the **wavelength** (Fig. 6–3). The rate at which a disturbance moves is the **speed** of the wave. The number of disturbances that pass a given point per unit time is the **frequency.** Think of frequency as how often (how frequently) something happens. Anything. How often your clock ticks, how often the waves break against the shore, how often the geese fly south. These are events that repeat themselves; we say that they recur in cycles. The units of frequency are therefore repetitions of something per unit of time. Since a repetition is called a cycle, and a unit of time is the second, we say the unit of frequency is "cycles per second."

> In calculations, only the "per second" is used, so we express frequency as $\frac{1}{\text{sec}}$ or sec^{-1}. The official name given to this unit is the Hertz (abbreviated Hz). One Hz $= \frac{1 \text{ cycle}}{1 \text{ sec}} = \frac{1}{\text{sec}}$.

Thus, if a wave travels so that one crest, or one trough, passes a given point every second, the frequency is 1 cycle/sec. The speed, frequency, and wavelength of a wave are related as shown in the following equation:

$$\text{Speed} = \text{wavelength} \times \text{frequency} \quad [6.1]$$

The speed of any electromagnetic wave in a vacuum is always 3.0×10^8 m/sec. Other waves, such as water waves or sound waves, travel at different speeds (see Chapter 11).

If you slap the surface of a pond gently once per second with a spoon, you will make waves at a frequency of 1 cycle/sec. If you slap the water hard once per second with a paddle, you will still make waves at a frequency of 1 cycle/sec; they will not travel any faster than those made with a spoon, but they will be bigger. The intensity of the disturbance is called the **amplitude** of the wave. Thus waves on a sheltered lake with a mild wind blowing will have a small amplitude, whereas ocean waves on a stormy day will have a large amplitude. Note that the amplitude is measured from the zero point, or the flat undisturbed level, and is one-half the vertical distance between the crests and the troughs.

Waves commonly interact with each other. If two different waves reach a single point in space at the same time, they will combine in a process known as **interference.** The new wave is formed by an addition of the two components. If the two waves are of the same frequency and shape, and if they meet crest to crest and trough to trough, they are said to be **in phase** and combine to produce a wave of equal frequency and double the amplitude. If they combine 180° out of phase, they cancel out and the wave is destroyed. If two waves of different frequencies combine, the situation becomes more complicated, for they reinforce part of the time and cancel part of the time (Fig. 6–4).

6.4 THE WAVE NATURE OF LIGHT

For many years, scientists had attempted to establish whether or not light travels in waves. Then, in 1801, Thomas Young, a British physicist, decided that the best way to resolve the question would be to determine

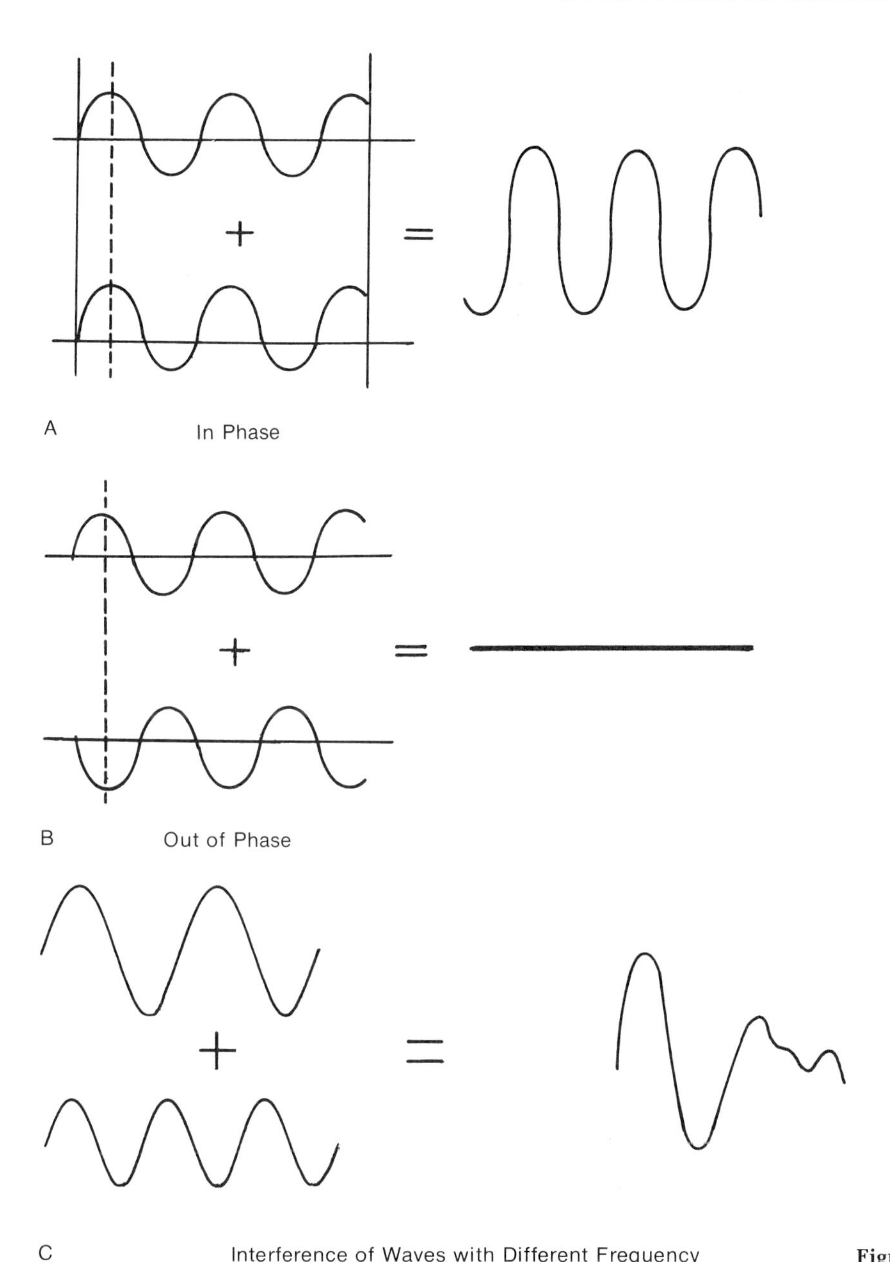

Figure 6–4. Interference of waves.

whether or not light could exhibit interference. If so, its behavior would resemble that of known waves such as water waves. Young knew that if a wave such as a water wave came against a narrow opening, the opening would act as a "point" source of new waves. As a result, concentric-shaped waves would be produced on the other side of the barrier. If two narrow openings were positioned close to each other, two independent waves would be produced. As these waves met, some would be in phase and some out of phase with each other. As a result they would interfere with each other, as shown in Figure 6–5. Alternate patterns of wavy and quiet water would be produced.

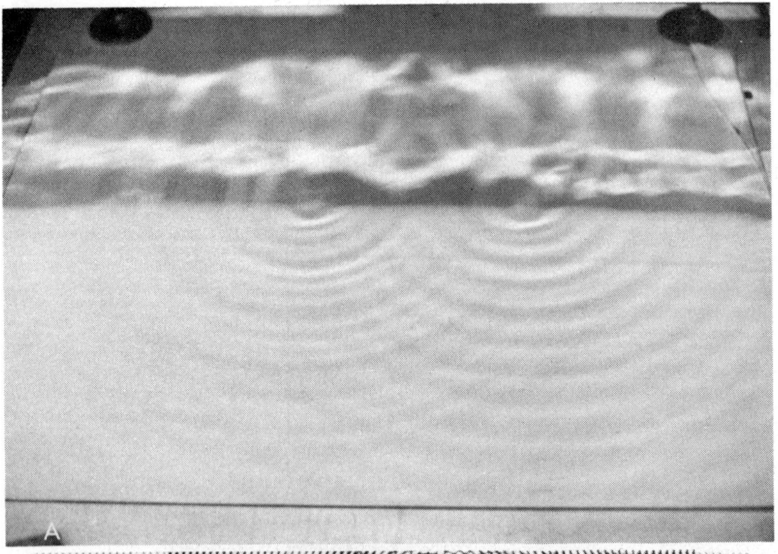

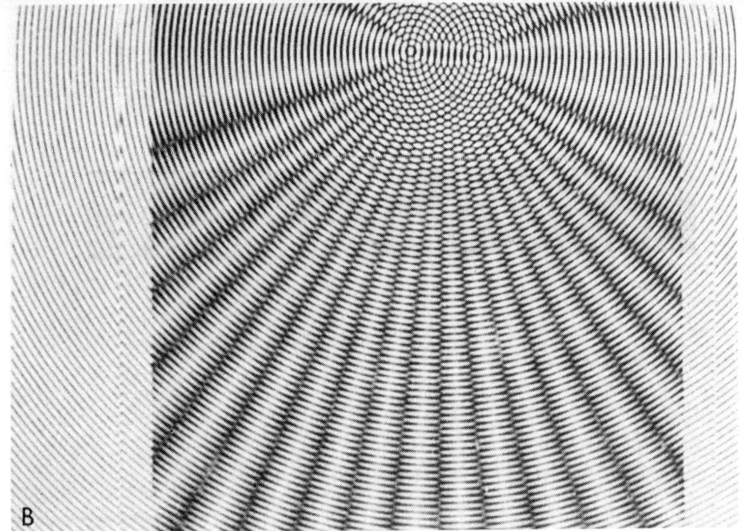

Figure 6–5. *A,* Two point source waves will interfere with each other, producing alternate patterns of wavy and quiet water. *B,* An artist's graphical representation of the alternate patterns produced when two point source waves interfere.

Young's experiment was amazingly simple, yet the results were extremely significant. He took a metal sheet, cut two slits in it, and placed it in front of a viewing screen, as shown in Figure 6–6. When he shined the light at the slotted place, alternate bands of light and dark appeared on the screen. This was an interference pattern analogous to the effect produced by water waves. Young therefore concluded that light exhibits wave behavior. Thus, every ray of light is characterized by a certain frequency and wavelength. For example, the frequency of red light is approximately 4×10^{14} cycle/sec and its wavelength is about 7.5×10^{-7} m.

Figure 6–6. Interference fringes observed by Young.

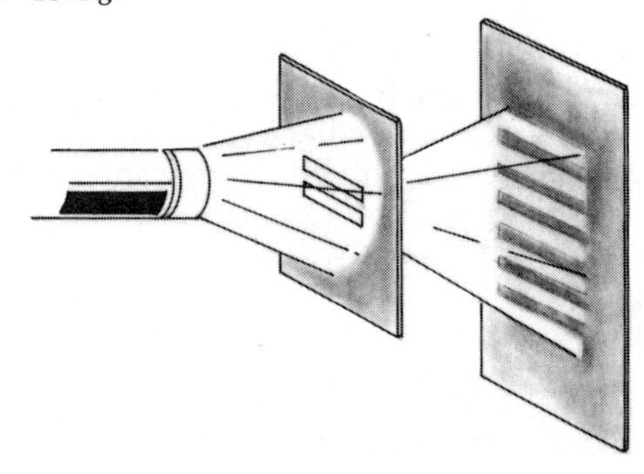

6.5 THE PARTICLE NATURE OF LIGHT

The outermost electrons of certain metals such as potassium and cesium are not held very strongly by the nucleus. If a beam of light of a certain frequency is shined on such metals, electrons will be "knocked off"—dislodged from the surface. This movement of electrons is, of course, an electric current. Since a ray of light can initiate an electric current, this process has been called the **photoelectric effect.**

There is nothing surprising about the fact that light can knock electrons off a metal surface. After all, we know that water waves can dislodge pebbles from a sandy beach, and a loud noise can knock down a delicate tower of cards, so why shouldn't light waves dislodge electrons from a metal surface? However, further experiments with photoelectric apparatus led to some results that could not be explained satisfactorily by assuming that light acts as a wave.

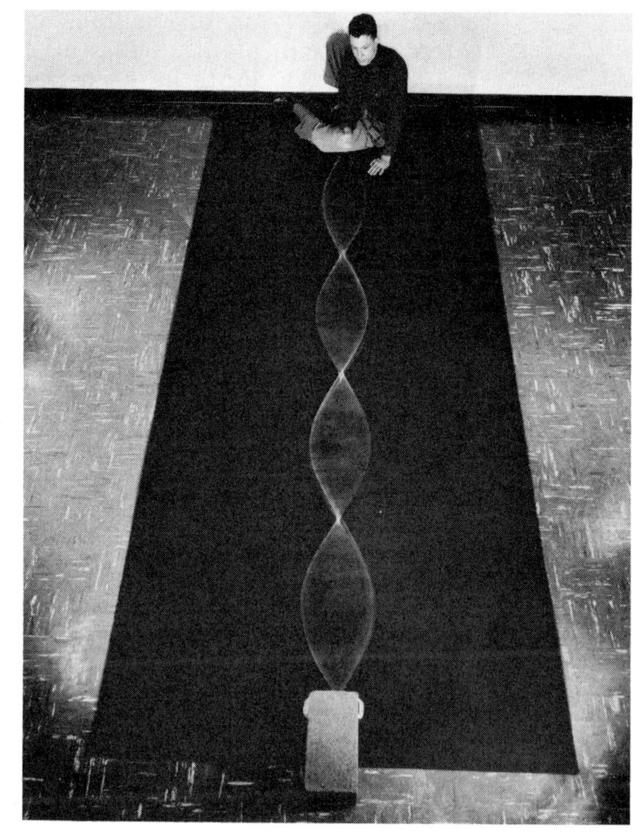

Standing waves in a piece of string.

The key observation was that the *kinetic energy* of the emitted electrons was related to the *frequency* of the incident light and not to the intensity (Fig. 6–8). Thus a very bright, low-frequency light could release a lot of low-energy electrons but no high-energy ones. On the other hand, a dim, high-frequency light would dislodge electrons with high kinetic energy. If light of very low frequency was used, no electrons at all would be dislodged, even if the light was very bright. To relate this to everyday experience, one can get a sunburn (a chemical change

Figure 6–7. Apparatus for observing photoelectric effect.

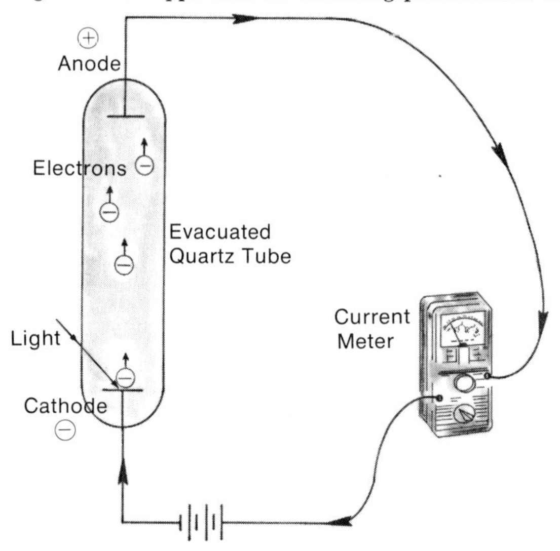

Figure 6–8. Electron emission as a function of light frequency in the photoelectric effect experiment.

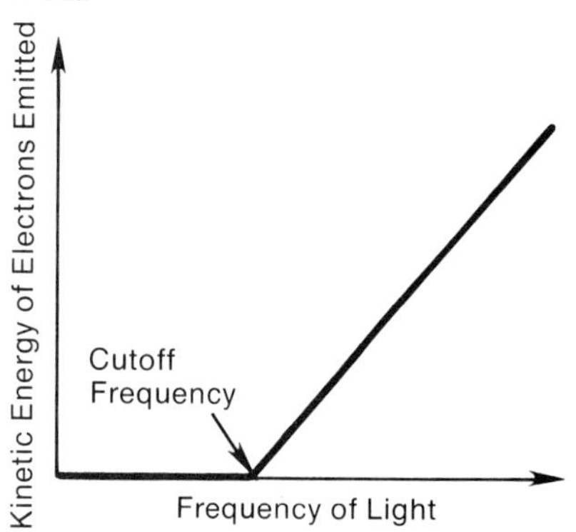

caused by excitation of electrons in molecules of skin pigment) in winter sunlight, which contains high-frequency ultraviolet radiation. But you can sweat all night near a hot stove (low-frequency infrared) and not get a trace of tan.

The ability of light to initiate an electric current is used in certain types of automatic doors and burglar alarms. A beam of light shines across a doorway onto a photoelectric cell. When a person passes through the door and interrupts the light, the electric current is turned off. This current change activates a switch that opens the door, sounds an alarm, or performs some other function.

The experimental data just outlined simply cannot be explained by assuming that light exhibits classic wave behavior. Think of water waves hitting a beach and dislodging rocks from hard-packed sand. The amplitude of the waves can be considered to be analogous to the brightness of the incident light, and of course the frequency of the water waves is defined (in the same manner as is the frequency of any wave) as the number of wave fronts passing a given point per second. If water waves behaved like light waves, then violent water waves appearing every now and then would not dislodge any rocks, whereas frequent gentle ones would have the power to move rocks. Furthermore, if we measured the kinetic energies of the dislodged rocks, we would find them to be proportional to the frequency of the waves and not to their height. In other words, if hurricane-force waves rolled in at low frequency, they would move rocks around more slowly than if many gentle waves came to shore in a short period of time. We know that water waves do not act like this at all. Big waves dislodge rocks easily and push them out with great force, and the kinetic energies of the displaced rocks are much more closely related to the heights of the waves than to their frequencies. Thus, light waves behave very differently from water waves.

The results of the photoelectric effect were most puzzling, but in 1905 Albert Einstein published a theory that explained the paradox. Five years earlier, another theoretical physicist, Max Planck, had postulated that light was emitted *discontinuously*, in **quanta.**

A quantum (plural, *quanta*) is a small discrete quantity. Physicists refer to quanta, or "bundles," of energy. To understand this concept, consider the following analogy. If a person is trying to hoist a stone into the air with a pulley, he can lift it to *any* desired height, say 5 m, or 5.1 m, or 5.01 m, or 5.00004 m. But if the task were to lift a stone up a flight of steps, the stone could not be placed just anywhere, it must be placed on one of the steps. If each step were 1 m high, the stone could rest at a height of 1 m, or 2 m, or 3 m, but not at 1.5 m or any other fractional value. Thus, since the potential energy of the stone is proportional to its height, the stone on the pulley can be given any potential energy, but only certain energies are *allowed* for the stone on the stairs. We say then that the energy we can give the stone is **quantized.**

Planck had theorized that the energy in a light ray is likewise quantized. Individual packets of light can have only one of a definite set of quan-

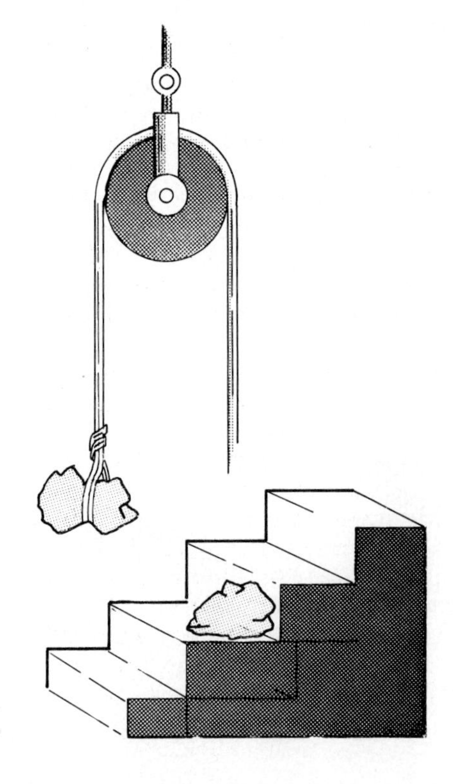

tized values of energy, like the levels of steps on a stairway, and nothing in between. Moreover, the allowed energies depend on the frequency, according to the equation

$$\text{Energy} = \frac{\text{Planck's}}{\text{constant}} \times \frac{\text{Frequency}}{\text{of the light}} \quad [6.2]$$

Planck's constant is equal to 6.625×10^{-34} J sec/particle. Thus a burst of light with a frequency of 10^{14} Hz (10^{14} cycles/sec) has an energy equal to

$$E = 6.625 \times 10^{-34} \frac{\text{J sec}}{\text{particle}} \times \frac{10^{14}}{\text{sec}}$$

$$= 6.625 \times 10^{-20} \text{ J/particle}$$

The smallest burst or particle or packet of light energy is called a **photon.** Therefore we say that the energy of this radiation is 6.625×10^{-20} J/photon. In summary, Planck postulated the following:

(1) Light energy is quantized and is available only in discrete packets. The smallest packet is called a photon.

(2) The energy of a photon is proportional to the frequency of the radiation; photons with high frequency have a lot of energy, and photons with low frequency have less.

Five years after Planck postulated the idea that light is quantized, Einstein used Planck's theory to explain the photoelectric effect and resolved the paradox so well that Planck's ideas became the basis of modern quantum physics. Let us see how quantum theory explains the photoelectric effect. For reference, the results of the experiments are set alongside the explanations.

There is no parallel to this behavior in classical physics. If we have a collection of ping-pong balls glued to a table top and tap them gently but frequently with a hammer, we would gradually loosen the glue and eventually knock them off. Thus, many low-energy taps dislodge the balls. But if we have a collection of electrons attracted to a nucleus and we bombard them with many low-energy photons, we never loosen or dislodge any of them.

Results of the Photoelectric Experiment	**Explanation in Terms of Quantum Theory**
(a) High-frequency radiation knocks electrons off the surface of a metal. The higher the frequency of the light, the greater the kinetic energy of the ejected electron.	(a) Each electron emitted in a photoelectric apparatus carries the energy of one photon. Some of this energy separates the electron from the surface of the metal. The remaining energy is converted into energy of motion (kinetic energy) of the electron.
(b) If the radiation is below a certain frequency, no electrons are knocked off the metal.	(b) If the energy of the photon is too low to remove the electron from the metallic surface, there is no photoelectric effect.
(c) The energy of the electron emitted from the surface of a metal depends only on the frequency of the photon and not on the brightness of the light.	(c) To repeat; each electron emitted in the photoelectric apparatus carries the energy of one photon. Thus, bright, low-frequency light contains many low-energy photons. They can knock many electrons off the surface with low kinetic energy, but do not produce any highly energetic electrons. If the frequency is too low, no electrons are knocked off.

In many scientific textbooks, including this one, the term "ray of light" is commonly used in verbal descriptions and is represented as an arrow in diagrams. These are simplified representations, because they do not take into account both the wave and the particle nature of light. These simplifications are useful in that they make it easier to understand reflection and other phenomena.

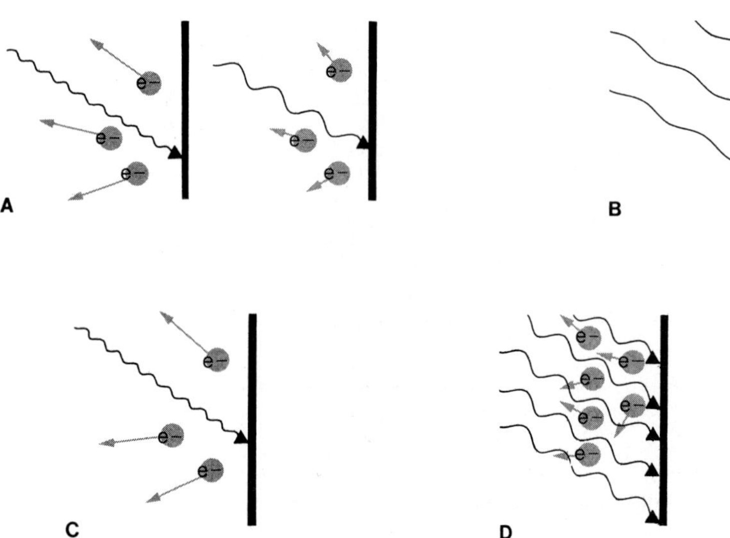

A, High-frequency radiation dislodges electrons with greater kinetic energy than low frequency radiation of the same brightness. *B*, No electrons at all are dislodged by a very low–frequency radiation even if it is quite bright. *C*, Low-intensity, high-frequency radiation generates a few highly energetic electrons. *D*, Whereas high-intensity, low-frequency radiation generates many low-energy electrons, but no very fast ones.

6.6 EMISSION AND ABSORPTION

In the last section we learned that if a photon of the proper frequency strikes certain metals, an electron will be ejected from the surface. But what happens to the photon? It vanishes; it simply disappears; it is absorbed. Conversely, if a bar of iron is heated, it glows bright red; photons are emitted. These photons appear where an instant ago there were none, and the photons are "born" in motion, traveling at 3×10^8 m/sec. Light is a truly unique phenomenon.

To understand emission and absorption we must appreciate the close association between radiation and the movement of charged particles.

Emission

Whenever a charged particle accelerates, an electromagnetic wave is emitted. This rule is a general one. If a charged ping-pong ball, an ion or electron in a gas, or an electron in a wire is accelerated, some form of radiation is emitted. Most commonly we deal with the acceleration of an oscillating particle, such as an electron wiggling back and forth in a wire or two atoms in a molecule vibrating back and forth. Thus, when an iron bar is heated, iron atoms accelerate rapidly and vibrate within the solid structure. These vibrating atoms emit light, and the bar glows red.

Absorption

Alternatively, any electromagnetic field may cause a charged particle to accelerate. Thus if a photon of light of the proper frequency strikes an electron, the electron will absorb the photon and gain its energy. The photon disappears, but energy is conserved because the electron accelerates.

Consider the case of a hydrogen atom. Hydrogen is the simplest atom; it has one proton in the nucleus and one electron in the outer shell. In the normal condition of the hydrogen atom (called the **ground state**), the electron may be considered to be separated from the nucleus by one "energy step." Think of this separation as analogous to the energy involved in lifting a stone to the first step of a flight of stairs. Since the electron and the proton are oppositely charged, they attract each other, and energy is required to move the electron further away (more energy steps) from the nucleus. We can think of another gravitational analogy. If a space satellite is in orbit around the Earth, and scientists wish to move it further out into space, then rocket engines must be fired to push the craft against the force of gravity. Returning to our hydrogen atom, once the electron has moved further away from the nucleus it has gained potential energy. It is called an excited electron and said to be in an **excited state.** Remember that when we say something has potential energy, we imply that it can undergo some change that can release energy. The electron could "fall" back to a position closer to the nucleus and release its energy (Fig. 6–9).

How do you excite an electron from one energy level to another? Our analogy of the satellite in orbit is of no help because no rocket is small enough to push an electron. But an electron is a charged particle and can be excited by a photon.* If radiation of the proper frequency strikes a hydrogen atom, the radiation will be absorbed and the electron will be promoted to a higher energy level. Thus, electromagnetic energy is converted to the potential energy of an electron. Similarly, if an excited electron "falls" back to a lower energy orbital, it will emit radiation, and the energy it loses will be converted to the energy of an emitted photon.

Recall that electrons can move only in quantum steps. An electron in a hydrogen atom cannot absorb just any amount of energy. An electron can absorb a photon and jump one, two, three, four, or more energy levels, but can never jump 1½ or 1¾ or any other fractional number of levels.

We can now understand why low-frequency light cannot eject electrons from the surface of a metal. If a low-energy photon approaches an electron, there may be insufficient energy to promote the electron one or more quantum steps, and the photon is simply not absorbed. Therefore, the electron is not affected. It is as if a weak person were to try to move a heavy stone up a flight of steps. If the person could not lift the stone one complete step, the stone would never go anywhere.

So what is light, anyway? Is it a wave traveling through space or is it a series of high-energy photons? In a way, that is an unfair question, because it engenders inappropriate images like ocean waves or streams of bullets. So we had better not try to answer it. Instead, let us just describe how light acts. It does exhibit wave behavior such as interference. Furthermore, as with other waves, there is a frequency associated with light and all other electromagnetic radiation. But it also does act

*There are various ways that an electron can be excited; absorption of a photon is only one of these ways.

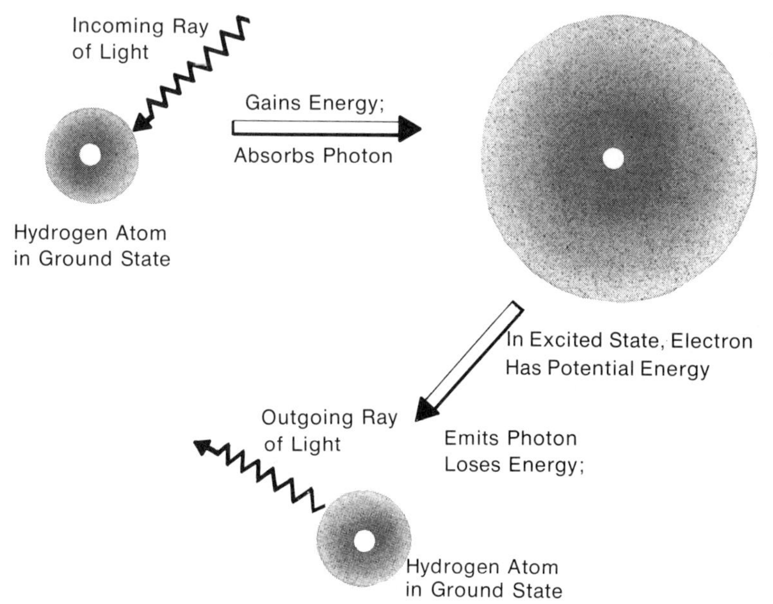

Figure 6–9. Emission and absorption of light.

like a series of high-energy particles. Since these particles can appear and vanish, light acts like something other than a classical wave or a classical particle. All we can say is that when light is interfering through a series of slits it acts like a wave, and when it dislodges electrons from a metal it acts like a series of photons, which are "packets" of energy.

6.7 MATTER WAVES

One fascinating sequel to the discovery that light is simultaneously a wave and a particle is the discovery that all matter has both wave and particle properties and can also, under the proper conditions, lose mass and become pure energy. For example, electrons are clearly particles and have a measurable mass, yet it has been shown that electrons traveling at certain speeds have a wavelength of about 10^{-8} cm. This distance is the same order of magnitude as interatomic distances, and electrons have been observed to interfere through the naturally occurring spaces between atoms in crystals. We cannot observe the wave behavior of large objects such as a chair or your pet goldfish, but, in theory at least, all matter exhibits wave behavior.

6.8 REFLECTION

Any electromagnetic wave moving through a vacuum or a uniform medium travels in a straight line. If a wave meets a second medium, it can either move through it or bounce back from it. For example, if a radio wave moving through air comes against a wooden house, the wave will travel right through the wood and enter the interior air space. Then it can be detected by the antenna on your radio. On the other hand, if a light wave meets a mirror, the wave will bounce back from it. When electromagnetic waves bounce back from an object they are said to be **reflected.** Light is reflected from the surface of wood, paper, metal, soil, most living tissue, some plastics, and anything else we describe as opaque or nontransparent. Transparent substances such as glass or water allow most of the light to pass through them. We say that the light is **transmitted** through such materials.

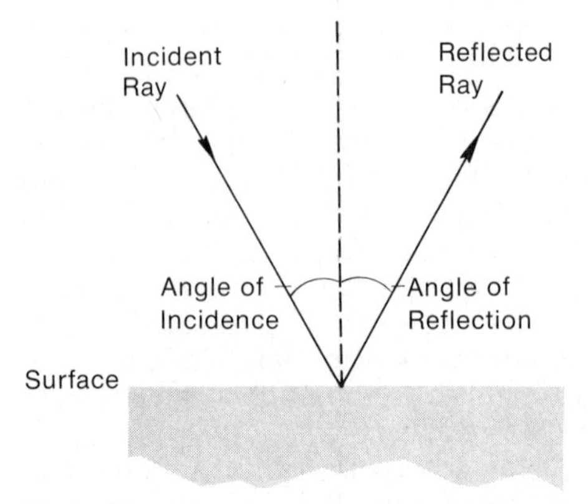

Figure 6–10. Angle of incidence equals angle of reflection.

A mirror and a sheet of white paper both reflect light well, but you can see your image only in the mirror and not on the paper. What is the difference? To answer this question, we must examine the nature of a reflected wave. Imagine a ray of light reaching a surface as shown in Figure 6–10. It strikes the object at a certain angle. The **angle of incidence** is defined as the angle between the light ray and a line drawn perpendicular to the surface. When this ray is reflected, it bounces off on the other side of the perpendicular line but at the same angle at which it approached the surface. *The angle of reflection always equals the angle of incidence* (Fig. 6–10).

Now suppose that the surface is rough, as shown in Figure 6–11. As a

Figure 6–11. Scattered reflections from a rough surface.

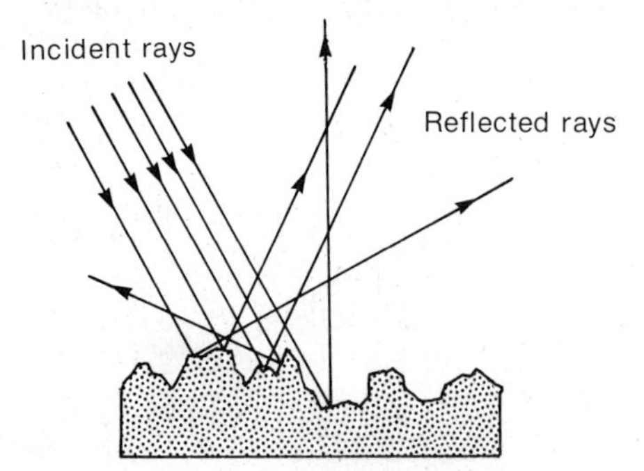

Figure 6–12. ***A,*** **This mountain is clearly reflected in a still, calm lake. The smooth water is an effective mirror.** ***B,*** **When the lake surface is disturbed by waves, reflected light is scattered and the image is blurred. Rough surfaces reflect light but do not make good mirrors.**

group of rays approaches the surface, different ones strike different areas. Since each wave is reflected from each microscopic area of the surface according to its own particular angle of incidence, the waves will be scattered, as shown. Therefore light is scattered randomly from the surface of a sheet of paper or a desk, and as a result the surface appears dull and diffuse. If light strikes a smooth surface such as that of a polished silver dish or a still body of water, light is reflected uniformly, as shown in Figure 6–12. Such an object is a **mirror.** Thus, mirrors are smooth, and non-mirrors reflect light but do so diffusely because they are not smooth. Figure 6–12 shows the reflection of a mountain from a still lake. When the region was windy and the surface of the lake was rough, a photograph of the same water taken from the same angle showed no image, because the surface was uneven and the reflected light was diffuse.

Now suppose a woman is standing in front of a mirror and a light is shining on her. The light from the light source strikes her and is reflected at all angles. We will consider only those, drawn as solid lines in Figure 6–13, that are reflected from her to the mirror and back through her eye. Think of a light ray reflected from her foot to the mirror to her eye. Its path is marked by the solid line traveling from point A to

Figure 6–13. Formation of an image in a flat mirror.

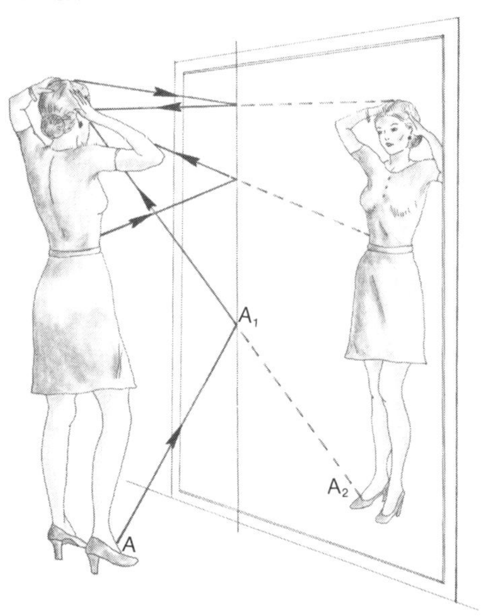

We see the image behind the mirror because we respond as if light travels only in straight lines.

point A_1 to the eye. The eye does not see this erratic path; it sees only a straight light ray coming from point A_1. However, the eye draws no conclusions; it simply sends its signal on to the brain. Therefore, the brain assumes that this ray came from point A_2 instead of from its true origin, point A. Thus the foot appears to be behind the mirror. Since the deception occurs for all parts of the body, a full image appears to be standing behind the mirror.

Curved mirrors are used in many practical applications. If light strikes a curved surface, it will be reflected at an angle as shown in Figure 6–14. If an entire mirror is curved into a specific shape known as a **parabola,** most of the light that reaches the surface will be reflected to focus on one specific point in space (see Figure 6–15). The parabolic mirror would be considered to be a device that "collects" light. A reflective disk 1 m in diameter concentrates enough sunlight to boil water, cook a hamburger, or bake a chicken, and outdoor solar barbeques are commercially available. A multistory parabolic mirror built in France can concentrate proportionally larger amounts of solar energy. This solar tower can produce enough steam to power a small electric generating station. It is now being used for research applications. Similarly, parabolic antennas that reflect radio waves are used to collect signals from outer space. In recent years, many important astronomical discoveries have been made with these "telescopes," for objects in outer space emit radio waves as well as visible light.

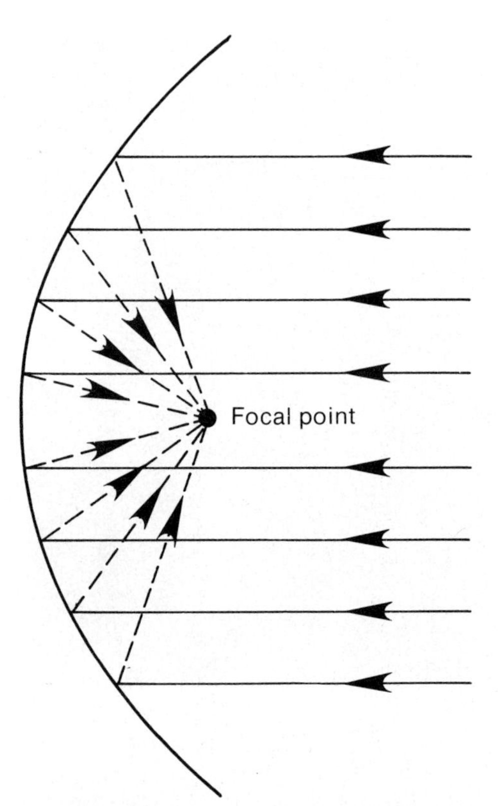

Figure 6–15. Reflection from a parabola. Light from a broad area is focused to a small point called the focal point.

Figure 6–14. Reflection from a curved surface. The angle of incidence equals the angle of reflection with respect to a line drawn perpendicular to the tangent of the surface, as shown.

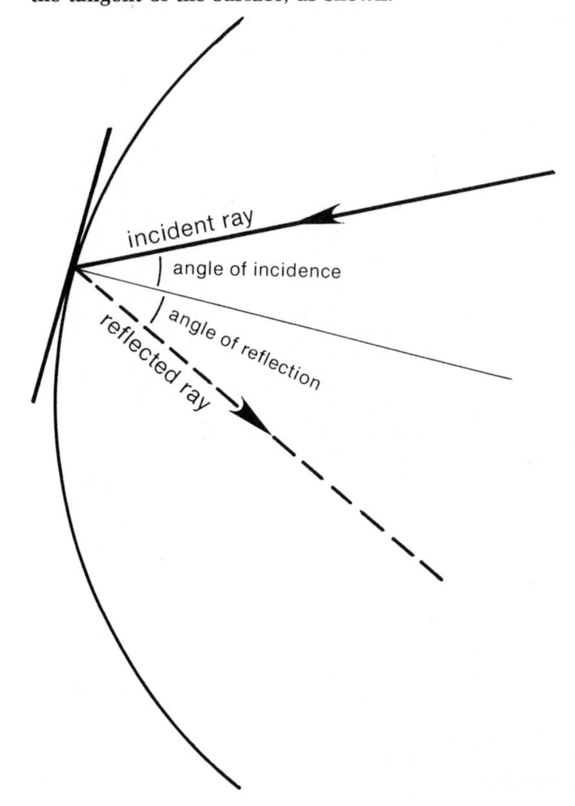

6.9 REFRACTION

Electromagnetic radiation always travels at 3.0×10^8 m/sec in a vacuum, never faster and never slower. But light travels through various substances such as air or glass or water at slower speeds. If a ray of light (or a radio wave

A solar parabolic heater. Sunlight, reflected from the surface, is focused onto the plate above the mirror, where high temperatures are attained. A clock mechanism drives the collector to follow the sun throughout the day. (Courtesy of Solar Energy Research Institute, SERI).

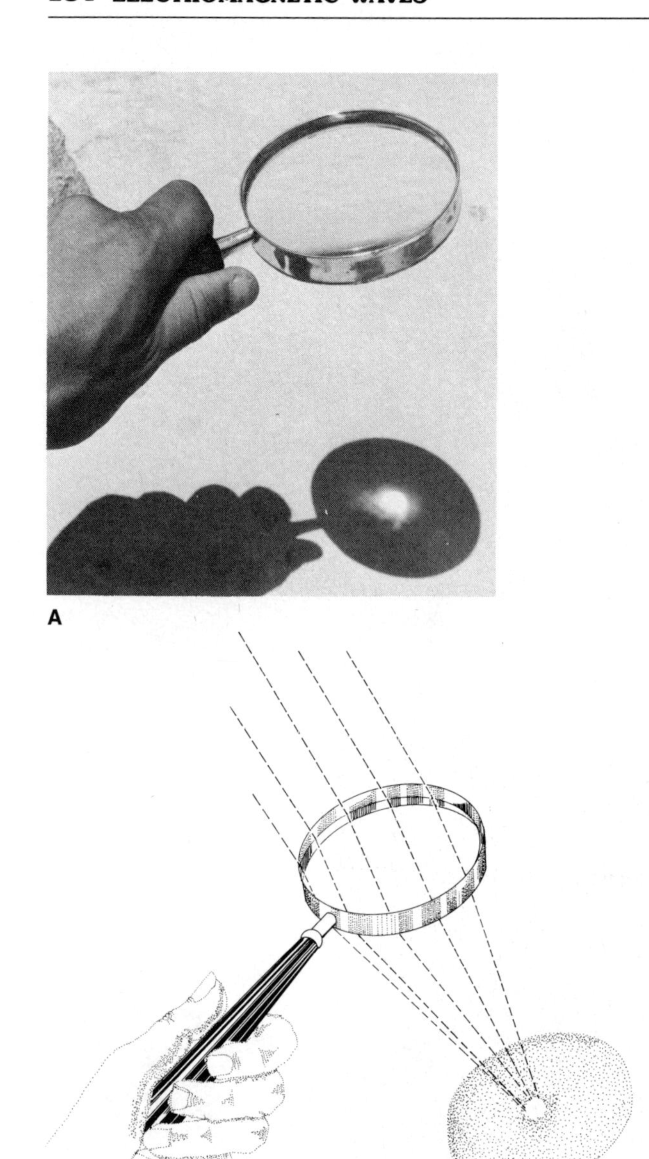

Figure 5–16. *A*, **A magnifying glass focusing sunlight. Note that even though the lens is made of clear glass, it casts a shadow around the outside rim. This occurs because the Sun's rays are bent (refracted) to concentrate in the center. Since the sunlight does not pass straight through the lens, a shadow is cast.** *B*, **This drawing shows how the Sun's rays are bent by the magnifying glass in the accompanying photograph.**

or any other electromagnetic radiation) moves from one transparent medium to another, such as from air to water, and strikes the second medium at an angle, the ray of light bends. This bending is called **refraction.** Thus, if a straight pencil is placed obliquely in a glass of water, it no longer appears straight. It is not the pencil that has bent, but the light. Similarly, if light is shined on a triangular prism or a curved glass lens, it bends as shown in Figure 6–16.

To understand why light bends as it slows down upon entering a different medium such as water, consider the analogy of a sled gliding down a snowy hill onto a cleared, paved roadway: The sled is analogous to the light ray, the snowy surface to the air, and the paved roadway to the water. Just as the sled slows down as it moves from the snowy surface to the cleared one, light slows down as it moves from air to glass or water. Suppose you are sledding down a snowy hill and hit a roadway dead on, perpendicular to it. The sled will slow down but will not turn. On the other hand, if you hit the road at an angle, one runner will reach it before the other, as shown in Figure 6–17. The runner that hits the pavement first will slow down while the other runner, still on the snow, continues to travel at a rapid speed. The result is that the sled will turn abruptly. Light waves act in a comparable manner. If light enters a dense medium from the perpendicular, it slows down but does not bend. However, if it moves at an angle from one medium to another, it will turn, just as a sled turns when it hits a road. (Note that the reverse is also true: Light refracts when it moves from a more dense medium to a less dense one.)

Refraction of light causes many familiar optical phenomena. Consider the pencil that appears to bend as it is placed in a glass of water. The ray of light traveling from the tip of the pencil to the eye is refracted as shown by the solid line in Figure 6–18. But once again, when the eyes sees light, the brain assumes that the light rays move in a straight line from the object. Thus you see the light as if it came from point A_1 instead of from its true origin, point A. If the light gets bent, we get fooled. Since this deception occurs for

Figure 6–17. Refraction analogy
sled = light ray
snowy surface = air
roadway = water

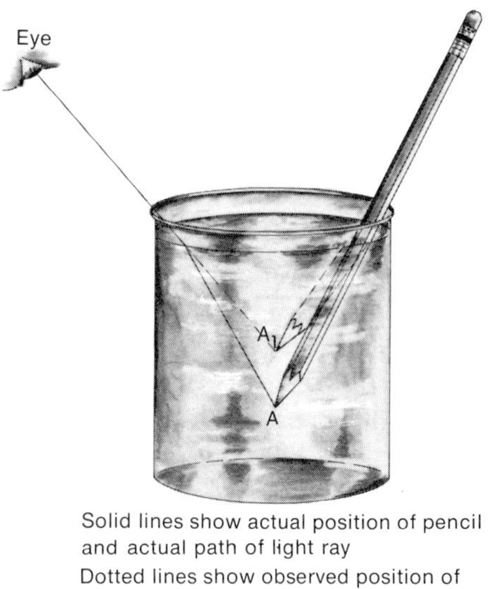

A

B

Figure 6–18. Optical illusion caused by refraction in water.

all parts of the submerged pencil, the whole thing appears bent.

A mirage in the desert is a well-known optical illusion caused by refraction. Travelers in the desert have reported "seeing" water only to find out that no such pool ever existed. On a hot day in the desert, the earth is very warm, and thus the air close to the earth is also warm. Warm air is less dense than cool air, so there is an atmospheric density gradient. Light reflected from the top of an object, say, a palm tree, may move directly toward an observer's eye, or alternatively it may move toward the ground. If a ray moves toward the ground, it reaches the low-density regions of the atmosphere and is refracted upward, as shown in the figure. The observer sees one ray of light coming from the top of the tree and the other apparently coming from the ground. The brain is fooled and assumes that the ray coming from the ground originated below the ground. Thus the observer sees the tree and its reflected image. The desert novice then assumes that the reflection is of a tree in the water, and he moves toward the mirage, only to be disappointed.

Figure 6–19. A desert mirage.

6.10 LENSES

Think for a moment of how you judge the size of an object that you are looking at. If you see a lion in the distance, walking across the African savannah, it appears small because your eye sees a very narrow angle between the lion's feet and head, as shown below.

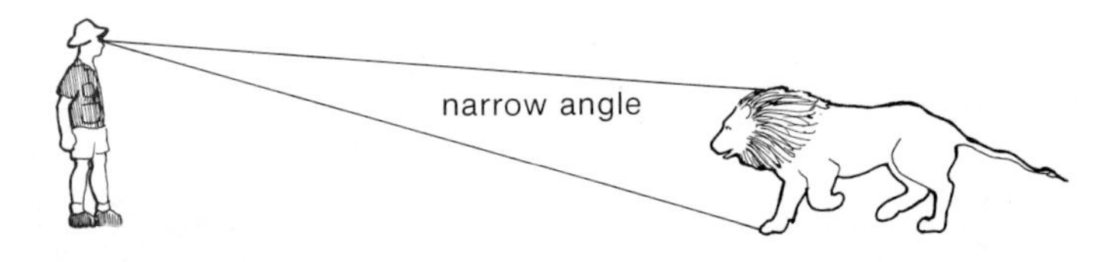

But if the lion is very close, it looks much larger because it is viewed through a much wider angle.

A lens is a device that makes an object appear to be larger or smaller than it really is. This illusion is created by bending light rays so that the apparent angle of view is altered. Thus, a distant lion can be made to appear larger (and closer) by bending the light so that it appears as though the lion is being viewed through a wider angle.

In order to understand how lenses work, let us first examine the simplest type of converging lens, which is the magnifying glass. The lens of a magnifying glass is made up of a curved piece of transparent glass or plastic. Light entering the lens is refracted as shown.

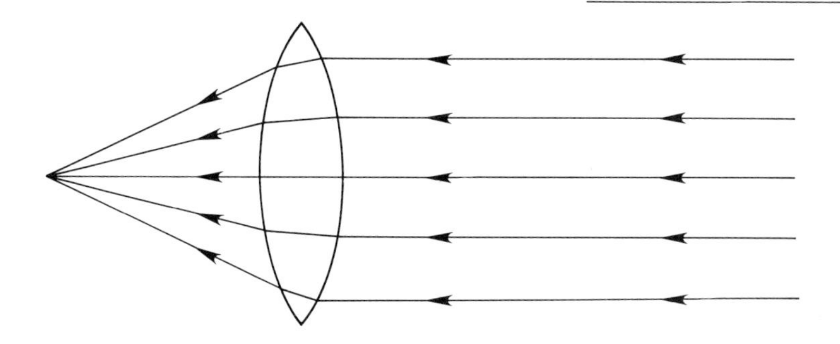

Now suppose that you are looking at a small object, such as a mosquito. If you look at the insect without the use of a magnifying glass it looks small because the light enters your eye through a small angle.

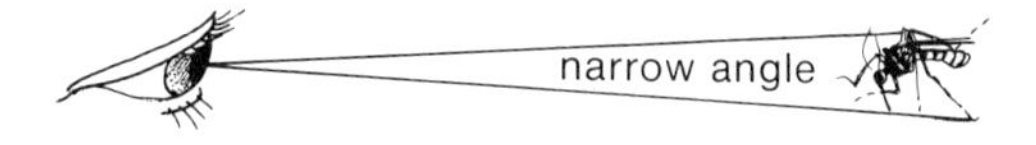

But, if a magnifying glass is placed between your eye and the mosquito, the light will be bent as shown.

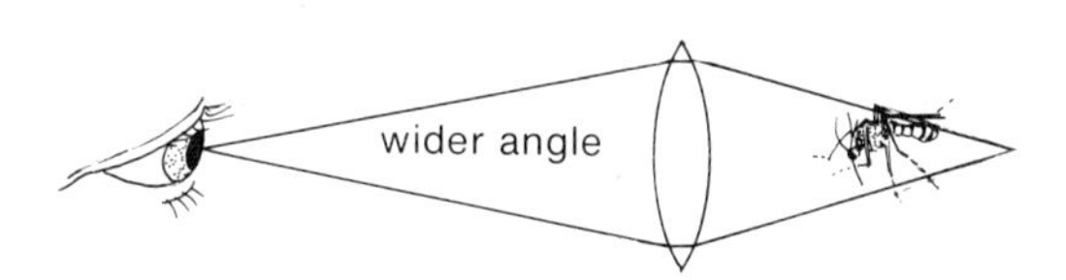

The eye sees the light as if it had been traveling in a straight line, as illustrated by the two dotted lines in the drawing.

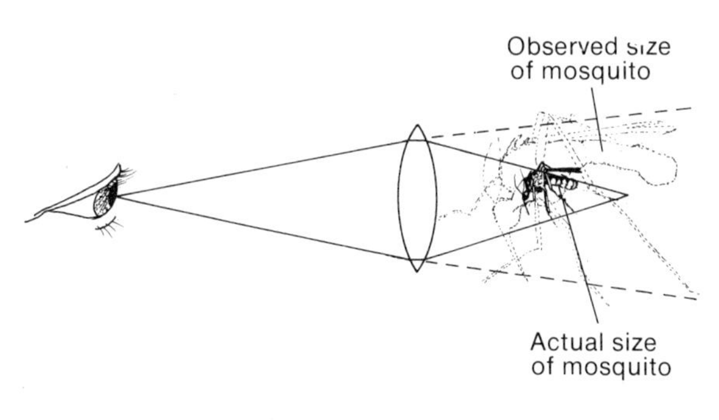

In this case, the mosquito is viewed by your eye through a wide angle, and thus it appears to be much larger than it really is; it is magnified.

Microscopes and telescopes work on the same general principle, only they use various combinations of lenses to achieve the desired effects.

A
Magnification by a telescope

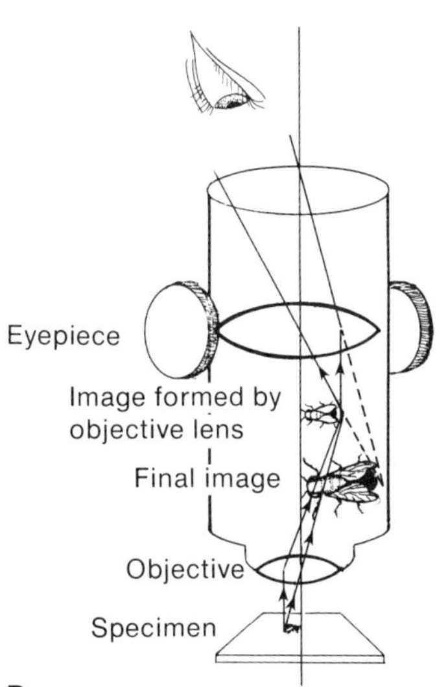

B
Magnification by a microscope

6.11 THE ELECTROMAGNETIC SPECTRUM

Electromagnetic radiation can exhibit a whole range of frequencies. In practice we deal with radiation from as low as about 60 Hz to gamma rays with a frequency up to about 60×10^{20} Hz. As we learned previously, the energy of a photon is proportional to its frequency. Therefore, gamma rays with a frequency 10^{20} times as great as 60-Hz rays carry 10^{20} times as much energy per photon.

Waves of different frequencies affect our environment differently. Some can barely be detected, others warm our bodies, and still others can destroy living tissue. There are many radiation sources in our environment. Sunlight, the ultimate source of most of the Earth's energy, contains a large range of different frequencies. Some of this energy strikes us directly, some is absorbed in the upper atmosphere and readmitted at still other frequencies, and the rest is reflected out to space. Other natural forms of radiation include high-energy rays originating from outer space.

There are also technological sources of electromagnetic energy such as communication systems, radar, light bulbs, and X-ray machines, to name but a few. In order to appreciate the significance of electromagnetic energy in our environment, we will dissect the entire spectrum into various ranges of frequency and consider each in turn.

6.12 LOW-ENERGY WAVES

Since any oscillating charge produces an electromagnetic wave, there are a great many different sources of radiation. Recall that current in household wiring alternates at 60 Hz. This alternating current generates low-frequency waves. Using Equation 6.1, we can readily calculate the wavelength of electromagnetic disturbance emanating from household wiring:

$$\text{Speed} = \text{wavelength} \times \text{frequency}$$

$$\text{Wavelength} = \frac{\text{speed}}{\text{frequency}}$$

$$\text{Wavelength} = \frac{3 \times 10^8 \text{ m/sec}}{60/\text{sec}}$$

$$\text{Wavelength} = 5 \times 10^6 \text{ m or } 5 \times 10^3 \text{ km}$$

Thus, a wave emanates from any household wire with a speed of 3×10^8 m/sec, a frequency of 60 Hz and a distance from crest to crest of 5000 km.

Although electromagnetic waves from electric wires are all about us, they have little effect on the environment. Recall that the energy inherent in a given wave is proportional to the frequency of the wave; high-frequency waves are energetic, whereas low-frequency waves carry little energy. Electromagnetic waves with a frequency of 60 Hz can barely be detected and do not significantly affect biological or physical systems.

6.13 RADIO WAVES

Radio waves have a significantly higher frequency and therefore have a great deal more energy than 60-Hz waves. In theory the radio waves could be generated by a conventional electric generator such as the one discussed in Section 5.6. If the generator were connected to an antenna and the rotor spun at a rate of one million revolutions per second, a one-megahertz radio wave would be generated, just as a 60-Hz electromagnetic wave is produced from the alternating current generated by a generator rotating at 60 revolutions per second. The only problem with this approach is that no one can build a generator to rotate at one million revolutions per second. Therefore, for radio transmission, a rapidly alternating current is established by use of special electronic circuits.

6.14 MICROWAVES

We must remember that even though people have a habit of classifying electromagnetic radiation into distinct categories, there are no sharp transition points in nature. Thus, we cannot say exactly where conventional radio waves stop and the microwave region starts. Perhaps the most convenient artificial borderline between radio waves and microwaves is at about 1000 megahertz (10^9 Hz), since the circuits that generate radio waves cannot be built to function properly at higher frequencies.

RADIO WAVES	MICROWAVES
frequencies 10^5 Hz to 10^9 Hz	frequencies 10^9 Hz to 10^{11} Hz
wavelengths 3×10^5 cm to 30 cm	wavelengths 30 cm to 0.3 cm

Radar

Although our eyes can see light in a narrow portion of the electromagnetic spectrum only, there are a great many circumstances in which it is helpful to detect radiation of other frequencies. For instance, visible light is rapidly dispersed by water droplets in the air, and thus it is impossible to see far on misty, foggy days. On the other hand, microwave transmission is relatively unaffected by fog, so scientists have studied microwave emission and reflection in detail.

If we wish to use our eyes to find an object, we need, first, some source of visible light. The source may be the Sun, or at night a candle or a flashlight. When light is shined on an object, it is reflected, and we see the reflected light. Similarly, we can "see" an object through the fog (or through the dark or, for that matter, on a clear day) by transmitting a beam of microwaves and then searching for the reflected radiation with some sort of electronic receiver. A system that accomplishes this task is called **radar.** A radar set consists of a pulsed transmitter and a receiver. A very short burst (about one millionth of a sec) of microwave radiation is beamed out. Then the transmitter is electronically turned off, and a receiver is switched on. If the pulsed signal strikes a solid object, it will be reflected back to the source and received by the antenna and amplified. By measuring the time required for the signal to make one round trip, the distance from the radar set to the receiver can be computed. The electronics of such a device must be highly precise, since a pulse of radiation will travel to an object 1 km away and return in about 7.0×10^{-6} sec.

It is technically difficult to generate high-frequency microwaves, so the earliest radar sets operated at low frequencies, corresponding to wavelengths of several meters. But if the wavelength of the transmitted radiation is longer than the object in its path, the waves may pass by without being reflected. Therefore, small planes and boats were often able to travel undetected right through the range of early radar sets. Modern radar is transmitted at wavelengths of the order of a few centimeters and is extremely sensitive.

Radar is an acronym for (ra)dio (d)etecting (a)nd (r)anging.

Microwaves and the Solar-Power Satellite

Imagine an electric generating station that consumed no fossil fuels, emitted no pollution, produced no radioactive wastes, and could operate 24 hours a day, 365 days a year. Some scientists believe that such a power plant could be built in the near future. They propose to launch a large satellite in orbit around the Earth. This space station would be fitted with an array of solar cells that would collect sunlight and transform it into electrical energy. The electrical energy could then be beamed to Earth as microwave radiation, where it would be collected by giant antennas, and fed into a conventional electric power grid. Proponents of this idea stress that a solar-powered plant in space has many advantages over a similar plant on Earth. There are no clouds to block the Sun, and with proper orientation, the satellite could

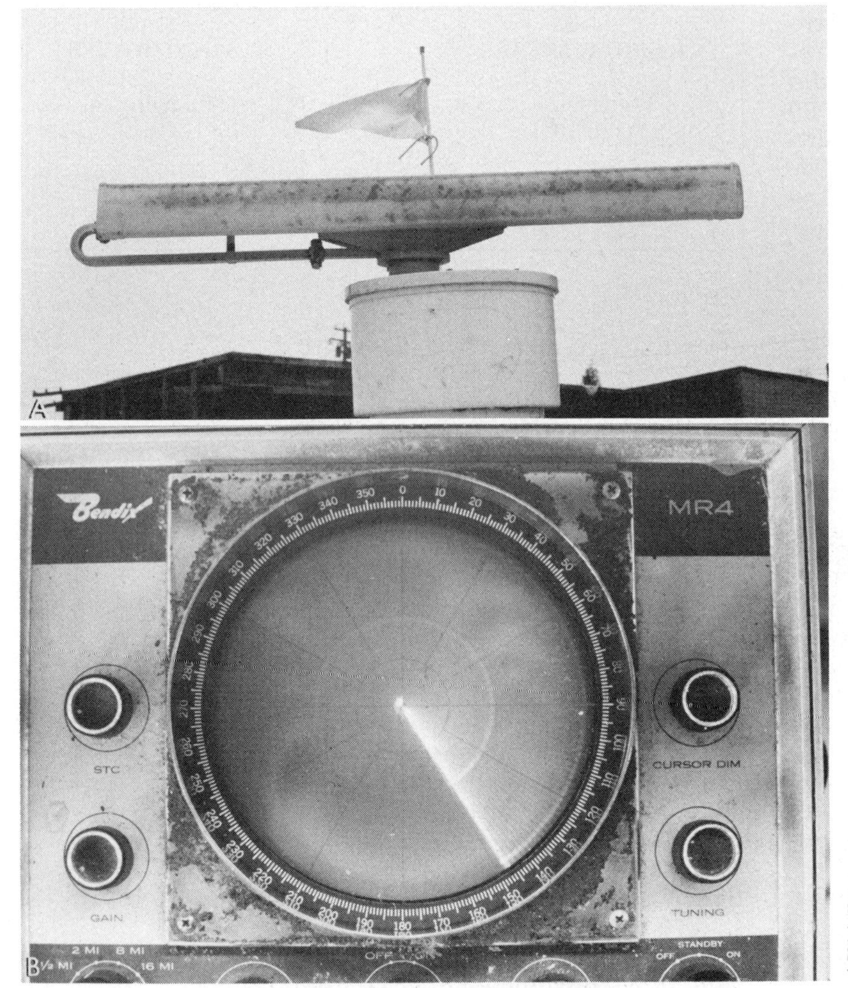

A, **Radar antenna on a small boat.**

B, **Look into the radar scope. The small white dot at 92° indicates the presence of a small boat. (Courtesy of Somethin' Fishy Fish Co., La Conner, Washington.)**

collect direct sunlight 24 hours a day, since there is no night in space.

If the technical problems of such an ambitious project could indeed be solved, there is widespread concern over the effects of microwaves on human health. Even with the most careful design, some of the radiation emitted by the power station would be refracted or scattered in the upper atmosphere and would miss the collecting antennas. As a result, measurable quantities of radiation would strike residential areas.

Microwaves are low frequency and therefore carry little energy, far too little to destroy molecules or alter genes. However, it is known that high doses of low-energy radiation can affect biological tissue. Microwave ovens are used to cook many types of food. The microwaves cause the atoms and molecules in the food to rotate rapidly; molecular motion is heat, and, presto, dinner is ready.

But what about much lower dosages of radiation? If you stand in a busy airport, microwaves from hundreds of different radar transmitters are absorbed by your body. Do they have an effect? Soviet scientists report that low levels of microwave exposure lead to headaches, eye strain, weariness, dizziness, irritability, emotional instability, depression, diminished intellectual capacity, partial loss of memory, and loss of appetite. They believe that the electromagnetic energy may somehow interact with the normal functions of the brain. Many investi-

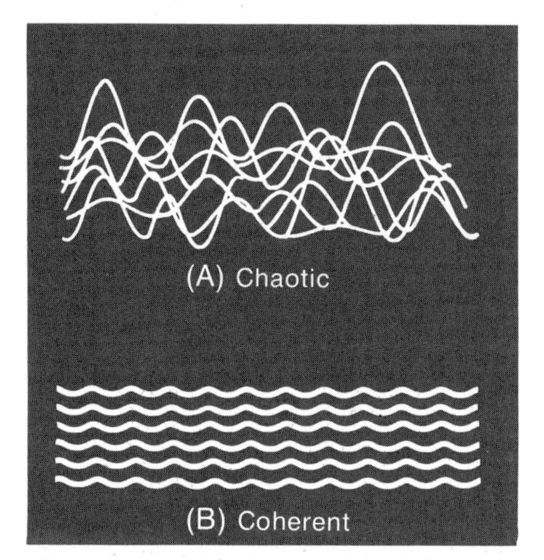

Figure 6–20. Chaotic and coherent light.

A laser generates a type of light that can be focused into a narrow beam. One difference between laser light and sunlight or a flashlight beam is that laser light is coherent, ordered, nonchaotic. Each wave has the same frequency, phase, and direction. This light is carefully aligned within the laser generator and is emitted as a concentrated beam. Since the waves are aligned, they do not spread out or become diffuse as easily as normal light does. Therefore, space scientists have been able to send laser light beams to the Moon and detect the reflection. If, on the other hand, powerful conventional light sources had been used, the beam would have been extensively dispersed into space and its reflection would have been impossible to detect.

There are many different kinds of lasers. To understand how one type is generated, recall that the energy that an atom gains by absorbing a photon can promote an electron to a higher energy level. Such a condition is called an **excited state.** When such an excited atom is struck by another photon of the proper frequency, a **stimulated emission** occurs: The electron falls to a lower, nonexcited state and emits a photon in phase, at the same frequency, and in exactly the same direction as the incoming photon. This is the start of a laser beam—two light waves traveling together coherently. The trick of making a laser is to repeat the process many times until a powerful, coherent light beam is produced.

A laser does not create energy, for it must be activated by an outside light source. In fact, most are highly inefficient, losing much of the input light energy to the environment. Rather it is simply a device to produce coherent light, which can concentrate a lot of energy in a narrow beam. Recall from our earlier discussion that power = energy/time. A laser delivers a moderate amount of energy in an extremely short period of time and is therefore extremely powerful. In addition, this energy can be focused onto a small area, thereby concentrating this power.

The first lasers were operated in 1960, and since then they have found a wide variety of uses. The pinpoint beam of extremely concentrated light, which can be easily focused, has been used for various kinds of specialized welding. High temperatures can be achieved quite rapidly—a temperature of 6000°C can be reached in about half a millisecond. Thus a selected region of metal can be melted without destroying nearby areas. Eye surgeons are using lasers to "weld" displaced retinas back into position without disturbing

The word laser is an acronym for (l)ight (a)mplification by (s)timulated (e)mission of (r)adiation.

Stimulated emission.

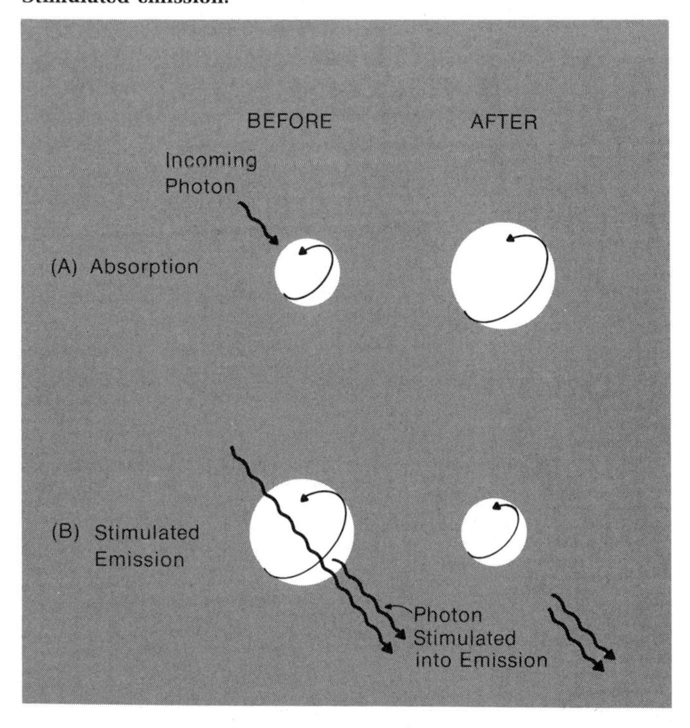

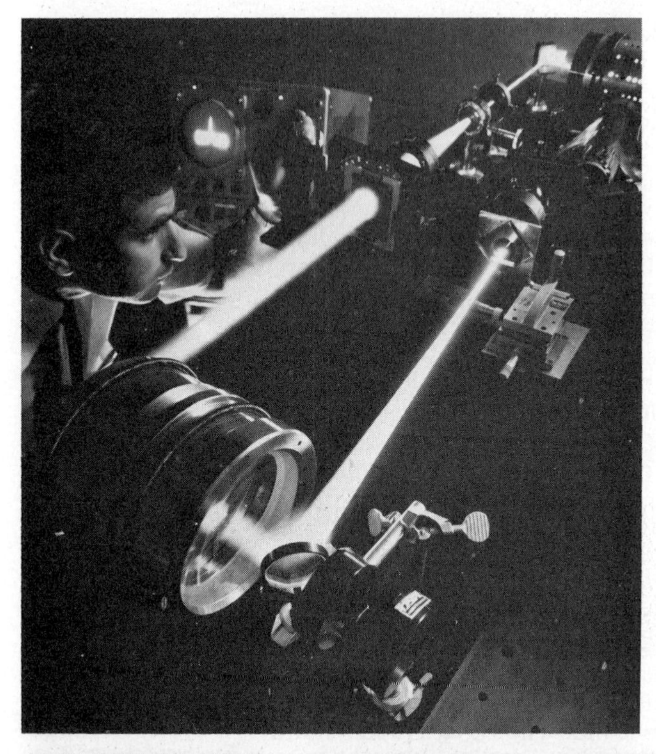

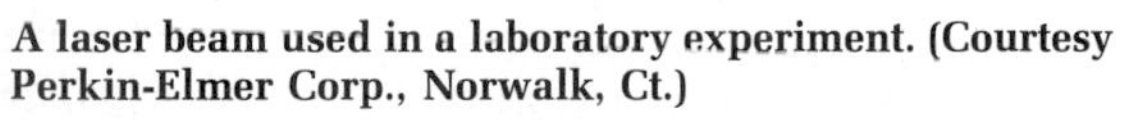
A laser beam used in a laboratory experiment. (Courtesy Perkin-Elmer Corp., Norwalk, Ct.)

A laser being used to cut metal. (Courtesy of Metrological Instruments.)

the rest of the eye. Machinists have used the beams to melt tiny holes in small jewels used as bearings in watches or other precision machinery. Pinpoint holes made by lasers are so small that they are being used in computer technology to burn microscopic spots in computer tape. Each hole represents a single piece of information, and because the holes are so small, a trillion pieces of data can be recorded on a single reel of tape.

The straight unvarying beam of laser light has been used in seemingly impossible surveying tasks. Recently scientists from two different continents have simultaneously bounced laser beams off the Moon. By accurately measuring the angle of the emitted beam with respect to the Earth and the time required for the round trip, and by using some simple trigonometry, the distance between continents has been measured to within 30 cm or so.

The list could go on and on, from laser-operated pencil erasers to devices for cutting cloth, to global surveying, to three-dimensional photographs called **holograms.** Perhaps the most significant application of lasers will be their use in the development of nuclear fusion reactors. This subject is discussed in Chapter 10.

CHAPTER OBJECTIVES

Understand the nature of light and how it simultaneously exhibits both wave and particle properties. In particular, you should be able to explain the photoelectric effect experiment and how that study demonstrates that light energy is quantized. Emission and absorption phenomena follow directly from a comprehension of the quantum nature of light.

Study reflection, refraction, and lenses.

Understand how various frequencies of electromagnetic radiation affect our environment differently, with particular reference to the following eight categories: low-energy waves, radio waves, microwaves, infrared, visible, ultraviolet, X-rays, and gamma rays. When you study the various regions of the electromagnetic spectrum, it is more important to be able to relate the type of wave (such as infrared or ultraviolet) to the type of effect it can produce than to memorize wavelengths and frequencies. Study lasers and the differences between laser light and ordinary light.

KEY WORDS

Electromagnetic field
Speed of light
Wave
Crest
Trough
Wavelength
Frequency
Amplitude
Interference
In phase/out of phase
Photoelectric effect
Quantum
Photon
Planck's constant
Matter waves
Reflection
Transmission
Angle of incidence
Angle of reflection
Mirror
Refraction
Emission of light
Absorption of light
Ground state
Excited electron
Excited state
Electromagnetic spectrum
Radio waves
Microwaves
Radar
Infrared
Visible light
Ultraviolet
X-ray
Gamma ray
Laser
Coherent light
Stimulated emission

FORMULAS TO KNOW

1. $\text{speed of a wave} = \text{wave length} \times \text{frequency}$
2. $\text{energy of a photon} = \text{Planck's constant} \times \text{frequency}$

TAKE-HOME EXPERIMENTS

1. **Interference.** Take a piece of paper and cut a thin slice in it with a razor blade. Look at a light source through the slit. Do you see a sharp image? You should see a series of dark lines, called interference fringes, appearing through your opening. Try it with two closely spaced slits. Would these fringes appear if light exhibited only particle behavior? Explain your observations.

2. **Refraction.** (a) Pour some rubbing alcohol (isopropyl alcohol) into a small glass (or a test tube if you have one). Now add a little water, which is denser than alcohol and tends to fall to the bottom of the glass. As the two liquids mix imperfectly, hold the glass up to the light and note that the mixture is not quite transparent; what you see through it appears distorted. Now stir the mixture thoroughly and look again—all seems clear. Explain.

(b) Could you use this procedure to test whether two clear liquids that dissolve in each other were the same or different substances? Try it by mixing water with antifreeze (ethylene glycol); antifreeze with rubbing alcohol; rubbing alcohol with a solution of ethyl alcohol (vodka or gin); rubbing alcohol with glycerine. Try it also with two identical liquids: water with water, etc.

3. **Mirrors and Lenses.** (a) Hold this book up to a mirror and try to read the words. (b) Hold an ordinary magnifying glass about 7 to 10 cm away from this book and try to read the words. (c) Place the book about 1.5 m from your eyes. Hold the magnifying glass at arm's length and try to read the words. Record your observations in each case and explain what you see.

4. **Different energies in the visible spectrum.** For this experiment you will need a few pieces of a type of photographic paper called "contact printing-out" (PO) paper. One such product is Kodak Studio Proof paper, which you can get from a photographic shop or studio. If it must be specially ordered, the minimum packet is 25 sheets of 8 × 10 inch paper, which is enough for an entire class, since as little as one sheet will do for the experiment. You will also need some red and some blue clear plastic, such as cellophane, or colored transparent vinyl report covers.

(a) Cut about an 8-cm square of the red and the same size square of the blue clear plastic. Now go into a dimly lighted room, remove one sheet of the "printing-out" (PO) paper, and cut three squares out of it, each about 5 cm square. Staple or clip the blue plastic over one of the PO squares, making sure the shiny part of the PO paper touches the plastic. Do the same with the red plastic over another 5-cm square of the PO paper.

(b) Now put a small flat object such as a key on each piece of PO paper. Cover two of the keys with the colored plastic flaps, and leave the third key, which has no plastic on it, exposed. Place the three assemblies inside the front cover of a book. Close the book, *keep the entire assembly flat,* and walk outside with it. If it is not convenient to go outdoors, set the book in front of the window.

(c) Now lift the book cover so that the three photographic assemblies are exposed to sunlight at exactly the same time. Keep the book cover lifted up until the bare PO paper becomes fairly dark. This should take about a minute (more or less) on a cloudy, overcast day, but only a few seconds in bright sunlight. Then close the book cover.

(d) Walk back into the room, open the book, and remove the plastic covers and the keys. Note the sharpness of the images and the darkness of the areas of paper exposed to light. Which is darkest, which lightest , and which is intermediate?

Now interpret the results in terms of what you learned in the chapter. Remember, transparent blue plastic allows mainly blue light to pass through. The red plastic allows mainly red to pass through. Which light consists of photons of higher energy? How would you rate unfiltered sunlight by comparison?

Use your imagination to devise various other experiments with PO paper. For example, use a photographic negative instead of a key and make positive prints. Or compare outdoor light on a cloudy day with a bright tungsten light, such as that from a high-intensity lamp. (Which do you think will work faster? Why?) How about a warm source, which emits infrared radiation— for example, a hot-water radiator that heats a room in winter. Try the PO paper in front of the radiator during the night, with all the lights turned off. Interpret your results.

18. **Reflection.** Curved mirrors in amusement parks can make a person appear to be fat, skinny, or even wiggly. Using a diagram, explain briefly how a curved mirror distorts an image.

19. **Refraction.** If you place a pencil straight down into a glass of water and look at it from above, it does not appear to be bent. But if you place it in the water at an angle and eye it obliquely, it does appear bent. Explain.

20. **Refraction.** If you look obliquely at a fish in the water and estimate its depth, is the fish likely to be deeper or shallower than it appears to be? Explain.

21. **Refraction.** A ray of light bends as it enters the body of a lens and bends again when it emerges. Explain.

22. **Refraction.** The Earth's atmosphere is denser near the surface than at high altitudes. If a scientist were trying to locate the exact position of a weather balloon flying in the upper atmosphere, would the density gradient of the atmosphere be a factor to consider? Explain.

23. **Lenses.** Describe how a magnifying glass works. How does it make something look bigger?

24. **Electromagnetic spectrum.** What is the electromagnetic spectrum? Is there a sharp distinction between radio and microwave radiation? Microwave and infrared radiation? Infrared and visible radiation? Explain.

25. **Spectra.** How do the various regions of the electromagnetic spectrum differ from each other?

26. **Spectra.** List in order of increasing energy: ultraviolet, visible, X-ray, microwave, radio, infrared.

27. **Radar.** Explain briefly how a radar device works. Could you build an effective radar set using a one-megahertz radio wave? Using visible light? Explain.

28. **Infrared.** When the infrared picture shown on page 192 was taken, the photographer wished to filter out some of the more energetic visible light entering the camera. Do you think he used a filter that removed mostly blue light or mostly red light? Explain.

29. **Visible light.** A person who is enlarging a photograph in a darkroom by shining white light through the negative onto photosensitive paper generally uses a low-intensity red light in order to see. Would a dim blue light work just as well? Explain.

30. **Visible light.** The flame of a welding torch is blue at the inner tip, white in the middle, and red on the outside. Which part of the flame is the hottest? Explain.

31. **Photoelectric effect.** When the photosensitive cell of a light-meter is exposed to light, a small electric current is produced that moves a needle to register the amount of light present. Could you obtain a true light-meter reading near a powerful radio transmitter, or would the radio waves be likely to affect the instrument? Explain.

32. **Ultraviolet light.** Imagine that you have two beams of light with the same number of photons in each beam, but one is composed of ultraviolet frequencies and the other of visible light. Which beam carries more energy, or are they the same? Which required more energy to generate or are they the same? Explain.

33. **Visible light.** A fire inside a pot-bellied stove emits visible light. However, the stove itself does not change color when it gets hot. What has happened to the energy of the visible-frequency photons?

34. **X-rays.** Explain why X-rays are more apt to damage living tissue than are ultraviolet rays.

CHAPTER 7

This is the first of a set of chapters covering the subject of chemistry. The chapter consists of two major portions. The first portion (Sections 7.1 through 7.5) deals with atoms and molecules and includes an introduction to the periodic table and to the electronic structures of atoms.

The second portion (Sections 7.6 through 7.11) deals with the physical states of matter—gases, liquids, and solids. The properties of matter in these states are described and are explained in terms of the arrangements of molecules in matter. The interconversions between different states of matter are also discussed.

ATOMS, MOLECULES, AND MATTER

7.1 MATTER

Wherever you may be as you start to read this chapter—your room, the library, outdoors—look at the things that surround you. Most of them are items whose shape or construction has some particular function or some recognizable identity—a chair to sit on, a cup to drink from, a book to read, a rock that is interesting to look at. These things are **objects.** Now imagine that each of these objects were cut into little pieces: the chair then is no longer a chair but slivers of wood; the cup is granules of porcelain; the book is paper; the rock is coarse sand. Wood, porcelain, paper, sand are no longer called objects; they are **materials.** And materials are samples of **matter,** which is simply the stuff of which the universe consists.

If you brought all your cut-up objects to a recycling center, you would put shredded books, shredded newspapers, and shredded milk cartons into the same bin. You recognize that although they come from different objects, they are all of the same material, paper. Paper has some resemblance to wood, because they both can burn. And ground porcelain is a little like sand, because both contain hard grains of noncombustible matter. Thus by noting these resemblances, you have begun to classify materials. Classification therefore makes us recognize that different materials in the same class must have something in common. It might occur to you that the various materials observed have a complex inner structure, and are in fact combinations of simpler, more fundamental kinds of matter. By this reasoning, if two materials are similar, perhaps their resemblance results from the fact that they do indeed have some fundamental component in common.

Let us then think what might be done to put to test the thought that wood and paper, say, have some component in common. Suppose you shred each particle into smaller and smaller portions with the finest blade available. No luck—all you get is one pile of tiny fibers of paper and another of wood dust. Heating might be a better method. When a piece of paper is heated in the absence of air, it loses shape, chars, emits gases, and finally leaves a black residue, carbon. A similar procedure with the wood yields the same final product. The experiment thus confirms the idea that paper and wood have some material in common, namely carbon. Perhaps even more important, the results now suggest many other experiments; for example, do all things that burn contain carbon? We heat sugar and find that it does. Magnesium is also combustible, but heating magnesium in the absence of air just makes it get hot and melt. It does not produce any carbon nor any other new substances. The answer to the question "Do all things that burn contain carbon?" is *no*—one exception is sufficient to disprove the rule. But now our exchange between ideas and experiments suggests another thought: Is there a special class of substances, like magnesium and carbon, that cannot be decomposed but rather are the elemental building blocks out of which all other materials are compounded? Many experiments support this notion, and we call these nondecomposable substances **elements.**

The ancient Greeks pondered these questions about the nature of matter and speculated that all matter was composed of four elements—earth, air, fire, and water. Different substances, then, consisted of different *proportions* of these elements. Interconversions among the elements were related to four "principles"—hot, cold, moist, and dry—as shown below:

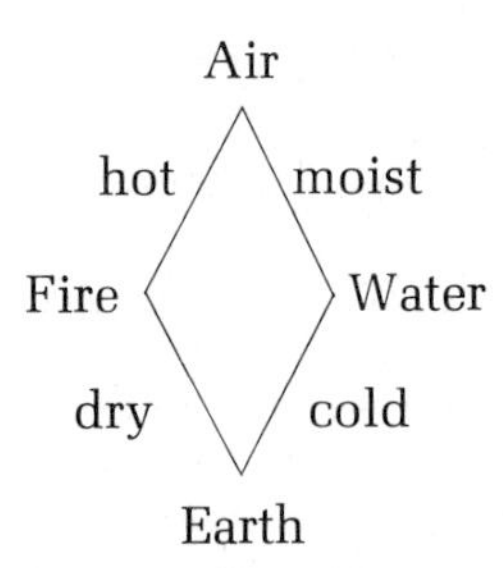

The concept of an element developed slowly over the centuries. The alchemists of the Middle Ages carried out many kinds of chemical transformations but did not distinguish clearly between elements and compounds. They tried to convert lead into gold but failed because these elements cannot be chemically transformed. The nature of elements became better understood as our ideas about atoms grew clearer.

The beaker on the left contains sugar. The beaker on the right contains carbon produced by the decomposition of this quantity of sugar.

7.2 ATOMS

Think of a gold bar that has a mass of 1 kg. The volume of such a bar would be about 52 cm^3. Does this statement mean that there is nothing in this volume but gold—no empty space? We cut the bar in half, and the two resulting pieces are still solid gold—nothing else. Imagine that we keep cutting the bar again and again, indefinitely. Will we *always* produce smaller and smaller pieces of gold? The ancient Greek philosophers worried about such matters, and two of them (Leucippos and Democritus) could not accept the idea that such cutting could go on forever. Ultimately, they speculated, the process must end when it produces a particle that can no longer be cut. In Greek, *a tomos* means "not cutting," from which we get the word **atom** to describe the smallest, ultimate particles of matter. The space between the atoms was considered to be empty, or void.

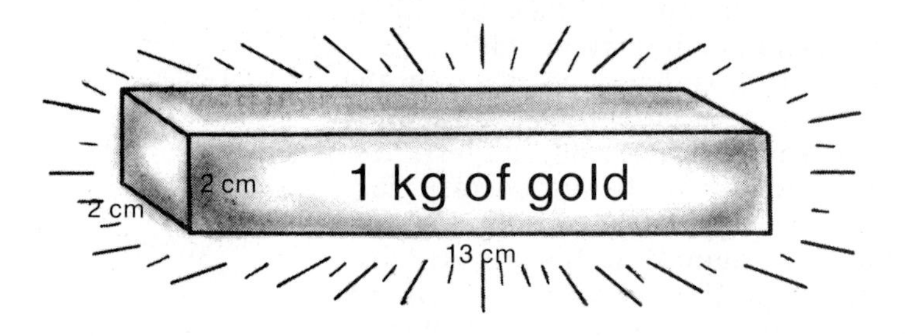

Many centuries later, in 1803, John Dalton established the atomic theory on a less speculative, more scientific basis by relating atoms to chemical changes.* Dalton recognized that atoms are the fundamental units of the elements. Whole atoms—not parts of atoms—can combine in various ways to form many different substances. The combinations of bonded atoms are called **molecules.** Furthermore, Dalton understood that atoms of different elements have different masses. But that was as far as he went. Like the ancient Greeks, Dalton still considered atoms to be ultimate, indivisible little particles. Their makeup, or internal structure (if any), was not questioned.

This concept of a structureless atom began to change in the nineteenth century as a result of experiments with electricity. The first important breakthrough was the finding that all matter contains small particles that carry a negative electrical charge. This conclusion is demonstrated by the following experiment: A sealed glass tube contains two electrodes, which are the terminals of an electric circuit (Fig. 7–1). The positive electrode is the **anode;** the negative one is the **cathode.** The inside of the tube is a vacuum—it contains nothing. When a voltage is applied across the two electrodes, an electric current passes through the vacuum. What particles carry the current, and where do they come from? Experiment shows that the conducting electrical particles are coming directly out of the negatively charged plate (cathode) in the tube and going toward the positive plate. These particles are **electrons,** which were stripped off the cathode. But matter cannot consist only of electrons. Since matter as we know it is electrically neutral, it must also contain positive electricity to balance the negative electrons. How are these positive electrical charges arranged—uniformly, as if each atom were itself a little crystal? Or are the electrical charges concentrated in some way?

To answer this question, Ernest Rutherford, with his colleagues Hans Geiger and Ernest Marsden, in 1909, carried out what we consider to be one

*John Dalton, 1766–1844, an English chemist and physicist, also worked on the properties of gases and on color blindness.

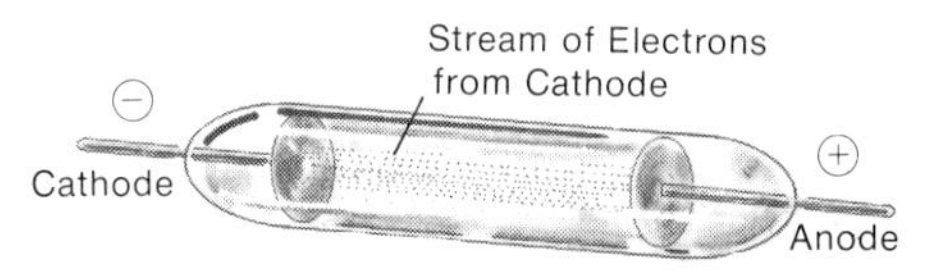

Figure 7–1. A "cathode ray" tube. The "ray" is a stream of electrons coming from the cathode.

of the greatest experiments of this century. The experiment is not hard to understand. What Rutherford did was to shoot a beam of positively charged particles at a thin metal foil. The particles were charged helium atoms, called **alpha particles,** which are emitted by radium and other radioactive elements (see Chapter 10).

Alpha particles are very heavy in comparison with the mass of electrons. The metal target was surrounded by instruments that could detect alpha particles. It had been assumed previously that the positive electricity in an atom is uniformly distributed and that the electrons are embedded here and there, like raisins in a cake. If this were true, Rutherford's alpha particles would encounter a uniform electric field, the forces on them would be equal in all directions, and they would pass right through the foil with little or no deflection. As expected, most of them did. But to everyone's amazement, a few did not, but instead were deflected through large angles. In Rutherford's own words, "It was almost as incredible as if you fired a 15-inch shell at a piece of tissue paper and it came back and hit you."

To explain these results, Rutherford concluded that the atom is mostly empty space, which accounts for the fact that *most* of the alpha particles passed through the foil in a straight line. However, to account for the occasional deflections, Rutherford also concluded that the positive electricity of the atom must be concentrated in a very small volume, which he called the **atomic nucleus.** Furthermore, since the heavy alpha particles were bounced back from the nucleus, the nucleus must contain most of the mass of the atom. Since atoms are electrically neu-

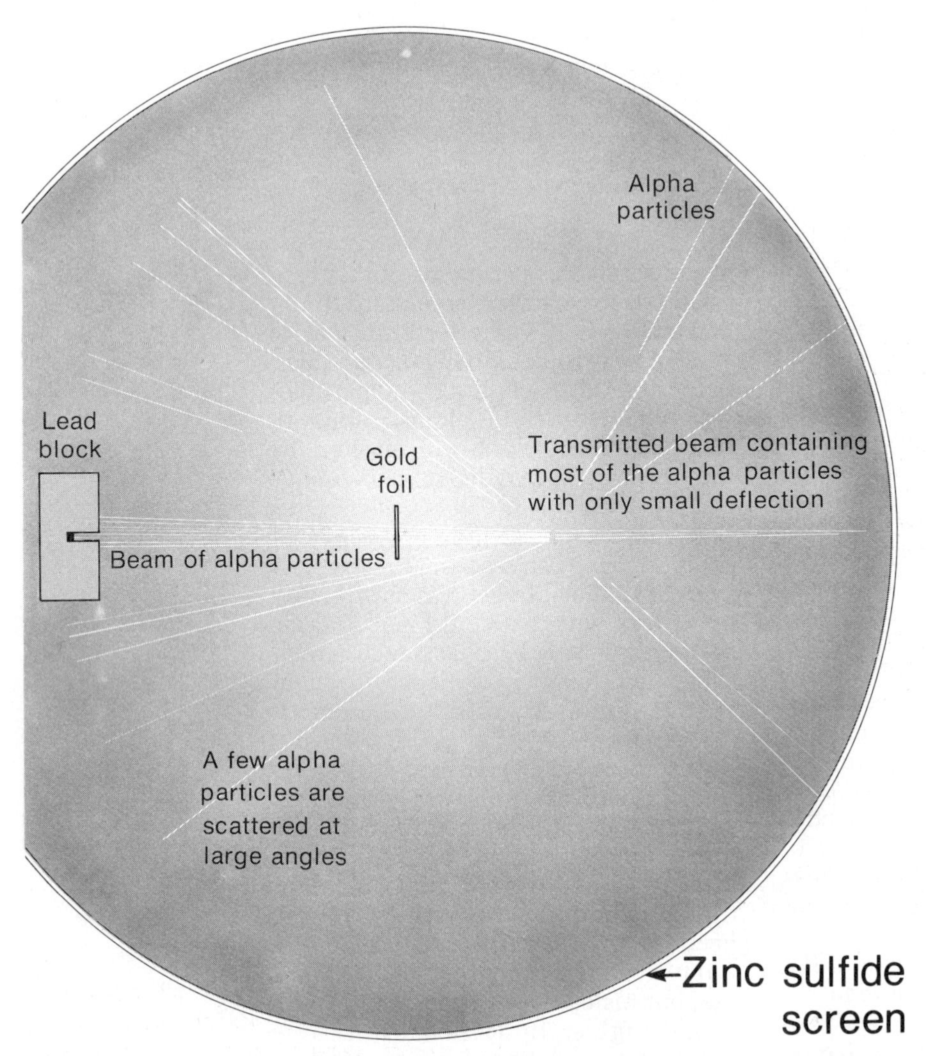

Rutherford's experiment with alpha particles, demonstrating the nuclear structure of the atom.

The structure of an atom.

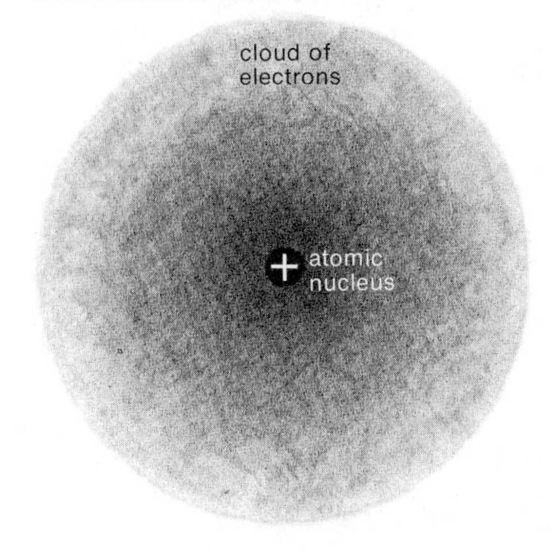

tral, each atom must have enough electrons so that their total negative charge equals the total positive charge of the nucleus. These electrons occupy the space around the nucleus. The mass of the electron is negligible compared with that of the nucleus.

The unit of positive charge in the atom is the **proton,** and the **atomic number** is the number of protons, or unit positive charges, in the nucleus. It is also the number of electrons in the neutral atom. A hydrogen atom, atomic number 1, consists of a proton with a charge of +1 as its nucleus, surrounded

TABLE 7–1. PARTICLES IN THE ATOM

Particle	Electrical Charge	Mass Number
Electron	−1	0
Proton	+1	1
Neutron	0	1

by one electron with a charge of −1. An atom of carbon, atomic number 6, contains 6 protons and 6 electrons.

However, the protons account for only about half the mass of the carbon atom. The remainder is attributed to neutral particles, called **neutrons,** in the nucleus. The neutron has about the same mass as the proton. The **mass number** of an atom is the total number of protons and neutrons in its nucleus.

The properties of the three fundamental atomic particles are shown in Table 7–1.

The chemical elements are named after planets, ancient gods, modern scientists, geographical places, and Greek or Latin words. They are also referred to by symbols which are one- or two-letter abbreviations of the English or foreign names.

Study at least the names and symbols shown in Table 7–2. (No need to memorize the atomic numbers.) The complete list appears inside the front cover of this book.

We will now look more closely at three of the elements from Table 7–2—carbon, calcium, and uranium. The tabulation below gives nuclear composition, atomic number, and mass number.

Name and Symbol		Nuclear Composition		Atomic Number	Mass Number
		Protons	*Neutrons*	*(Protons)*	*(Protons + Neutrons)*
Carbon-12	^{12}C	6	6	6	12
Carbon-14	^{14}C	6	8	6	14
Calcium-40	^{40}Ca	20	20	20	40
Calcium-44	^{44}Ca	20	24	20	44
Uranium-235	^{235}U	92	143	92	235
Uranium-238	^{238}U	92	146	92	238
Uranium-239	^{239}U	92	147	92	239

TABLE 7–2. ELEMENTS TO REMEMBER

Atomic Number	Name	Symbol
1	Hydrogen	H
2	Helium	He
6	Carbon	C
7	Nitrogen	N
8	Oxygen	O
9	Fluorine	F
10	Neon	Ne
11	Sodium	Na
12	Magnesium	Mg
13	Aluminum	Al
14	Silicon	Si
15	Phosphorus	P
16	Sulfur	S
17	Chlorine	Cl
18	Argon	Ar
19	Potassium	K
20	Calcium	Ca
26	Iron	Fe
29	Copper	Cu
47	Silver	Ag
78	Platinum	Pt
79	Gold	Au
80	Mercury	Hg
82	Lead	Pb
86	Radon	Rn (for Chapter 10)
88	Radium	Ra (for Chapter 10)
92	Uranium	U (for Chapter 10)
93	Neptunium	Np (for Chapter 10)
94	Plutonium	Pu (for Chapter 10)

SOURCES OF NAMES OF SOME ELEMENTS

ELEMENT	SYMBOL	SOURCE OF NAME
Uranium	U	The planet Uranus, which was the outermost known planet of the Solar System when uranium was the end of the series of known elements. (More distant planets and heavier elements have since been discovered, however.)
Mercury	Hg	Mercury, the messenger god, who is quick. The element is a shiny metal that is liquid at room temperature. It flows quickly and looks alive—hence its other name, *quicksilver.*
Hydrogen	H	Greek, *hydōr,* water; and *genēs,* producing. (Water is produced from hydrogen and oxygen.)
Lead	Pb	Latin, *plumbum.* Think of plumbers and lead pipe.

Note that a given element may have more than one mass number. Atoms of the same element (that is, atoms with the same atomic number) that have different mass numbers are called **isotopes.** Thus, ^{12}C and ^{14}C are carbon isotopes. Both ^{12}C and ^{14}C represent carbon atoms (or carbon nuclei), because they both have six nuclear protons. They are isotopes because they have different mass numbers. This difference results from the fact that there are different numbers of neutrons in the two nuclei. Isotopes of an element are chemically equivalent (or very nearly so): they have the same ability to combine with other atoms. Thus, ^{12}C and ^{14}C are both chemically the same element, carbon. If the carbon is converted to some other compound, such as carbon dioxide, the isotopes themselves are not altered but retain their separate identities in the carbon dioxide molecules.

The general formula that relates these terms is

$$\text{mass number} = \text{protons} + \text{neutrons} \quad [7.1]$$

or,

$$\text{mass number} = \text{atomic number} + \text{neutrons} \quad [7.2]$$

The complete symbol of an isotope indicates both the mass number and the atomic number. For example,

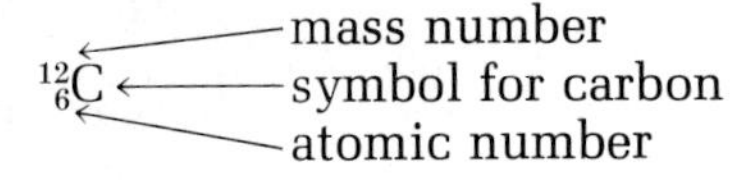

Example 1
(a) How many neutrons are in the nucleus of chlorine-37?
(b) What are the symbol and mass number of an isotope of an element containing 19 protons and 22 neutrons per nucleus?

Answer: **(a) From Equation 7.2, the number of neutrons is the mass number minus the atomic number. Looking up chlorine in the table of elements (inside back cover) we see that its atomic number is 17. Then,**

$$\begin{aligned}\text{neutrons} &= \text{mass number} - \text{atomic number}\\ &= 37 - 17\\ &= 20\end{aligned}$$

(b) If the atom contains 19 protons per nucleus, its atomic number is 19. Searching for atomic number 19 in the table of elements, we find it is potassium, K. From Equation 7.1, the mass number must be protons + neutrons = 19 + 22 = 41. The isotope is therefore potassium-41, or ^{41}K.

7.3 MOLECULES

Now let us return to our sugar, which, you will recall, yields carbon when it is decomposed. If you would buy a bag of, say, Jack Frost brand granulated white sugar and analyze it for its content of elements, you would find that it consists of 42.11 per cent carbon, 51.41 per cent oxygen, and 6.48 per cent hydrogen by mass. If you analyzed Domino, or any other brand of granulated sugar, you would get the same results. All other properties, such as sweetness and crystal shapes, would also be the same. This sugar, called *sucrose*, is obtained from sugar cane or sugar beets. The original sweet plant hardly resembles the white crystals that you purchase at the grocery, nor is its elemental composition the same. Of course, you could carry out various procedures to extract the sugar from the cane or beet. For example, knowing that sugar dissolves in water, you might try to soak the plant in warm water, filter the fibers that do not dissolve, then evaporate the water to recover the sugar. You now compare your product with the store-bought white granules. They are both sweet, but your prepared material is brown, not white, and their elemental compositions do not quite match.

It would be possible, eventually, to purify your sugar to the point where additional operations would produce no further changes. Your product would then be the same as other samples of sucrose purified in other laboratories. Such substances, which have a fixed composition associated with a specific set of properties, are said to be pure. A pure substance, such as sucrose, that is made up of more than one element is called a **compound.** **Pure substances** are entirely composed of like **molecules,** which are groups of atoms bonded together.

7.4 ELEMENTS AND THE PERIODIC TABLE

So far we have learned two things about elements: First, that they are the fundamental substances which make up all matter as we know it under ordinary terrestrial conditions. Second, elements consist of fundamental particles called atoms.

Let us now briefly survey some similarities and differences among the properties of the elements. One approach to learning about the elements would be to make a collection of them. Let us pursue this objective as an imaginary exercise, and see what can be gained from it.

Since this is an imaginary exercise, take an imaginary few thousand dollars, and go out to buy a sample of each natural element for your exhibit. You would soon find that some are cheap, some expensive, some easy to handle, some deadly, and that most are solids, some are gases, and two are liquids. You would note that two of the gases are colored—fluorine and chlorine are both greenish yellow. Some of the elements would react so rapidly with the atmosphere that they would have to be protected from it, perhaps by being stored in a vacuum, or in an inert medium, such as mineral oil. Most of your specimens would be shiny metals. You might wish to divide your collection into categories—the solids here, the liquids there, or perhaps a separation of metals from nonmetals, or reactive elements from inert ones. As you tried different arrangements, you would be following a respected chemical tradition, for many chemists, starting especially in the nineteenth century, made similar attempts. At first they were hardly taken seriously, for most of these arrangements were of no help at all in understanding chemical principles. But interesting and significant results began to emerge when the elements were arranged in the increasing order of their atomic weights.*

In 1869 Dmitrii Ivanovich Mendeleev in Russia and, several months later, Julius Lothar Meyer in Germany published independent versions of an arrangement that came to be called a **periodic table of the elements.** Chemists' views of the idea of such a table were transformed. Instead of looking on it as an idle curiosity, they recognized it as a broad and useful concept that could correlate a wide range of physical and chemical properties of the elements. A modern form of the periodic table is shown as Table 7–3, and a complete listing of the elements and their atomic numbers and weights is shown on the inside back cover.

Note the following characteristics of the periodic table:

1. Each box contains the symbol of the element and its atomic number.
2. The elements appear in the increasing order of their atomic numbers (except for two long sequences that are set off as footnotes).
3. The vertical columns (called **groups**) contain elements with similar sets of properties. Thus, for example, Group 7A (fluorine, chlorine, etc.), called the halogen family, consists of colored, highly reactive elements that are normally gases or that evaporate readily. The Group 1A elements (except for hydrogen, which is unique) are all soft, shiny, reactive metals.

*Modern periodic tables are based on atomic numbers, not weights. However, the two sequences match each other with only a few exceptions.

Some of the other designations of the table are of less importance to us here, but the reader may nonetheless be curious. The letters A and B in the group designations (2A, 3B, etc.) refer to **representative** and **transition** elements, respectively. These designations refer to different categories of atomic structure. The footnoted sequences called lanthanoids (elements starting with lanthanum) and actinoids (elements starting with actinium) refer to yet another category of atomic structure. The dotted boxes are for elements that have not yet been discovered.

TABLE 7–3. PERIODIC TABLE, LONG FORM†

PERIODS	1A	2A	3B	4B	5B	6B	7B	8B	8B	8B	1B	2B	3A	4A	5A	6A	7A	8A
			TRANSITION ELEMENTS															
1	H 1																	He 2
2	Li 3	Be 4											B 5	C 6	N 7	O 8	F 9	Ne 10
3	Na 11	Mg 12											Al 13	Si 14	P 15	S 16	Cl 17	Ar 18
4	K 19	Ca 20	Sc 21	Ti 22	V 23	Cr 24	Mn 25	Fe 26	Co 27	Ni 28	Cu 29	Zn 30	Ga 31	Ge 32	As 33	Se 34	Br 35	Kr 36
5	Rb 37	Sr 38	Y 39	Zr 40	Nb 41	Mo 42	Tc 43	Ru 44	Rh 45	Pd 46	Ag 47	Cd 48	In 49	Sn 50	Sb 51	Te 52	I 53	Xe 54
6	Cs 55	Ba 56	57– 71	Hf 72	Ta 73	W 74	Re 75	Os 76	Ir 77	Pt 78	Au 79	Hg 80	Tl 81	Pb 82	Bi 83	Po 84	At 85	Rn 86
7	Fr 87	Ra 88	89– 103	? 104	? 105	? 106	? 107	108	109	110	111	112	113	114	115	116	117	118
8(?)	119	120	121															

Lanthanoids	La 57	Ce 58	Pr 59	Nd 60	Pm 61	Sm 62	Eu 63	Gd 64	Tb 65	Dy 66	Ho 67	Er 68	Tm 69	Yb 70	Lu 71
Actinoids	Ac 89	Th 90	Pa 91	U 92	Np 93	Pu 94	Am 95	Cm 96	Bk 97	Cf 98	Es 99	Fm 100	Md 101	No 102	Lr 103

† The heavy line approximately separates the metallic from the nonmetallic elements.

Among Groups 4A, 5A, and 6A there is a marked trend from non-metallic elements (at the top) to more metallic ones (as we go down). Look at Group 4A, for example, which starts with carbon (non-metal), goes on to silicon and germanium (semimetals, used in transistors), and finally tin and lead (metals). Similarly, Group 5A starts with nitrogen (non-metal) and ends with bismuth (metal). In between lie phosphorus, arsenic, and antimony, all known for their poisonous compounds. (See Figure 7–2 for the poisons found in poor Mr. Baum, who died in 1892.) Note also the middle elements of Group 6A—sulfur, selenium, and tellurium (Fig. 7–3). Selenium, which lies smack in the middle, exists in both metallic and non-metallic forms.

4. The horizontal rows (called **periods**) contain sequences of elements whose electronic configurations vary in characteristic patterns.

Figure 7–4 is a sketch of what a collection of the A-groups of elements might look like. The noble gases (Group 8A) are all colorless, but if enough energy is put into them, they exhibit characteristic colors, as in "neon lights." Therefore, they would show up best in glass tubes at low pressure under high voltage.

Thus, the study of chemical periodicity teaches us that there are categories of elements which resemble each other, or whose properties are related to each other in some regular manner. The important inference is this: if two elements are similar, perhaps their atoms have some structural features in common. But since their atoms are different, this thought implies that the *atoms are not ultimate particles*. Thus the classification of elements, and especially the recurrence of their properties in some sequence, dimly foreshadowed our present understanding of atomic structure and particularly the role of the electrons in the atom, to which we now turn our attention.

7.5 ELECTRONIC STRUCTURES OF ATOMS

Imagine that you heat a piece of iron in a hot flame. You now take your hot iron into a perfectly dark room. If

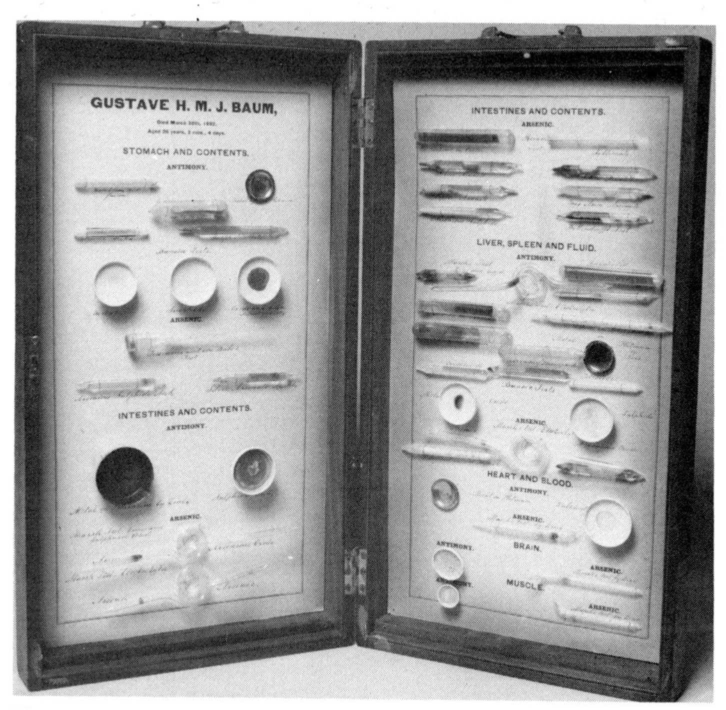

Figure 7–2. Arsenic and antimony form poisonous compounds.

Figure 7–3. Sulfur, selenium, and tellurium.

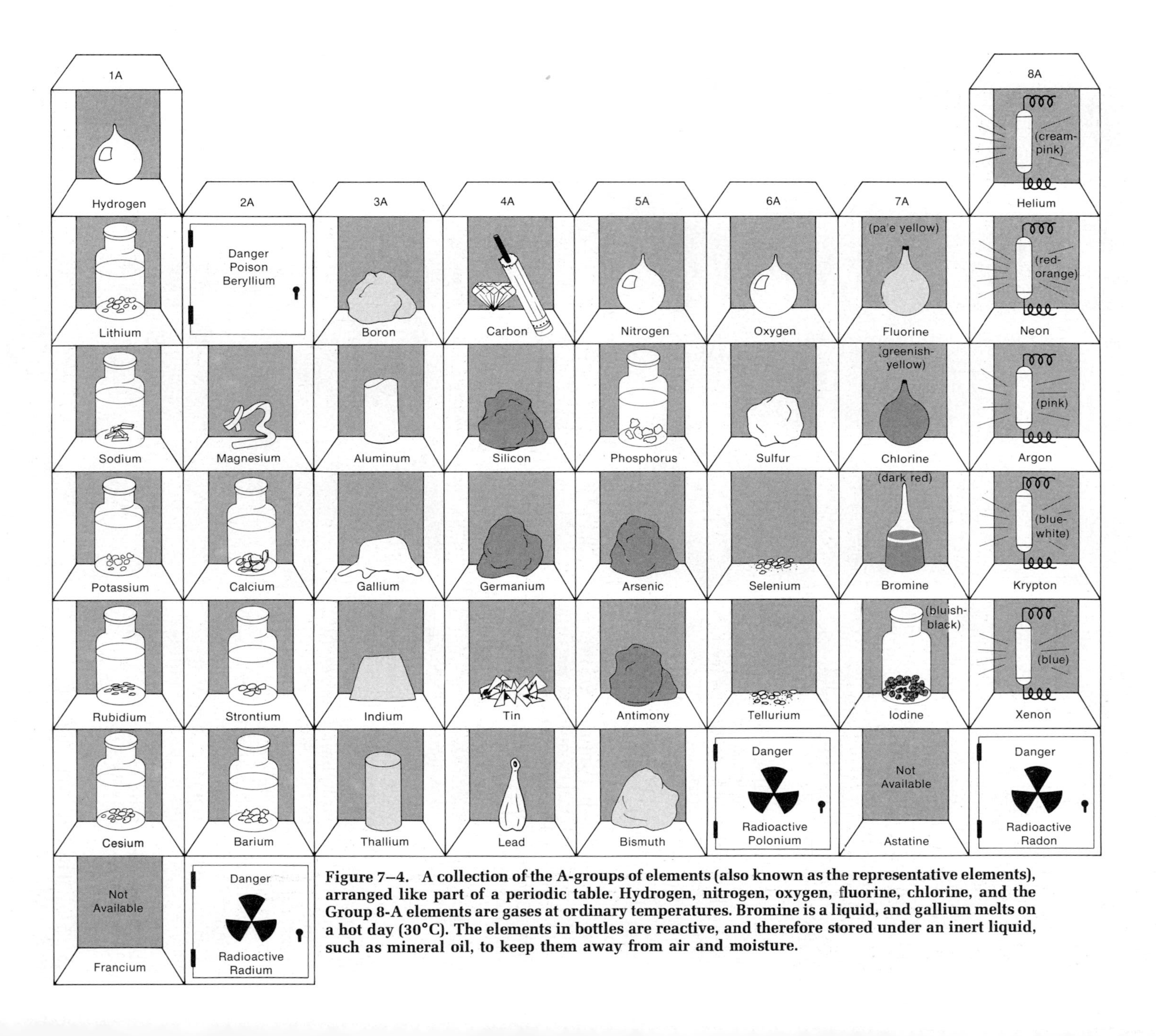

Figure 7–4. A collection of the A-groups of elements (also known as the representative elements), arranged like part of a periodic table. Hydrogen, nitrogen, oxygen, fluorine, chlorine, and the Group 8-A elements are gases at ordinary temperatures. Bromine is a liquid, and gallium melts on a hot day (30°C). The elements in bottles are reactive, and therefore stored under an inert liquid, such as mineral oil, to keep them away from air and moisture.

the iron was heated to a very high temperature (over 1100°C) it will glow with a white light. We say it is "white hot." As it cools, the color changes first to yellow (about 1000°C), then orange (800°C), then cherry red (700°C). The light gradually turns to a dull red and finally becomes invisible below about 500°C. Remember, the iron is no longer being heated by anything, it is cooling. Furthermore, there is no other source of light in the room, so the light is not being reflected from anything; it is coming out of the iron.

The source of this energy is the photons emitted when excited electrons (electrons at higher energy levels) fall back to lower energy levels. Energy was needed to force the electrons away from the nucleus which attracted them. As the iron cools, this energy is returned in the form of emitted photons (radiation). Each photon has a specific frequency, which depends on the difference between the higher energy from which the electron starts and the lower one to which it falls. This radiation can be separated into an **emission spectrum.**

Each element has a unique spectrum, different from that of all other elements, so that spectra can be used to identify elements, much as fingerprints can identify people.

Intuitively, one might think that, since an electron is a particle of matter, it might someday, somehow, be possible to "see" one. Is there such a possibility? That is to ask, "Could any instrument ever be invented that could measure both the precise position and the precise energy of an electron in an atom?" The answer is no; the task is considered to be theoretically impossible. Measurement affects the object that is measured. The reason is that measurement always involves some use of energy—even if it is only through the light that illuminates what is being measured. For example, imagine that you wished to use radar to locate a ship at sea. The radar beam (microwaves) would be transmitted to the ship, bounce off of it, and return to the sender. Its reflection would provide information about the location of the ship. Of course, the ship itself is hardly affected by the energy of the radar beam. However, if you wish to locate an electron, the problem is quite different. When a photon strikes an electron, the energy it transmits to it is enough to displace it appreciably. The electron will then be in a different location from where it was when the measurement was being attempted. The original position and energy of the electron remain a mystery. Each succeeding attempt at measurement fails in the same way. Thus, the electron is elusive. This conclusion, called the **uncertainty principle,** was formulated by Werner Heisenberg in 1927.

However, it is valid to calculate the *probability* of finding an electron at any given distance from the atomic nucleus. If we draw a diagram of a hydrogen atom by making darker shadings where there is a greater chance of finding the electron and lighter shadings where there is less chance, the result looks like a spherical cloud of negative charge around the nucleus (Fig. 7–5). In fact, such a picture is called an **electron cloud diagram,** and the space in which an electron may be found is called its **atomic orbital.**

The available energy levels for electrons fall into a limited number of categories, and each level can accommodate only a limited number of electrons. For our purposes we shall consider only the main categories, which are called **electron shells.** The energy levels corresponding to the electron shells are called the **principal quantum levels,** designated by the numbers 1, 2, 3 . . ., etc.

The higher the quantum level, the greater the energy of the electrons in that shell. The electron that can be separated most easily from its atom will therefore be an electron in the highest shell. (As an analogy, it takes less energy to blast a rocket off the top of Mt. Everest than would be needed for the same rocket at sea level.) We have learned that electrons can be knocked away from their atoms by photons (Section 6.5). Chemical reactions, too, involve separations of electrons from their atoms. The electrons in the highest shells are the ones involved in

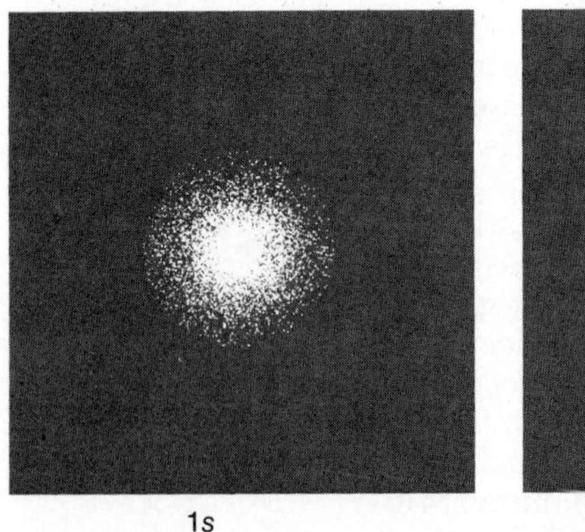

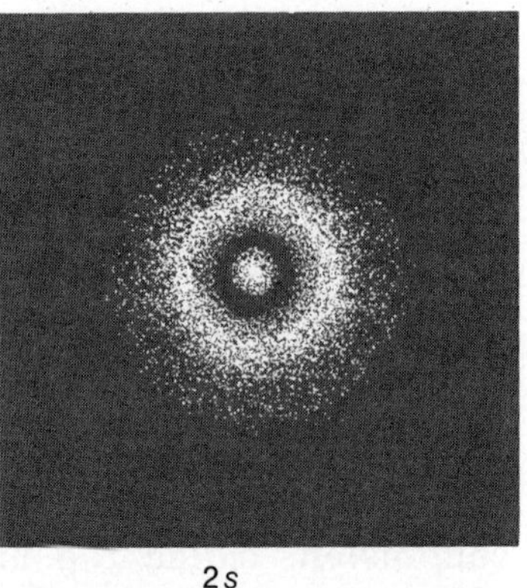

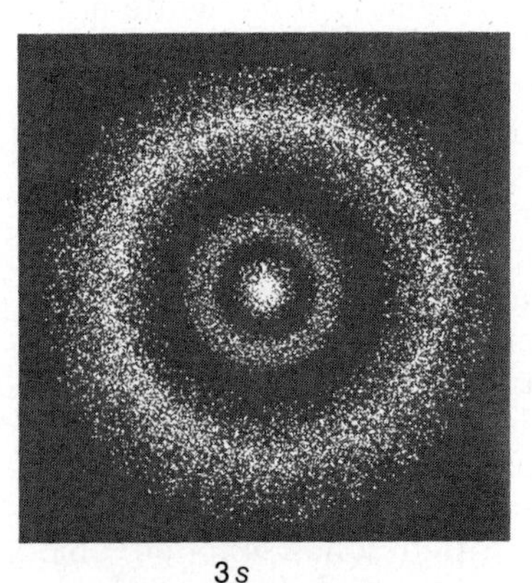

Figure 7–5. Electron cloud diagrams representing the shapes of atomic orbitals of hydrogen. These should be visualized as three-dimensional clouds surrounding the *nucleus* of the hydrogen atom. The density of the cloud is related to the chances of finding the electron in the cloud. *Note:* These are photographs *not* of electrons but of models based on a mathematical theory of the atom. (Modified from White, H.E.: *Physical Reviews, 37:*1416, 1931.)

The highest atomic number among the "natural" elements is 92—uranium. Elements 43, 61, 85, and 87 have been called the "missing" elements, because they occur in such insignificant quantities in nature that their only practical sources are synthetic. Hence, 92 − 4 = 88 natural elements. Some elements beyond 92 are naturally present on Earth, but so far as we know their quantities are also insignificant.

TABLE 7–4. ELECTRON CONFIGURATIONS OF ELEMENTS 1 to 12*

Atomic Number	Element and Symbol	Number of Electrons in Each Shell			Total Number of Electrons
		First	*Second*	*Third*	
1	Hydrogen, H	1			1
2	Helium, He	2 (full)			2
3	Lithium, Li	2	1		3
4	Beryllium, Be	2	2		4
5	Boron, B	2	3		5
6	Carbon, C	2	4		6
7	Nitrogen, N	2	5		7
8	Oxygen, O	2	6		8
9	Fluorine, F	2	7		9
10	Neon, Ne	2	8 (full)		10
11	Sodium, Na	2	8	1	11
12	Magnesium, Mg	2	8	2	12

*Among the heavier elements, the distribution of electrons becomes more complicated because of the division of shells into subshells.

chemical changes; these shells are therefore called the **valence shells.** The concepts of valence and chemical bonding are the subject of the next chapter, but for now it is sufficient to know that in the A-group elements (the representative elements), the number of electrons in the highest shell is the same as the group number.

Example 2
How many electrons are in the highest shell of (a) an oxygen atom; (b) a sodium atom; (c) a carbon atom?

Answer: **(a) Oxygen is in Group 6A, so its highest shell has 6 electrons; (b) sodium, Group 1A, 1 electron; (c) carbon, group 4A, 4 electrons.**

The larger atoms have larger clouds of electrons around them. The higher the principal quantum level, the more electrons that can be accommodated within the shell. The relationship is:

$$\text{maximum number of electrons per shell} = 2n^2$$

where n is the principal quantum number.

Example 3
What is the maximum number of electrons in the electron shell for which n =

1? for the $n = 2$ shell? for the $n = 3$ shell?

Answer: **The maximum number is $2n^2$. Therefore when $n = 1$, the number of electrons is $2 \times 1^2 = 2$.**
For $n = 2$, it is $2 \times 2^2 = 8$
For $n = 3$, it is $2 \times 3^2 = 18$.

Table 7–4 shows the distribution of electrons in the shells of the first dozen elements. Note that the first shell is full before electrons enter the second shell, and that the second shell is full before electrons enter the third. Atoms in which all the electrons are in the lowest possible energy levels are said to be in the **ground state.** If an electron absorbs a photon that promotes it to a higher energy level, the atom is said to be in an **excited state.**

There are some 105 known elements. (The number is indefinite because some of the claims of discovery of the last elements are still in dispute.) Not all of these occur naturally on Earth, nor do all the elements possess stable isotopes. "Unstable elements" are those whose nuclei are unstable; we shall discuss these in Chapter 10.

Table 7–5 shows the relative abundance of the most common elements on Earth. The most abundant in the universe, the principal component of the stars, is the simplest element, hydrogen.

TABLE 7–5. RELATIVE ABUNDANCE OF ELEMENTS ON EARTH (%)

Iron	35.9
Oxygen	28.5
Silicon	14.3
Magnesium	13.2
Calcium	1.9
Sulfur	1.8
Aluminum	1.8
All others	2.6

The States of Matter

7.6 CLASSIFICATION OF PHYSICAL STATES

Up to this point we have been dealing with atoms and molecules, and with the internal structures of atoms. Ordinary samples of matter, however, consist of collections, or aggregations, of very large numbers of atoms and molecules. How do these "collections" stay together? This question goes to the very heart of chemistry. We will approach the problem in two parts. The first part, which is the subject of the remainder of this chapter, will deal with the *physical* aspects of the states of matter. The second part, which is the subject of the next chapter. will take up the topic of chemical bonds.

Electrical forces are responsible both for binding atoms to each other to form molecules and for holding molecules to each other in their physical states. However, the forces between molecules (intermolecular forces) are relatively weak, and they are not considered to be chemical bonds. Nevertheless, these forces are important because they account for many of the properties of materials.

The **physical states** of matter are generally grouped into three categories: gases, liquids, and solids. These states can often be altered by changing the temperature of a substance, as when ice melts, water freezes, or alcohol evaporates.

Gases are substances that have no

Not everything that moves freely in space is a gas. Cigarette smoke consists of small solid particles and liquid droplets. The "steam" from a tea kettle consists of some true gas and some liquid water droplets—the gas is invisible, and the water droplets are seen as a mist.

definite shape. Instead, they disperse rapidly in space and occupy any volume available to them. All gases are transparent, and most of them are colorless. (Chlorine gas, which is green, and nitrogen dioxide, which is reddish brown, are some exceptions.) The molecules of a gas exert very little attraction for each other.

Liquids do not disperse in space but they do change shape easily. A liquid therefore occupies a definite volume. Under the influence of the Earth's gravity, a liquid fills the lower part of its container. The molecules of a liquid do exert significant attractive forces on each other.

Solids are rigid and maintain their own shape. Their molecules are held together by comparatively strong forces.

7.7 GASES

Let us think about gases from our practical experience and see how they differ from each other and what properties they have in common. Air is a gas; so is the "natural gas" that we burn in a kitchen stove. (The "gas" used as automobile fuel is not in this category, but refers to gasoline, which is a liquid.) The aroma of a flower and the stench of a rotten egg are gases. When

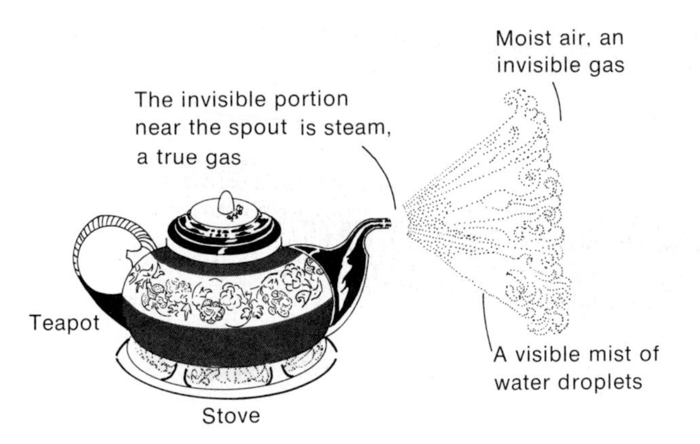

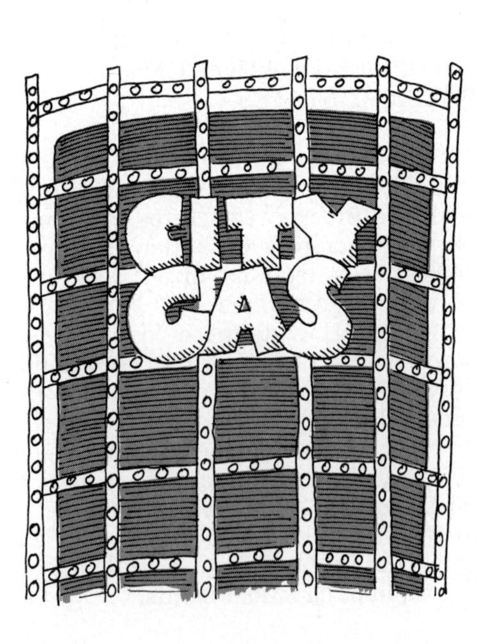

Gases.

water or "dry ice" evaporates, it turns into a gas. Some gases, such as chlorine, are poisonous; others, such as oxygen, are necessary for the maintenance of life; still others, such as nitrogen, are chemically inert in the human body.

The properties of gases can be illustrated by experiments with samples of gas inside a hypodermic syringe.* There are four variable properties of the sample of gas inside the syringe that are related to each other; that is, if any one of these variables is changed, there *must* be a change in at least one of the other three. These four variables are

1. The volume of the gas.
2. The temperature of the gas.
3. The pressure of the gas.
4. The number of molecules of the gas.

It will be best to do experiments in which any two of the variables are kept constant, so that the relationship between the other two can be observed.

We start with a given amount of gas at room temperature and at normal atmospheric pressure. It occupies a definite volume.

EXPERIMENT 7.1

Warm the gas with a heating lamp as in Figure 7–6 *A;* do not change the pressure or let any gas get in or out. We observe that the plunger rises, which means that the gas expands (its volume increases). If the gas is cooled, its volume decreases.

If the gas volumes in such an experiment are measured carefully, it is found that they change by a constant amount for every 1°C change in temperature. Thus, for every 1°C drop in temperature, a gas shrinks by the *same constant loss of volume.* This means that if a gas were cooled sufficiently, it would shrink to nothing—a miracle that does not occur because the molecules themselves occupy some volume, and besides, cold gases liquefy first. But if the constant shrinking continued without liquefaction, and if the mole-

*This is not an easy experiment to do. However, the plunger of a syringe can be made to function as an almost gas-tight and frictionless piston by lubricating it and spinning it at high speed.

Who cares about how gases behave under different pressures and temperatures?

Automotive tire mechanics
Scuba divers
Heating and air-conditioning workers
Meteorologists
Users of compressed gases (welders, physicians, respiratory therapists, etc.)
Gas utility workers
Perfumers
Astronauts
. . . and many others

Pressure is related to force, which discussed in Chapter 2. The relationship is:

$$\text{pressure} = \frac{\text{force}}{\text{area}}$$

The pressure exerted by the water over a submerged object (such as a submarine) may be considered to be the force exerted on each square meter of the object's surface by the weight of the column of water above it. The pressure is exerted equally in all directions.

The SI unit of pressure is the **pascal,** which is 1 N/m². Still in common use, however, is the **atmosphere,** which is the pressure exerted by a column of mercury 76 cm high. This is equivalent to the normal pressure exerted by the Earth's atmosphere at sea level.

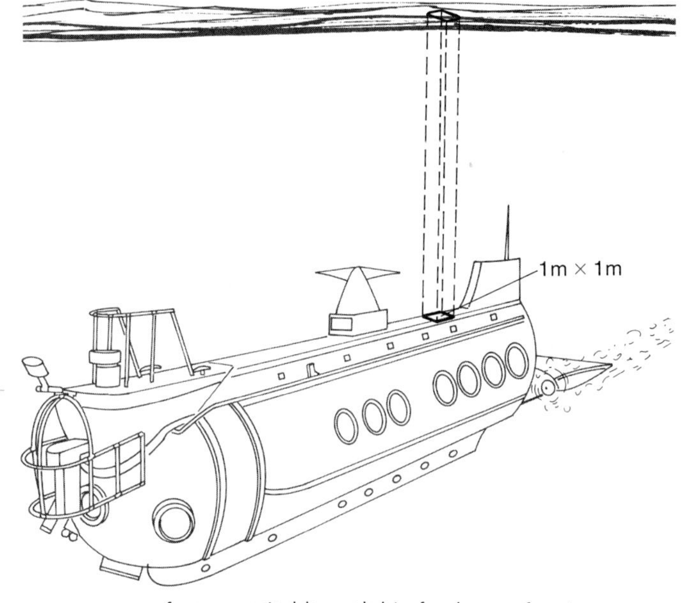

$$\text{pressure} = \frac{\text{force exerted by weight of column of water}}{1\ \text{m}^2 \text{ of surface of object}}$$

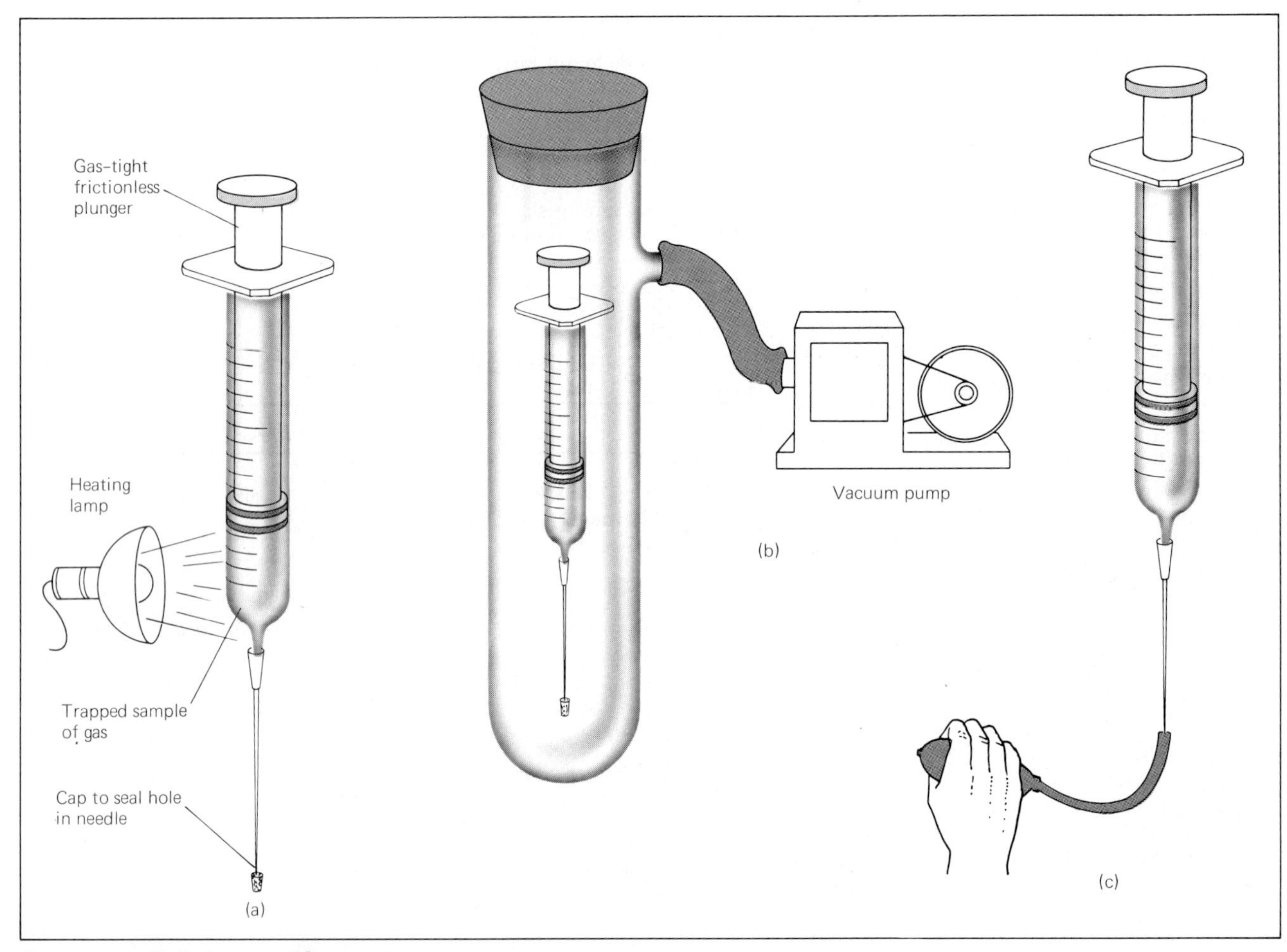

Figure 7–6. Experiments with gases.

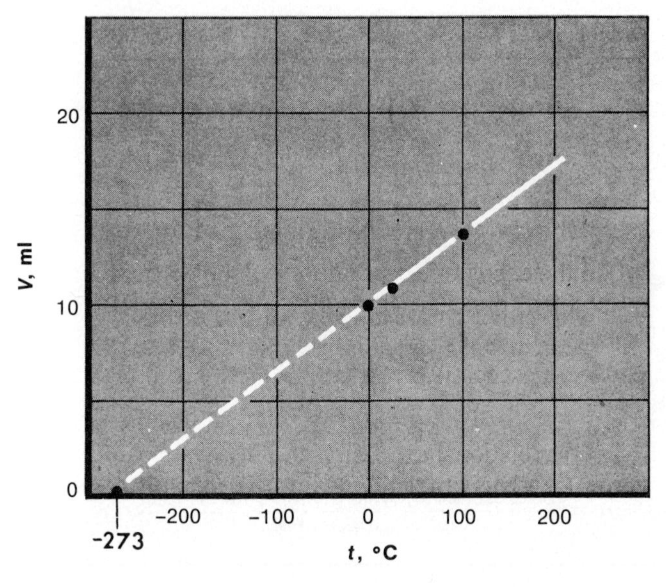

Figure 7–7. A plot (graph) of volume vs. temperature shows that gases expand when heated at constant pressure.

melts, so there is nothing but water in the pot. The fire under the pot continues to add heat to the water and the temperature of the water now starts to rise. The water continues to get hotter until it reaches its boiling point (100°C at sea level). Again the temperature stops rising, even though heat is still being added. Instead of getting hotter, the water begins to boil. If more fuel is added to the fire, the fire burns faster and more heat goes into the water. The water then boils more rapidly, but the temperature still remains constant at 100°C.

If our explorer now leaves the pot of hot water outdoors overnight in the cold Arctic, the whole process goes backwards. The hot water cools to 0°C, then ice starts to form as the temperature remains constant at 0°C. When all is ice, the temperature starts to fall again.

Now let us define the terms that describe these transformations. We will also do some simple calculations. Recall from Chapter 3 that the **specific heat** is the heat absorbed when 1 g of a substance is warmed by 1°C. (This is the same as the heat released when 1 g of a substance cools by 1°C.)

The **heat of fusion** is the heat absorbed when 1 g of a solid melts (or the heat released when 1 g of a liquid freezes) at constant temperature.

The **heat of vaporization** is the heat absorbed when 1 g of a liquid vaporizes (or the heat released when 1 g of a vapor condenses) at constant temperature.

Much more heat is required to vaporize a gram of water at constant temperature than to warm a gram of water 1°C. Similarly, much more heat is needed to melt a gram of ice than to warm it 1°C, say from −10°C to −9°C. Table 3–1 (page 57) gives the specific heats of various substances. Table 7–6 shows some values of heats of fusion and vaporization.

Example 9
How much heat is needed to vaporize (a) 100 g of ethyl alcohol, (b) 100 g of water?

Answer: **Multiply the heat of vaporization by the mass in grams:**

(a) $854\ \mathrm{J/g} \times 100\ \mathrm{g} = 8.54 \times 10^4\ \mathrm{J}$
(b) $2258\ \mathrm{J/g} \times 100\ \mathrm{g} = 2.258 \times 10^5\ \mathrm{J}$

Example 10
How much heat is needed to convert 200 g of ice at 0°C to steam at 100°C?

Answer: **Here we have three processes. The heat for each process must be calculated separately and the three heats added.**

First process: **Melt the ice.**
Heat needed =
$$333\ \mathrm{J/g} \times 200\ \mathrm{g} = 66{,}600\ \mathrm{J}$$

Fusion is another word for melting, although in common usage it also connotes "sticking together"; you may think of "fused" as meaning "united by melting."

Second process: **Heat the water from 0°C to 100°C.**
Heat needed
$$= \text{specific heat} \times \text{mass} \times \text{change of temperature}$$
$$= 4.184\ \mathrm{J/(g^\circ\ C)} \times 200\ \mathrm{g} \times 100^\circ\ \mathrm{C}$$
$$= 83{,}680\ \mathrm{J}$$

Third process: **Boil the water.**
Heat needed
$$= 2258\ \mathrm{J/g} \times 200\ \mathrm{g} = 451{,}600\ \mathrm{J}$$

Sum of these processes
$$= 66{,}600\ \mathrm{J} + 83{,}680\ \mathrm{J} + 451{,}600\ \mathrm{J}$$
$$= 601{,}880\ \mathrm{J}$$

This figure should be rounded off (see Appendix A) to 6.02×10^5 J.

TABLE 7–6. HEATS OF FUSION AND VAPORIZATION*

Substance	Melting Point, °C	Boiling Point, °C	Heat (J/g) of Fusion	Heat (J/g) of Vaporization
Water†	0	100	333	2258
Ethyl alcohol	−114	78.5	104	854
Mercury	−39	357	12	295

*The heat of fusion is given at the melting point; the heat of vaporization is given at the boiling point. They are slightly different at other temperatures.

†The values for water are widely used and are often given in calories. The conversions are obtained by dividing the value in joules by 4.184, which gives us 79.6 cal/g for the heat of fusion of ice and 539.7 cal/g for the heat of vaporization of water.

CHAPTER OBJECTIVES

Make sure you know the relationships between mass number, atomic number, and the composition of the atomic nucleus.

Become familiar with the general structure of the periodic table, particularly the relationships among elements in a given group, and among elements in a given period. Also, learn the electron configurations of the first 12 elements.

Understand how the forces between molecules and their arrangements in space account for the different states of matter.

KEY WORDS

Object
Material
Matter
Element
Atom
Molecule
Compound
Electron
Proton
Neutron
Atomic nucleus
Alpha particle
Atomic number
Mass number
Isotope
Periodic table
Period
Group
Ground state
Excited state
Electron shell
Principal quantum level
Atomic orbital
State of matter
Gas
Liquid
Crystalline solid
Noncrystalline solid (glass)
Pressure
Boyle's law
Charles' law
Avogadro's law
Kinetic-molecular theory
Kelvin scale
Density
Crystal
Melting
Evaporation
Freezing
Condensation
Sublimation
Heat of fusion
Heat of vaporization

FORMULAS TO KNOW

1. Mass number = protons + neutrons
= atomic number + neutrons

2. K = °C + 273

Example 11
(a) Convert −10°C, 0°C, and 100°C to the Kelvin scale.
(b) Convert 10 K, 200 K, and 300 K to Celsius temperature.

Answer: (a)

$$-10°C + 273 = 263\ K$$
$$0°C + 273 = 273\ K$$
$$100°C + 273 = 373\ K$$

(b) Rearranging the equation gives

$$°C = K - 273$$

Therefore

$$10\ K - 273 = -263°C$$
$$200\ K - 273 = -73°C$$
$$300\ K - 273 = +27°C$$

TAKE-HOME EXPERIMENTS

1. **Gases.** Use a tire gauge to measure the air pressure in an automobile tire after it has been standing overnight in a cool spot. Then check it again when the tire is warm, after the car has been driven or has been standing in sunlight. What is the rise in pressure?

The tire gauge tells you, in lb/in², how much pressure there is *in addition to atmospheric pressure,* which is about 15 lb/in². The ratio is therefore:

Per cent increase in absolute pressure

$$= \left(\frac{\text{pressure of hot tire} + 15}{\text{pressure of cold tire} + 15}\right) \times 100\%$$

You can also feel with your hand that the temperature of the tire (and therefore of the air inside) has increased. Finally, the volume of the tire has expanded somewhat, though this may be hard to see.

2. **Liquids.** Fill a long test tube or a tall drinking glass with water. Set it where it can lean over a bit but is still stable. A good place is on a piece of rug in a corner of a room. Now roll a small glass or metal ball, such as a ball bearing, down the inside of the tube, and time its descent to the bottom. Repeat the experiment using the following liquids (always keeping the glass at exactly the

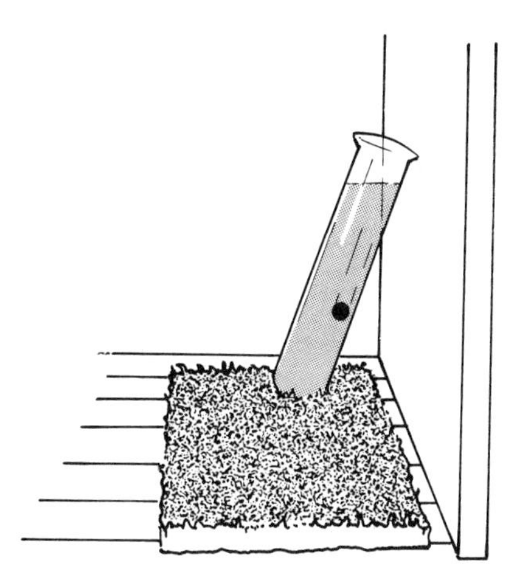

same angle): honey, cooking oil, rubbing alcohol, permanent antifreeze (ethylene glycol). You have been measuring the resistance to flow, called the **viscosity,** of the various liquids.

3. **Density.** A solid will float on a liquid only if it is less dense than the liquid; if it is more dense, it will sink. When two liquids that do not dissolve in each other are mixed, the less dense liquid will float on the more dense one. Use pairs of the following substances to determine which substance in each pair is more dense: water, cooking oil, glass (use a glass marble), wood, paraffin (use a piece of candle wax), graphite (use a piece of "lead" from a pencil), iron (use a paper clip).

4. **Crystal models.** One of the hobbies of Dr. Felix Hoenikker, the fictional scientist of Kurt Vonnegut's novel *Cat's Cradle,* was "photographing how cannonballs are stacked

A steel ball floats on mercury, showing that steel is less dense than mercury.

Cannonballs on a courthouse lawn.

on different courthouse lawns." The point is that the doctor was studying models of crystalline patterns. Try it yourself, starting with pennies, which you may visualize as the shadows of spheres. You could arrange them so that their centers make a bunch of squares, for example, or hexagons. A curious result will emerge: There are not many ways to arrange the pennies compactly on the surface in an orderly pattern, In fact, there is only *one way* to arrange them as compactly as possible—the hexagonal way. If we step up now from two dimensions to three, we find that we can arrange spheres in various cu-

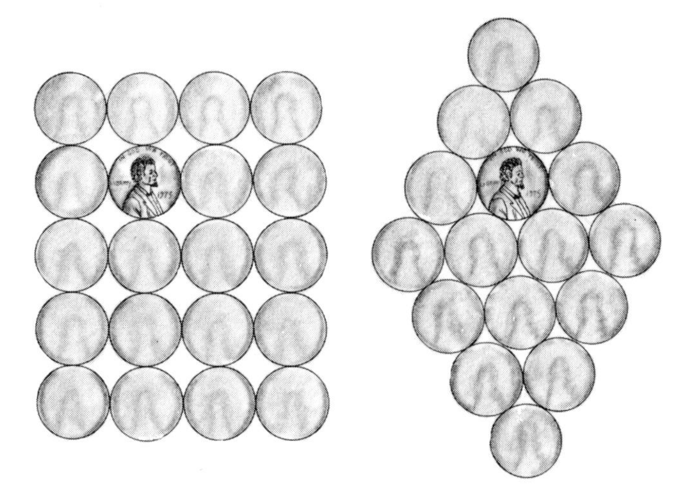

bical and hexagonal patterns, which fill space with different densities.

You can try this out yourself by sticking candy gumballs together, using a little water as your glue. Get about five or six dozen gumballs of one color and an equal number of some other color. To make a cubic arrangement, set out the first 25 of one color in a 5×5 square. Then, using a second color, stick another 25 gumballs directly on top of the first 25. Alternate colors this way for five layers, making 125 balls in all. As you do this, can you see how many gumballs can touch a given gumball in the center of the pile? Measure the length of your pile, in cm. (Since it is a cube, all three lengths will be the same.) Calculate the density from the following formula:

$$\text{density} = \frac{125 \text{ gumballs}}{\text{length}^3} = \underline{\qquad}\text{gumballs/cm}^3$$

Now break up your pile and start over, but this time pack them in the hexagonal way. Now build up other layers, changing colors for each layer, and resting your gumballs in the depressions of the layer beneath. In this arrangement, how many gumballs can touch a given gumball? Assume that the "length" of this pile consists of the sum of five gumball diameters, and is therefore the same as the length of the cubical pile you just broke up. Now measure the width and the height of your pile (which should be the same). Calculate the density from the formula

$$\text{density} = \frac{125 \text{ gumballs}}{\text{length} \times \text{width} \times \text{height}} = \underline{\qquad}\text{gumballs/cm}^3$$

What conclusion can you draw about the relationship between density and packing patterns?

5. **Real crystals.** Real crystals are easy to make and fun to watch. Prepare saturated solutions of as many of the following solids as you can by stirring the solid in about one glassful of water until no more will dissolve: table salt, sugar, Epsom salt, bicarbonate of soda, washing soda. Let the undissolved solid settle out, and pour off the clear solutions into clean glasses. Label each glass with the name of the dissolved solid. Now cover each glass with a piece of paper towel held around the rim by a rubber band. Let the solutions evaporate through the paper, and observe them from time to time. (This will be slow, but be patient. It may take weeks.) Describe the crystals.

PROBLEMS

1. **Definitions.** Define the following terms: (a) element, (b) compound, (c) pure substance.

2. **Materials and objects.** List 10 objects that are near you. List 10 materials.

3. **Atomic structure.** Explain the difference between the mass and the mass number of an atom.

4. **Atomic structure.** Complete the accompanying table by substituting the correct numerical value where a question mark appears. (Note that atomic numbers, but not mass numbers, appear in the table of elements on the inside back cover.)

Isotope	Atomic Number	Mass Number	Number of Neutrons in Nucleus
Oxygen-18	?	?	?
Strontium-90	?	?	?
Uranium-?	?	?	141
Iodine-?	?	131	?
?	17	35	?
?	?	226	138

5. **Definitions.** Define and explain: (a) isotope, (b) neutron, (c) proton.

6. **Atomic structure.** Which of the following particles are electrically positive; which are negative; which are neutral? (a) a proton, (b) a hydrogen atom, (c) a neutron, (d) an alpha particle, (e) an electron.

7. **Compounds.** Dry ice, which is used as a coolant, is made either from the gases produced from fermentation or by burning oil. From either source, the dry ice is 27.3 per cent carbon and 73.7 per cent oxygen, and the properties of the substance from the two sources are the same. Do you think dry ice is an element, a compound, or an impure mixture of several compounds? Defend your answer.

*8. **Elements.** Ozone is a gas that, upon heating, produces oxygen and nothing else. When carbon is subjected to extremely high pressure, it is converted to diamond and no other product. From these results would you

*Indicates more difficult problem.

conclude (a) that ozone and carbon are elements, (b) that they are not elements, or (c) that you cannot decide. If your answer is (a) or (b), explain your conclusion. If it is (c), suggest what other experiments you would carry out to help you reach a conclusion.

9. **Elements.** When yellow crystalline sulfur is heated, it melts to a light, straw-colored liquid, which on further heating turns dark and sticky. When this dark liquid is cooled rapidly, it becomes a rubbery, plastic solid which, on standing, slowly reverts to the original solid crystalline form. From these results would you conclude that sulfur is an element, or a compound, or that you cannot decide?

*10. **Molecule.** Webster's Dictionary defines molecule as "the smallest part of an element or compound that can . . . still retain the characteristics of the element or compound." One characteristic of sugar is its sweetness. But one molecule of sugar cannot be detected by taste. Is Webster's definition faulty? Defend your answer.

11. **Elements.** Distinguish among stable elements, unstable elements, natural elements, and "missing" elements. Select one element to fit each of the empty boxes in the table.

	Stable	Unstable
Natural		
"Missing"		

12. **Periodicity.** Define period and group, as related to Table 7–3, page 210. How many groups are in the table? How many periods? (Ignore the lanthanoids, actinoids, and dashed boxes.)

13. **Periodicity.**

(a) If the elements were arranged in the increasing order of their atomic weights rather than atomic numbers, would the sequence of elements be largely the same as in Table 7–3? (To answer this question, pick five or six small sets of elements with consecutive atomic numbers, such as N, O, F, Ne, and check whether the numbers of each set appear in the increasing order of their atomic weights.)

(b) Referring to question (a), would the sequence *always* be the same? (Check the set Cl, Ar, K, Ca, the set Fe, Co, Ni, Cu, and the set Te, I, Xe).

14. **Electronic structure.** (a) What is the maximum number of electrons in the electron shell for which $n = 4$? (b) Predict the number of electrons in each shell of elements 13 through 18.

15. **States of matter.** (a) Using your own words, distinguish among gases, liquids, crystalline solids, and glasses. (b) Fluids are substances that flow readily. Which of the four states of matter listed in (a) are fluids?

*16. **States of matter.** Identify the state of matter of each of the following substances: (a) A hard lump of matter cannot be bent by hand. However, on being struck with a hammer, it shatters. Many of the resulting fragments have flat surfaces that form angles of 120° with each other. (b) A rigid bar, held horizontally, sags slowly over a period of years. When the bar is smashed, the fragments seem more random than those from the previous object; no typical face angles are observed. (c) A brown transparent material is in a closed container. When the container is opened, the brown color becomes lighter, first near the top, then throughout the container. Finally, the material disappears entirely from the container. (d) A spherical object starts to fall to Earth. As its speed increases it becomes pear-shaped, the wide end downward. It falls into a pore in a rock and assumes the shape of the pore.

17. **Properties of gases.** The warning on a gas tank reads: "CAUTION. Contents of this tank are under pressure. Do not store in direct sunlight. Do not use or store near heat or open flame." What is the reason for this warning?

18. **Properties of gases.** A novice diver asks the old-timer, "How full is this oxygen tank?" The old-timer raps up and down the tank with his knuckles, stops about halfway, and says, "It's down to here!" Explain what was foolish about the novice's question and how the old-timer was kidding him. How should the novice have asked the question if he wanted a straight answer?

19. **Kelvin scale.** (a) Convert −40° C, 10° C, and 273° C to the Kelvin scale. (b) Convert 5 K, 273 K, and 1000 K to Celsius temperature. (c) Which of the following temperatures of a substance is/are too low to be possible: −200° C, −3 K, −300° C, −273 K?

*Indicates more difficult problem.

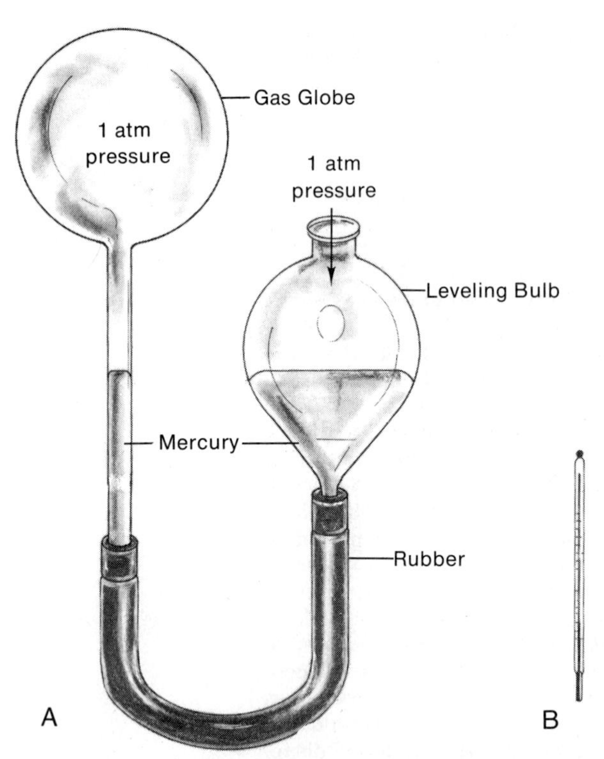

Figure 7–12. *A,* **Gas thermometer.** *B,* **Liquid-in-glass thermometer.**

$PV = 12$	
V	P
1	
2	
3	
4	
6	
12	

20. **Charles' law.** (a) A sample of helium gas occupies 12 L at 100 K. What volume will the helium occupy at 200 K? at 400 K? (Assume that the pressure remains constant.) (b) A sample of air occupies 300 mL at 0° C. What volume will the air occupy at 273° C at the same pressure? (*Hint:* First convert Celsius to Kelvin temperature.)

*21. **Charles' law.** (a) Imagine that an automobile tire is filled with cold compressed air to a certain pressure. You now drive the car rapidly on a warm road; the air in the tire warms up, and the pressure increases. To reduce the tire pressure back to its original value, you bleed out some air and catch the leaked air in a balloon. Would the volume of air in the balloon tell you anything about the warming of the air in the tire? Explain.

(b) Look at Figure 7–12*A*, which is a **gas thermometer.** The leveling bulb can be raised or lowered so as to keep the two liquid levels equal and thus maintain atmospheric pressure inside the gas globe. Describe how you could use this device as a thermometer. Where would you place the temperature markings? Do you think that such a thermometer would be more sensitive than the ordinary liquid-in-glass thermometer (Fig. 7–12*B*), or less sensitive? Explain.

22. **Boyle's law.** A sample of argon gas occupies 12 mL at ½ atm pressure. What volume will the argon occupy at 1 atm? 2 atm? ¼ atm? Assume no change in temperature.

23. **Gases.** Give the name of the gas law that is illustrated by each of the following observations: (a) As a bubble of air rises from a diver's helmet to the surface of the water, it continuously expands. (b) As a rubber balloon filled with air cools during the night, it shrinks in size. (c) A 1-L volume of neon at a certain temperature and pressure contains 2×10^{20} molecules, and a 2-L volume of argon under the same conditions contains 4×10^{20} molecules.

24. **Boyle's law.** Another statement of the law is that the pressure multiplied by the volume of a gas is constant at constant temperature, or $PV = k$. Assume that the value of k is 12, and complete the table shown in the margin by solving for P. Now plot your results on a graph of P (x-axis) vs V (y-axis). What is the shape of the curve? If you have ever pumped air into a bicycle tire by hand, can you say whether any single stroke is harder to push near the beginning or near the end of the stroke? Explain how the shape of your curve expresses this experience. Remember, you are compressing the air from a larger volume (tire + pump) into a smaller volume (tire alone).

25. **Kinetic-molecular theory.** What are the basic assumptions of the kinetic-molecular theory of gases? Explain how the theory accounts for the physical properties of gases.

*26. **Density and crystal patterns.**
   (a) The accompanying sketch shows four circles in a square. Let the radius of each circle be equal to 1 cm. The side of the square is therefore 4 cm. Calculate (i) the area of the square, (ii) the combined areas of

*Indicates more difficult problem.

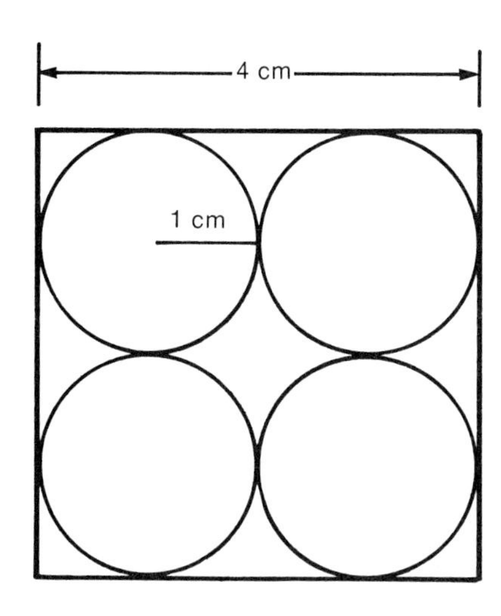

the four circles, (iii) the empty area, which is (i)−(ii), and (iv) the percentage of empty space, which is (iii/i) × 100.

(b) Do you think your answer to part (iv) would have been different if the radii of the circles had been 1 mm instead of 1 cm? If they had been 1 km? Any value?

(c) Two empty swimming pools of the same size are filled with uniform spheres of ice packed as closely as possible. The spheres in the first pool are as large as grains of sand; those in the second pool are as large as oranges. The ice in both pools melts. In which pool, if either, will the water level be higher?

(d) The density of a solid depends on the masses of its atoms and on the geometry of their packing arrangements. Does it also depend on the sizes of the atoms? Explain.

27. **Solids.** Enter each of the following four solids into the appropriate box shown in the table: lead, aluminum, diamond, iridium (a metal used for penpoints). If you are not sure of the properties of these substances, make your best guess, or ask someone who works in a machine shop. What factors account for the hardness and densities of solids?

	Harder than iron	Softer than iron
Denser than iron		
Less dense than iron		

28. **Liquids and solids.** The note on page 217 lists groups of people who are concerned with the physical behavior of gases. Make a similar list for liquids and for solids.

29. **Changes of state.** (Refer to Figure 7–11 to help you answer this question.) State whether your body would receive or lose heat in each of the following circumstances: (a) You hold an ice cube in your hand until it melts. (b) As you enter a room you find that your eyeglasses or your watch crystal becomes fogged with water droplets. (c) You are in a room with a freezer that is making ice cubes. (d) You step out of a shower and allow the water to evaporate from your body.

30. **Liquid and glassy states.** A zinc metal rod and a glass rod are each heated in the absence of air. At a sufficiently high temperature, liquid zinc begins to drip from the zinc rod, although the rod itself remains rigid. The glass rod sags, but does not drip. Account for these phenomena.

31. **Changes of state.** Referring to Table 7–6, state which of the following changes in each set requires more energy: (a) melting 1 g of ice or boiling 1 g of water, (b) vaporizing 1 kg of water or vaporizing 1 kg of alcohol, (c) vaporizing 1 g of water or vaporizing 5 g of mercury.

32. **Changes of state.** How much heat in joules is needed to (a) melt 50 g of ice, (b) vaporize 15 g of alcohol, (c) convert 10 g of water at 50°C to steam at 100°C?

*Indicates more difficult problem.

CHAPTER

This chapter deals with the most fundamental aspect of chemistry—the nature of chemical bonds. The chapter opens with brief treatments of chemical formulas, valence, and the balancing of chemical equations. The major topic is then introduced by means of simple electrical experiments with four common substances—salt, ice, sand, and silver. These substances represent the four major types of chemical bonding—ionic, covalent, network covalent, and metallic. Each type is then discussed in more detail and serves to illustrate various chemical principles. The study of ionic substances teaches us about electron transfer and its relationship to the electronic structure of the noble gases. Covalent substances introduce us to structural formulas, including double bonds, triple bonds, and cycles. Network covalent bonding brings in three-dimensional structures and "giant molecules." Finally, metals add the concepts of "loose" electrons, closely packed atoms, and the nature of electrical conductivity.

All these ideas flow naturally from our four simple electrical experiments. The reader should see this chapter not as a series of separate topics, but rather as a study of the one force that underlies all chemical change—the electrical force of attraction and repulsion.

CHEMICAL BONDS

8.1 CHEMICAL CHANGES

Iron rusts, plants grow by taking sustenance from their surroundings, rocket fuel burns, an egg hardens as it is heated, the muscles of a child at play help to convert the sugar in his blood to carbon dioxide and water. In all of these transformations, some substances are used up and others are produced. Such processes are called **chemical changes.** All these changes result from the *making and breaking of chemical bonds,* the ties that hold atoms together. Therefore we must look into the nature of the force that make these ties and to the processes by which they are altered and by which atoms rearrange their linkages.

But first, we must learn how to express ourselves in simple chemical language.

8.2 FORMULAS AND EQUATIONS

As we have learned, substances consist of molecules, which are combinations of atoms. Substances or molecules are represented by **formulas,** such as H_2O for water. The subscript 2 refers to the H. Therefore this formula tells us that one molecule of water consists of two atoms of hydrogen and one atom of oxygen. Other examples are:

Formula	Molecule or Substance
CO	Carbon monoxide. The formula shows 1 atom of carbon and 1 atom of oxygen per molecule of carbon monoxide.
H_2	Hydrogen. Each molecule contains 2 atoms.
Ne	Neon. One atom per molecule.
H_2O_2	Hydrogen peroxide. Four atoms per molecule.
H_2SO_4	Sulfuric acid. Seven atoms per molecule.
$Ca(OH)_2$	Calcium hydroxide. One Ca, 2 O, and 2 H atoms per molecule.

Example 1
Give the number of atoms of each element and the total number of atoms per molecule in (a) H_3PO_4, (b) $Ba(OH)_2$, (c) $Cu(NO_3)_2(H_2O)_6$, (d) $(NH_4)_6Mo_7O_{24}(H_2O)_4$.

Answer: **Remember, the subscript** ***follows*** **the number of atoms it represents. If the subscript follows a parenthesis, it is a multiplier for everything within the parentheses. The answers are: (a) 3 H, 1 P, and 4 O atoms, total eight atoms; (b) 1 Ba, 2 O, and 2 H, total five; (c) 1 Cu, 2 N, 12 O, (6 O in the $[NO_3]_2$ portion of molecule and 6 O in the $[H_2O]_6$ portion), 12 H, total 27; (d) 6 N, 24 H, 7 Mo, 24 O, 8 H, and 4 O. Combining, we have 6 N, 32 H, 7 Mo, and 28 O, for a total of 73.**

Chemical changes are represented by **chemical equations,** which show the starting materials, final products, and the relative numbers of molecules involved. Atoms are not created or destroyed in chemical changes. Therefore the products must contain the same number and kinds of atoms as the starting materials. An equation that shows this conservation is called a **balanced equation.**

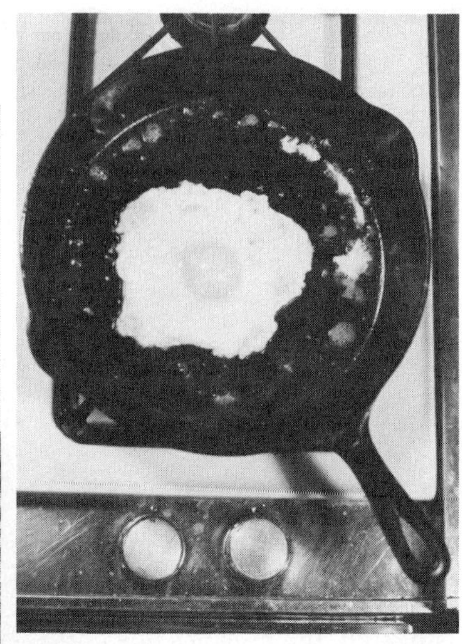

Chemical changes.
Iron rusts
Plants grow and rocket fuel burns (Courtesy of NASA)
An egg hardens
Muscle action consumes sugar

To learn how to balance equations, let us start with a reaction expressed in words:

Hydrogen reacts with chlorine to produce hydrogen chloride.

or

Hydrogen + chlorine → hydrogen chloride

The formulas of these substances and diagrams of their molecules are:

Hydrogen, H_2, (H H)
Chlorine, Cl_2, (Cl Cl)
Hydrogen chloride, HCl (H Cl)

An H atom is smaller than a Cl atom.

We can now rewrite the equation with diagrams:

(H H) + (Cl Cl) → (H Cl) (incomplete)

The above equation is incomplete because there are two H atoms and two Cl atoms on the left and only one of each on the right. We can balance the equation only by changing the *numbers* of molecules, not the *kinds* of molecules:

(H H) + (Cl Cl) → (H Cl) (H Cl)

or

$H_2 + Cl_2 \rightarrow 2HCl$
(correctly balanced)

It will not be necessary to use diagrams to balance equations. You need only adjust the numbers of molecules. Try the following exercise.

Example 2
Balance the following equations:

(a) hydrogen + oxygen → water
$$H_2 + O_2 \rightarrow H_2O$$

(b) methane + oxygen → carbon dioxide + water
$$CH_4 + O_2 \rightarrow CO_2 + H_2O$$

(c) iron oxide + carbon monoxide → iron + carbon dioxide
$$Fe_2O_3 + CO \rightarrow Fe + CO_2$$

Answer:

(a) First note that the O atoms are not balanced. To balance them, we need two H_2O molecules:
$H_2 + O_2 \rightarrow 2H_2O$ (still unbalanced)
The H atoms now need to be balanced:
$2H_2 + O_2 \rightarrow 2H_2O$ (balanced equation)

(b) This one is a bit more complex because there are three kinds of atoms, C, H, and O. The C's are already balanced. The O's occur in both products, so we save them for last. First balance the H atoms:
$CH_4 + O_2 \rightarrow CO_2 + 2H_2O$ (still unbalanced)
Now balance the O's:
$CH_4 + 2O_2 \rightarrow CO_2 + 2H_2O$ (balanced)

(c) First balance the Fe's, which is easy:
$Fe_2O_3 + CO \rightarrow 2Fe + CO_2$
To balance the O's, note that the CO and CO_2 molecules must be kept equal, so as not to upset the balance of C atoms. Therefore we must increase both equally to add more O atoms to the right side. The balanced equation is:
$$Fe_2O_3 + 3CO \rightarrow 2Fe + 3CO_2$$

8.3 VALENCE

Consider the following formulas of some well-known chemicals:

HCl	Hydrogen chloride
NaCl	sodium chloride
CaO	calcium oxide
H_2O	water
NH_3	ammonia
CH_4	methane
CaH_2	calcium hydride

The first two formulas, HCl and NaCl, show that the atoms of hydrogen,

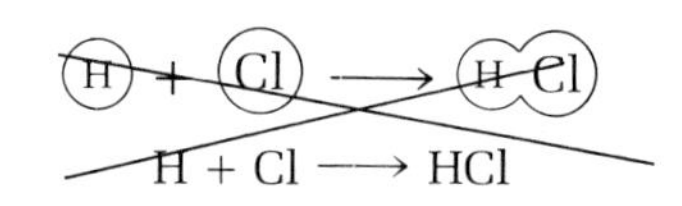

(WRONG, because hydrogen is H_2, not H, and chlorine is Cl_2, not Cl)

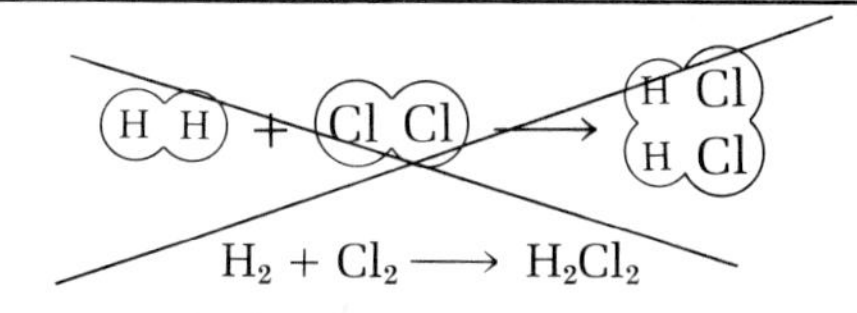

(WRONG, because hydrogen chloride is HCl, not H_2Cl_2)

chlorine, and sodium are all equal to each other in **combining capacity;** they combine one atom with one atom. The formula CaO shows that the atoms of calcium and oxygen also have equal combining capacities; one Ca atom combines with one O atom. But the formulas H_2O, NH_3, CH_4, and CaH_2 clearly show that not all atoms are equal in combining capacity. In fact, these formulas show that *more than one* atom of hydrogen can combine with *one* atom of the other element. Other elements can thus have higher combining capacities than hydrogen.

The combining capacity of an atom is known as its **common valence** (Latin, *valentia*, "capacity"). By convention we assign hydrogen a valence of 1. Then we can define the common valence of an element as the number of hydrogen atoms that combine with one atom of that element. Then the common valences of the other elements in the above formulas must be Na (sodium) and Cl (chlorine), 1; O (oxygen) and Ca (calcium), 2; N (nitrogen), 3; C (carbon), 4.

These assigned valences make it possible to predict other formulas. The rule is that two elements combine in such a way that the total valences of each element are equal. For example, calcium hydride is a compound of calcium and hydrogen. What is its formula? The valence of H is 1, and the valence of Ca is 2. In the formula, the total valences of H must equal the total valences of Ca. The formula must be

$$CaH_2$$

total valence 2 — total valence $1 + 1 = 2$

The subscripts are generally reduced to their least common denominators.* Thus, for calcium oxide we write CaO, not Ca_2O_2.

Example 3
Write the formula for the compound formed by the combination of (a) Ca and Cl; (b) N and Cl; (c) C and Cl; (d) Ca and N; (e) C and O.

Answer: **Since the Cl has a valence of 1, its subscript in a formula will be the valence of the other element. Thus: (a) $CaCl_2$; (b) NCl_3; (c) CCl_4; (d) Ca has a valence of 2 and N has a valence of 3. In order for the total valence of each element to be equal, 3 Ca atoms must combine with 2 N atoms, giving both Ca and N a total valence of 6. This gives the formula Ca_3N_2. (e) The same procedure yields a formula of C_2O_4, which reduces to CO_2. This formula actually corresponds to the composition of the molecule.**

The prediction of a formula from valences does not guarantee that the compound exists. For example, the valences of 2 for Ca and 4 for C lead to the prediction of the formula C_2Ca_4 or CCa_2. However, there is no such compound. Conversely, many compounds whose formulas cannot be predicted from valences do exist. Therefore, common valences are a useful but not infallible guide to the prediction of formulas of simple substances composed of two elements.

*This is not always the case. When the molecule has a definite and known structure, the formula includes all the atoms in one molecule. An example is hydrogen peroxide, H_2O_2.

IMPORTANT SAFETY NOTE

The descriptions of these four experiments are not instructions for the reader to carry out. Do not attempt to do so.

8.4 TYPES OF CHEMICAL BONDS

We will illustrate the four major types of chemical bonding with four familiar substances: a piece of silver (Ag), a large crystal of table salt (sodium chloride, NaCl), an ice cube (H_2O), and some pure sand (silicon dioxide, SiO_2). We will also use the simple electrical circuit shown in Figure 8–1, which consists of an ordinary light bulb plugged into a household socket (110 volts); however, there is a gap in the circuit so that no current flows and the bulb does not light. For convenience, we attach the two bare ends of wire to sticks of graphite (carbon). These pieces of graphite which are separated by the gap in the circuit are called the **electrodes.** If the gap is bridged by anything that conducts electricity, the bulb will light. We will now do experiments with our four substances.

EXPERIMENT 8.1

We touch the electrodes to the piece of silver. The bulb lights up and stays lit. If we remove the piece of silver after a few hours, or a few days or months, we note that it has not changed in any way. Nor has any of it been used up; its weight is exactly the same as it was at the start. Silver is a typical metal. Metals are good conductors of electricity.

EXPERIMENT 8.2

We touch the electrodes to the salt crystal. No luck, the bulb does not light. Next we put the salt in a porcelain dish and melt it (at about 800°C). We then insert the ends of the wire into the molten salt. Now the bulb lights. But we note that other things are happening, too—the molten NaCl is undergoing chemical change. Chlorine (a pale yellow gas) and sodium (a shiny metal) are being produced. Thus the NaCl is being decomposed as the electric current passes through it. This behavior is very different from that of metals. NaCl is a typical ionic compound. Ionic compounds conduct electricity in the liquid state (or in solution) but not in the solid state.

EXPERIMENT 8.3

We now try the ice. No light. We melt the ice and try the pure water. Still no light. Water is a typical covalent compound. Covalent compounds do not conduct elec-

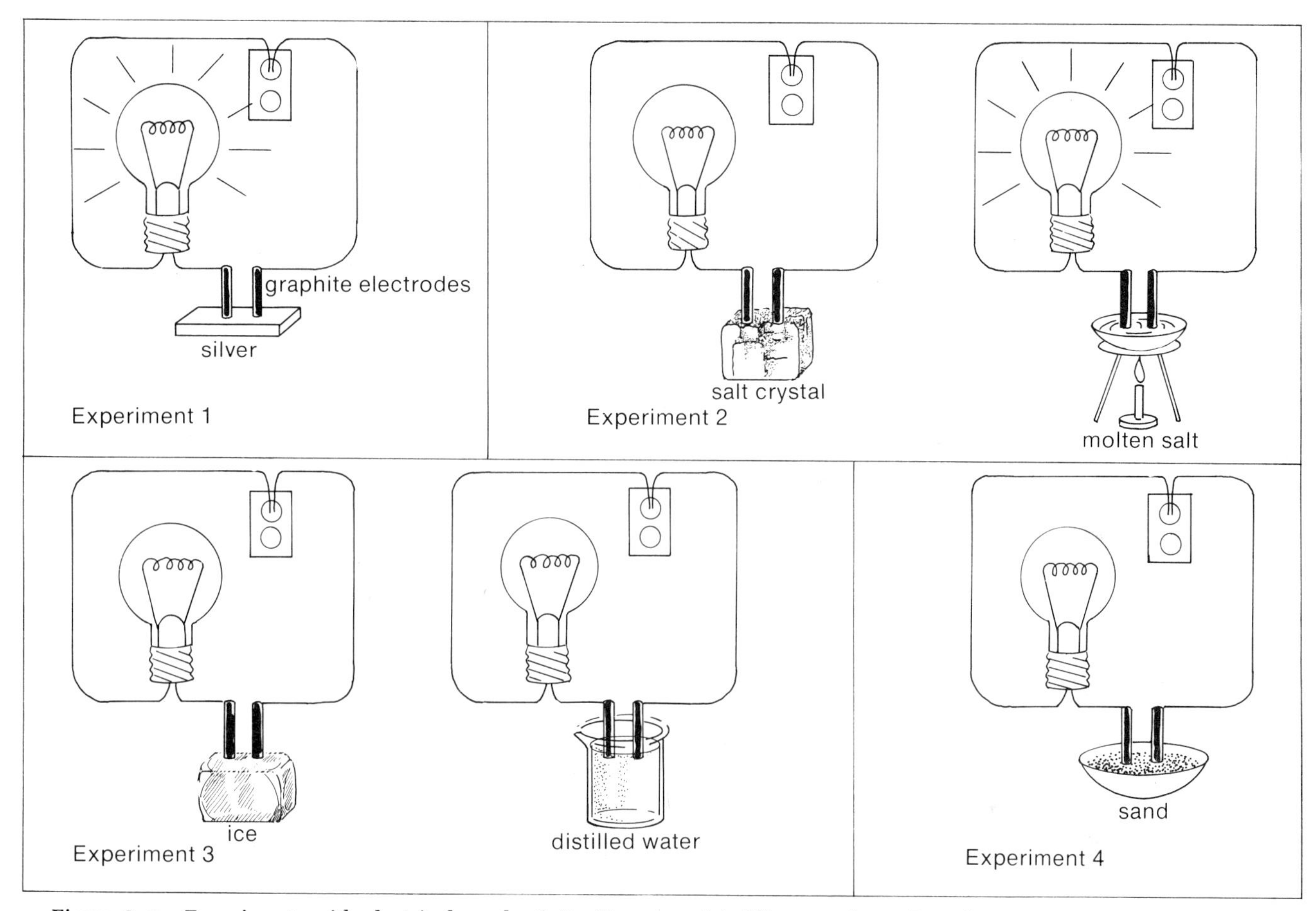

Figure 8–1. Experiments with electrical conductivity. Experiment 1: Silver conducts. Experiment 2: Salt crystal does not conduct, but molten salt does. Experiment 3: Neither ice nor water conduct. Experiment 4: Sand does not conduct.

tricity either in the solid or in the liquid state.*

EXPERIMENT 8.4

We repeat the test with the sand. No light. When we try to melt the sand, however, we find that a gas flame is not hot enough. The melting point of sand is 1710°C. If molten sand were used to complete the circuit, it would not work—the bulb would not light. Sand, like water, is a covalent compound, but the very large differences in their melting points indicates that there must be differences in the chemical bonding. Sand, or SiO_2, is a typical network covalent compound.

We will now discuss these four classes of substances and their chemical bonds in more detail. We will start with ionic substances, then take up the two kinds of covalent substances, and end with metals.

8.5 IONIC SUBSTANCES

You learned in Chapter 5 that an electric current consists of a movement of electrically charged particles. In molten NaCl the current is carried by electrically charged atoms called **ions.** The chloride ion, Cl^-, has one extra electron, giving it a negative charge. The sodium ion, Na^+, is missing one

*The distinction between electrical conductors and non-conductors is not an absolute one. Water does have a very slight electrical conductivity. The electrical experiments described here, however, do distinguish between different types of chemical bonding.

electron, giving it a positive charge. When a direct electric current (dc) is passed through molten NaCl, the ions move to opposite electrodes. The positively charged Na^+ ions are attracted to the negative electrode, where each one picks up the missing electron. In doing so, they become neutral atoms of sodium, which is a metallic element. Thus a chemical change occurs, as follows:

$$\underset{\text{ion}}{Na^+} + 1 \text{ electron} \rightarrow \underset{\text{neutral atom}}{Na}$$

Similarly, Cl^- ions move to the positive electrode, where they give up their extra electrons and become neutral Cl atoms:

$$\underset{\text{ion}}{Cl^-} - 1 \text{ electron} \rightarrow \underset{\text{neutral atom}}{Cl}$$

Chlorine atoms combine with each other to form Cl_2:

$$Cl + Cl \rightarrow Cl_2$$

Some ions have higher charges, although rarely greater than 3+ or 3−. Furthermore, the combinations of atoms that are known as **groups** may also carry an electrical charge. Table 8–1 lists some common ions, both positive and negative, and their names.

The names and formulas of common ionic compounds can be obtained directly from Table 8–1, simply by combining the names and formulas of the separate ions. When you write a formula, remember that the + and − charges must balance each other.

TABLE 8–1. A FEW COMMON IONS

Positive Ions	Negative Ions
Ammonium, NH_4^+	Bromide, Br^-
Potassium, K^+	Chlorate, ClO_3^-
Silver, Ag^+	Chloride, Cl^-
Sodium, Na^+	Fluoride, F^-
Barium, Ba^{2+}	Hydroxide, OH^-
Calcium, Ca^{2+}	Iodide, I^-
Copper(II) (cupric), Cu^{2+}	Nitrate, NO_3^-
Lead, Pb^{2+}	Carbonate, CO_3^{2-}
Magnesium, Mg^{2+}	Oxide, O^{2-}
Mercury(II) (mercuric), Hg^{2+}	Sulfate, SO_4^{2-}
	Sulfide S^{2-}
Tin(II) (stannous), Sn^{2+}	Sulfite SO_3^{2-}
Zinc, Zn^{2+}	Phosphate, PO_4^{3-}
Aluminum, Al^{3+}	
Iron(III) (ferric), Fe^{3+}	

Example 4
Write the names and formulas of the ionic compounds formed by a combination of (a) ammonium ion with bromide ion, with chloride ion, with sulfate ion; (b) calcium ion with hydroxide ion, with carbonate ion, with phosphate ion.

Answer:
(a) Combining the names of the + and − ions gives us
ammonium bromide, NH_4Br
ammonium chloride, NH_4Cl
ammonium sulfate. Here the formula cannot be NH_4SO_4 because the charges do not balance. It must be $(NH_4)_2SO_4$. Note that the procedure for writing formulas from ionic charges is the same as that which we used for writing formulas from common valences.
(b) The combinations give us
calcium hydroxide, $Ca(OH)_2$
calcium carbonate, $CaCO_3$
calcium phosphate, $Ca_3(PO_4)_2$, in which 6 + charges neutralize 6− charges.

We now ask the questions, "How can the charges on ions be accounted for? Why are some positive and some negative? Why are some charges greater than others?" To help us toward an answer, recall the electronic structures of O, F, Ne, Na, Mg, and Al from p. 214:

Atomic Number	Atom	Electrons Per Shell: *First*	*Second*	*Third*
8	O, oxygen	2	6	
9	F, fluorine	2	7	
10	Ne, neon	2	8	
11	Na, sodium	2	8	1
12	Mg, magnesium	2	8	2
13	Al, aluminum	2	8	3

Except for Ne, each of these elements forms a common ion. Let us look at the electronic structures of these ions. Remember, a − charge adds electrons, a + charge subtracts electrons.

Atomic Number	Ion or Atom	Electrons Per Shell: First	Second	Third
8	O^{2-}	2	8	
9	F^-	2	8	
10	Ne	2	8	
11	Na^+	2	8	
12	Mg^{2+}	2	8	
13	Al^{3+}	2	8	

This list shows us what these five ions have in common: They all have the same electronic structure as neon. They are said to be **isoelectronic** with neon and with each other. Neon itself forms no chemical compounds; it is an inert gas whose molecules are single atoms, Ne.

Similar relationships exist among the ions of elements whose atomic numbers are close to those of the other noble gases in Group 8A of the periodic table. These observations lead to the following reasoning:

- Electrons in atoms are involved in chemical bonding.
- Atoms bond with one another so as to acquire new and more stable electron configurations.
- The noble gases are chemically inert.* They do not readily gain or lose electrons, nor do they generally enter into chemical reactions. The filled shells of the noble gases must therefore represent stable arrangements of electrons. Other atoms form ions by gaining or losing electrons so as to acquire the stable electronic arrangement of a noble gas.
- As we have seen, when atoms react by electron transfer, the number of electrons gained and lost *must* be equal because the resulting ionic salt is neutral.

Notice that the number of electrons lost or gained by an atom in forming an ionic bond is equal to its valence. The charge on the ion formed from the atom is the valence of the element. Atoms that lose electrons to form positive ions are generally the metals. Atoms that gain electrons to form negative ions are generally the non-metals.

1A	2A	3A	4A	5A	6A	7A	8A
					O^{2-}	F^-	Ne
Na^+	Mg^{2+}	Al^{3+}					

These species are all isoelectronic.

Now we summarize these concepts about the formation of ionic compounds:

(1) There are six noble gases: helium, neon, argon, krypton, xenon, and radon. They have stable electronic configurations, characterized by eight electrons in their highest shells (except for helium, which has only two).

(2) Elements whose atomic numbers are one or two (sometimes three) higher than that of a noble gas can enter chemical reactions in which they lose just enough electrons to become isoelectronic with their noble-gas neighbor. Thus they become positive ions.

(3) Elements whose atomic numbers are one or two lower than that of a noble gas can enter chemical reactions in which they gain just enough electrons to become isoelectronic with their noble-gas neighbor. Thus they become negative ions.

(4) When elements in categories (2) and (3) are brought together, electron gains and losses occur in the same reaction, resulting in an **electron transfer** to form an ionic compound.

(5) Electrons are not created or destroyed in chemical reactions, so electrons gained = electrons lost. For example,

$$Mg \rightarrow Mg^{2+} + 2e^- \text{ \textit{two electrons lost}}$$
$$2F + 2e^- \rightarrow 2F^- \text{ \textit{two electrons gained}}$$

The resulting ionic compound is therefore MgF_2.

*For many years the noble gases were thought to be entirely inert. In fact, the word "noble" was used to convey the idea that these elements did not associate with the ordinary ones by entering into chemical combinations with them. However, in 1962 Neil Bartlett synthesized $XePtF_6$, and later other compounds of Xe and Kr were made. Bartlett's discovery showed that these gases could also show "common" chemical properties.

Example 5

Write formulas of ions of elements number 35, 37, and 38 that are isoelectronic with krypton.

Answer: **Krypton is number 36, so any element before krypton will need *more* negative charge to become isoelectronic with it, and elements after krypton will have to lose electrons and hence become positive. The ions are Br^-, Rb^+, and Sr^{2+}.**

Example 6

Write formulas for the ionic compounds rubidium bromide and strontium bromide.

Answer: **To conserve charge, the formulas must be RbBr and $SrBr_2$. In all ionic formulas the *total* positive charge must equal *total* negative charge.**

Ionic solids are very stable because the forces of attraction between oppositely charged ions are very strong. The solids do not conduct electricity because the ions, though charged, are rigidly held in the crystal structure and do not migrate. Figure 8–2 shows a model of the NaCl crystal lattice, in which the ions are in a cubic pattern. Note that each Na^+ ion inside the crystal is equally close to six Cl^- ions, and each C^- is equally close to six Na^+ ions. Since opposite charges attract each other, such an array is very stable. When the ionic solid melts, however, or is dissolved in a solvent like water, the ions are free to move and the substance can conduct electricity.

Figure 8–2. Portion of the NaCl crystal lattice.

8.6 COVALENT SUBSTANCES

Since pure liquid water does not conduct electricity, it cannot be an ionic substance. Yet the formula for water, H_2O, can be predicted from the common valence of hydrogen (1) and oxygen (2), just as the formula for sodium oxide, Na_2O, can be predicted from the ionic charges, Na^+ and O^{2-}. Thus, the chemical bonding in H_2O must be related in some way to that in ionic compounds, yet H_2O is not ionic. To interpret these facts, we turn again to the electronic structures of these elements and to their nearest noble gas neighbors. The noble gas nearest to H is helium, He; the one nearest to O is neon, Ne.

Atomic Number	Atom	Electrons Per Shell: *First*	Electrons Per Shell: *Second*
1	H	1	
2	He	2	
8	O	2	6
10	Ne	2	8

Hydrogen could become isoelectronic with He by gaining an electron. Oxygen could become isoelectronic with neon by gaining two electrons. These requirements cannot *both* be satisfied by electron transfer, because then one atom would have to lose electrons. Instead, the atoms *mutually share their electrons*. Then, the bond between H and O consists of two shared electrons, one contributed by each atom. The H now has two shared electrons, which makes it isoelectronic with He, but does not convert it into an ion. The O now has seven electrons in its $n = 2$ shell—the two that it shares with H and five others of its own. It is still one electron short of being isoelectronic with neon. This deficiency is satisfied by another sharing of two electrons with the second H atom, which gives us the formula H_2O. Such a sharing of a pair of electrons is called a **covalent bond** and is depicted by a dash or a pair of dots

$$H—O—H \text{ or } H{:}O{:}H$$

This description may sound very reasonable, but it doesn't explain just what holds the atoms together in a covalent bond. It is clear that in an ionic compound such as Na^+Cl^- the attractive force is electrical. What, then, is the covalent force? Let us examine the simplest covalent substance, H_2 (H—H, or H:H). Remember that these atoms are not points in space; they consist of separate nuclei and electrons. We must therefore consider separately the attractions between each electron and each nucleus of each atom and the repulsions between the two electrons and between the two nuclei. Then, if the sum of all the attractions exceeds the sum of all the repulsions, the molecule is stable. The strength of the bond results from the fact that the two *electrons are concentrated between the two nuclei to a greater degree than they would be if the atoms were unbonded.* Note that whenever plus and minus electrical charges alternate

$$+ - + - + - \ldots$$

opposite charges, which are attracting, are closer to each other than are like charges, which repel. Hence attractions exceed repulsions, and the array is stable.

The attractive force in a covalent bond, like that in an ionic bond, is electrical.

To find out *how many* covalent bonds each atom can form, we turn for help to the periodic table. Look at the portion below, which shows only the first three periods and highlights nine elements among them. Let us consider each of these elements:

Carbon is in Group 4. It needs four more electrons in order to resemble Ne. Carbon donates one electron for each covalent bond, and the other atom to be bonded also donates one electron, thereby forming a bonding pair of two electrons. Thus, each covalent bond adds a net of *one* electron per bonded atom. Therefore a carbon atom needs *four* covalent bonds to reach a total of eight and resemble Ne. We say that the covalency of carbon is 4.

Silicon: Same as carbon.

Nitrogen is in Group 5. It needs three more electrons and therefore forms three covalent bonds.

Phosphorus: Same as nitrogen.

Oxygen and sulfur: Group 6. Need two more electrons and therefore form two covalent bonds.

Fluorine and chlorine: Group 7. These elements form one covalent bond.

Note the following general equation that applies to all the above elements except hydrogen:

$$\text{Covalency} = 8 - \text{group number}$$

Hydrogen (a special case): Group 1. Needs one more electron to resemble helium. Forms one covalent bond.

8.7 FORMULAS OF COVALENT SUBSTANCES

The structural formula is a remarkably useful chemical tool. In its simplest form, a structural formula illus-

Group Number

	1A	2A	3A	4A	5A	6A	7A	8A
	H							He
	Li	Be	B	C	N	O	F	Ne
	Na	Mg	Al	Si	P	S	Cl	Ar
Covalency:	1			4	3	2	1	

trates the types and sequences of covalent bonds in a molecule. We have already seen the structural formula for water, H—O—H, which provides more information than the simple molecular formula H_2O. The structural formula shows that both H atoms are bonded to O. The formula H—H—O would be *incorrect*, because it shows a wrong sequence of bonds. Since structural formulas depict the arrangements of atoms in space, they can also show the angles formed by any two covalent bonds, as well as the relative lengths of the bonds. To do this properly for H_2O, we would have to write

```
H
 \ 105°
  O—H
```

showing that the bond angle is 105° and that the two H—O bonds are of equal length. In this chapter, however, we will concern ourselves not with bond lengths or angles but only with the sequences and types of bonds.

Single Bonds

With nothing more than the covalences of the nine elements shown in the accompanying figure, we can construct an astonishingly large number of structural formulas. The task is this: Given the following covalent bonds for each element,

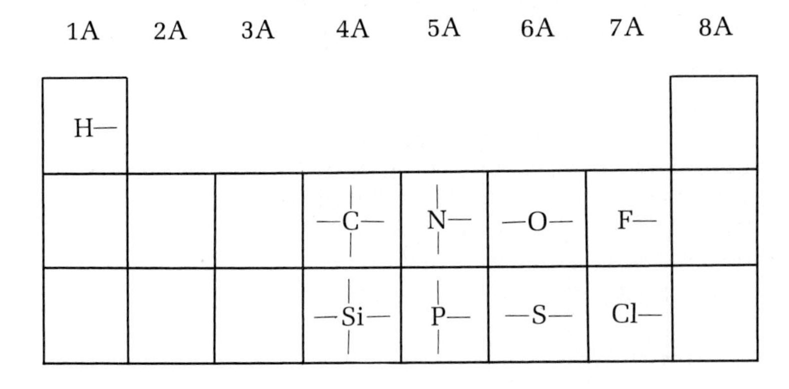

connect the atoms so that no bonds are left over.

Example 7
Write the molecular and structural formulas for the simplest covalent compounds that can be formed from (a) H and Cl; (b) H and S; (c) C and F; (d) P and Cl.

Answer:
(a) The formula can only be H—Cl.
(b) Since the covalency of S is 2, each S atom needs two H atoms. Therefore the formula must be H_2S, or H—S—H (analogous to water).
(c) Similar reasoning gives CF_4 or

```
   F
   |
F—C—F.
   |
   F
```

(d) PCl_3 or

```
Cl—P—Cl
   |
   Cl
```

More complex covalent compounds can be formed by unions of more than two elements, or by bonding of atoms of the same element with each other. If you are given the molecular formula of a covalent compound, and are asked to write the structural formula, the best procedure is to start with the highest covalency and work down to the lowest.

Example 8
Write the structural formula for (a) CH_4O; (b) CH_5N.

Answer:
(a) Start with

```
  |
—C—
  |
```

Add an oxygen,

```
  |
—C—O—
  |
```

Now satisfy the other covalencies with hydrogen,

```
  H
  |
H—C—O—H (methyl alcohol)
  |
  H
```

(b) Using the same procedure, we get

```
    H  H
    |  |
H—C—N—H (methylamine)
    |
    H
```

Carbon forms a unique series of compounds of extraordinary diversity. Moreover, living organisms on Earth consist largely of carbon compounds, and the processes of life involve, in large measure, the making and breaking of bonds to carbon atoms. The reasons for this uniqueness lie, in part, in the ability of carbon atoms to bond to each other in sequences of very extensive length and in continuous or branched patterns. Thus

```
            H  H
            |  |
C2H6 is H—C—C—H        ethane
            |  |
            H  H

          H  H  H
          |  |  |
C3H8 is H—C—C—C—H      propane
          |  |  |
          H  H  H
```

and the straight-chain octane (eight carbons) is

```
   H  H  H  H  H  H  H  H
   |  |  |  |  |  |  |  |
H—C—C—C—C—C—C—C—C—H
   |  |  |  |  |  |  |  |
   H  H  H  H  H  H  H  H
```

Eight carbon atoms can also be bonded to each other in highly branched patterns, such as

```
          H
          |
        H—C—H
   H      |     H     H     H
   |      |     |     |     |
H—C——————C—————C—————C—————C—H
   |      |     |     |     |
   H      |     H     |     H
        H—C—H       H—C—H
          |           |
          H           H
```

"iso-octane"

Now let us try this one: Write the structural formula for C_2H_6O. If we follow the rule of starting with the highest covalences and working down, we would get

```
 |  |              |  |
—C—C—, then  —C—C—O—,
 |  |              |  |

                 H  H
                 |  |
and finally, H—C—C—O—H
                 |  |
                 H  H
```

ethyl alcohol

But there is another possibility:

```
   H      H
   |      |
H—C—O—C—H   dimethyl ether
   |      |
   H      H
```

Both answers are equally correct, and in fact, both compounds are well known. Such existence of different substances with the same molecular formula is called **isomerism,** and the different substances, like ethyl alcohol and dimethyl ether, are **isomers.** However, their properties are quite different. Ethyl alcohol is a product of fermentation and is an intoxicant. It is a liquid that boils at about 78°C. Dimethyl ether is a colorless gas, sometimes used in refrigeration.

Example 9
Write the structural formula for (a) C_4H_{10} (two possibilities); (b) C_5H_{12} (three possibilities).

Answer:
(a) The carbons must all be linked to each other, since the hydrogens, with a covalence of 1 can only be linked to carbon. The two possible carbon skeletons are

```
C—C—C—C    and    C—C—C
                     |
                     C
```

If you now add enough bonds to *each* carbon to reach a total of 4, and attach a H atom to each such bond, you will

see that 10 H atoms are needed in each case:

```
    H  H  H  H
    |  |  |  |
 H—C—C—C—C—H
    |  |  |  |
    H  H  H  H

    H      H      H
    |      |      |
 H—C——C——C—H
    |      |      |
    H      |      H
        H—C—H
           |
           H
```

(b) The three possible carbon skeletons are

```
C—C—C—C—C,   C—C—C—C
                 |
                 C

           C
           |
 and   C—C—C
           |
           C
```

Adding the H atoms to give each C a covalence of 4 will yield the complete structural formulas:

```
    H  H  H  H  H
    |  |  |  |  |
 H—C—C—C—C—C—H ,
    |  |  |  |  |
    H  H  H  H  H

    H     H     H     H
    |     |     |     |
 H—C——C——C——C—H ,
    |     |     |     |
    H     |     H     H
       H—C—H
          |
          H

          H
          |
       H—C—H
    H     |     H
    |     |     |
 H—C——C——C—H
    |     |     |
    H     |     H
       H—C—H
          |
          H
```

Double and Triple Bonds

Natural gas contains, among other compounds, ethylene, whose molecular formula is C_2H_4. What is its structure? If we write

```
 H       H
  \     /
   C—C
  /     \
 H       H
```

we satisfy the composition and the covalencies of the H atoms, but not of the carbons. However, if we assume that there can be more than one covalent bond between the C atoms, we can write

```
 H       H
  \     /
   C═C          ethylene
  /     \
 H       H
```

and satisfy all the requirements. Are we merely playing pencil-and-paper games, or does the doubly bonded formula represent some molecular reality? We do know from experiment that the bonding between the carbon atoms in ethylene is shorter and stronger than it is in ethane, and this means that the attraction between the positive nuclei of the carbon atoms and the electrons between them is greater in ethylene. Therefore the electronic charge between the carbon nuclei must be greater in ethylene. *It is this greater electronic charge between the atoms that the double bond represents.* Specifically, the double bond denotes two electron pairs (four electrons) shared by the bonded atoms.

We can extend the concept of multiple bonding to the gas acetylene, C_2H_2, whose structure is represented as

```
H—C≡C—H
```

The triple bond is shorter and stronger than the double bond and denotes three shared electron pairs.

Example 10
Write structural formulas (with one or more double bonds) for (a) C_2H_3Cl; (b) COS.

Answer: **(a) H and Cl each has a valence of 1, so they cannot have any**

double bonds. The double bond must there be between the two carbon atoms. The formula must be

```
H       H
 \     /
  C═C
 /     \
H       Cl
```

(b) With equal numbers of atoms of different elements, it is good strategy to put the element with the highest covalence in the center and group the other elements around them. This would give S—C—O, and it is then obvious where the double bonds belong, to yield the correct formula S═C═O.

Cycles

There is no reason why the ends of a chain cannot find each other and form a bond. The result is a cycle. Note that a formula like C_3H_6 can represent either a doubly bonded or a cyclic structure:

```
           H
           |
H          C—H
 \       / |
  C═C    H
 /     \
H       H
```

propylene

```
     H   H
      \ /
H      C      H
 \   /   \   /
  C ——————— C
 /           \
H             H
```

cyclopropane

The Miller-Urey Experiment

Having seen how structural formulas are written, you may wonder whether these exercises are merely games chemists play, or whether they really reflect the properties of atoms. If you cut out all the squares of a crossword puzzle and tossed them into the air, you would hardly expect the letters to fall down again in the same word pattern, or indeed in any arrangement that made sense. What happens, then, when some simple covalent compounds are "zapped" with particles or photons of high energy to break them into various molecular fragments? Do the pieces bind themselves together again? Can new products be formed? Are the normal covalences reestablished? A very interesting experiment was carried out in 1953 by Stanley Miller and Harold Urey to explore what the chemistry of the Earth's atmosphere might have been before life existed. It is speculated that the primitive Earth's atmosphere consisted largely of hydrogen (H_2), water (H_2O), methane (CH_4), and ammonia (NH_3). Miller and Urey passed an electric spark through a mixture of these gases (see Figure 8–3) to imitate the action of lightning. The molecules broke into a variety of fragments, which then recombined spontaneously to form various amino acids, which are the building blocks of proteins. The structural formulas of some of these amino acids are:

```
     H     O
     |    //
  H—C—C
     |    \
     N     OH
    / \
   H   H
```

glycine

```
      H
      |    O
 H3C—C—C//
      |    \
      N     OH
     / \
    H   H
```

alanine

```
 O     H H     O
  \\   | |   //
    C—C—C—C
  /    | |    \
HO     H N     OH
        / \
       H   H
```

aspartic acid

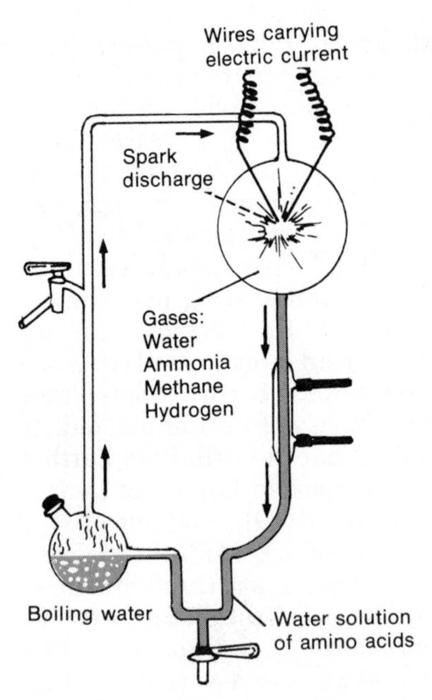

Figure 8–3. Miller-Urey experiment.

Thus the interplay of energy and probability (which molecular fragments hit each other and in what ways they collide) favors the formation of specific compounds from a chaotic mixture of molecular fragments.

8.8 NETWORK COVALENT SUBSTANCES

Recall our electrical experiment with sand. Sand (which is particles of quartz) does not conduct electricity and does not melt until it is heated to a very high temperature. The molecular formula of quartz, SiO_2, is analogous to that of carbon dioxide, CO_2. (Both Si and C have a covalence of 4.) But the structural formulas are different because CO_2 has double bonds while SiO_2 has only single bonds.

Why should this fact be so important? As we have just noted, double bonds are shorter than single bonds. This means that doubly bonded atoms are closer to each other than are singly bonded atoms. But large atoms cannot get as close to each other as smaller atoms can, because at closer range the repulsions of the more numerous electrons in the lower shells become too great. As a result, it is more difficult for the larger atoms to form double bonds. To see how important this difference is, let us try to write structural formulas for the oxides CO_2 and SiO_2, using double bonds for carbon but only single bonds for silicon. Carbon dioxide gives us no problem. Using double bonds, we write O═C═O, and the structural formula is complete. But using only single bonds for Si, we start with

```
        |
        O
        |
   —O—Si—O—.
        |
        O
        |
```

This satisfies the covalence of 4 for Si, but not the covalence of 2 for O. As we continue, the formula grows larger but the covalences of the outermost Si and O atoms are still not satisfied:

```
        |
        O
        |       |
   —O—Si—O—Si—O—
        |       |
                O
                |       |
           —O—Si—O—Si—O—
                |       |
                O
                |
```

To satisfy the covalencies with single bonds requires endless writing. What this means is that the covalent bonding in SiO_2 continues indefinitely; it is not limited to a small molecule. Therefore a sample of silicon dioxide is not composed of molecules in the ordinary sense but rather is a continuous three-dimensional network of single Si—O covalent bonds. It may be considered to be a **giant molecule** (see Fig. 8–4).

There have been science fiction accounts of intelligent life elsewhere in the Universe that is based on the chemistry of silicon, in contrast to the carbon-based life on Earth. Is silicon-life plausible? Most chemists think it is not, because the Si—Si bond is much weaker than the C—C bond. Consequently, structures with Si—Si bonds would react rapidly with oxygen to form giant-molecule compounds with Si—O bonds as in SiO_2 or silicate rocks. Furthermore, Si does not tend to form double or triple bonds.

Life may exist elsewhere and its forms may be different, but we can be sure of one thing. Only carbon has the variety of bonding to furnish the multitude of compounds needed for life as we know it.

8.9 THE METALLIC BOND

We return now to our first experiment with electrical conductivity—the one with silver. Like other metals, silver is an excellent conductor of electricity (one of the best, in fact), either in its solid or its liquid state. Moreover, metals are distinctive enough in other properties so that we can recognize them as such after only casual observation—by looking at them, feeling them, hefting them. (You could not tell just by looking at a white powder, or some blue crystals, whether the substance was ionic or covalent.) What is it, then, that is unique about metals, and what kind of bond holds their atoms together? Let us first look more carefully at their physical properties.

The most conspicuous attribute of metal is **luster**—the bright, highlighted appearance of a substance that reflects light well. A smooth silver surface, for example, throws back over 90 per cent of the light that shines upon it. The adjective "silvery" is often used in the general sense of having high luster. Two metals, gold and copper, are colored but nonetheless lustrous. Of course, many metallic objects (such as cast-iron frying pans) look dark or dull, but if we polish them enough, the natural luster of the metal reappears, and we realize that the dullness was a coating of foreign, nonmetallic matter.

In the Arctic winter you don't dare place your bare hand on a piece of metal—it would freeze right onto the surface. And if one end of a metal bar is in a flame, don't touch the other end, for it is too hot. *Metals are good conductors of heat.*

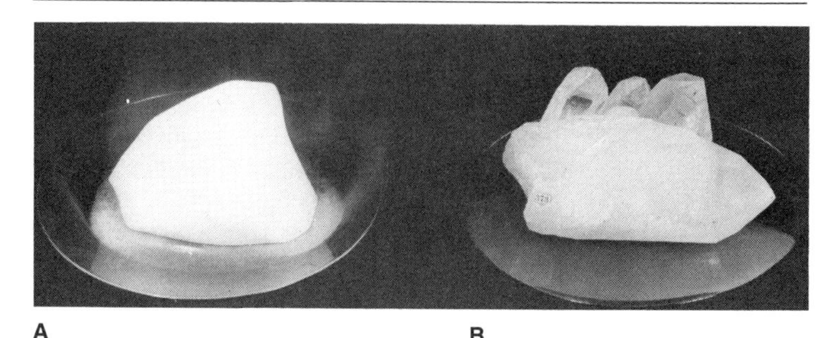

Figure 8–4. *A,* "Dry ice" (solid CO_2); the temperature of the solid is about $-79°C$. It is rapidly subliming to gaseous CO_2, and the cold fumes are generating a visible mist. The day after the photograph was taken, the dry ice was all gone. *B,* A specimen of a quartz (SiO_2) crystal borrowed from a museum case. It will keep its shape long after the museum is gone.

The electrical conductivity of metal is *far* greater than that of molten or dissolved salts. Copper, for example, is about a 60 million times better conductor than salt water (Table 8–2). Furthermore, when metals conduct electricity, no chemical change occurs. Thus, a silver bar or copper wire can carry an electric current indefinitely without decomposition. Ionic substances, on the other hand, undergo chemical change when electric currents pass through them.

The densest substances we know are metals. Lead is 11 times as dense as water, mercury over 13 times. Osmium and iridium, about 22 times as dense as water, top the list; they are denser than any other substances we know on Earth. A piece of osmium the size of a grapefruit (about 15 cm in diameter)

TABLE 8–2. APPROXIMATE ELECTRICAL CONDUCTIVITIES* AT ROOM TEMPERATURE

Silver or copper	600,000
Iron	100,000
Mercury	10,000
Salt water	0.01
Pure water	0.00000006
Rubber	0.000000000000001

*The units of electrical conductivity shown here are "reciprocal ohms/cm," but it is not the purpose of this table to emphasize such absolute values. Rather, attention should be given to the relationships among the different substances. Thus, if we compare samples of mercury and salt water *of equal physical dimensions,* we find that the mercury is more conductive by a factor of 10,000 to 0.01 or 1,000,000 to 1.

would surprise anyone who tried to pick it up, for it would weigh about 40 kg or close to 90 lb. By contrast, granite rock or concrete, which we commonly think of as "heavy" materials, are only about two or three times as dense as water. Of course, there are "light" metals, like aluminum (which, however, would sink even in the Dead Sea). But if we compare aluminum with solid nonmetallic elements of comparable or even greater atomic weight, such as sulfur or phosphorus, we find that aluminum is denser.

One of the most remarkable and unique properties of metals is their ability *to maintain their crystal structure even when their shape is deformed.* We say that metals are **malleable** (can be hammered flat, as with a mallet) and **ductile** (can be drawn into a wire). No other *crystalline* solids have this ability. Thus, if you strike a crystal of salt or sugar with a hammer, it will shatter, not flatten.

These sets of metallic properties are not at all consistent with our concepts of ionic or covalent bonding. The metallic bond must be related in some way to "loose" electrons in the crystal structure, for the following reasons:

1. The atoms of metallic elements, when they do enter into ionic bonding, tend to lose electrons.

2. When metals serve as conductors of electricity, it is electrons that actually carry the current.

3. Electrons are also the means by which metals conduct heat.

Considerations of metallic properties and the role of "loose" or "free" electrons in metals have led to a theory of the metallic bond. One important clue is that metals crystallize in lattice structures in which the atoms are closely packed (see Section 7.8 and Take-Home Experiment 4 in Chapter 7). In such close packing, one metal atom may be equally close to as many as 12 other atoms. In these arrangements, there simply are not enough valence electrons to provide ordinary two-electron covalent bonds between adjacent atoms. Therefore, a given valence electron is not associated with only two atoms but rather with *all* the atoms in a given sample of metal. In a metallic crystal, then, we have a large number of such "unattached" electrons scattered about everywhere. The energy levels of these "loose" valence electrons are very closely spaced—that is, the energy differences among them are very small. Taken together, the energy levels of these "loose" electrons form what amounts to a continuous band, called a **conduction band.**

Now, how does this idea of the metallic state account for the known properties of metals? The key must lie in the behavior of electrons in the conduction band. It is these electrons that can be promoted to slightly higher energy levels when an electrical potential (voltage) is applied; they are then free to move in the direction of the applied potential. Hence metals conduct electricity. Electrons in the conduction band can also absorb thermal (heat) energy readily; hence, metals conduct heat well. These electrons also absorb light energy, which promotes them to higher energy levels within the conduction band. When they fall back to their lower levels, the light is re-emitted; therefore metals reflect light. Metals are ductile and malleable because under mechanical stress the atoms of the crystal can move past each other with relatively little resistance and without breaking the metallic bonds, because the valence electrons in the conduction band "belong" to all the atoms and are not localized to individuals or pairs of atoms.

8.10 EPILOGUE

Let us not forget that in this chapter we have been dealing with environments that are common to us on Earth. Most molecules that are stable at ordinary temperatures are destroyed above about 5000°C and single atoms, small molecules, and small ions predominate. At still higher temperatures, such as those found in stars, electrons are extensively stripped from their atomic nuclei, resulting in a mixture of electrons and nuclei called a **plasma.**

At very high pressures (about a million atmospheres) atoms of non-metallic substances are squeezed together as tightly as are atoms in metals at room temperature, and materials such as hydrogen become metallic conductors.

> The temperature of a gas flame is about 2000° C. The chemistry of flames is entirely different from that of substances at ordinary temperatures.

CHAPTER OBJECTIVES

Know how chemical formulas are written and be sure to practice balancing chemical equations. Predict formulas from common valences or from ionic charges. Understand the meaning of "isoelectronic with a noble gas" and how this concept helps to predict the formulas of ionic and covalent substances. Study the natures of ionic and covalent bonding. Practice writing structural formulas with single, double, and triple bonds, and with cycles. Review the relationships between metallic properties and the conduction band in metals.

KEY WORDS

Chemical change
Symbol (of an element)
Formula (of a compound)
Chemical equation
Valence
Isoelectronic
Ionic bond
Covalent bond
Network covalent structure
Single bond
Double bond
Triple bond
Cyclic structure
Isomerism; isomer
Giant molecule
Metallic bond
Malleability
Ductility
Conduction band
Plasma

FORMULAS TO KNOW

Typical covalency = 8 − group number
(except for hydrogen)

TAKE-HOME EXPERIMENTS

1. **Reactions of some metallic elements.**

(a) "Steel wool" consists of iron fibers. Stuff a little of the nonsoapy variety into the bottom of a test tube and invert the tube into a glass ¼ filled with water. Leave the experiment alone for a few days until the iron wool looks quite rusty. What has happened to the water level in the test tube? Why has the volume of air in the tube decreased? The formula of the rust is Fe_2O_3. Write the balanced equation for the reaction.

(b) In the bottom of a wide-mouth jar (such as a peanut butter jar), put a piece of sponge soaked in salt water. Now place on the sponge a shiny piece of copper (a penny will do), a piece of silver (a shiny pre-1965 dime), and a piece of iron (a nail). Do not allow the metals to touch each other. Cover the jar and observe the metals daily for a period of time. Note any changes. Which metal seems most reactive? (The reactions involve the metals, air, and water. The salt helps to speed up the reaction.)

Experiment 1

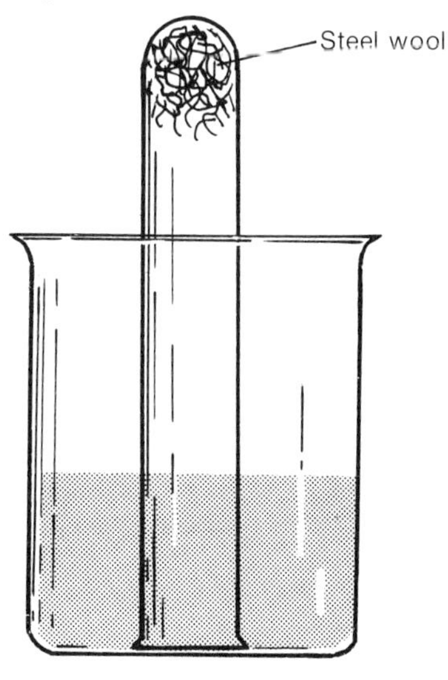

2. **Sugar, sand, and salt.** You know that salt is ionic and that sugar is not. Now let us compare these substances, together with sand, with regard to their hardness and stability to heat. Place a pinch of each substance on a cast-iron skillet or frying pan, keeping them in separate piles. Start to heat the pan, slowly. What do you observe? Which substance has the least stability to heat?

Now take a clean glass surface (such as the outside of a glass jar that you intend to discard) and rub it, in separate areas, with each of the three substances, using your thumb to try to grind the powder into the glass. Which substance is hard enough to scratch the glass? Explain your results.

3. **Carbon dioxide.** "Dry ice" is solid carbon dioxide, CO_2. To show that dry ice evaporates readily to produce CO_2 gas, place a small piece of dry ice in the bottom of a dry drinking glass. (*Caution:* Do not touch dry ice with your bare hands. It can freeze your skin and cause injury. Use a forceps, or wear gloves.) Let the dry ice remain there for a while, until at least part of it has evaporated. Now dip a lighted match or splint into the glass. What happens to the flame?

CO_2 is denser than air. "Pour" the CO_2 out of the glass onto a lighted match or candle. What do you observe? Explain.

Experiment 3

PROBLEMS

1. **Definitions.** Define or illustrate: (a) chemical change; (b) chemical equation; (c) chemical bond.

2. **Formulas.** For each of the following formulas, give the number of atoms of each element, and the total number of atoms, per molecule. (Assume that each formula represents one molecule.) (a) $KMnO_4$; (b) $Al(OH)_3$; (c) $CuSO_4(H_2O)_5$; (d) $Ba_3(PO_4)_2$; (e) $Co(NH_3)_3(NO_2)_3$.

3. **Equations.** Balance the following equations:

(a) $Cu_2O \rightarrow Cu + O_2$

(b) $MnCl_3 \rightarrow MnCl_2 + MnCl_4$

(c) $C_3H_6 + O_2 \rightarrow CO_2 + H_2O$

(d) $H_2S + SO_2 \rightarrow S + H_2O$

4. **Formulas and valence.** Using the following valences: F (fluorine), 1; Ba (barium) and S (sulfur), 2; PO_4 (phosphate), 3; Si (silicon), 4, write the formulas of (a) barium fluoride; (b) barium phosphate; (c) barium sulfide; (d) silicon fluoride; (e) silicon sulfide.

5. **Types of chemical bonds.** What are the four major types of chemical compounds, based on the nature of their chemical bonds? Which type conducts electricity without chemical change? Which conducts electricity only in the liquid state? Which two are non-conducting types? Which typically has higher melting points?

6. **Isoelectronic species.** Write the formulas of (a) ions of elements number 15, 16, 17, 19, and 20 that are isoelectronic with argon; (b) ions of elements number 1 and 3 that are isoelectronic with helium.

7. **Ionic compounds.** Using the information obtained by answering question 6, write the formulas for the following ionic compounds: (a) lithium hydride, which is a compound of lithium and hydrogen, (b) calcium chloride, (c) potassium sulfide, (d) calcium hydride, (e) lithium chloride.

8. **Ionic crystals.** Would a salt crystal in which the ions alternated in sets of two of each kind ($Na^+Na^+Cl^-Cl^-Na^+Na^+Cl^-Cl^-$. . .) be (a) more stable than, (b) less stable than, or (c) as stable as the arrangement shown in Figure 8–2? Defend your answer.

9. **Structural formulas** (single bonds only). Write structural formulas, consistent with the covalencies shown on page 242, for each of the following: (a) H_2S; (b) SiF_4; (c) $CClF_3$; (d) PH_3; (e) C_3H_7Cl (two possibilities); (f) NH_2Cl; (g) $C_2H_3Cl_3$ (two possibilities); (h)

Figure 9–1. The Copper Basin at Copperhill, Tennessee. A luxuriant forest once covered this area until fumes from smelters killed all of the vegetation. (U.S. Forest Service photo. From Odum: *Fundamentals of Ecology,* 3rd ed. Philadelphia, W. B. Saunders Co., 1971.)

useful chemical. In the United States, however, sulfur has been available more cheaply from natural deposits.

9.3 CASE HISTORY: POLLUTION BY AUTOMOBILE EXHAUST

By the early 1900's, many industrial cities were heavily polluted. The major sources of pollution were no mystery. The burning of coal was number one. Other specific sources, such as a steel mill or a copper smelter, were readily identifiable. The major air pollutants were mixtures of soot and oxides of sulfur, together with various kinds of mineral matter that make up fly ash. When the pollution was heavy, the air was dark. Black dust collected on window sills and shirt collars, and new-fallen snow did not stay white very long.

Imagine now that your grandfather had decided to go into the exciting new business of making moving pictures. Old-time photographic film was "slow" and required lots of sunlight, so he would hardly have moved to Pittsburgh. Southern California, with its warm, sunny climate and little need for coal, was more like it. A region of Los Angeles called Hollywood thus became the center of the movie industry. Population boomed, and after World War II, automobiles became almost as numerous as people. Then the quality of the atmosphere began to deteriorate in a strange way. Four classes of effects were noted: (a) A brownish haze settled over the city area (see Fig. 9–2); (b) people felt irritation in their eyes and throat; (c) various vegetable crops became damaged; and (d) the side walls of rubber tires began to crack (Fig. 9–3).

The air pollution "experts" of those days were found, of course, in the Pittsburgh area. They were called in to diagnose the problem. They looked for the same sources they knew so well—especially sulfur, but the facts did not fit the theory. Then in the early 1950's, A. J. Haagen-Smit, a chemist from California, proved conclusively that the mysterious Los Angeles smog was produced when automobile exhaust was exposed to sunlight.

The general principle of Haagen-Smit's experiments is easy to understand. He piped automobile exhaust into a sealed room equipped with sun lamps. The room contained various plants and pieces of rubber. The room was also provided with little masklike windows that permitted people to stick their faces in and smell the inside air. With the automobile exhaust in the room but the sun lamps off, the room smelled like automobile exhaust, and not like Los Angeles smog. But when the sun lamps were turned on, the symptoms developed. After a time, the air brought tears to the eyes, the plants showed the typical smog damage, and the pieces of rubber developed cracks. These were the crucial experiments that pointed the accusing finger at the automobile. Chemists then searched for reactions that caused this pollution.

Gasoline is a very complex mixture of chemicals, mostly hydrocarbons containing seven or eight carbon atoms per molecule. A typical formula is C_8H_{18}, which represents a set of 18 isomers known as "octanes." One of the isomers, called "iso-octane" in the petroleum industry, is the standard for 100-octane gasoline. Its structural formula is shown on page 243.

When an automobile engine is running, the piston moves so rapidly (typically 1500 to 3000 strokes per minute) that the gasoline vapor spends very little time in the cylinder. Not enough time, in fact, for the combustion to progress completely to CO_2 and H_2O. Some of the incompletely burned fragments are released through the exhaust pipe into the atmosphere. Here they react with ozone or other chemically active forms of oxygen to produce a new reactive molecule such as

$$\begin{array}{ccccccccc} & & H & & O & & & & \\ & & | & & \| & & & & \\ H & - & C & - & C & - & O & - & O - . \\ & & | & & & & & & \\ & & H & & & & & & \end{array}$$

Note that the covalence of the last oxygen atom is not satisfied; this incompleted valence is what makes the molecule reactive.

The next step is critical. These fragments react with NO_2 to produce a

Figure 9–2. Three views of downtown Los Angeles. *Top:* a clear day. *Middle:* pollution trapped beneath an inversion layer at 75 meters. *Bottom:* pollution distribution under an inversion layer at 450 meters. (Photos from Los Angeles Air Pollution Control District.)

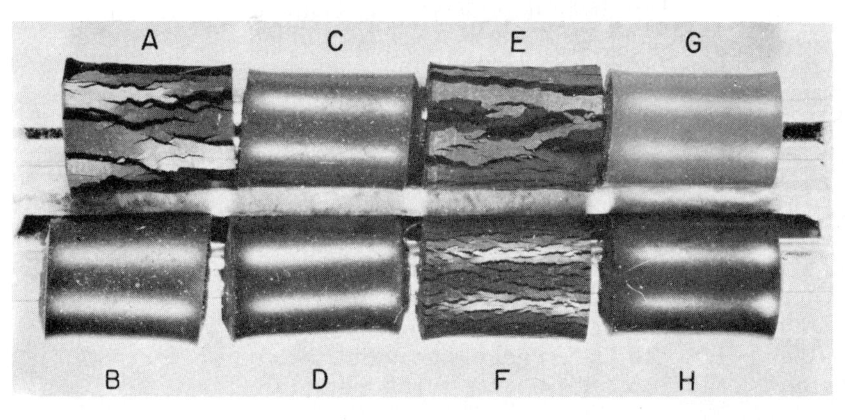

Figure 9–3. Effect of ozone exposure on samples of various rubber components. *A,* GR-S; *B,* Butyl; *C* and *D,* Neoprene; *E,* "Buna-N"; *F,* Natural rubber; *G,* Silicone; *H,* "Hypalon." (Photo courtesy of F. H. Winslow, Bell Telephone Laboratories. From Stern: *Air Pollution,* 2nd ed. New York, Academic Press, 1968.)

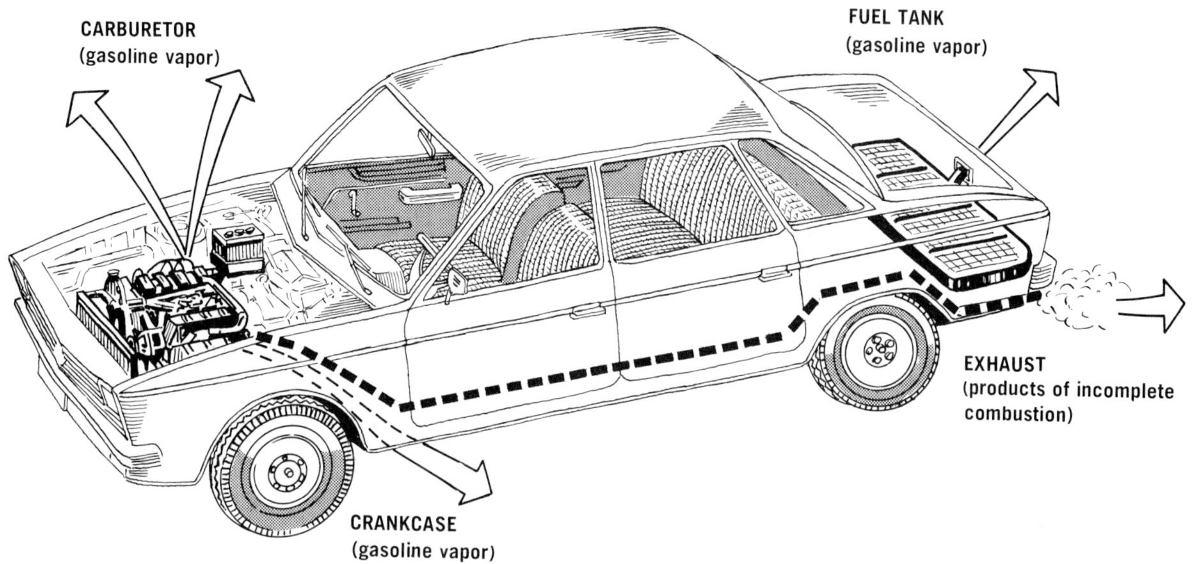

Potential sources of air pollutants from an automobile.

major class of atmospheric pollutants called peroxyacylnitrates (PAN). One example is:

$$\begin{array}{ccccccccccc} & & \mathrm{H} & & \mathrm{O} & & & & & & \\ & & | & & \| & & & & & & \\ \mathrm{H} & - & \mathrm{C} & - & \mathrm{C} & - & \mathrm{O} & - & \mathrm{O} & - & + \ NO_2 \rightarrow \\ & & | & & & & & & & & \\ & & \mathrm{H} & & & & & & & & \end{array}$$

$$\begin{array}{ccccccccccc} & & \mathrm{H} & & \mathrm{O} & & & & & & \mathrm{O} \\ & & | & & \| & & & & & & // \\ \mathrm{H} & - & \mathrm{C} & - & \mathrm{C} & - & \mathrm{O} & - & \mathrm{O} & - & \mathrm{N} \\ & & | & & & & & & & & \backslash \\ & & \mathrm{H} & & & & & & & & \mathrm{O} \end{array}$$

PAN

These compounds are very strong eye irritants and are extremely toxic to plant life.

The rates of these various reactions change during the course of the day as the intensity of the sunlight changes. In fact, the whole story—all the reactions and their rates—is not yet known. But we do know this: If hydrocarbons and other organic compounds were not introduced into the atmosphere, the polluting process would not take place. The remedy, then, is to drive the combustion of gasoline to completion, to produce *only* CO_2 and H_2O:

$$\text{hydrocarbon} + O_2 \rightarrow CO_2 + H_2O$$

There are fundamentally two ways to reduce hydrocarbon emission from automobile exhaust. One is to improve the design of the engine itself so that the gasoline is burned more completely. Such a design approach also improves the engine efficiency and results in substantial fuel savings. The other approach is to oxidize unburnt fuel before it is released into the air.

The second objective is achieved with the aid of a **catalyst** (Fig. 9–4). A catalyst is a compound that speeds up a reaction without itself being consumed. The best catalysts for speeding up the oxidation of organic molecules to CO_2 and H_2O are the heavy metals of Group 8B of the periodic table, especially platinum and palladium.

However, two major problems arise. For many years, a lead compound

Figure 9–4. Cutaway view of catalytic converter showing catalyst pellets.

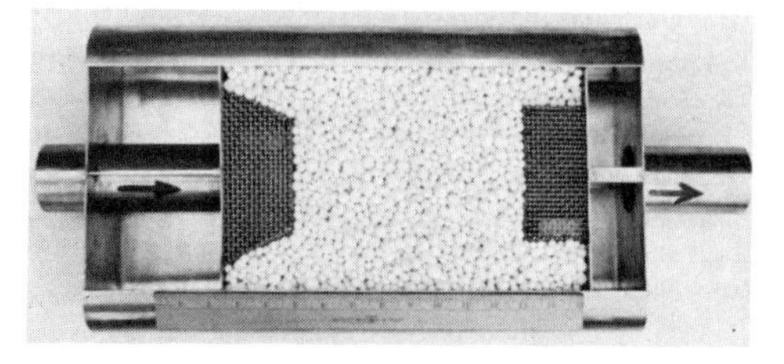

```
                H
                |
              H—C—H
                |
              H—C—H
                |
   H  H         |      H  H
   |  |         |      |  |
H—C—C———Pb———C—C—H
   |  |         |      |  |
   H  H         |      H  H
                |
              H—C—H
                |
              H—C—H
                |
                H
```

Tetraethyl lead (TEL)

was added to gasoline to improve engine performance. But the lead poisons the catalyst, destroying its effectiveness. It is for this reason that automobiles equipped with catalytic converters must use unleaded gasoline. The second problem is that the catalytic oxidation of the gasoline hydrocarbons generates heat within the catalytic converter that promotes other, environmentally unfavorable oxidations. Probably the most harmful of these is the increased conversion of N_2 to NO and NO_2.* The production of oxides of nitrogen is just what we want to avoid, since these compounds are also involved in the photochemical smog sequence.

The technical development of antipollution systems for automobiles is far from complete, and the next step may well be directed to the objective of minimizing the production of oxides of nitrogen. Our experience with the problems of atmospheric pollution from automobiles shows that the environmental aspects of this single process are extremely complex. Of course, decisions of public policy are also involved; pollution from the use of gasoline can be effectively reduced by using less gasoline—by driving fewer miles in smaller cars with more efficient gasoline consumption.

* The N_2 is part of the air drawn in to the cylinder. Since only a little of it reacts there, most of it goes out with the exhaust gases and enters the catalytic converter.

9.4 CASE HISTORY: CANCER-PRODUCING CHEMICALS (CARCINOGENS)

Normal cells in our bodies are being replaced all the time. Sometimes cells start to reproduce in an unorganized, uncontrolled way. They spread beyond their normal limits and invade other areas of the body. This abnormal growth is called **cancer,** and a clump of such cells is called a **tumor.** There are many different kinds of cancer, and there may be many different causes of this disease as well. We do know that certain chemical substances in the environment can convert normal cells into cancer cells. This fact was noted as early as 1775 by Dr. Percival Pott, who described the cancers of chimney sweepers whose bodies were exposed to soot. In more recent years, exposure to cigarette smoke has been implicated.

It is a fairly straightforward task to identify those who sweep chimneys and those who do not, as well as those who smoke and those who do not. As a result, we know that chimney soot and cigarette smoke are carcinogenic. However, for many other substances, the task of identification is far more difficult. How, then, can we establish whether or not a particular chemical is a carcinogen? It isn't easy. We do not conduct such experiments on human beings for two reasons. First, it is immoral to do so. Second, even if we would consider such a wrongful act, it would not be very helpful to have to wait 15 or 20 years for results. We could experiment by feeding concentrated food additives to humans, but this is something we should not even think about.

So the next step is to experiment on animals. Even here there are many people who would hesitate to do so because of their concern for animal rights. Nevertheless, most people assume that we, as humans, take priority over animals in such matters. The usual choices are small animals (mice, rats, guinea pigs, cats, dogs, and small monkeys). Of course, a rat is not a person. However, a rat will dine quite happily on the food that people eat and can be poisoned by chemicals that are harmful to people. (People shouldn't eat rat poison either.) We can't wait 20 years to see whether a rat that eats a synthetic chemical will get cancer. For one thing, the rat doesn't live that long. So we do to the rat what we would never do to a human being—we feed the rat a *concentrated* diet of the suspected chemical. If the rat gets cancer, the chemical is a carcinogen. Can we then set up some sort of an equation, such as, "If the rat gets cancer from the concentrated chemical in one month, then a person would get cancer from a dilute mixture of the chemical in 20 years?" No, we can do no such thing. All we can say is that if the rat gets cancer, then the chemical is a carcinogen for the rat. Since rats and people are both mammals, we can also say that the chemical is *probably* a carcinogen for people. Period. That is about as far as we can go. We can't say much about the chances that one person will get cancer, nor how long it will take.

In this case history, we will describe several categories of carcinogens.

Soot, tobacco smoke, and charcoal-grilled steak

The complete oxidation of a hydrocarbon yields only CO_2 and H_2O. But the oxidation in a fireplace, furnace, automobile cylinder, or candle flame is never complete. The reaction slows down in the cooler parts of the flame, and some materials escape before they are fully oxidized. The chemistry of flames is very complex, but in general the oxygen of the air bonds to the H atoms (to form H_2O) faster than it does to the C atoms. As a result, incomplete oxidations generate compounds that are enriched in carbon relative to hydrogen. This is an important point; we will illustrate it by using hydrocarbons with six carbon atoms per molecule as examples.

The formula for hexane, which is a component of gasoline, is C_6H_{14}. Like other hydrocarbons, it produces CO_2 and H_2O when it burns completely:

$$2C_6H_{14} + 19O_2 \rightarrow 12CO_2 + 14H_2O$$

As just noted, however, this reaction does not occur rapidly enough to go to completion in an ordinary flame. Products other than CO_2 and H_2O are formed. Some of these are

```
                           H  H  H  H  H  H
                           |  |  |  |  |  |
C6H14, hexane,          H—C—C—C—C—C—C—H
                           |  |  |  |  |  |
                           H  H  H  H  H  H
   ↓
                        H           H  H  H  H
                         \          |  |  |  |
C6H12, hexene,             C=C—C—C—C—C—H
                         /      |  |  |  |  |
                        H       H  H  H  H  H
   ↓
                                    H  H  H  H
                                    |  |  |  |
C6H10, hexyne,          H—C≡C—C—C—C—C—H
                                    |  |  |  |
                                    H  H  H  H
   ↓
                               H
                               |
C6H6, benzene,          H      C      H
                          \  /   \\  /
                           C       C
                           ||      |
                           C       C
                          /  \   //  \
                        H      C      H
   ↓                           |
                               H
C, soot
```

Note that the number of hydrogens per molecule *decreases* from compound to compound in the series just listed. Think now of pictures of a gasoline fire in a petroleum refinery or at an oil well you may have seen on a TV news broadcast. The most prominent feature is the towering cloud of black smoke.

What does all this have to do with cancer? It is this: Benzene is a carcinogen. So are many other hydrocarbons that are formed in flames during incomplete combustion. These carcinogenic hydrocarbons typically have several benzene-like rings, and contain fewer H atoms than C atoms per molecule. Soot and cigarette smoke are full of them. They are also found in smoked foods and in the burnt fringes of your charcoal-grilled steak. The structural formulas of some carcinogenic hydrocarbons are:

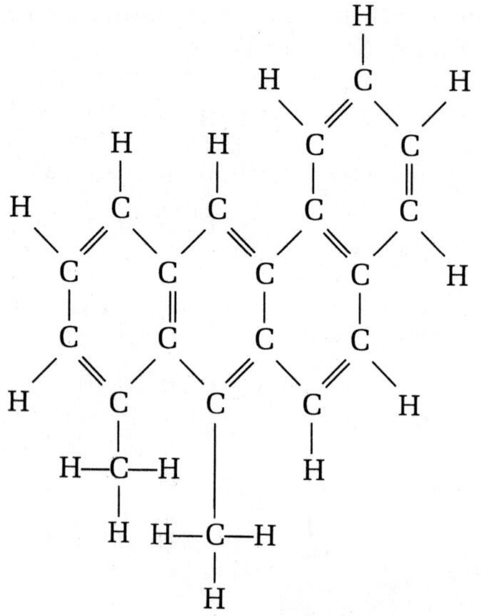

dimethyl benzanthracene

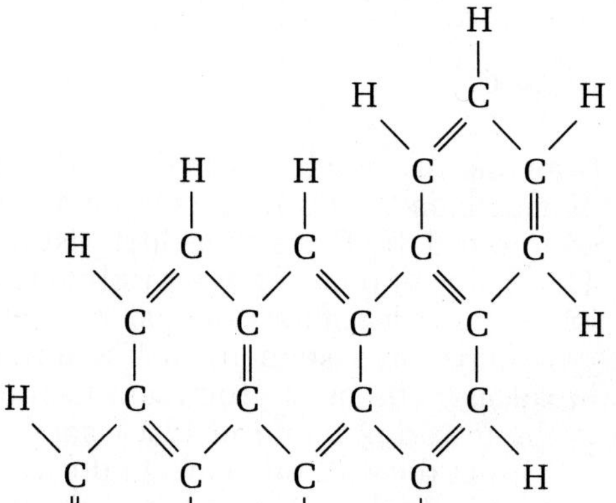

dibenzanthracene

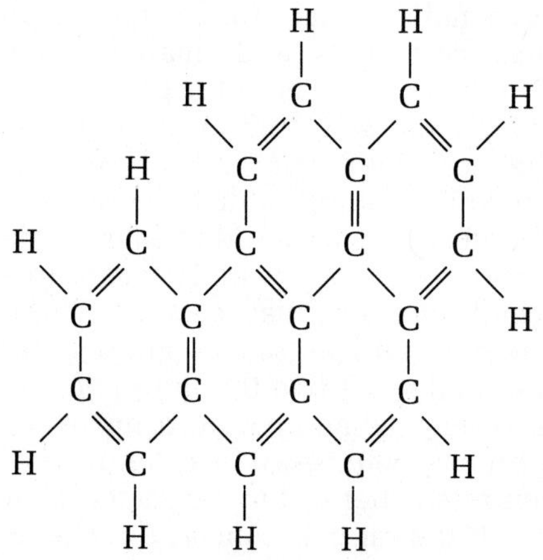

benzpyrene

Nitrosamines

An amine is an organic derivative of ammonia, NH_3, in which one or more of the hydrogens is replaced by a hydrocarbon portion (R), such as CH_3. A primary amine is

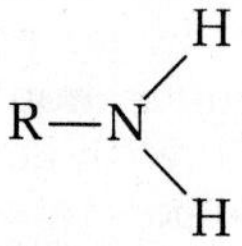

$$R{-}N{<}^{H}_{H}$$

; a secondary amine is

$$^{R}_{R}{>}N{-}H$$

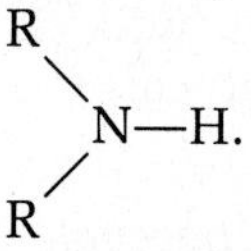

. A nitrite has an NO_2 group, as in sodium nitrite ($NaNO_2$).

Secondary amines react with nitrites in acid solution to form nitrosamines, which are potent carcinogens. For example,

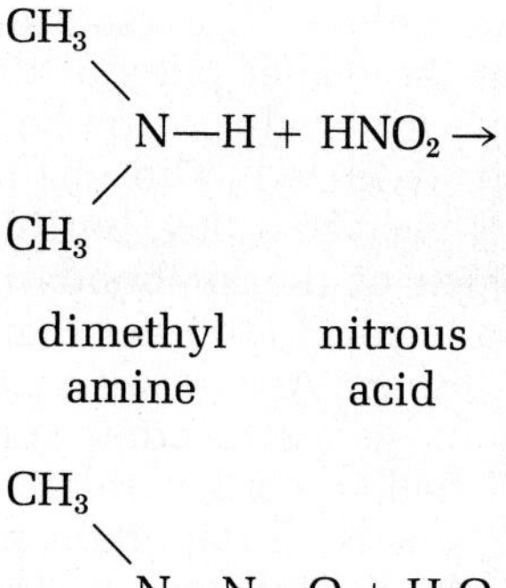

$$(CH_3)_2N{-}H + HNO_2 \rightarrow$$

dimethyl amine   nitrous acid

$$(CH_3)_2N{-}N{=}O + H_2O$$

dimethyl nitrosamine

tle in the vicinity of aluminum plants. Modern methods of air purification (see Chapter 12) can prevent such effects.

9.7 CASE HISTORY ON DISTURBANCE OF NATURAL CONDITIONS: THE OZONE LAYER IN THE STRATOSPHERE

An example of how human activity can have serious consequences is the possible depletion of stratospheric ozone by the chemical action of certain pollutants. The possible effects on terrestrial life are of serious concern.

The solar radiation that reaches the Earth contains high-energy photons in the ultraviolet range. Such radiation would be injurious to life if it penetrated to the land surface. However, most of this energy is absorbed in a series of reactions involving the small concentrations of ozone (about one molecule in 10,000,000) in the upper atmosphere:

Step 1:
O_3 + UV radiation $\rightarrow O_2 + O$
Description:
Ozone absorbs UV radiation: the energy gained ruptures a bond to produce O_2 and O

Step 2:
$O_2 + O \rightarrow O_3$ + IR radiation
Description:
The O_2 and O recombine, thus releasing IR radiation (heat)

If we add the two preceding equations, we get the following sum:

$$O_3 + \text{UV radiation} + O_2 + O \rightarrow O_2 + O + O_3 + \text{IR radiation}$$

If we now cancel terms that appear on both sides, everything cancels out except

$$\text{UV radiation} \rightarrow \text{IR radiation}$$

Thus, stratospheric ozone is a catalyst that provides a chemical pathway for converting solar ultraviolet radiation, which is hazardous to our health, into a warming effect in the upper atmosphere, which is harmless.

Ozone is produced and destroyed by natural processes. In the absence of

A cow afflicted with fluorosis.

pollution, these processes balance each other so that the natural concentration of ozone remains high enough (about 10 ppm) to screen out much of the solar ultraviolet radiation, thus providing the conditions under which life on Earth exists. However, pollution can initiate several other processes that upset this natural balance. One of these processes involves nitrogen oxide (NO).

$$NO + O_3 \rightarrow NO_2 + O_2$$
$$NO_2 + O \rightarrow NO + O_2$$
$$\text{net equation} \quad O_3 + O \rightarrow 2O_2$$

Note that the sum of the two equations is the destruction of ozone. Furthermore, the NO is not destroyed in the process. It acts as a catalyst, and therefore small quantities of NO can destroy large quantities of ozone.

These considerations have implied that a fleet of supersonic transport (SST) aircraft, flying in the stratosphere, would upset the ozone balance because the NO in the jet exhaust could initiate the ozone depletion sequences shown here. However, the fact that these reactions are known to occur does not prove that the ozone layer is at risk from SST jet exhaust. The reactions shown are only a very few of many different processes that go on at the same time.

Another mechanism for depletion of the ozone layer involves chlorine atoms, and is generally considered to be a more serious threat than the NO pathway. As shown in the following equations, chlorine atoms catalyze the ozone depletion reaction:

$$
\begin{array}{ll}
 & Cl + O_3 \rightarrow ClO + O_2 \\
 & ClO + O \rightarrow Cl + O_2 \\
\hline
\text{net equation} & O_3 + O \rightarrow 2O_2
\end{array}
$$

(same as reaction catalyzed by NO)

The important stratospheric sources of atomic chlorine are the chlorofluoromethanes, often referred to as **Freons,** which are DuPont trade names. $CFCl_3$, called Freon-11, is used as a propellant in aerosol cans, and CF_2Cl_2, called Freon-12, is a refrigerant. These compounds are stable in the lower atmosphere. As a result, they persist long enough to diffuse into the stratosphere. There they become exposed to solar ultraviolet radiation that is energetic enough to break the C—Cl bonds and release Cl atoms. The most recent studies have indicated that the chlorine pathway is an effective one for the removal of atmospheric ozone. The chlorofluoromethanes are a serious threat to the natural condition of the upper atmosphere.

The C—F bonds are stronger than C—Cl bonds and are not broken by the solar ultraviolet radiation. C—Br bonds are weaker and would be broken even more easily than C—Cl bonds.

Depletion of the ozone layer by chlorofluoromethanes.

CHAPTER OBJECTIVES

The six case histories presented here are interesting in themselves. Follow your instructor's guidance as to which ones to emphasize.

The chemical principles presented in this chapter should enable you to achieve the following objectives: Understand the nature of acidity and the meaning of the pH scale. Recognize molecules that are likely to be reactive because some of their atoms have less than their normal covalence. Practice adding chemical equations to obtain a net overall equation, and identify the catalyst in such a sequence. Know how to complete the structural formula of a benzene-like hydrocarbon if you are given only the outlines of the rings. Explain the function of roasting sulfide ores. Understand why an ionic solid like Al_2O_3 is much more stable than one like NaCl. Know how photons of different energies can be involved in a sequence of chemical reactions.

KEY WORDS

Acids	Roasting (of an ore)	Carcinogen
pH	Catalyst	Slag

TAKE-HOME EXPERIMENTS

1. **Food additives.** Makes lists of ingredients of various packaged foods in your kitchen. Classify the function of each ingredient as preservation, nutritional supplement, colorant, flavorant, emulsifier (to disperse oil and water in each other so that they do not separate), thickener, or some other purpose. If the function is not as obvious as, say, vitamins for nutritional supplements, or is not stated on the label, see whether you can get information from some other source. The best single reference volume is the Merck Index, which lists some 10,000 chemicals alphabetically and gives their uses. It should be in your school or public library.

2. **Iron and its oxides.** For your experiments with iron, use unsoaped "steel" wool (really iron wool). If you cannot get any of the unsoaped variety in the grocery store, try the hardware store. You will also need a magnet and a tweezers or forceps.

Take a small wad (about the size of a grape) of iron wool in a forceps or tweezers and burn it in a gas flame on a stove or bunsen burner. Remove the burnt iron from the flame and examine it carefully. Note the small, rounded black globs. The rounding shows that the material melted in the flame and turned into droplets. The black product is the magnetic oxide of iron (Fe_3O_4), known as **magnetite.** The ancient name of this substance is **lodestone.** It was used as a compass magnet by sailors as early as the eleventh century. Use your magnet to demonstrate that these tiny black globs are magnetic. The melting point of both Fe and Fe_3O_4 is about 1500° C.

Now take another small portion of your iron wool and leave it in an open dish containing a little water until it is completely rusted. This will require some days or weeks. The product is the red oxide, Fe_2O_3. In mineral form it is known as **hematite.** Verify with your magnet that this oxide is not magnetic.

Both hematite and magnetite are important iron ores.

3. **Automobile exhaust.** Go to your friendly neighborhood gasoline station and request the attendant's permission to let you ask a few questions. (Interview hint: Do not use a notebook, clipboard, or any other writing material. Know your questions by heart. Remember the answers—it takes a little practice but you can do it. When the interview is over, leave the gas station and only then should you fill out your questionnaire form. This informal method will be much more acceptable.) The questions are

(a) Can you tell the difference between cars that take leaded gas and those that take non-leaded gas just by the smell of the exhaust? (If the answer is no, your interview is over. If the answer is yes, ask the second question.) (b) What do the two exhausts smell like? Remember the *descriptive* words that the attendant uses. Some of the probable chemical equivalents are:

Like gas Gasoline	hydrocarbons
Pungent Acidic Tickling	Partially oxidized hydrocarbons
Cabbage Skunk	Sulfur compounds

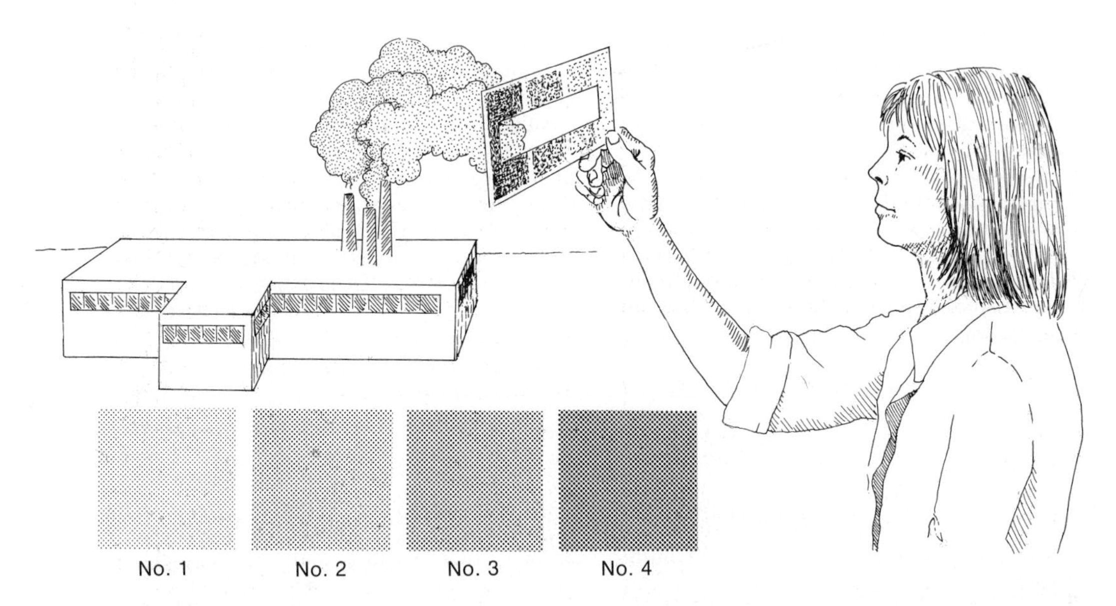

What are your conclusions regarding the action of catalytic converters which are used on automobiles that require non-leaded gasoline?

4. **Observation of smoke shade.** When fuel burns inefficiently, some of the unburned carbon particles are visible as a black or gray smoke. The density of such smoke coming from the stack of a factory or power plant can be estimated visually by comparing it with a series of printed grids. These grids, first suggested by Maximilian Ringelmann in 1898, are formed from squares of black lines on a white background, as follows:

Ringelmann No.	Black (%)	White (%)
1	20	80
2	40	60
3	60	40
4	80	20

Select a suitable location for observing a smoke plume from a stack. Hold the chart in front of you and view the smoke while comparing it to the chart. The light shining on the chart should be the same as that shining on the smoke. For best results, the sun should be behind you.

5. **Acids and bases in water.** Acidic and basic impurities occur as pollutants in water. They can be detected conveniently by substances whose color depends on acidity or basicity; these substances are called **indicators.**

Prepare an acid solution by mixing tap water with a little vinegar or lemon juice.

Prepare a basic solution by mixing tap water with a little dishwasher soap or other strong soap.

Many juices from naturally colored foods or flowers will serve as indicators. Purple grapes, red cabbage, or blueberries are among the best choices. Grind up one of these materials and extract the juice. This juice is your indicator. Place a few drops of your indicator in the acid solution and note the color. Repeat with the basic solution. The base and acid can neutralize each other. Verify this by testing various mixtures with your indicator.

PROBLEMS

1. **Oxides of sulfur.** What are the two major sulfur oxides? Write the balanced equation for the formation of each of these oxides from S and O_2.

2. **Sulfur acids.** Write the balanced chemical equations for the reaction of each sulfur oxide with water to form an acid.

3. **pH.** What is the pH of a solution in which the H^+ concentration (in moles/L) is (a) 10^{-4}; (b) 10^{-3}; (c) 10^{-10}; (d) 10^{-11}?

*4. **pH.** Could a solution be so strongly acidic that its pH is 0? A negative number?

*Indicates more difficult problem.

What is the pH of a solution whose H^+ concentration is one mole/L? Ten moles/L?

*5. **Sulfuric acid.** At flame temperatures SO_3 tends to decompose to SO_2 and oxygen. At room temperature, the reaction tends to go the other way, but it proceeds quite slowly. However, the reaction of SO_3 with water to form sulfuric acid is very rapid at room temperature. From this information, would you expect sulfuric acid mists to be found only in close proximity to combustion sources, or to be widely dispersed in the atmosphere of industrial societies? Defend your answer.

6. **Roasting of ores.** (a) What is the advantage of roasting a sulfide ore before reducing it to the metal? (b) Write the balanced chemical equation for the roasting of iron pyrite, FeS_2 (also called "fool's gold"), assuming that the iron is oxidized to Fe_3O_4.

7. **Hydrocarbons.** What is a hydrocarbon? Which of the following substances are hydrocarbons: (a) methane gas, CH_4; (b) glucose, $C_6H_{12}O_6$; (c) "gasohol," a mixture of octanes and ethyl alcohol, C_2H_5OH; (d) cetane, $C_{16}H_{34}$, a component of diesel fuel?

8. **Lead additives.** Another anti-knock agent is tetramethyl lead (TML). The methyl group is CH_3—. Write the structural formula for TML.

*9. **High octane gasoline.** "Lead-free" gasoline must have a sufficient resistance against engine knock to compensate for the absence of the lead additive. One approach is to provide a large proportion of highly branched hydrocarbons, which have good anti-knock properties. One such hydrocarbon is known as "triptane," C_7H_{16}; it is the isomer with the most CH_3 groups and has an octane rating greater than 100. Write the structural formula for triptane.

10. **Smog.** Write the balanced chemical equations for each of the following "smog" reactions: (a) the formation of nitrogen dioxide and atomic oxygen from NO and O_2; (b) the formation of nitrogen dioxide from NO and ozone; (c) the decomposition of one molecule of NO_2; (d) the formation of ozone from two other forms of oxygen.

11. **Smog.** The "acyl" in PAN is the $R-\overset{\overset{\displaystyle O}{\|}}{C}-$ portion, where R is a hydrocarbon group. When R is CH_3, this portion is called "acetyl;" when R is C_2H_5, the portion is "propionyl." Write the structural formula for peroxypropionylnitrate. What is the name of the PAN shown on page 259?

*Indicates more difficult problem.

12. **Food additives.** Name five functions that may be served by food additives. List them in what you think is the order of importance to consumers. Defend your priorities.

13. **Carcinogenic hydrocarbons.** A molecule of the carcinogenic hydrocarbon chrysene, represented by the skeleton

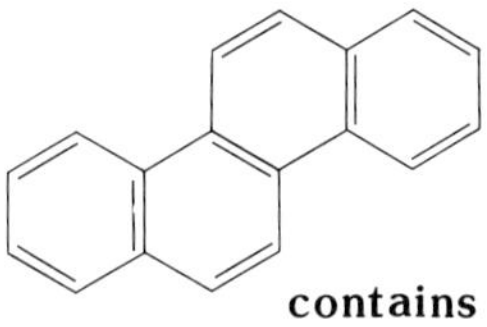

contains ____ C atoms and ____ H atoms.

14. **Carcinogenic hydrocarbons.** Write in all the C and H atoms in the beautiful structural formula of the carcinogenic hydrocarbon coronene.

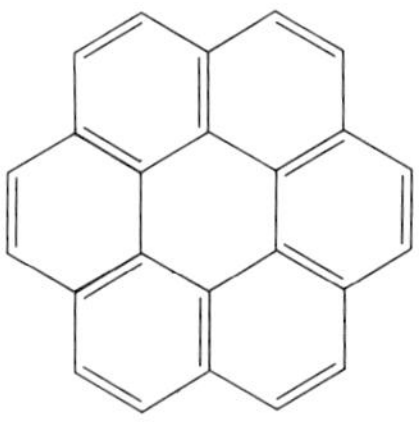

15. **Iron.** Write balanced chemical equations for each of the following reactions: (a) the reduction of Fe_3O_4 to iron by CO; (b) the reduction of Fe_2O_3 to iron by CO; (c) the production of lime, CaO, by the decomposition of limestone, $CaCO_3$; (d) the reaction of lime with sand to produce slag.

16. **Silicates.** A known cyclic silicate ion, $Si_3O_9^{6-}$, has the following structure:

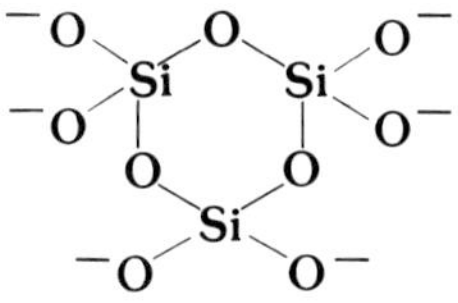

Write a balanced chemical equation to show how this anion can be broken down into three SiO_4^{4-} ions by the action of oxygen ions from lime, CaO.

17. **Aluminum.** Sand and bauxite, which are the raw materials for glass and alumi-

num, respectively, are plentiful in the Earth's crust. If we are in no danger of depleting these resources in the near future, why should we concern ourselves with recycling glass bottles and aluminum cans?

18. **Aluminum.** Aluminum is made by reducing bauxite, Al_2O_3, with an electric current. The process produces pollutants that contain fluorine. Where does the fluorine come from?

19. **Aluminum.** The reduction of Al_2O_3 to Al requires a high temperature and considerable energy. Most other common metals can be produced more easily. What makes Al_2O_3 so difficult?

20. **Ozone layer.** Ozone in the stratosphere protects us from solar UV radiation by converting it to IR radiation. Write the chemical equations that describe this transformation.

21. **Ozone layer.** Write the chemical equations that show how NO can act as a catalyst to destroy ozone.

22. **Ozone layer.** Write the chemical equations that show how Cl atoms can act as a catalyst to destroy ozone.

23. **Ozone.** Ozone is a natural component of air, produced by the action of lightning and solar radiation. It is also a product of photochemical smog. Ozone is toxic to people and it weakens rubber. However, its presence in the upper atmosphere helps protect us from the effects of high-energy radiation. Finally, ozone imparts an odor to air that many people describe as "fresh." (a) Would you classify ozone as an air pollutant? Explain. (b) Various ozone-producing devices have been sold as "air-fresheners" or "air purifiers." Would you buy one? Why or why not?

24. **Ozone layer.** (a) The following volatile liquids have been used as dry-cleaning solvents: carbon tetrachloride, CCl_4 (now banned because of its very high toxicity); methylchloroform, CH_3CCl_3 (1,1,1-trichloroethane, a preferred solvent); and naphtha (a mixture of hydrocarbons). Which one(s) of these would threaten the ozone layer if its vapor reached the stratosphere? Explain. (b) Methyl bromide, CH_3Br, is used as a fumigant in agriculture. Some of this vapor may also reach the stratosphere. Would this threaten the ozone layer?

CHAPTER 10

The three preceding chapters, which dealt with chemistry, were concerned with the changes among the electrons of the atoms. The energies absorbed or emitted during these changes are associated with transitions of electrons between different energy levels.

In this chapter we probe beneath the electron clouds to examine nuclear structure and the nature of the force that holds protons and neutrons together. We shall also take up various nuclear reactions, such as radioactivity, artificial transmutation, fission, and fusion. Finally, we will discuss several interesting applications, such as nuclear energy and the controversy surrounding it, radiochemical dating, and the use of radioisotopes in medicine.

NUCLEAR SCIENCE AND THE ENVIRONMENT

10.1 RADIOACTIVITY

Alchemy was the chemistry of the Middle Ages. One of its fundamental assumptions was that ordinary metals could be changed into gold—a process called **transmutation.** The alchemists never did it. Their consistent failures gradually led to the conclusion that elements are fundamental building blocks of matter that cannot be altered. This conviction was strengthened by the successes of the atomic theory in the nineteenth century. Elements could enter into various combinations with each other—that's chemistry—but they could not break down or be converted to other elements—that would be transmutation.

It was therefore somewhat eerie when the French physicist Henri Becquerel discovered in 1896 that uranium minerals spontaneously emit energy in the form of radiation. Thus, if a piece of photographic film is held near a uranium mineral in the dark, the film becomes exposed, just as it would be if it were held near a light. This emission of radiation from an element was called **radioactivity.** If elements were stable, however, where could such energy come from?

Several significant facts soon emerged from further studies. The pure uranium compounds that were extracted from the mineral were *less* radioactive than the crude mineral itself. This difference implied that there were other more highly radioactive substances mixed with the uranium. A series of careful, tedious separations carried out by Marie and Pierre Curie (wife and husband) resulted in the discovery of new radioactive elements, the most important of which was **radium.**

The Curies also learned that the radioactivity of substances is associated with their elements, not with compounds. Thus, a gram of radium has the same radioactivity in the form of the pure metal, Ra, as in the form of any of its compounds, such as radium bromide, $RaBr_2$, or radium carbonate, $RaCO_3$. Since chemical bonding involves the electrons of the atom but does not affect radioactivity, we are led to the conclusion that *radioactivity is associated with atomic nuclei.*

When a naturally radioactive source such as a uranium mineral is placed at the bottom of a long narrow hole in a block of lead, most of the radioactivity is absorbed by the lead, but a thin beam comes out of the hole. In

Madame Curie's laboratory. (From Weeks and Leicester: *Discovery of the Elements,* 7th ed. *J. Chem. Ed.,* Easton, Pa., 1968.)

an electric field, this emission is split into three beams, as shown in Figure 10–1, where they are labeled alpha (α), beta (β), and gamma (γ). The experimental results are interpreted as follows:

Beam	Deflection	Interpretation
Alpha	Toward negative plate.	The α-rays consist of positive particles. Further evidence shows that when these particles are neutralized by electrons, helium gas is produced. Therefore α-particles are helium nuclei.
Beta	Toward positive plate, more sharply deflected than α-particles.	The β-rays consist of negative particles, which are lighter than the alpha particles. Further evidence shows that they are electrons.
Gamma	Not deflected.	The γ-rays are electromagnetic radiation, which do not bear any electrical charge. Further evidence shows that they have higher frequency and therefore higher energy than X-rays.

Let us pause again for a moment and consider what happens to the atomic nuclei of radioactive elements. If a particle is emitted by a nucleus, the *nucleus must be unstable*—it gives up part of itself and loses its identity in the process. Thus the nucleus of one atom is converted—transmuted—into the nucleus of another. This conclusion was reached by Ernest Rutherford and Frederick Soddy in England in 1902.*

*"Soddy turned to his colleague and blurted: 'Rutherford, this is transmutation!' Rutherford rejoined: 'For Mike's sake, Soddy, don't call it *transmutation*. They'll have our heads off as alchemists.' Rutherford and Soddy were careful to use the term 'transformation' rather than 'transmutation.'" (*Scientific American*, August, 1966, p. 91.)

Figure 10–1. The behavior of alpha, beta, and gamma emissions in an electric field.

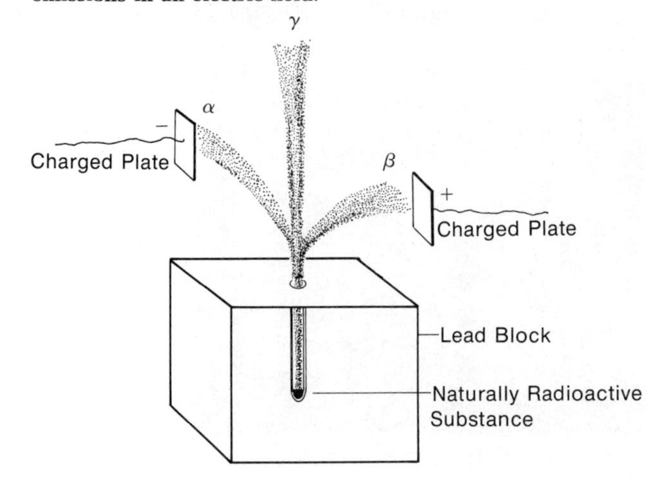

Radioactive disintegration can be represented by nuclear equations, which are simple to balance. For example,

$$^{226}_{88}\text{Ra} \rightarrow {}^{4}_{2}\text{He} + {}^{222}_{86}\text{Rn}$$

radium α-particle   radon

Remember from Chapter 7 that the superscripts represent mass numbers, which are conserved in these reactions. Thus, 226 = 4 + 222. The subscripts represent atomic numbers of nuclear charge, which are also conserved. Thus, 88 = 2 + 86. Note that when a radioisotope decomposes, a new atom is left behind. In some cases this leftover atom is stable (nonradioactive); in others it is radioactive. In the preceding example, radon is a radioactive gas which also decomposes to produce an alpha-particle and still another radioisotope, polonium-218. The decompositions continue for seven more steps until a stable isotope, lead-206, or $^{206}_{82}\text{Pb}$, is formed.

Example 1
Complete the following nuclear equation.

$$^{222}_{86}\text{Rn} \rightarrow {}^{4}_{2}\text{He} + ?$$

Answer: **The superscripts must add up to 222, so the mass number of the unknown element is 222 − 4 = 218. Similarly, from the subscripts, its atomic number must be 86 − 2 = 84. Searching for element 84 in the periodic table (inside back cover), we find that it is polonium, Po. Therefore the isotope must be $^{218}_{84}\text{Po}$ and the complete equation is**

$$^{222}_{86}\text{Rn} \rightarrow {}^{4}_{2}\text{He} + {}^{218}_{84}\text{Po}$$

In any radioactive disintegration, the element that decomposes is called the **parent,** and the new elements that

Figure 10–6. Control-rod driving mechanisms of a pressurized water reactor (PWR), partially disassembled. (From D. R. Inglis: *Nuclear Energy: Its Physics and Its Social Challenge.* Reading, Mass., Addison-Wesley, 1973, p. 91.)

it is a neutron moderator, which must be avoided. Furthermore, water boils at relatively low temperatures even under high pressures, and steam is a poor heat conductor. The coolant of choice is liquid sodium. Sodium is a silvery, soft, chemically active metal. It reacts with water to produce hydrogen gas; if air is present, the heat of the reaction can spark the explosion of the hydrogen. The sodium becomes highly radioactive when exposed to the reactor core. But its saving virtue is its ability to carry heat away from the reactor core rapidly, since it is an excellent heat conductor and it remains in the liquid state over a very wide temperature range, from 98°C to 890°C at normal atmospheric pressure.

The heat exchanger in which steam is produced to drive the turbine must be shielded from the radioactive sodium. This is accomplished by an intermediate loop of non-radioactive sodium. The entire arrangement is shown schematically in Figure 10–7*A*. A more detailed illustration of a breeder reactor is given in Figure 10–7*B*.

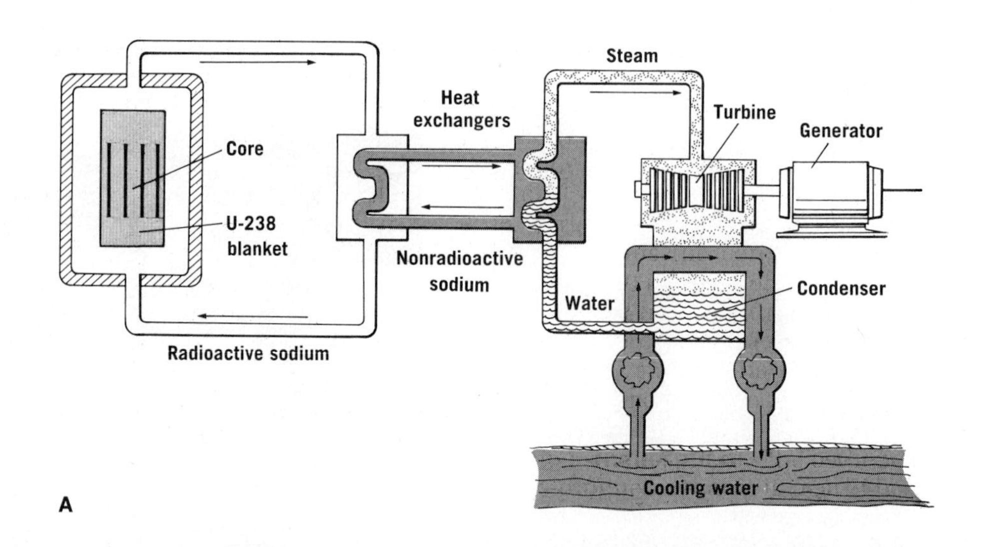
Steam
Heat exchangers
Turbine
Generator
Core
U-238 blanket
Nonradioactive sodium
Condenser
Water
Radioactive sodium
Cooling water

A

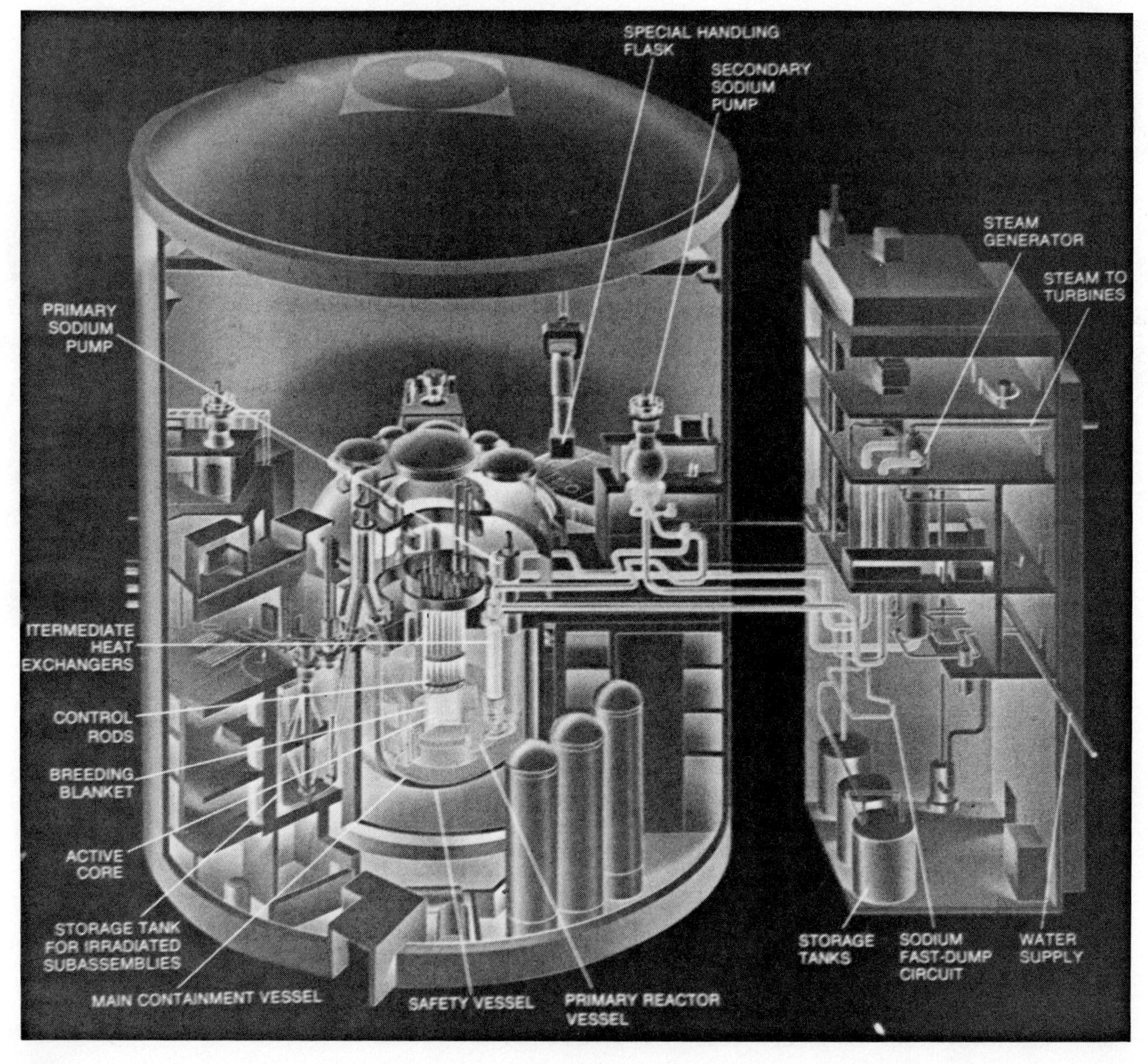
SPECIAL HANDLING FLASK
SECONDARY SODIUM PUMP
STEAM GENERATOR
STEAM TO TURBINES
PRIMARY SODIUM PUMP
ITERMEDIATE HEAT EXCHANGERS
CONTROL RODS
BREEDING BLANKET
ACTIVE CORE
STORAGE TANK FOR IRRADIATED SUBASSEMBLIES
MAIN CONTAINMENT VESSEL
SAFETY VESSEL
PRIMARY REACTOR VESSEL
STORAGE TANKS
SODIUM FAST-DUMP CIRCUIT
WATER SUPPLY

Figure 10–7. *A*, Schematic diagram of a fast breeder reactor. *B*, Vertical section of the French Superphenix reactor building and one of the four identical steam-generating buildings shows the main operating components of the plant. Superphenix is classified as a pool-type breeder reactor, which means that the active core, the primary sodium pumps, and the intermediate heat exchangers are all located within a single large vessel; in this particular design the main steel containment vessel, which is hung from a steel-and-concrete upper slab, is 21 meters across, and is filled with 3300 tons of molten sodium. A cylindrical structure welded to the main vessel supports the control-rod mechanism and the fuel subassemblies, which constitute the active core of the reactor. The four primary pumps convey the sodium upward through the core. The primary reactor vessel separates the "cold" sodium, which enters at the bottom of the subassemblies at a temperature of 395° C, from the "hot" sodium, which leaves at the top at 545° C. The hot sodium then flows downward through the eight intermediate heat exchangers, which form part of a secondary circuit of nonradioactive sodium, inserted for reasons of safety between the primary sodium circuit and the water-steam circuit. Each of four secondary loops consists of two intermediate heat exchangers, a secondary pump installed inside a spherical expansion tank, and a steam generator in the adjacent building. (From George A. Vendryes: "Superphenix: A Full-Scale Breeder Reactor." *Sci. Am.*, March, 1977, p. 28. Copyright © 1977 by Scientific American, Inc. All rights reserved. Drawing by George V. Kelvin.)

10.6 THE NUCLEAR FUEL CYCLES

The availability of nuclear fuels is discussed in Chapter 3. From mine to factory to disposal to ultimate death by radioactive decay, these materials will become more and more intimately involved with human activities if the nuclear industry continues to grow. It is therefore important to understand the steps involved in the processing, utilization, and disposal of nuclear fuels.

There are two different sequences to consider. The first applies to nonbreeder reactors, and is really better characterized as a "once-through" process rather than a cycle (except that the wastes *do* eventually return to earth). The second applies to breeder reactors, which may represent the nuclear economy of the future, sometimes called the "plutonium economy." Both cycles are described below.

The "Once-Through" Uranium Cycle

Uranium ore is mined in various areas of the Earth as a black deposit containing perhaps 0.3 per cent uranium. It is concentrated by a series of physical and chemical processes to a yellow mud that is about 80 per cent uranium oxide, U_3O_8. After further processing, the uranium is obtained as a brilliant orange oxide, UO_3.*

Recall that only about 0.7 per cent of natural uranium is the fissionable uranium-235 isotope. The next step is therefore **enrichment,** which is the most difficult and costly portion of the fuel cycle. Since the isotopes are for all practical purposes chemically identical, the separation must be carried out by physical processes. The method that has been in use since the beginning of the nuclear program is called **gaseous diffusion.** The uranium must first be converted to the gaseous uranium hexafluoride, UF_6. Then the UF_6 molecules that contain the lighter uranium-235 move through porous barriers slightly faster than the heavier $^{238}UF_6$ molecules. The enriched material is reconverted to an oxide form and fabricated into the fuel pellets used by the power plant. The diffusion plants are very costly to build and to operate, and few countries can afford them. Methods that operate on the principle of a centrifuge (whirling lighter particles away from heavier ones) promise to be cheaper.

After a year or more, when an appreciable portion of the uranium-235 has been consumed and fission products have accumulated, the fuel assemblies are removed from the reactor. At this time the waste products are at their most intensely radioactive state, and they are too dangerous to ship. They are therefore stored underwater at a site on the plant premises for a few months to allow the most highly radioactive components to decay. The partially decayed fuel is then shipped to a fuel processing plant. Here the pellets are cut

* Many American homes contain old (pre-World War II) orange-colored kitchen pottery prepared from this uranium oxide pigment. The radiation level from such materials is low. However, it would be well to get them out of your kitchen. Donate them to the nearest university.

up, dissolved, and chemically processed to recover uranium and plutonium (which was produced during the time the fuel was in the reactor).

The uranium can be reconverted to UF_6 and recycled for enrichment, but this is not advantageous as long as rich uranium ores can be mined. Meanwhile, most of it is stored. Plutonium is also stored for possible future use in reactors or as an explosive. Some of the radioisotopes that have special applications in science, medicine, or industry are also separated and set aside for such uses. The remainder is a solution of **radioactive waste.** The question of how and where to keep this material is the subject of Section 10.8.

The Plutonium Breeder Fuel Cycle

Review the earlier description of breeder reactors and recall that the breeder *produces* plutonium from uranium-238. This circumstance affects the fuel cycle in two important ways. First, the uranium enrichment step can be skipped because the reactor breeds its own fuel. Second, the fuel it breeds, which is plutonium, must be recovered and incorporated again into pellets. Since these operations do not all take place at the same location, the breeder fuel cycle has the effect of introducing plutonium in a highly enriched form into channels of commerce and transportation, with possible consequences that will be discussed later in this chapter. Figure 10–8 is a schematic diagram of the two cycles.

10.7 THE PRACTICE OF SAFETY IN NUCLEAR PLANTS

Questions about safety and hazards are at the heart of the nuclear controversy. It will be helpful, in approaching this very complex issue, to consider first some of the basic principles of industrial safety, and then to describe how they are applied in nuclear plants.

To become familiar with the general concepts of safe design, let us return to a familiar example, the automobile. You must first recognize that cars are inherently dangerous because there are many ways for an accident to occur. Therefore, the first requirement is that *safe operation must be part of the original design*. For example, brakes should operate smoothly and reliably; the driver should be able to see the road clearly on all sides, even at night or during rain or snow; and the automobile body must be able to absorb shocks from irregularities of the road surface. But we all know that mechanical devices are far from perfect. Things can go wrong, and, given enough time, we may be confident that they will. There are two possible responses to such dangers. One of them is to *provide "back-up" or duplicating systems that will take over in cases of failure.* This approach is sometimes called **redundancy.** An example in the automobile is an independent braking system that will operate if the primary one fails. The other response is to *provide a warning,* so that the operator can act to avoid an impending accident. Thus a light or buzzer can indicate overheating or loss of oil. Since materials and components wear out, we must also *provide a schedule of inspection and maintenance.* Finally, if all these systems fail and an accident does occur, the design should *provide features that prevent or minimize injury to people.* Such features are safety belts, air bags, helmets, asbestos suits, self-regenerative bumpers, and roll bars.

Nuclear plants, like automobiles, serve an inherently dangerous function—they process materials that are exceedingly harmful to living organisms. Therefore the five principles of safe practice described above must be followed. Their applications in nuclear plants may be outlined as follows:

Safe design

Recall that in a non-breeder reactor the uranium-238 is only modestly enriched with the fissionable uranium-235, so that the fuel is nothing like an atomic bomb. The control rods are inserted by pushing them down into the core, so that if power fails, they could simply fall. Ordinary water is both a coolant and a moderator. If excess heat

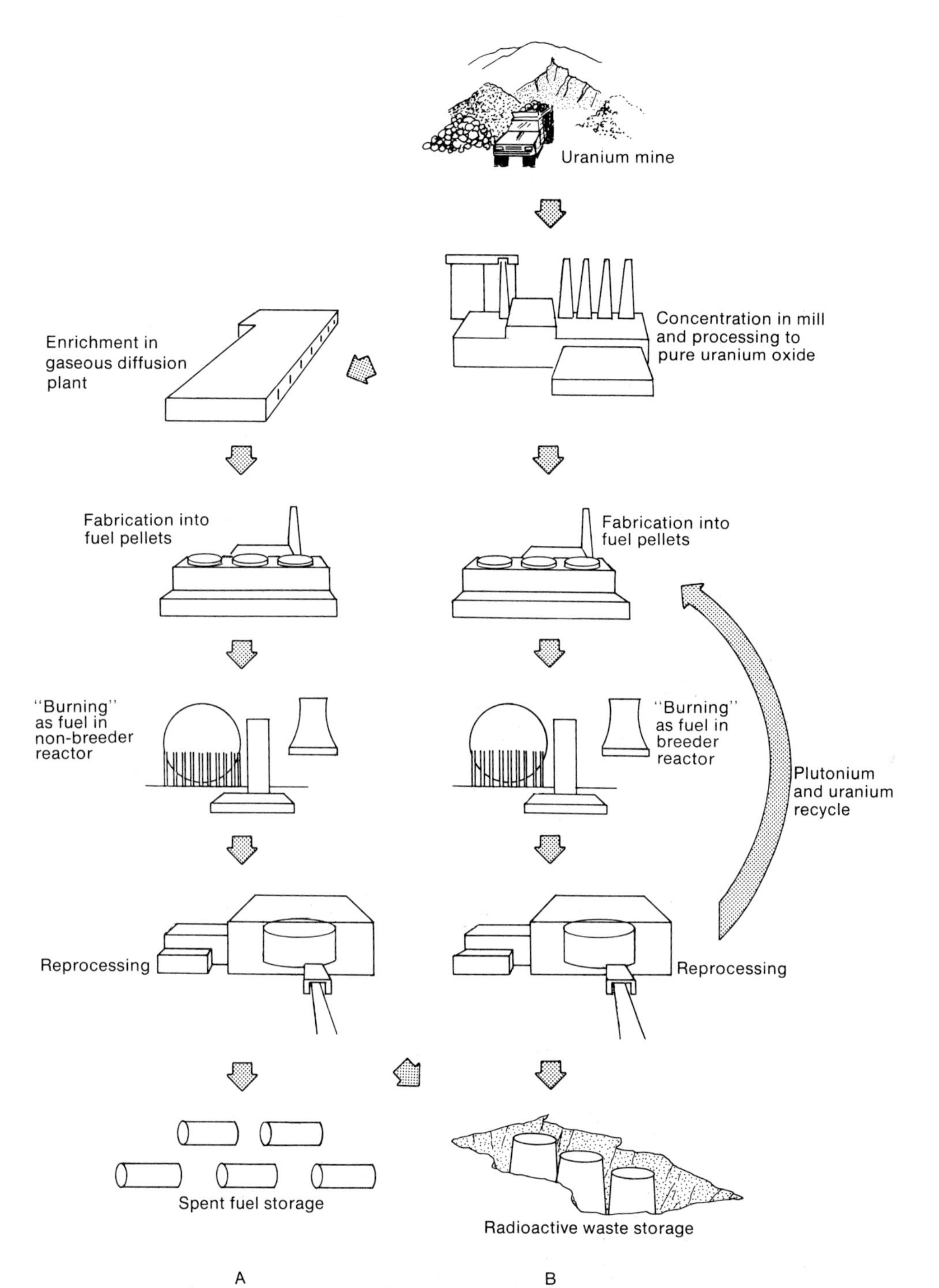

Figure 10–8. Nuclear fuel cycles. *A,* Once-through uranium cycle. *B,* Plutonium cycle.

should boil the water out, the loss of moderator would stop the chain reaction. Design specifications require that the materials of construction be of the highest engineering quality and be fully tested before use. As pointed out on page 287, the breeder reactor is inherently more dangerous, but this means only that safe design is, if anything, even more critical.

Redundancy

The system for which a back-up is most important is the one which cools the reactor core. If that should fail, there are generally at least *two* other independent cooling systems. If the power system on which the emergency measures depend should fail, an off-site source of power can be used. If *that* fails, on-site diesel generators or gas turbines can take over. Secondary systems of this type are quite complex and are interrelated in such a way that their responses are specifically appropriate to the nature of the emergency. Furthermore, these responses are fully automatic; they do not have to be initiated by a human operator.

Warning

The control room of a nuclear plant displays a panorama of gauges, dials, lights, buzzers, and bells. Individual workers are supplied with badges that are sensitive to radiation and that will monitor the degree to which the wearer has been exposed. Detection devices are distributed throughout the plant and are also set outdoors at various distances from the plant.

Inspection and maintenance

Reactor operators must go through strict licensing procedures, with periodic renewal. The plants themselves are inspected several times each year, penalities are applied to violators of regulations, and listings are kept of any defects or failures.

Protection in the event of accident

The reactor vessel, made of thick steel, is itself surrounded by an anti-radiation shielding several feet thick. As a final barrier, the entire system is surrounded by a vapor proof, steel-lined, reinforced concrete **containment structure** (Fig. 10–9). This barrier is designed to withstand earthquakes and

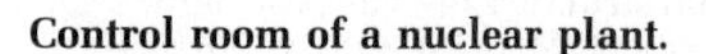

Control room of a nuclear plant.

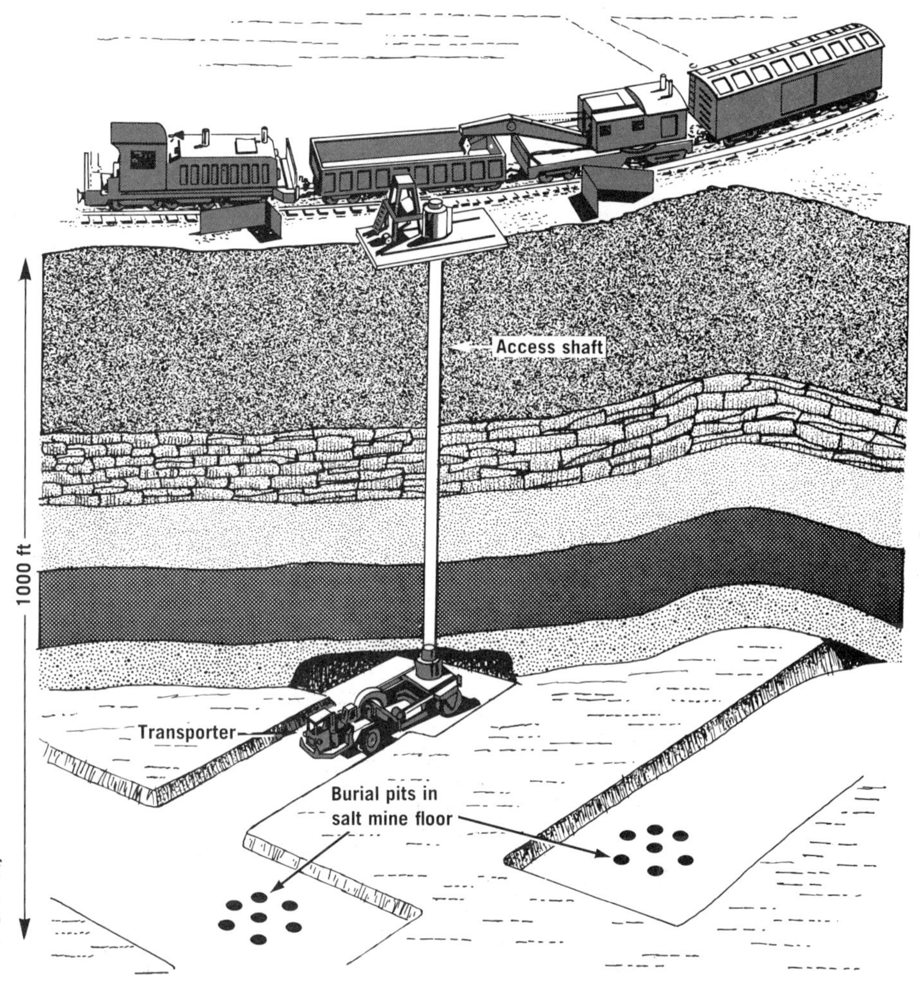

Figure 10–12. Final disposal of radioactive wastes in a salt mine. (© 1971 by The New York Times Company. Reprinted by permission.)

Figure 10–13. Engineering scheme, left, would involve freefalling canister with monitor attached. Canister would embed itself in soft, deep clay, and monitor could then be recovered. Other methods involve multiple-canister deposition.

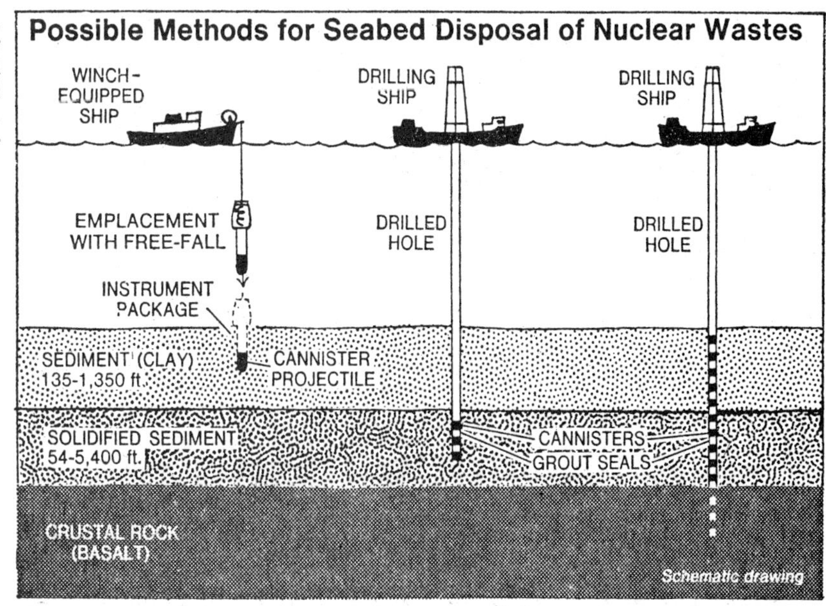

The New York Times/March 3, 1977

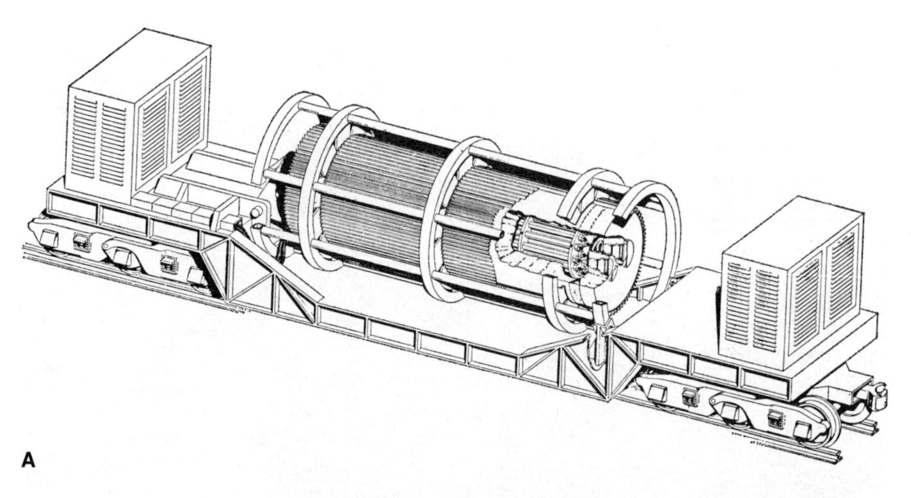

A

B

Figure 10–14. *Above,* Liquid metal fast breeder reactor spent-fuel shipping cask with 18 assemblies. (From *Science* *177*:31, July, 1972.) *Below,* Railroad accident showing a cylinder of uranium hexafluoride that fell off a flatcar in Wingate, North Carolina, on April 29, 1971. The cylinder was not damaged. (From *Science* *172*:1319, June 25, 1971. Copyright by the American Association for the Advancement of Science.)

A second question involves safe practice at the reprocessing plant, where the radioactive wastes are once again exposed to various physical and chemical operations. Some emission to the atmosphere (krypton and tritium, particularly), though small, seems to be unavoidable here. The United States experience with this problem has not been good. The first such reprocessing plant, near Buffalo, New York, operated from 1966 to 1971 but has since been shut down to correct various problems. It has not yet been reopened and its future is uncertain. Other plants have also experienced difficulties. In view of such circumstances, the critics of the nuclear program do not consider the technology of fuel reprocessing to be completely safe and reliable.

A third question involves the nuclear plants (and the reprocessing plants, too) themselves. What do we do with such a facility when its useful life is over? So far, we have no definite answers.

Still another problem involves so called "low-level" wastes. Think of it this way—imagine that you prepared an omelet for yourself, sat down to eat it, and just before you took the first bite someone rushed in and shouted, "Don't touch that food, the eggs are radioactive!" You would scoop up your omelet, plus the remaining eggs in your refrigerator, plus the broken shells, put them all in a lead box, and bury the box under a mountain somewhere. You would thus have disposed of the "high-level" wastes. But, to continue this fantasy, what about your plate, your frying pan, the other food in your refrigerator, maybe the refrigerator itself, and the kitchen counter? (Did any egg splash on it?) These materials are much less dangerous but much bulkier and more expensive. Would you bury everything that might possibly have been contaminated? In the real world of nuclear technology, such "low-level" problems are no fantasy, for they start with the tailings produced at the mine and continue through all portions of the fuel cycles. It seems nearly impossible to eliminate all low-level emissions.

Finally, with regard to the ultimate question of "permanent" storage of nuclear wastes at the end of the process, is the problem solved or is it not? The critics of the nuclear program emphasize the fact that political systems, on which we depend for reliable continuity of any public policy, do not last as long as radioactive isotopes.* Furthermore, the assumptions about the geological stability of salt caverns or rock formations are not *proven;* they are predictions.

There is no question that the risk of any single accident during any single day in the life of any particular batch of radioactive waste is very, very small. But it is also true that the consequences of an accident (for example, the contamination of a large supply of groundwater) could conceivably be very great. Furthermore, many batches of wastes are involved and there will be very, very many days. To judge the overall risks, we must multiply very small numbers (the risk of any one accident) by very large ones (serious consequences; long periods of time for storage of wastes). Any mathematician will tell you that such exercises approach indeterminate, or unknown, answers.

*Remember, the oldest major political system in the world today is only a bit over 200 years in age. It is the United States.

Terrorism and Sabotage

Uranium and plutonium inventories are not always fully accounted for. There are documented cases of substantial quantities of missing materials. Such discrepancies may not be real but may only be the results of errors in bookkeeping. Nevertheless, the question remains, "Can they be stolen, and, if so, can amateurs convert them into bombs?" A related question is, "Can saboteurs damage nuclear plants so that radioactive matter is released to the environment?" Some writers have speculated on this matter; some physics majors have written term papers on how to make a bomb (but they didn't make one); and some terrorist acts have actually been threatened and attempted. All these circumstances have led to increased security measures around nuclear installations. Since our past experience is (fortunately) so limited, we can only guess at the possibilities.

10.9 CASE HISTORY: THREE MILE ISLAND AND THE CHINA SYNDROME

The Three Mile Island nuclear plant in Middletown, Pennsylvania is a subsidiary of the General Utilities Corporation. Starting at 4 A.M. on March 28, 1979 a series of mishaps occurred. The sequence is enormously complicated—some 40 different events have been identified during the subsequent investigations. We will therefore try to highlight the key factors and address the two major questions:

1. What was the underlying cause of the accident? Was it the fault of the operators, or did it come about because the plant was incorrectly designed?

2. Was there ever a serious risk that the accident might have gone out of control, causing a meltdown (China Syndrome) that would endanger the people over a wide area (the state of Pennsylvania)?

The operation that seems to have started the trouble was a routine one—the change of a batch of water purifier in a piping system. For a nuclear plant, this job is considered to be as routine as, say, changing the oil filter in an automobile. But a problem developed; some air got into the pipe, causing an interruption in the flow of water. Of course, the back-up systems in a nuclear plant are designed to respond automatically to such an event, but, in this instance, several other things went wrong.

•Two spare feedwater pumps were supposed to be ready to operate at all times. However, the valves that control the water from these pumps were out of service for routine maintenance; therefore, the spare pumps could not deliver water. The controls for these valves were provided with tags to indicate they were being repaired. The tags hung down over red indicator lights that go on when the spare pumps are not feeding water. Since the lights were obscured by the tags, the operators did not see that they were lit and did not realize that no water was flowing.

•As a result, pressure built up in the reactor core. A relief valve in the primary coolant loop then opened automatically (as it should have) to let out superheated steam. *But the relief valve failed to close,* causing a dangerous drop in pressure. This malfunction is considered to be the crucial failure of equipment in the entire sequence.

•When the emergency core cooling system came on automatically, the

The Three Mile Island nuclear facility. (Photo courtesy of *Philadelphia Inquirer*/Chuck Isaacs)

ing, the method has not yet been successful, but research is continuing.

Could a fusion reactor get out of control and go off like a hydrogen bomb? Nuclear scientists are entirely confident that the answer is no, an explosion could not occur. The reason is that the hydrogen isotopes are continuously fed into the reactor and are continuously consumed; they do not accumulate. The total quantity of fuel in the plasma at any one time would be very small—about 2 g or so—very far below the critical mass required for a runaway reaction. If the temperature were to drop, or the plasma somehow dispersed itself, the reaction would stop; in effect, the fusion would turn itself off. The situation is rather analogous to that of a burning candle; if something goes wrong, the flame goes out, the candle does not explode.

Would there be a problem of environmental radioactivity? The answer here is yes, because both tritium and neutrons could be released. Tritium is radioactive (half-life, 12 years) and, being an isotope of hydrogen, combines with oxygen to form radioactive water. The tritiated water could conceivably enter food webs and harm living organisms. However, the energy released by tritium (in the form of fast electrons) is so weak that it would be virtually harmless if its source were outside the body. Furthermore, sound engineering practice should be able to restrict any tritium emissions to inconsequential levels.

Neutron release is another potential hazard, but we must remember that the neutrons stop when the reaction stops. However, neutrons are absorbed by atomic nuclei, and the new atoms that are thereby produced are radioactive. As a result, there could well be substantial quantities of radioactive matter to be disposed, but in general, the problem should be much less difficult than that of wastes from fission reactors.

A hydrogen bomb explosion. Note that the giant battleships are dwarfed by the cloud. (Photography by H. Armstrong Roberts.)

10.11 RADIOCHEMICAL DATING

Radioactivity can be used to estimate the age of a rock, a fossil skeleton, or an ancient shipwreck. The method, known as **radiochemical dating,** makes use of the pattern of radioactive decay, which can be expressed in terms of half-lives. The age of the object is measured by calculating how long it would take to return to the beginning if the pattern of radioactive decay were reversed. In other words, we calculate back into time.

As an example, consider the decay of uranium-238, whose half-life is 4.5 billion years. The final stable product is lead-206. (The intermediate products decay very rapidly compared with U-238, so we may ignore them.) Thus, if we start with pure U-238, the decay pattern would be

Time (Billions of Years)	Number of Half-lives	Composition	
		% U-238	% Pb-206
0	0	100	0
4.5	1	50	50
9	2	25	75
13.5	3	12.5	87.5
etc.			

Therefore, if we analyze a rock to contain 50 per cent U-238 and 50 per cent Pb-206, the age of that rock must be 4.5 billion years.

However, we cannot use uranium-lead ratios to date human fossils or antique works of art. In 1948, Willard Libby conceived of a method of radiochemical dating based on carbon. The principle is this: Atmospheric nitrogen is bombarded by neutrons generated from outer space so that a few nitrogen atoms are converted to a radioactive isotope of carbon, ^{14}C. The reaction is

$$^{14}_{7}N + ^{1}_{0}n \rightarrow ^{14}_{6}C + ^{1}_{1}H$$

Carbon-14 is radioactive, with a 5730-year half-life. This small concentration of radioactive carbon in the atmosphere enters the carbon cycle, becoming $^{14}CO_2$. It then participates in photosynthesis to become part of the tissues of all plants. Since animal life depends on the consumption of plants, C-14 enters the bodies of animals as well. Now, as long as a plant or animal is alive, it continues to exchange carbon with the atmosphere through photosynthesis or respiration, and therefore its C-14 content remains constant. The radioactivity from a living organism is about 14 disintegrations per minute for every gram of carbon. But when the organism dies its photosynthesis or respiration stops, and its small content of ^{14}C is no longer replenished by exchange with the atmosphere. The ^{14}C decays and the radioactivity slows down, as follows:

Time (Years)	Number of Half-lives	Radioactivity (Disintegrations/min/g of C)
0	0	14
5,730	1	7
11,460	2	3.5
17,190	3	1.75
etc.		

Thus, if the activity of the hair of an Egyptian mummy is seven disintegrations/min/g of carbon, the mummy is 5730 years old. Of course, the age need not be a whole number of half-lives. Recall from Section 10.2 that radioactive decay by half-lives occurs as a continuous function; it does not descend in steps. The graph in Figure 10–16 shows the decay curve of carbon-14. This graph can be used to estimate the age of any sample of carbon from the radioactivity of its carbon-14.

Figure 10–16. Radioactive decay of carbon-14.

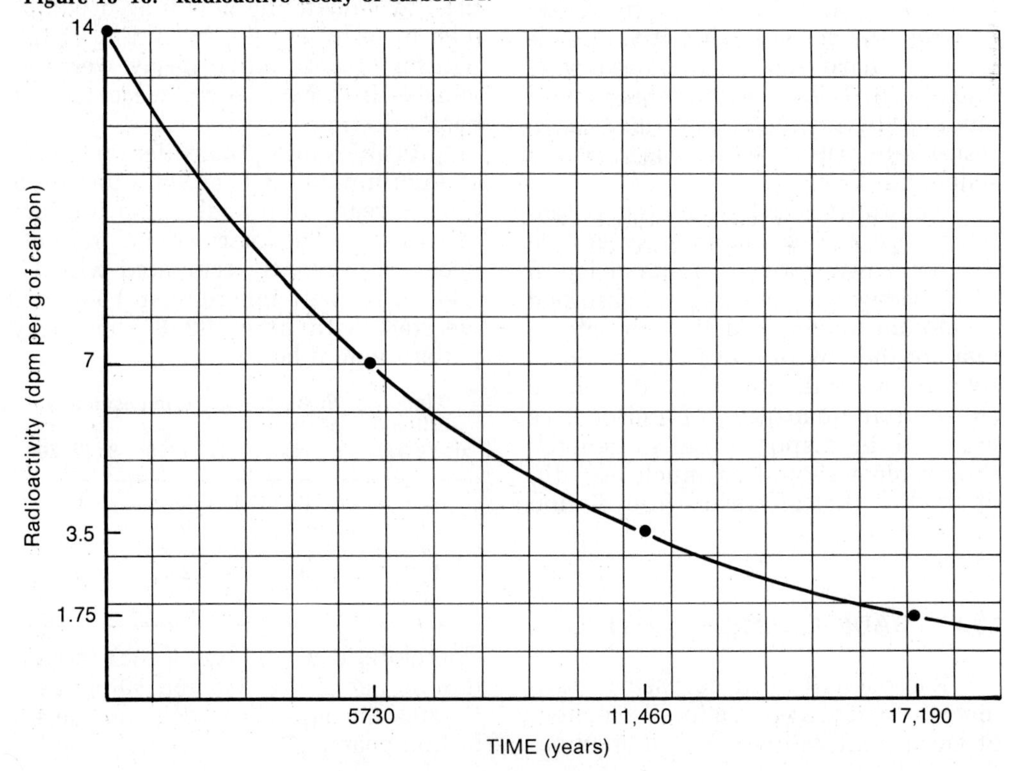

Carbon-14 dating of human fossils from East Africa has shown that the earliest humans lived there three to four million years ago.

A

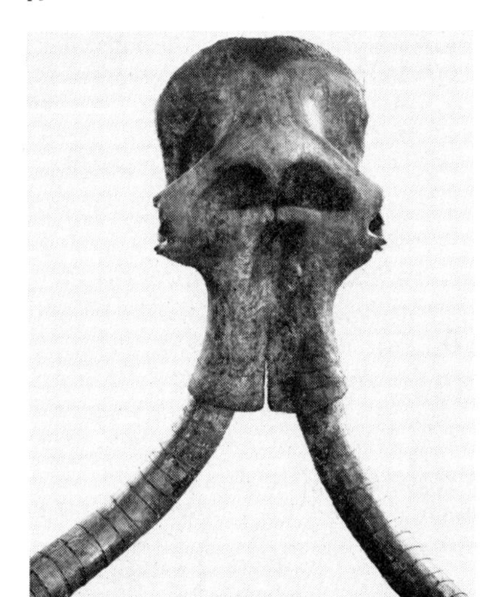

B

A, Columbian mammoth. (Painting by Charles R. Knight) B, Front view of mammoth skull, discovered in Indiana, 1904. The ages of such fossils are measured by carbon-14 dating. (Illustrations courtesy of American Museum of Natural History.)

10.12 BIOLOGICAL EFFECTS OF RADIATION

Effects of Radiation on Living Cells

We have learned that nuclear reactions can release energy. In our emphasis on chain reactions, we have paid most attention to energy in the form of speeding neutrons. However, nuclear reactions also release energy in the form of X-rays and gamma rays, both of which are highly energetic varieties of electromagnetic radiation.

Photons in the X-ray or gamma-ray range are energetic enough to knock electrons away from their atoms or molecules. Ions are thereby produced. If certain key molecules in a living cell are ionized, cellular function may be disrupted and the cell may die. Other effects of radiation may fall short of producing ions, but may nonetheless alter or break chemical bonds. The affected molecule may be essential to the cell. One such molecule is deoxyribonucleic acid, DNA, which contains all the genetic information that is required for the growth and maintenance of the cell. DNA is a sensitive target for radiation; when a cell is irradiated, the DNA strands tend to break into fragments. If the rate of delivery of the radiation is low, the cell's repair mechanisms can seal the breaks in the strands, but above a certain dose rate, the repair process cannot keep up, and the DNA fragmentation becomes irreversible.

Early somatic effects: radiation sickness

On several occasions during the past 75 years, groups of people have been exposed to large doses of ionizing radiation over periods of time ranging from a few seconds to a few minutes. The holocausts at Hiroshima and Nagasaki, together with accidents at civilian nuclear installations, have provided much information about what radiation can do when a lot of it is administered to the entire body over a short period of time. Let us consider first the simplest and most drastic measure of radiation effect—death. Figure 10–17 shows the relation between the dose administered to a population of animals and the per cent of the population remaining alive three weeks or more after the exposure. Up to a dose of about 250 rads (see Table 10–2 for definition of a rad), virtually everyone survives. When the dose is increased above this point, survival begins to

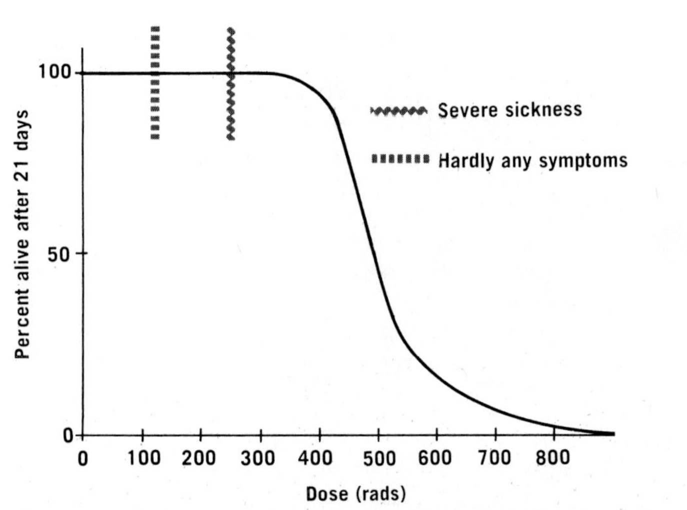

Figure 10–17. Curve showing the approximate relationship between the dose of radiation administered to a whole animal like a mouse or a man and the percent of the treated population which survives three weeks afterward. Mice have, of course, been extensively studied in the laboratory; accidents in industry and the nuclear explosions in Japan have provided the approximate data for man. (From *American Scientist* 57:206, 1969. Copyright 1969 by Sigma Xi National Science Honorary.)

drop sharply, and above a dose of 800 rads, everyone dies.

Does this mean that below doses of 250 rads there is no observable effect? Not at all. For even if the exposed individuals do not die, they may become quite ill. At doses between 100 and 250 rads most of the people will develop fatigue, nausea, vomiting, diarrhea, and some loss of hair within a few days of the exposure; the vast majority, however, will recover completely from the acute illness. For doses around 400 to 500 rads, however, the outlook is not so rosy. During the first few days, the illness is similar to that of the previous group. The symptoms may then go away almost completely for a time, but beginning about three weeks after the exposure, they will return. In addition, because the radiation has impaired bone marrow function, the number of white cells and platelets in the blood will decrease. This is of great significance, since without white cells the body cannot fight infection, and without platelets the blood will not clot. Looking at Figure 10–17 again, we can see that about 50 per cent of those exposed in this dose range will die, and of these, most will die of either infection or bleeding.

If, instead, the dose administered is about 2000 rads, the first week of the illness will again be the same as in the previous groups, but rather than waiting three weeks for symptoms to return, these people become very ill in the second week, with severe diarrhea, dehy-

TABLE 10–2. UNITS RELATED TO RADIOACTIVITY

Unit	Abbreviation	Definition and Application
Disintegration per second	dps	A rate of radioactivity in which one nucleus disintegrates every second. The natural background radiation for a human body is about 2 to 3 dps. This does not include "fallout" from manmade sources such as atomic bombs.
Curie	Ci	Another measure of radioactivity. One Ci = 37 billion dps.
Microcurie	μCi	A millionth of a curie, or 37,000 dps.
Roentgen	R	A measure of the intensity of X-rays or gamma rays, in terms of the energy of such radiation absorbed by a body. (One R delivers 84 ergs of energy to 1 gram of air.) The roentgen may be considered a measure of the radioactive dose received by a body. The dose from natural radioactivity for a human being is 5 R during the first 30 years of life. A single dental X-ray gives about 1 R, a full mouth X-ray series, about 15 R.
Rad		Another measure of radiation dosage, equivalent to the absorption of 100 ergs per gram of biological tissue.
Rem		A measure of the effect on man of exposure to radiation. It takes into account both the radiation dosage and the potential for biological damage of the radiation. The damage potential is based on the following scale of factors: X-rays, gamma rays, electrons : 1 neutrons, protons, alpha-particles :10 high-speed heavy nuclei :20 The rem is then defined by the relationship: Rems = Rads × Biological damage factor. Therefore, 100 ergs per gram (X-rays) = 1 rad × 1 = 1 rem, but 100 ergs per gram (neutrons) = 1 rad × 10 = 10 rems.

dration, and infection leading to death. At these dose levels, the cells of the gastrointestinal tract are affected before the bone marrow toxicity has a chance to become severe, and these patients may die even before their blood counts have dropped to life-threatening levels.

At doses above 10,000 rads, animal experiments have shown that death, which may occur within hours of administration of the dose, is due to injury of the brain and heart.

Delayed somatic effects

Of the late somatic effects of radiation (that is, those occurring months or years following the exposure), none is better studied or of more concern than the increased incidence of cancer in those with a history of prior exposure to radiation. Although the molecular mechanisms at work here are still largely obscure, the evidence that radiation does increase the incidence of cancer in exposed populations is overwhelming. Before the dangers of radiation were appreciated, early workers were careless in their handling of radioactive materials and suffered a greatly increased incidence of skin cancers. The famous case of the radium dial workers in the 1920's also deserves mention. These women were responsible for painting the dials of watches with the phosphorescent radium paint in use at that time and routinely tipped the end of the brush in their mouths before applying the paint to the dial face. In later years this group experienced a very high incidence of bone tumors. (Ingested radium, like strontium, is preferentially incorporated into bone.) The survivors of the atomic attacks at Hiroshima and Nagasaki, within a decade of the attacks, had far more leukemia than one would have expected from a group of this size, and subsequently the incidence of a variety of malignancies other than leukemia seems to be rising as well.

Genetic Effects

We must also consider those effects of radiation which do not manifest themselves in the irradiated individual himself but result in mutations in the genetic material of the **germ cells** (the sperm cells of the testis and the egg cells of the ovary) that are passed on to succeeding generations. In every experimental system studied in the laboratory, in organisms as diverse as viruses, bacteria, fruit flies, and mice, radiation has been shown to be a potent inducer of mutations. Though both ethical and practical considerations militate against genetic experiments with humans, scientists have attempted to find evidence of an increased mutation rate in irradiated populations such as the atomic bomb survivors. These investigations have yielded only equivocal results. Nonetheless, there is no reason to believe that humans should behave differently in this respect from every other well-studied species, and thus scientists and policy-makers must assume that radiation is also mutagenic in humans.

10.13 MEDICAL APPLICATIONS OF RADIATION

- Radiation has been successfully used in the treatment of cancer. Cancerous cells are more sensitive to radiation than normal cells. The idea is to select a dosage that destroys the malignant cells but not the normal ones.
- Hemoglobin contains iron. The rate at which injected radioactive ^{59}Fe appears in the blood provides a measurement of the red blood cell production.
- After a small amount of blood serum labeled with ^{131}I is injected into the body, the amount of blood pumped by the heart per minute can be determined by measuring blood activity with a detector placed over the heart.
- The volume of blood in the body is determined by measuring the dilution of ^{14}C activity after injecting a ^{14}C-labeled compound into the blood stream.
- Heart damage is very reliably appraised by use of thallium-201. ($^{201}_{81}Tl + e \rightarrow ^{201}_{80}Hg + \gamma$). Healthy heart tissue has a strong affinity for Tl. When ^{201}Tl is injected into a patient, the γ photons picked up by a detector held over the heart are converted into a pic-

ture on a screen. Scars and areas deficient in blood supply appear black. Heart conditions commonly overlooked by electrocardiograms are easily seen on the screen.

- Obstruction of a blood vessel by a clot or a bubble (embolism) is detected with fibrinogen, a soluble protein, labeled with ^{125}I. The labeled fibrinogen piles up at the obstruction and signals an above-average blood activity.
- Brain tumors can be located very accurately because of their greater tendency to absorb certain radioisotopes, such as ^{111}In and ^{64}Cu, from the blood stream.
- Gallium-67 has been proved 95 per cent accurate in locating deeply hidden lesions that result from Hodgkin's disease.

10.14 EPILOGUE—THE NUCLEAR CONTROVERSY

Nuclear energy burst onto the public consciousness in 1945, when two fission bombs were used against Japan. The initial reaction everywhere was a realization that World War II was about to end, and a sense that a new kind of energy had been unleashed. The public understood that the "new energy" could be used for human betterment as well as for war. There was much talk—and hope—for what was then called the "peaceful atom" and the "peaceful use of atomic energy." These expressions meant that nuclear energy could be utilized in power plants rather than in bombs.

The nuclear energy program was thus launched with widespread public approval and support. By the mid-fifties, the program was being rapidly accelerated, and the associated difficulties and dangers were only vaguely appreciated. However, the facts that radioactive materials could be deadly, that fission fuels could also become explosives, and that the development of nuclear weapons had not stopped with the end of the war led to a gradually widening sense of unease. Furthermore, accidents started to happen—one at Chalk River in Canada in 1952 and another at Windscale in England in 1957. In both cases, various amounts of radioactivity were released to the environment.

By the next decade, as the biological dangers of radiation came to be better understood, the nuclear debate became a recognized public issue. The "peaceful atom" was called the "careless atom."* Concern about nuclear safety became more urgent, but the development of nuclear energy and the plans for its further rapid expansion continued.

Despite these developments, neither the public nor the "experts" were prepared for the events of the 1970's. That was the decade of frightening near-catastrophes (at the Browns Ferry Nuclear Power Plant and at Three Mile Island), of the Rasmussen report and its repudiation, and of the world-wide energy crisis. For the first time, the debates about the advisability of continuing the nuclear program, or even the possibility of scrapping it, reached significant political levels. These considerations have in fact already resulted in a marked slowdown of new plant construction as compared with the anticipations of previous years.

One thing that has not slowed down has been the controversy. Furthermore, responsible and knowledgeable scientists (including what seems to be a required number of Nobel Prize winners) are found on both sides of the debate. The public sometimes feels that scientists, unlike politicians, should not have to argue, but rather should know the correct answers. Alas, it is not so simple. Different people, scientists or not, differ in the statements they believe to be true. They differ in the assumptions they make about the probability of accidents. They differ in the judgments they make about the value of the expected benefits and the human cost of the expected damages. But perhaps the most significant gap that separates the two sides lies in their views of the human condition. Those who favor a nuclear future point to the benefits that technology has brought us.

*S. Novick: *The Careless Atom.* Boston, Houghton Mifflin Co., 1968.

PROBLEMS

1. **Definitions.** Define radioactivity; isotope; radioisotope.

2. **Radioactivity.** Identify the α, β, and γ rays from radioactive disintegration with regard to (a) their electrical charge, if any; (b) their identity.

3. **Nuclear equations.** Complete and balance the following nuclear equations. Refer to the table of atoms (inside back cover) to identify the elements indicated by question marks.

(a) $^{25}_{12}Mg + ^{4}_{2}He \rightarrow ^{1}_{0}n + ?$
(b) $^{13}_{6}C + ^{1}_{0}n \rightarrow ^{4}_{2}He + ?$
(c) $^{95}_{42}Mo + ^{1}_{0}n \rightarrow ^{1}_{1}H + ?$
(d) $^{41}_{21}Sc \rightarrow ^{0}_{1}\beta + ?$

*4. **Half-life.** A Geiger counter registers 1024 cps (counts per second) near a sample of radioactive substance; six hours later the rate is 128 cps. What is the half-life of the radioactive substance? What rate will the counter register after an additional 10 hours?

5. **Half-life.** Cesium-137 is a radioactive waste product whose half-life is 30 years. It is chemically similar to potassium, which is an essential element in plants and animals. Its compounds are readily soluble in water.
(a) How long will it take for 64 mg of cesium-137 to decay to 2 mg?
(b) Since cesium compounds are soluble, would it be wise to dump this isotope into an open holding pond and let it dissolve and decay until only negligible quantities remain? Defend your answer.

6. **Half-life.** Strontium-90 is a product of radioactive fallout from atomic bomb tests. Its half-life is 28 years and it is chemically similar to calcium. (a) If 256 mg were to settle on a given area of farmland and were not transported elsewhere, how long would it take to decay to 1 mg? (b) If someone were to wait for the number of years calculated in (a), would it be likely that 1 mg of strontium-90 would actually remain on the original farm? More? Less? Explain.

*7. **Half-life.** One of the isotopes of technetium, a synthetic radioactive element used in cancer diagnosis, has a half-life of three months. Assume that a laboratory wished to keep a supply of 2 mg of this Tc isotope on hand, that it purchased 2 mg to start with, and that it checked its inventory every three months and decided at inventory time to bring its supply back up to 2 mg. (a) How much Tc would the laboratory purchase at inventory time? (b) What are the implications of your answer to the problem of storing radioactive wastes?

8. **Nuclear structure.** (a) What is the name of the particle that "carries" the electromagnetic force? (b) What is the name of the hypothetical particle that "carries" the nuclear force? (c) What is the name of the fundamental particle which makes up larger particles such as protons and neutrons?

9. **Chain reaction.** What is a chain reaction? Explain chain propagation (lengthening); chain branching; chain termination; critical condition. Can the spread of a rumor among a large group of people function as a chain reaction? If so, illustrate how the chain could branch or terminate. Define the critical condition of such a system.

10. **Nuclear reactions.** Complete and balance the following equations and identify the isotopes indicated by question marks.

(a) $^{27}_{13}Al + ^{4}_{2}He \rightarrow ^{1}_{0}n + ?$
(b) $^{238}_{92}U \rightarrow {}_{-1}^{0}\beta + ?$
(c) $^{236}_{92}U \rightarrow ^{95}_{39}Y + ? + 3^{1}_{0}n$
(d) $^{226}_{88}Ra \rightarrow ? + 5^{4}_{2}He + 4{}_{-1}^{0}\beta$
(e) $^{236}_{92}U \rightarrow ^{100}_{43}Tc + 3^{1}_{0}n + ?$
(f) $^{239}_{94}Pu + ^{1}_{0}n \rightarrow ^{144}_{58}Ce + ? + 11^{1}_{0}n$

11. **Reactors.** What are essential features of a nuclear fission reactor? Explain the function of each.

12. **Neutrons.** List the possible fates of neutrons in a fission reactor. Which of these events should be favored, and which should be inhibited, in order to (a) shut down a reactor, (b) breed new fissionable fuel, and (c) produce more energy?

13. **Breeder reactors.** Explain how breeder reactors differ from non-breeders in fuel, moderator, coolant, and any other features.

14. **The fuel cycles.** (a) Outline the steps in the "once-through" uranium fuel cycle. Do you think it is appropriate to use the word "cycle" in this context? Defend your answer. (b) Outline the steps in the plutonium fuel cycle. What are its major differences from

*Indicates more difficult problem.

the uranium fuel cycle? What new environmental hazards would the plutonium cycle produce?

15. **Nuclear explosion.** Explain why a critical mass of pure fissionable material must be exceeded if an explosion is to occur. Why is it thought that a nuclear reactor could not explode in the manner of a bomb?

16. **Safety.** (a) What are the five principles of industrial safe practice? (b) How are they applied to the construction and use of automobiles? of the place where you live? of a nuclear plant?

17. **Nuclear safety.** Outline the general concept and approach to safety used in nuclear power plants. Can you think of any specific series of events that would cause all of the safety features to fail and a radioactive cloud to be released to the atmosphere? If so, describe them.

18. **Nuclear safety.** Do you think it would be reasonable to set safety limits in nuclear power plants that would prohibit *any* release of radioactive matter? Defend your answer. If your answer is no, what criteria would you use to set the limits?

19. **Nuclear safety.** Some proponents of nuclear power argue that some release of radioactive material to the environment should be permitted and that some risks of accidents should be accepted. How are such arguments defended?

*20. **Nuclear safety.** Most uranium is mined underground, not in open pits. The rock in these mines is hard, so that the danger from collapse of the tunnel is much less than in coal mines. Also, there is no danger of gas explosions. However, there is a risk of lung damage from inhalation of silica dust. In addition, radon gas (radon-222, half-life 3.8 days) does seep into the mine from surfaces of exposed rock. Are the following statements true or false? Defend your answers.

(a) After the tunnel is opened, it should be ventilated for 38 days, or 10 half-lives, which would cut the radioactivity in half 10 times, or by a factor of 2^{10}, which is about 1000:1. This amounts to a 99.9 per cent reduction, which would make the mine safe.

(b) The danger of silicosis has nothing to do with the exposure to radioactive matter. Besides, the silica dust could be controlled simply by spraying the work area with water.

(c) The miners could be protected by gas masks that are provided with filters that remove particles of rock dust and the solid radioactive radon daughters, such as radioactive forms of polonium or lead.

(d) The miners could be protected by gas masks that are provided with filters to remove particles, and with activated carbon to remove radon gas.

*Indicates more difficult problem.

21. **Nuclear safety.** Describe the safety features of a nuclear plant that would operate if (a) pipe carrying cooling water would burst; (b) the source of electrical power would fail.

22. **Radioactive wastes.** List the various proposals for "permanent" storage of radioactive wastes. Suggest some advantages and some problems or uncertainties associated with each.

*23. **Radioactive wastes.** Sandlike radioactive leftovers from uranium ore processing mills, called "mill tailings," have been used to make cement for the construction of houses in Colorado, Arizona, New Mexico, Utah, Wyoming, Texas, South Dakota, and Washington. These tailings contain radium (half-life 1620 years) and its daughter radon (a gas, half-life 3.8 days), as well as radioactive forms of polonium, bismuth, and lead. Radon gas seeps through concrete, but is chemically inert. Are the following statements true or false? Defend your answer in each case:

(a) Since radon has such a short half-life, the hazard will disappear quickly; old tailings, therefore, do not pose any health problems.

(b) Even if the radon gas is present, it cannot be a health problem because it is inert and does not enter into any chemical reactions in the body.

(c) Continuous ventilation that would blow the radon gas outdoors would decrease the health hazard inside such a house.

24. **Fusion.** Suppose that someone claims to have found a material that can serve as a rigid container for a thermonuclear reactor. Would such a claim merit examination, or should it be ignored as a "crackpot" idea not worth the time to investigate? Defend your answer.

*Indicates more difficult problem.

25. **Fusion.** Outline the reasons why fusion reactors are expected to be far less serious sources of radioactive pollutants than fission reactors.

26. **Hydrogen isotopes.** If you use the symbols H, D, and T for the isotopes of hydrogen, it is possible to write six formulas for water. Write them. Identify the three that represent radioactive forms of water.

27. **Radiochemical dating.** (a) Organic matter found in a cave in Crete has an activity of 3.5 disintegrations/minute/gram of carbon. How old is the organic matter? (b) A sample of peat found under a glacier contains 10 g of carbon and has a total activity (of the entire sample) of 17.5 disintegrations/minute. What is the age of the peat?

28. **Radiochemical dating.** Cosmic ray bombardment maintains a low but constant level of tritium in atmospheric moisture. As a result, fresh groundwater contains 4800 tritium atoms for every mg of ^{1}H. The half-life of tritium is 12 years. The wine taken from a musty bottle contains 300 tritium atoms for every mg of ^{1}H. How old is the wine?

29. **Health.** Since a six-year-old girl is too young to bear children, there is no need to shield her body from the radiation produced by dental x-rays. True or false? Explain.

30. **Health.** Outline the types of damage to the body that can result from exposure to high-energy radiation. Can there ever be any benefits? Explain.

31. **Health.** Give two reasons why a 70-year-old woman does not face so serious a problem regarding the health effects of radiation as a 17-year-old.

32. **Health.** The formula for thyroxin, an essential chemical growth regulator, is $C_{15}H_{11}I_4NO_4$. Which of the following radioactive waste products of nuclear reactors pose a particular threat to the thyroid gland: CH_3I containing iodine-131; or radon? Justify your choice.

33. **Medical applications.** Describe five medical applications of radioisotopes.

CHAPTER 11

The sounds we hear can give us pleasure, provide information, annoy us, or even cause physical harm. It is important, therefore, that we learn about the physics as well as the environmental and other practical aspects of sound.

The chapter opens with a discussion of sound, music, and noise. The subject of loudness and the decibel scale is then taken up. (A treatment that involves logarithms is given in Appendix F.)

The chapter continues with a description of the effects of noise and offers practical methods of noise control. Finally, the special case of the SST and the sonic boom is discussed.

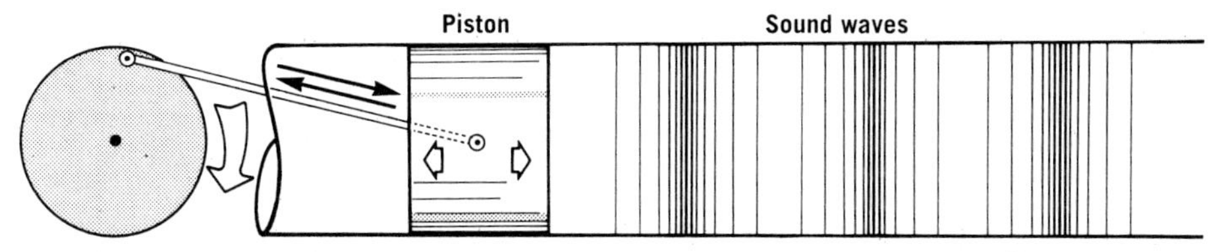

Figure 11–5. Generating a pure tone.

of steam is obviously higher pitched than a rumble of thunder, because the pressure variations in the hiss, even though they are not rhythmic, occur much more rapidly. These differences are shown in Figure 11–6.

It is an interesting observation that, in general, if any human experience is to be aesthetically pleasing, it must be complex (although, of course, complexity alone is not sufficient). In addition to the musical aspects described here, consider the following: no single pure chemical compound has a really interesting taste or enticing aroma; no monochromatic color, all by itself, is beguiling; no simple touch, without any other context, carries much message.

11.3 MUSICAL SOUNDS

A musical composition is impossible to describe in words or symbols; it carries an essence of its own. Even when we speak about a single note, we use nebulous, hard-to-define words such as "quality," "depth," or "richness." Suppose, for example, that we had ten different pianos, ranging from a cheap toy to a quality concert grand, and that we struck the note middle C on each. The fundamental pitch of each note would be the same, but the sound of the better instrument would be somehow "fuller," "richer." Middle C played on any piano is carried by a sound wave with a **fundamental frequency** of 262 vibrations per second. But in addition to the fundamental frequency, the string vibrates to produce sounds, called **overtones,** with frequencies two, three, four, five, six, or more times the fundamental frequency (Fig. 11–7). A note from any instrument contains a mixture of the fundamental frequency and its overtones. In a quality instrument, this mixture is more complex and therefore fuller than in an inferior one.

Figure 11–6. Wave forms of a hiss and a rumble. *A*, Hiss–higher frequency. *B*, Rumble–lower frequency.

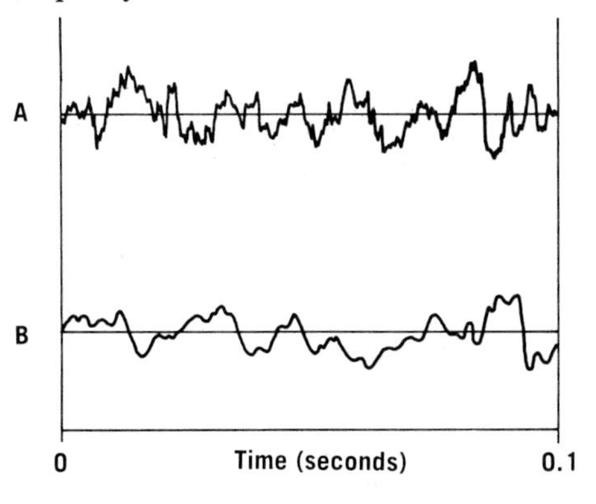

Figure 11–7. Fundamental frequency and overtones.

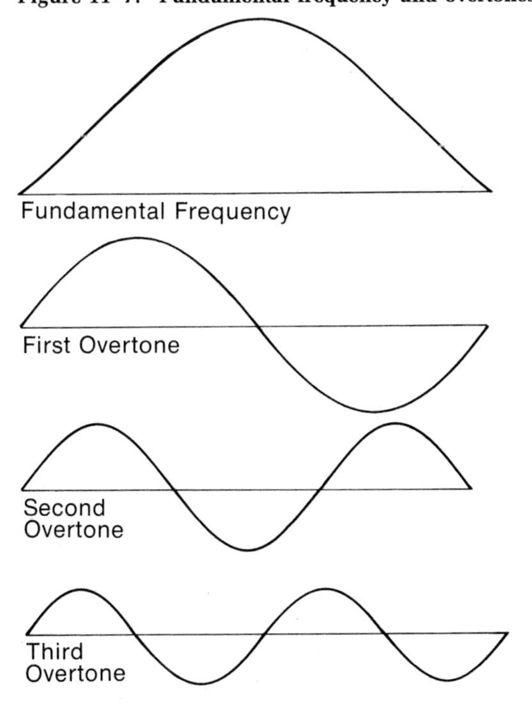

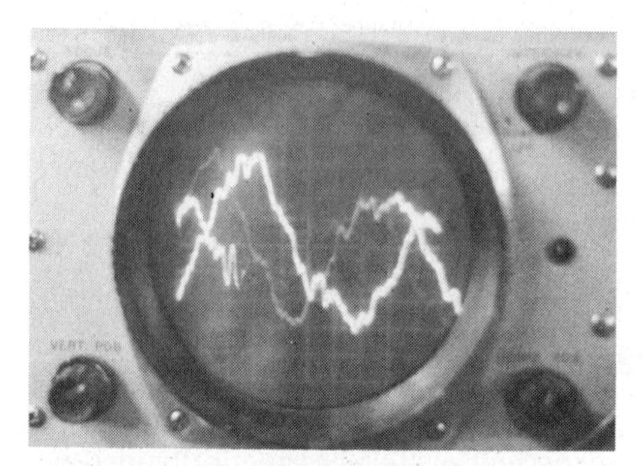

Figure 11–8. A rock-and-roll tune as seen on an oscilloscope.

If we compare two different instruments, say a piano and a clarinet, and listen to middle C on both, the fundamental frequency will be the same, but because the number and loudness of the overtones are different, the quality of the sound will be different.

When many instruments operate together, each playing different notes, the resultant sound wave contains many different fundamental frequencies, each mixed with its specific overtones. The agglomeration, which we call music, is a complex superimposed mixture of many pure sinusoidal sound waves (Fig. 11–8).

11.4 NOISE

The concept of noise is often related to the idea of randomness, but there are other connotations. The complete physical description of a given sound cannot establish whether you, as an individual, will like it or not. If you don't like a sound, that sound is noise. We now have two definitions of noise: (a) any erratic, intermittent, or statistically random oscillation, and (b) any unwanted sound.

The concept of "unwanted" sound seems straightforward enough, but it does not teach us how to predict which sounds will be disliked. After all, a given sound may be music to one person but noise to another, pleasant when soft but noise when loud, acceptable for a short time but noise when prolonged, intriguing when rhythmic but noise when randomly repeated, or reasonable when you make it but noise when someone else makes it. Of all the attributes that distinguish between wanted and unwanted sound, the one that we generally consider the most significant is loudness. There is ample evidence that exposure to loud sounds is harmful in various ways, and, in any event, loudness tends to be annoying; therefore, the louder a sound is, the more likely it is to be considered noise.

There are yet other subtleties to complicate matters. People often associate noise with power, and in that context noise becomes desired. For example, some homeowners choose noisier lawn mowers and vacuum cleaners over quieter ones in the mistaken idea that the noisier ones work better or faster. And some drivers of "hot rods" or of trucks remove the exhaust mufflers from their vehicles to help "soup them up." In these instances it is true that such removal reduces the resistance imposed on the exhaust gases and thereby may increase the efficiency of the engine, but the benefit is small (2 to

(TIGER, © King Features Syndicate, Inc., 1977)

Motorcycle noise.

Traffic noise.

Jack hammer noise.

Grinding noise.

3 per cent) and the cost is high (impaired hearing). Some of these attitudes date back to the 1940's, however, and have been undergoing a reversal in favor of quietness during the heightened environmental awareness of recent years.

More difficult to modify, perhaps, is the association of noise with social recognition. A loud noise connotes authority, even though what it utters may be nonsense. Such is the case, all too often, with loud speech, a loud motorcycle, loud music, or roaring toys, especially toy guns and firecrackers.

11.5 LOUDNESS AND THE DECIBEL SCALE

We have noted that, other things being equal, the louder a sound, the more likely it is to be considered noisy. And with good reason—loud sounds

DEFINITIONS AND UNITS RELATED TO SOUND

Acoustic power, or **sound power,** is the sound energy per unit time radiated by a source. It is measured in watts. **Sound intensity** is the sound power that passes through a unit area (watts/m^2). A point source of sound that radiates, say, 10 watts becomes the center of an everexpanding field of sound. The intensity of the sound diminishes as the radius of the field increases, though the power of the source remains unchanged. The "intensity of a barely audible sound" is usually taken to be one-trillionth of a watt per square meter, or 10^{-12} watt/m^2. **Sound pressure** is the force per unit area exerted by sound of a given intensity. **Loudness** is the listener's subjective judgment of the intensity of the sound as it is received.

tend to interfere with our activities and as we shall see, they can be physically harmful. But loudness is not energy, or pressure, or frequency, or anything else that can be measured with a physical instrument. Loudness is a sensation, and if you want to know how loud a sound is, you must get the answer from the person who hears it. However, it is possible to obtain useful information from instruments by measuring some physical property of sound that is *related* to the human perception of loudness. Air must vibrate against the eardrum before sound can be transmitted to the brain. Therefore, it is reasonable to use a device that responds to **sound pressure** and to relate its response to perceived loudness.

Figure 11–9. Decibel meter. Photo courtesy of GenRad, Inc. (formerly General Radio Company), Concord, Mass.

The instrument that measures sound is called a **decibel meter** (Fig. 11–9), and a scale of such values is called a **decibel** (abbreviated dB) **scale.** We know that the human ear is sensitive to sounds over an extremely wide range of intensities, so that if our scale were directly proportional to sound intensity, it would suffer the inconvenience of ranging from very small to very large numbers. Furthermore, the scale would be awkward, for it would not start at zero, but at some small number that represents the softest audible sound. To avoid these complications, the dB scale (Table 11–1) is set up as follows:

(a) The scale starts at zero dB, which represents the softest sound that is audible to the human ear.
(b) Each *tenfold increase* in sound intensity is represented by an *additional* 10 dB. Thus, a 10-dB sound is 10 times as intense as the faintest audible sound. (That still isn't very much.) The sound level in a quiet library is about 1000 times as intense as the faintest audible sound. Therefore the sound level in the library is 10 + 10 + 10 or 30 dB. To summarize:

Sound	Sound level in decibels
Faintest audible sound (threshold of hearing)	0
A leaf rustling, at 10 times the intensity of the threshold of hearing.	10
Sound level in a broadcasting studio, at 10 times the level of the rustling leaf. (This is also 100 times the level of the faintest audible sound.)	20
Sound level in a quiet library, at 10 times the level of the broadcasting studio. (We are now at 1000 times the threshold of hearing.)	30

Figure 11–15. Hydraulically operated shear has less impact noise than mechanically driven shear. (Courtesy of Pacific Industrial Manufacturing Company.)

sively noisy, an acoustical engineer may be called in to "soundproof" it. Under such circumstances, the engineer may be forced to accommodate to features of construction that should never have been accepted in the first place. Therefore, much of his effort may necessarily be applied, not to the source, but to the path between sound and receiver.

Interrupting the Path

We have learned that sound travels through air by compressions and expansions. It also travels through other elastic media, including solids such as wood. Such solids vibrate in response to sound and therefore do not effectively interrupt its transmission, as many residents of apartment houses will readily attest. However, we could use various materials that vibrate very inefficiently, such as wool or lead, and absorb the sound energy, converting it to heat. (Very little heat is involved; the sound power of a symphony orchestra will warm up a room about as much as a 15-W electric heater.) Sound-absorbing media have been developed extensively; they are called **acoustical materials.** We could also build interruption of the sound waves mechanically into more kinds of machinery; devices that function in this way are called **mufflers** (see Figs. 11–16, 11–17, and 11–18.)

Figure 11–16. Mounting of compressor and piping to isolate vibration noise. (From L. L. Beranek, ed.: *Noise Reduction.* Copyright © 1960 by McGraw-Hill Book Company. Used with permission of McGraw-Hill Book Company.)

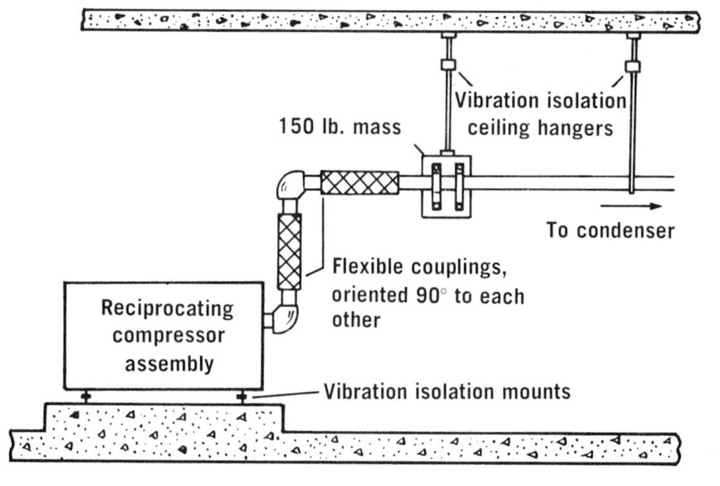

Figure 11–17. Sound absorbers suspended close to noise sources. (Courtesy of Elof Hannson, Inc., & Sonosorber Corporation.)

Figure 11–18. Vibration isolation of printing presses required to reduce noise in office on floor below. (From L. L. Beranek, ed.: *Noise Reduction.* Copyright © 1960 by McGraw-Hill Book Company. Used with permission of McGraw-Hill Book Company.)

Man wearing acoustical earmuffs while using chainsaw.

Finally, we may be able to deflect the sound path away from the receiver, as by mechanically directing jet exhaust noise upward instead of down. Such deflection is, in effect, an interruption between source and receiver.

Protecting the Receiver

The final line of defense is strictly personal. We protect ourselves instinctively when we hold our hands over our ears. Alternatively, we can use ear plugs or muffs as shown in Figure 11–19. (Stuffing in a bit of cotton does very little good.) A combination of ear plugs and muff can reduce noise by 40 or 50 dB, which could make a jet plane sound no louder than a vacuum cleaner. Such protection could prevent the deafness caused by combat training, and should also be worn for recreational shooting. Degrees of protection are shown in Figure 11–20.

We can also protect ourselves from a noise source by going away from it. In a factory, such reduction of exposure

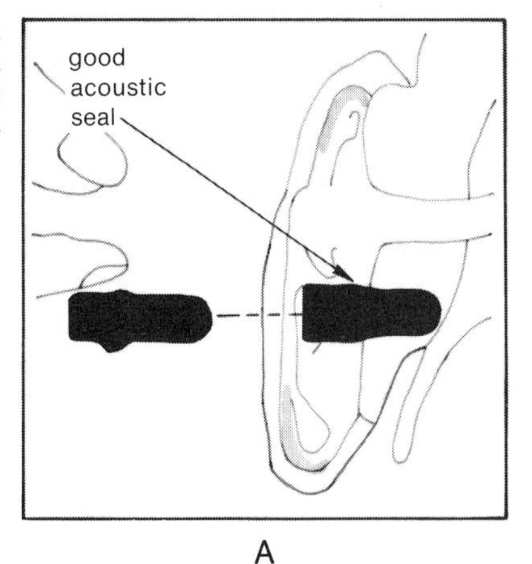

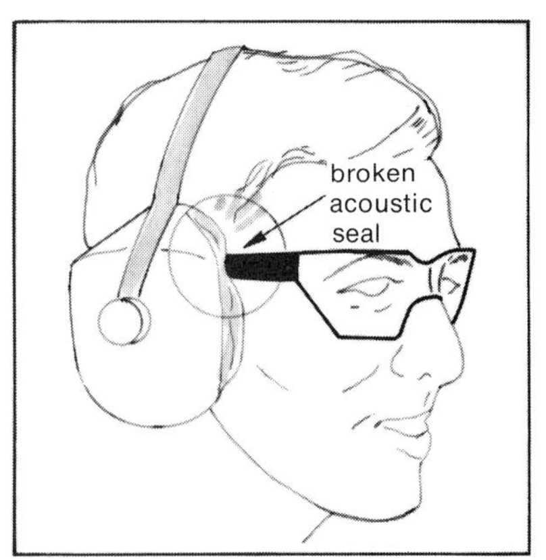

Figure 11–19. Protecting the receiver. *A,* Ear plugs must be inserted to a depth to ensure an acoustical seal. *B,* Placing ear muffs over eyeglass frames can break a proper acoustical seal.

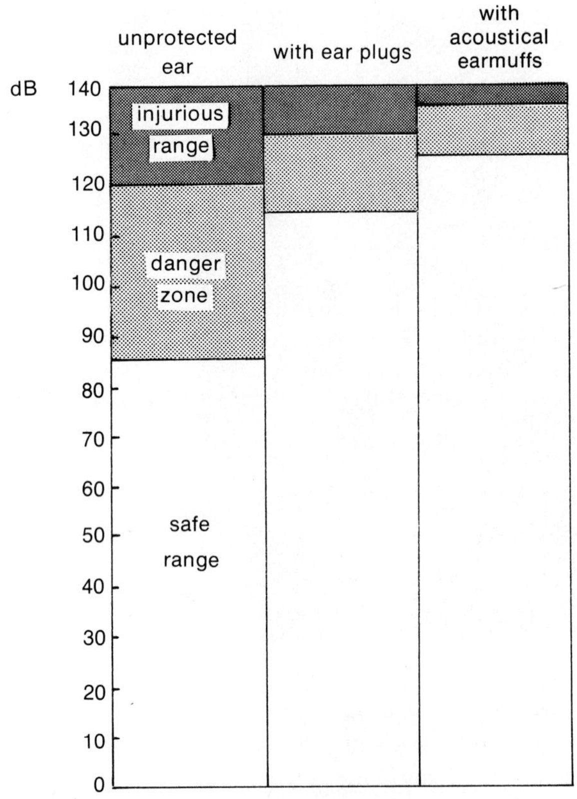

Figure 11–20. Using ear protectors reduces the risk of injury to hearing. The figure shows the danger zone at 1000 Hz.

may take the form of rotating assignments so that different workers take their turns at the noisy jobs.

11.9 A PARTICULAR CASE: THE SUPERSONIC TRANSPORT (SST)

The SST is a passenger aircraft that travels faster than sound and at much higher altitudes than subsonic airplanes. Higher speed requires more power, and more power makes more noise. Near airports, the noise problem is associated with the SST's approach and the rapid climb shortly after takeoff (Fig. 11–21), although the speeds at these times are subsonic. The engines on an SST must be small in diameter to provide optimal streamlining, and the noise from jet exhaust increases very rapidly (for a given engine thrust) as jet diameter is reduced and its speed increased.

When the SST reaches supersonic speed in flight, another effect, the **sonic boom,** occurs, and this, too, creates problems.

If there is one factor that has been common to all of the environmental controversies surrounding various SST programs, it is technical confusion. Just what is a sonic boom? Is it something that occurs when the aircraft "breaks the sound barrier," like cracking through some kind of wall? If an SST on takeoff were as loud as, say, ten ordinary jets, does that mean it is ten times as loud as one jet? Or ten times as annoying to people?

We can answer one of these questions directly from what we have learned about the decibel scale. Recall that a tenfold increase in sound intensity is represented by an increase of 10 dB, and that sound intensity is produced by sound power. Obviously, the sound power of ten jets is ten times as great as that of one jet. Therefore ten jets are 10 dB louder than one jet. And if the sideline noise of an SST sounds like that of ten ordinary jet planes, the SST is 10 dB louder than one ordinary jet plane. However, this answer does not tell you how much louder the SST sounds to you (remember, you are not a decibel meter), nor how much more annoyance it would cause you; nor does it tell what you would do about it. Experiments show that a sound 10 dB louder than another is judged to be "about twice as loud," but it sounds nevertheless just like ten of the weaker sounds all sounding simultaneously. Experiments on airport noise show that a single aircraft 10 dB louder than another produces about the same *annoyance* as ten separate flights of the quieter craft spread throughout the day. This relationship is used by the government and by airport operators in planning land use around airports.

Now let us consider the phenomenon most closely associated with the SST—the **sonic boom.** To visualize this effect, think of a speed boat moving rapidly in the water. Its speed is greater than that of the waves it creates, and it therefore leaves its waves behind it. Moreover, the wave energy is being continuously reinforced by the forward movement of the boat. The result is a high-energy wave, called a **wake,** that trails the boat in the shape of a V and that slaps hard against other vessels or against the shoreline. The sonic boom is a high-energy air wave of the same type. The tip of the wake moves forward with the airplane, while the sound itself moves out from the wake at the usual speed. The faster the airplane, the more slender is the wake.

To understand the geometry of the wake, study Figure 11–22. A stationary object (Fig. 11–22*A*) remains in the center of the circular waves it generates. The waves from a moving object will crowd each other in the direction of the object's motion (Fig. 11–22*B*). The object is, in effect, chasing its own waves. Recall that sound travels in air at sea level at a speed of 331 m/sec (1086 ft/sec, 741 mi/hr); any speed less than this is said to be **subsonic.** When the speed of the object equals the speed of the wave, the object will not see any waves before it; it will just be keeping up with them (Fig. 11–22*C*). In air, such a speed is said to be **sonic;** and speeds greater than this are **supersonic.** Such speeds are usually measured in Mach numbers:*

*After Ernst Mach, 1838–1916, a physicist who made important discoveries about sound.

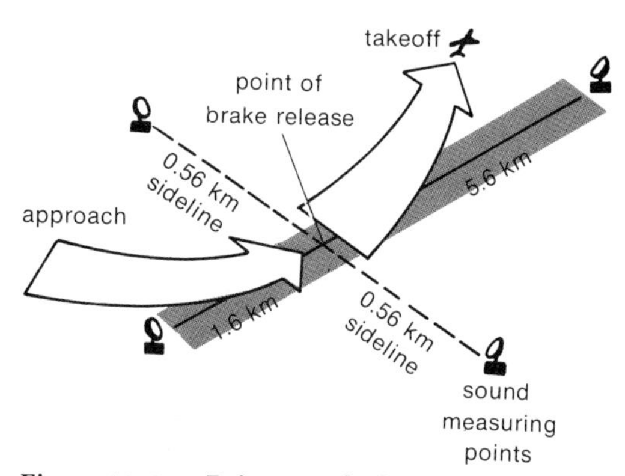

Figure 11–21. Points at which airplane approach, takeoff, and sideline noises are measured.

Speedboat wakes.

Sources of noise from jet engine.

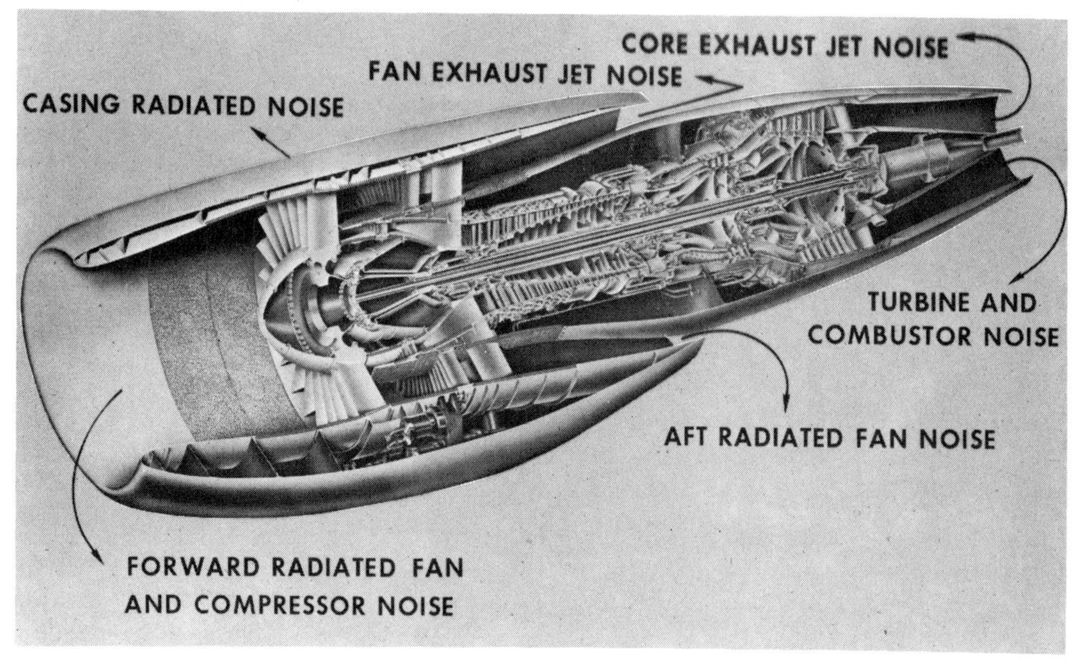

$$\text{Mach number} = \frac{\text{speed of object}}{\text{speed of sound}}$$

If an object is traveling at the speed of sound, then the numerator and the denominator of the equation are the same, and the Mach number equals 1. Mach 2 is twice the speed of sound, Mach 3 is three times the speed of sound, and so forth.

Figure 11–22*C* and *D* shows the wave patterns at supersonic speeds. Note that the object is always *ahead* of its waves. A passenger in an SST would therefore not hear the sound of its motion. Instead, the waves will crowd in on each other, and the effect will be a significant elevation of pressure at the advancing boundary of the overlapping wave fronts.

Of course, an airplane travels within its medium, and not, like a boat, on the surface of its medium. Therefore the outlines shown in Figure 11–22*C* and *D* are two-dimensional projections of what are really conical shapes. Furthermore, an airplane is more than a

Figure 11–22. Wave patterns of subsonic and supersonic speeds: *A*, stationary; *B*, subsonic; *C*, sonic, Mach 1; *D*, supersonic, Mach 1.5; *E*, supersonic, Mach 3. From left to right, the waves are shown at equal time intervals as they expand.

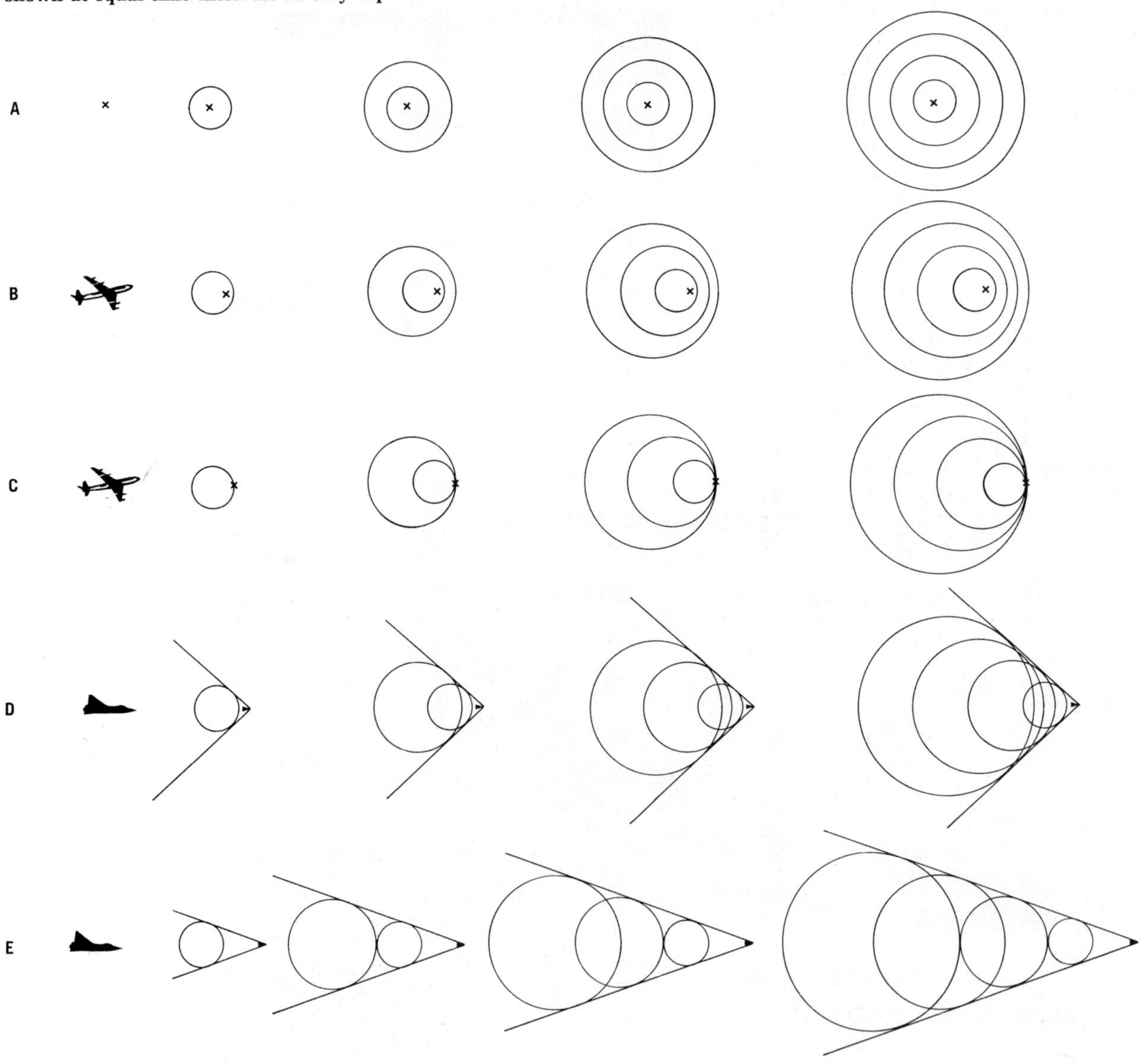

The Concorde SST.

point in space, and therefore a whole series of such cones will be generated. It is sufficient to consider only the nose and the tail of the plane, and represent the entire space between the forward and rear cones as the volume of the disturbance, as shown in Figure 11–23.

To be struck unexpectedly by a sonic boom can be quite unnerving. It sounds like a loud, close thunderclap, which can seem quite eerie when it comes from a cloudless sky. Depending on the power it generates, the sonic boom can rattle windows or shatter them or even destroy buildings. It is important to avoid the misconception that the sonic boom occurs only when the aircraft "breaks the sound barrier," that is, passes from subsonic to supersonic speed. On the contrary, the sonic boom is continuous and, like the wake of a speedboat, trails the aircraft all during the time that its speed is supersonic. Furthermore, the power of the sonic boom increases as the supersonic speed of the aircraft increases.

11.10 EPILOGUE

Noise is not a substance; it does not accumulate in the environment. Noise is a form of energy, and when its echo dies, something will be just a tiny bit warmer for it. But, as we have learned, this effect is entirely trivial as compared with other sources of thermal pollution, and it may be ignored.

We have seen that noise affects the quality and sometimes the health of human life. The effects on other living species have been less severe, because animals do not work in factories, and in

Figure 11–23. Sonic boom. *A,* Double Mach cones and their intersection with the ground surface. *B,* Profile of boom on ground surface.

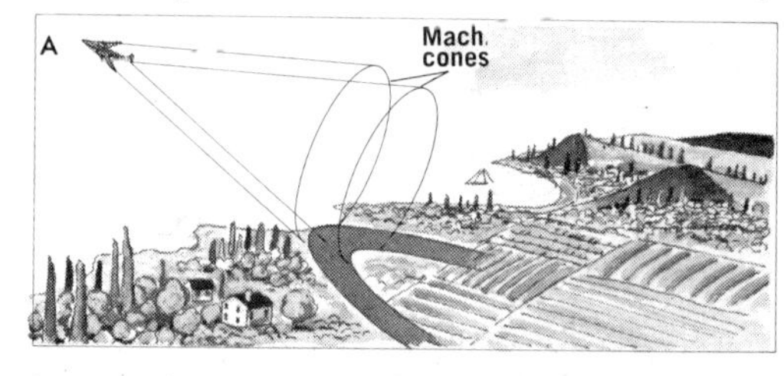

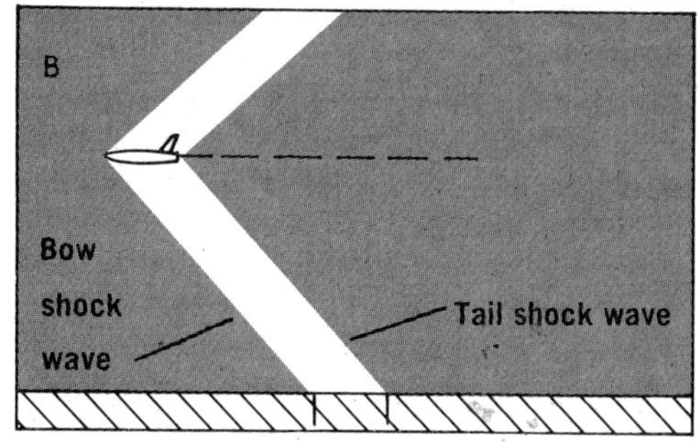

any event, we have more powerful means of displacing our non-human competitors. There are probably exceptions to this generalization, such as the disruption of animal life in winter by the roar of snowmobiles.

Noise, the "hustle and bustle" of industry and commerce, was once looked upon with favor as a sign of prosperity, like smoke from chimneys. Today, perhaps, it is most significant to think of the prevailing noise levels of our environment as an index of the price in human health, or in tranquility of spirit as well as of ear, that we have chosen to pay for the benefits of technology.

CHAPTER OBJECTIVES

Familiarize yourself with the capacity of the human ear.

Remember that sound is an elastic wave that must travel in some medium.

Understand the differences between sound, noise, and pure tones.

Study Table 11–1 carefully to appreciate the relationships between the dB scale and the effects of noise.

Learn the procedure for combining decibel levels.

Review how noise can interfere with communication, diminish our hearing, and affect our health and behavior, and how it can be controlled by controlling the source, interrupting the path of transmission, or protecting the receiver.

Understand the problems of the noise produced by the SST.

KEY WORDS

Eardrum
Cochlea
Sound
Noise
Elastic wave
Subsonic
Supersonic
Loudness
Decibel scale
Sine curve
Pure tone
Overtone
Subjective loudness scale
Phon
Infrasound
Ultrasound
Muffler
SST
Sonic boom
Wake
Mach number

FORMULAS TO KNOW

1. $\text{Wavelength} = \dfrac{\text{speed}}{\text{frequency}}$

Example 4
An organ pipe produces a sound whose wavelength is 2.0 m. What is the frequency of the sound?

Answer: **Solving the previous equation for the frequency gives us:**

$$\text{Frequency} = \frac{\text{speed}}{\text{wavelength}}$$

Substituting,

$$\text{Frequency} = \frac{331\,\dfrac{\text{m}}{\text{sec}}}{2.0\ \text{m}}$$

$$= 165.5\ /\ \text{sec, or } 165.5\ \text{Hz}$$

2. $\text{Mach number} = \dfrac{\text{speed of the object}}{\text{speed of sound}}$

The following formulas appear in Appendix E:

3. Difference in intensity between two sounds, X and Y, expressed in decibels

$$= 10 \log_{10}\left(\frac{\text{sound intensity of X}}{\text{sound intensity of Y}}\right)$$

4. Intensity in decibels of any given sound

$$= 10 \log_{10}\left(\frac{\text{intensity of the given sound}}{\text{intensity of a barely audible sound}}\right)$$

5. 1 Bel = 10 dB

TAKE-HOME EXPERIMENTS

1. **Loudness.** Carry this book around with you for a few days so you can refer to Table 11–1 (page 327). Make a diary of various sounds you hear, recording your information in a form such as that given in Problem 19. Estimate the decibel levels as well as you can from the columns in the table that show the sound levels of various sources and their perceived loudness. Try to include the following sources: (a) a television, or radio at normal listening volume in your room or apartment; (b) the central study area in the school library; (c) your physical science classroom; (d) the street outside your classroom; (e) the background noise in your room at night; (f) the school cafeteria; (g) a local factory or construction job site; (h) your own activities. Which sounds are annoying? Offer suggestions for reducing the perceived loudness in each of the instances where the sound is annoying.

2. **Sound.** Select a convenient constant source of sound, such as a ringing alarm clock, and try to reduce the loudness you hear from it by the following means: (a) stuff some cotton loosely into your ears; (b) hold your hands over your ears; (c) use both the cotton and your hands; (d) submerse your head in the bathtub (face up) until your ears are underwater; (e) if you can borrow a pair of earmuffs of the kind used in factories or at airports, try them. (*Safety Note:* Don't try to stuff any small hard objects in your ears; the results could be harmful.)

Inaudible (zero loudness)	Loudness to naked ear

Draw a straight line (of any length) in your notebook, labeling one end "inaudible" and the other end "loudness to naked ear." Mark the positions of each of the sound-reducing methods on the line at a point that corresponds to the loudness you heard. For example, if you think that one of the methods reduced the loudness by half, mark its position halfway along the line. If you think it reduced it by only 25 per cent, mark it at 1/4 of the length away from the "naked ear" end. Discuss the reasons for your findings.

3. **Sound power.** Hang a strip of tissue paper in front of the loudspeaker of a sound system (see sketch). Shut off the sound, close the windows, and turn off any fan or air conditioner in the room. The paper should hang motionless. Now switch the sound on and turn up the volume. Describe the effect on the paper and explain your observations.

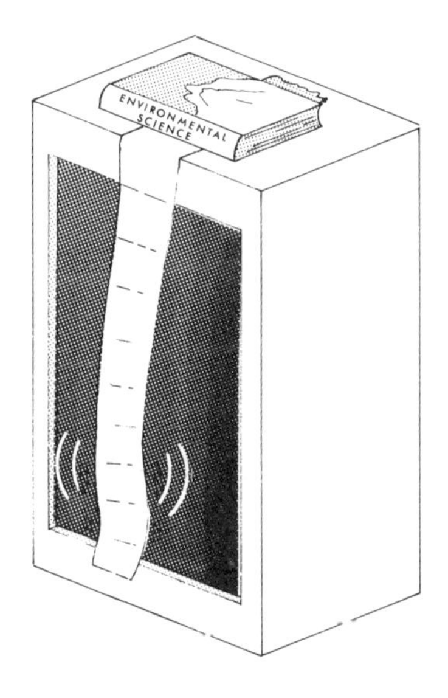

PROBLEMS

1. **Definitions.** Define or explain: Elastic wave; subsonic; supersonic; overtone; Mach number; sonic boom.

2. **Hearing.** Briefly describe the functions of (a) the eardrum; (b) the middle ear; (c) the inner ear.

3. **Sound.** As stated in Section 11.6, the scale of subjective loudness is based on a pure tone of 1000 Hz. Calculate the wave length of this tone if the speed of the sound is 334 m/sec.

4. **Pure tone.** What is a pure tone? Which of the following sounds would you consider to be the purest: the croak of a frog; the sound of an orchestra; the sound of a tuning fork?

5. **Musical sound.** Explain the difference between a pure tone and a musical sound.

*6. **Pure tone.** When we say that the shape of a "pure tone" is sinusoidal, which of the following statements do we imply? (a) The molecules move along in a wavy motion like water waves. (b) A graph of air density vs. distance will be a sine curve. (c) A graph of the degree of increase or decrease of

*Indicates more difficult problem.

air pressure above or below atmospheric pressure vs. distance will be a sine curve. (d) A graph of pressure vs. time at any one point will be a sine curve. (e) The molecules move back and forth like the inking of the paper in Figure 11–4*B*. (f) Since the air does not ripple, there is no real sine function, but rather we are using a figure of speech to compare a "pure" tone with the pure symmetry of a rotating wheel.

7. **Noise.** What is noise? Do you think it would be feasible to develop an instrument that would indicate how noisy a given sound is? Defend your answer.

8. **Noise.** The first definition of "noise" in Section 11.4 does not include the word "sound." Which of the following phenomena would you be willing to classify as noise? Defend your answers. (a) Mysterious blips on a radar screen that is scanning an area near an airport for approaching aircraft; (b) "snow" that interferes with your television picture but not with the sound; (c) smells from burning garbage that interfere with the chemical trail-making signals from the scent glands of the red deer.

9. **Signal vs. noise.** Which of the following proportionalities do you think better expresses the discussion in Section 11.7 on "interference with communication"?

(a) Communication $\propto$ (signal − noise)
(b) Communication $\propto$ (signal/noise)

Defend your answer.

10. **Decibels.** A person hears a cry in the woods that is 1000 times the intensity of the faintest audible sound. What is the sound level in decibels?

11. **Decibel scale.** Table 11–1 lists sound intensity factors as well as sound levels (dB). How are these two lists related to each other? Can you express the relationship in equation form?

12. **Sound intensity.** The sound intensity of a motorcycle at a distance of 8 m is 90 dB. How many times more intense than the faintest audible sound is this motorcycle sound?

13. **Sound intensity.** (a) The sound intensity of a garbage disposal unit is 80 dB. How many times more intense than the faintest audible sound is this garbage disposal sound? (b) How many times more intense is the sound of a 120 dB thunderclap than the sound of a garbage disposal unit?

14. **Combinations of sounds.** The sound intensity of a vacuum cleaner is 70 dB. What is the sound intensity of two vacuum cleaners? Is the difference between the sound intensity of two vacuum cleaners and one vacuum cleaner the same as that between two jet engines and one jet engine? Explain your answer.

*15. **Decibel scales.** Can there be a negative decibel level? A dog can hear sounds inaudible to a human. Suppose a dog could just hear a sound whose intensity is 10^{-13} W/m^2; what is the decibel level to which he would be sensitive?

*16. **Combinations of sine waves.** Given two sine curves of different frequencies, as shown in Figure 11–24: (a) Construct the combination of these curves by adding them, using the numerical values on the vertical scale. (b) If one of the curves were shifted slightly to the right or left, would the sum of the two curves still show a periodic variation?

*17. **dBA scale.** If you turned Figure 11–12 upside down and held it in front of a mirror, would it look something like Figure 11–11? Explain the relationship.

*Indicates more difficult problem.

Figure 11–24. Combination of two sine waves.

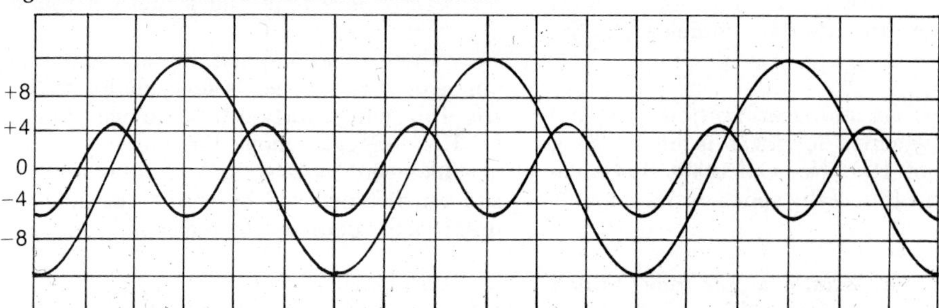

18. **Loss of hearing.** Explain why curve *C* of Figure 11–14 is said to characterize deafness, even though it shows no loss of hearing below 500 Hz.

19. **Noise control.** A man carries a decibel meter with him for a day and records the following readings in his diary:

7:00 A.M.	Baby crying.	84 dB
7:30	Dishwasher in kitchen.	70
7:45	Garbage truck, 150 feet away.	90
8:00	Traffic noise while waiting for bus.	81
8:45	Arrived at entrance to office. Noise of jackhammer on sidewalk.	106
9:00–12:00 Noon	Average sound in office.	45
12:00–1:00 P.M.	Noise in restaurant—dishes, etc.	45
5:00–5:30	Rode home on subway (windows open).	90–110
6:00	Mowed lawn with power mower.	93

Offer suggestions for reducing the perceived loudness of each of these various noises.

20. **Noise control.** Figure 11–25*A* shows a simplified sketch of a section of interior house wall made up of two sheets of wallboard attached to vertical wooden supports, called studs. A plan of the same wall section (looking down) is shown in Figure 11–25*A′*. Three other plans are also shown: *B*, sheets of lead (a good sound absorber) are placed between the wallboards and the studs; *C*, sheets of lead are placed between the studs; and *D*, alternate studs touch each wallboard, with sheets of lead snaked in between. Rate these structures according to their ability to serve as sound insulators. Defend your rating.

21. **Mach numbers.** A rocket is moving through the lower atmosphere, where the speed of sound is 334 m/sec, at Mach 1.5. What is the speed of the rocket?

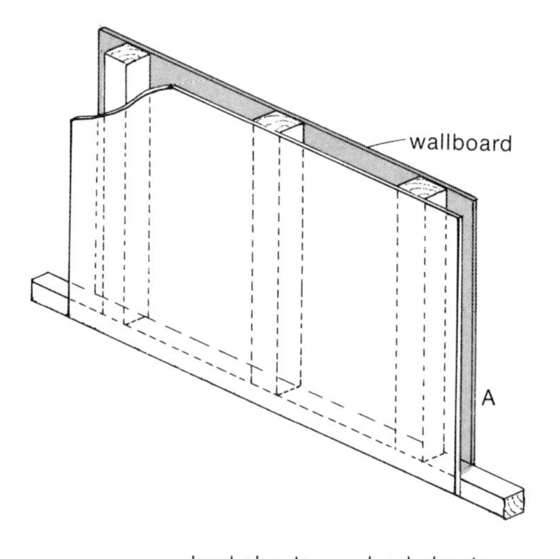

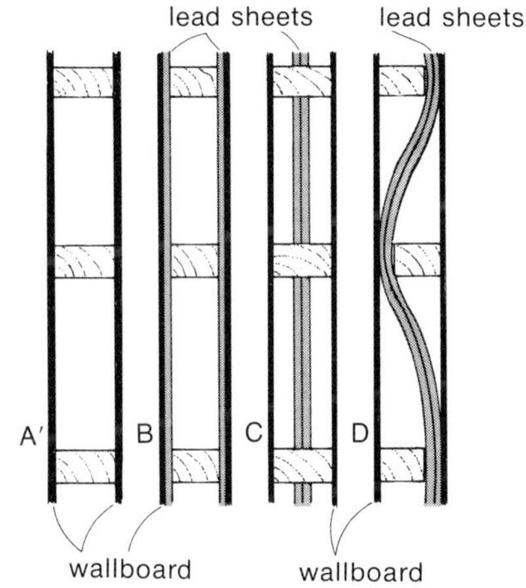

Figure 11–25. Sections of interior house walls. *A* and *A′*, No insulation. *B*, *C*, and *D*, Various arrangements of lead insulation.

CHAPTER 12

Engineering is the science of the design of practical objects such as bridges, roads, buildings, mechanical devices, automobiles, airplanes, spacecraft, computers, nuclear power plants, and pollution control devices. It is a broad field with many different specialties, but in all instances the engineer must combine theoretical knowledge with such practical considerations as cost, space requirements, and availability of materials. The constraints placed on various design problems are quite varied. For example, an aerospace engineer must build a satellite to be as light, small, and durable as possible, but he is generally free to use expensive materials such as titanium or gold; on the other hand, a civil engineer designing a bridge must use cheaper materials such as steel and concrete, but he is not nearly so concerned about the size and weight of the final product.

This chapter discusses some fundamental aspects of mechanical, civil, and pollution control engineering.

ENGINEERING

12.1 INTRODUCTION

When we think of problems in design and engineering we often visualize such complex constructions as skyscrapers, bridges, highway systems, oil refineries, automobiles, or airplanes. Perhaps we can appreciate the work of an engineer better if we start by studying the construction of a simple object such as a knife. Everyone knows that a knife is a relatively flat piece of steel with a handle at one end and a sharpened edge at the other. Yet anyone who set out to manufacture knives would be confronted with a host of design problems. What kind of steel should be used? How thick and how long should the blade be? Should it be curved or straight, flat or fluted? How should the handle be constructed to ensure a pleasing appearance, a firm grip, and long life? How much would the whole assembly cost?

To answer these questions, one would first decide on the exact function of the proposed knife—is it to be used primarily to slice fruits and vegetables in the kitchen, or just to peel them, to cut meat in a butcher's shop, or to skin small game in the field? Of course, the shape, size, weight, and appearance of the knife would be dictated by its proposed use. But the engineer must also choose the type of steel to be used—hard, soft, rigid, or flexible. The materials in the handle must also be considered—is it important for them to be machine-washable, resistant to impact, or protected against corrosion?

As an example, a good kitchen knife used primarily for cutting vegetables should have a flat blade surface so that a person can chop down on a cutting board and slice vegetables through with one sharp blow. The blade is generally thin, so that a cut will be clean and precise. Kitchen knives are usually constructed with a relatively soft steel so that they can be sharpened easily, and they are often built to be machine-washable. A hunting knife, on the other hand, is not designed for use against a cutting board. The blade is curved so that a person may develop an easy, smooth motion while skinning or whittling. The blade is generally strong and stiff for cutting between bone joints or for general hard use. Hunting knives are often made of fairly hard steel so that they will hold an edge for a long time, for many people do not like to carry sharpening stones in the field. Handles are made of some rugged material that resists abrasion, such as bone, horn, hard wood, or plastic.

The engineering problems involved in designing more complex objects are much more difficult. Consider the manual transmission of a car or truck. Given the speed (in revolutions per minute) and power of the engine, the transmission must have (a) one gear sufficiently low so that the vehicle can accelerate from a dead stop, move up a hill, or pull a load; (b) a high gear that enables the vehicle to cruise at highway speed; and (c) some number of intermediate gears to ensure smooth acceleration. But a well-designed transmission needs many other qualities as well. It must be relatively long-lasting, yet inexpensive to build. Preferably it should be easily taken apart and repaired. It must be shaped so that

Knives are designed in many shapes and sizes to perform a variety of tasks.

it readily bolts to the clutch assembly and the drive shaft, and it must not interfere with other parts such as a fuel line or brake system. Its overall size must be compatible with that of the entire vehicle, so that it does not produce an uncomfortable or unsightly hump in the passenger compartment or hang dangerously low to the ground. Finally, there are production considerations. The automobile assembly plant will need to build transmissions in quantities, so all parts—such as the gears, the case, and the bearings—should be available from manufacturers with sufficient production capacity to guarantee a large and steady supply. Countless problems arise, and it is the engineer who must solve them.

Similarly, an engineering team designing a new bridge must not only consider how to build a structure that will support the required load but also must be concerned with cost, with risks from floods or earthquakes, and with wear due to corrosion from rain or saltwater spray. In addition, the environmental impact that the bridge may create must be considered. Thus, the task of a modern engineer goes well beyond designing a structure that stands up, a machine that works, or an airplane that flies. Costs, space, aesthetics, availability of material, longevity, ease of repair, and environmental problems must all be taken into account.

Engineering and design constitute a broad field with many different specialties. The **mechanical engineer** is concerned with all types of devices that are primarily mechanical in their operation, such as automobiles, sewing and knitting machines, printing presses, or typewriters. **Electrical engineers**

Aerospace engineers are considering the design of large microwave collection and transmission systems to be built in space and used to beam electrical energy to Earth. (This artist's drawing of the microwave power satellite that might be built someday in the future is supplied courtesy of NASA.)

Civil engineers are involved in the design of bridges, dams, and roads. (Hoover Dam courtesy of Bureau of Reclamation, U.S. Department of the Interior).

Mechanical engineers design machinery of all types, such as this large rolling mill that produces steel plate. (Courtesy of Bethlehem Steel.)

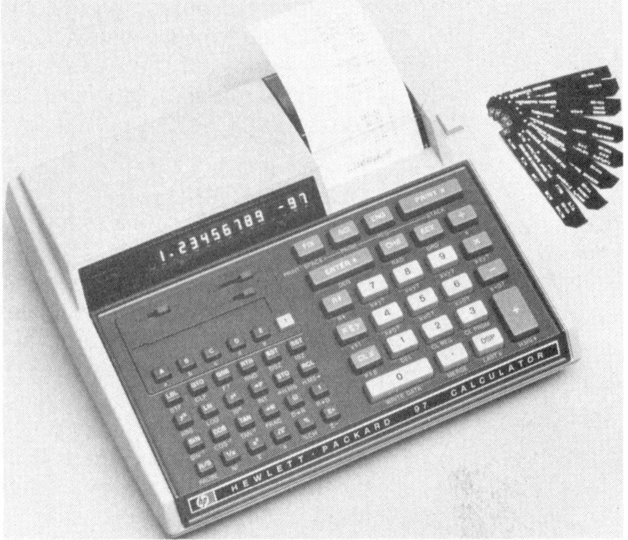

Electrical engineers designed this desk calculator. (Courtesy of Hewlett Packard.)

Chemical engineers are responsible for developing chemical processes that are conducted on a large scale. This photograph shows Exxon Oil Company's Baytown Refinery, Baytown, Texas. (Courtesy of Exxon.)

This water purification facility was designed by a pollution engineer. (Courtesy of Bethlehem Steel.)

Some of the many different branches of engineering

design and build electronic equipment—radios, record players, radar equipment, calculators, computers, scientific instrumentation, and many others. People who design public works projects such as bridges, roads, dams, harbors, and buildings are called **civil engineers. Chemical engineers** organize manufacturing processes for the synthesis and purification of various types of chemicals. Thus, after research chemists discovered how to synthesize nylon in the laboratory, teams of chemical engineers designed factories to produce this material on a large scale. **Aeronautical engineers** design airplanes, and **aerospace engineers** design rocket ships. New engineering specialties have recently become significant: the **environmental engineer** is responsible for constructing air and water purification systems and other environmental protection equipment, whereas **nuclear power engineers** work with atomic power plants. Because of space limitations, we will focus on only three types of engineering in this chapter—mechanical, civil, and environmental.

12.2 MATERIALS

Every object that is built and put to use is subject to various **stresses.** A building is stressed when the wind blows against it, a bridge is stressed when automobiles drive over it, a transmission gear is stressed when the vehicle accelerates, and a sewing machine needle is stressed when it is forced through a piece of cloth. Stress is defined as force per unit area:

$$\text{Stress} = \frac{\text{force}}{\text{area}}$$

An object can be stressed in three different ways. **Tensile stress** occurs when forces act to pull an object apart.

> Note that stress is expressed in the same terms as pressure. Therefore, a stress may be considered to be a pressure that has the potential to distort, damage, or destroy something. The units of stress and pressure are therefore the same; N/m^2. The older English units are lb/ft^2 or lb/in^2. The official SI name for N/m^2 is the Pascal, and lb/in^2 is frequently abbreviated "psi" for "pounds per square inch."

Figure 12–1. Types of stress.

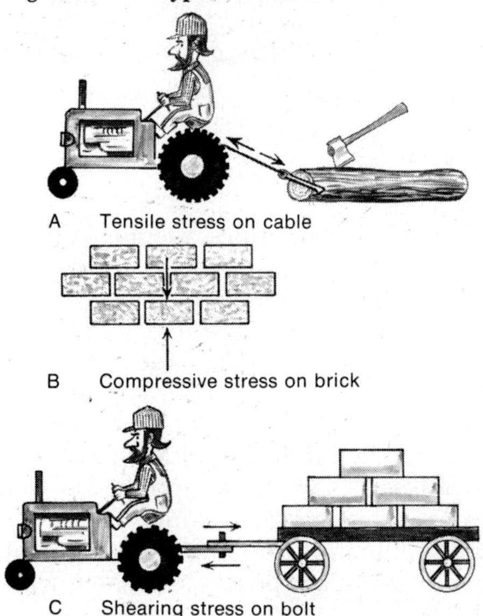

Thus if a cable is connected from a tractor to a log, and the tractor is pulling the log along the ground, the cable is under tensile stress (Fig. 12–1*A*). If an object is being squeezed or forced together it is said to be compressed, or subject to **compressive stress.** A brick in a wall is being compressed by the weight of the bricks above it (Fig. 12–1*B*). If we hold one section of a piece of material in a fixed position and attempt to slide another section across the fixed one, a **shearing stress** is exerted on that material. If a trailer is bolted to a tractor as shown in Figure 12–1*C*, the bolt is not being pulled or pushed as a unit. Instead, one part of it is being pulled in one direction while the other part is pressured to slide in the other direction. The net effect, which tends to destroy the bolt by pushing and pulling at the same time, is a shearing stress.

Different materials possess different types of strengths. For example, brick has high compression strength and is a valuable building material for walls and foundations that must support a great deal of weight, but it does not have great tensile or shearing strength. Therefore you would never construct a beam or a tow bar out of brick.

Whenever we stress an object, it changes size or shape. Thus when we pull a cable, it stretches somewhat; when we compress a brick, it becomes smaller; and when we exert a shear against a bolt, it bends a little. The distortion that results from stress is called **strain.** Since there is a measurable strain for every stress, there is no perfectly rigid object. Walk out on a bridge some day and wait until traffic flows by. Cars and trucks will cause the structure to bounce, and the bounce is easily felt. Similarly, buildings sway in the wind; the top of the World Trade Center in New York City may sway up to 28 cm. Next time you ride on an airplane, sit behind the wing, and if you watch it closely, you will see that it moves up and down noticeably, especially in turbulent weather.

All materials deform somewhat when a force is exerted against them. The **elasticity** of a material is a measure of how easily it deforms and how quickly it recovers its original shape

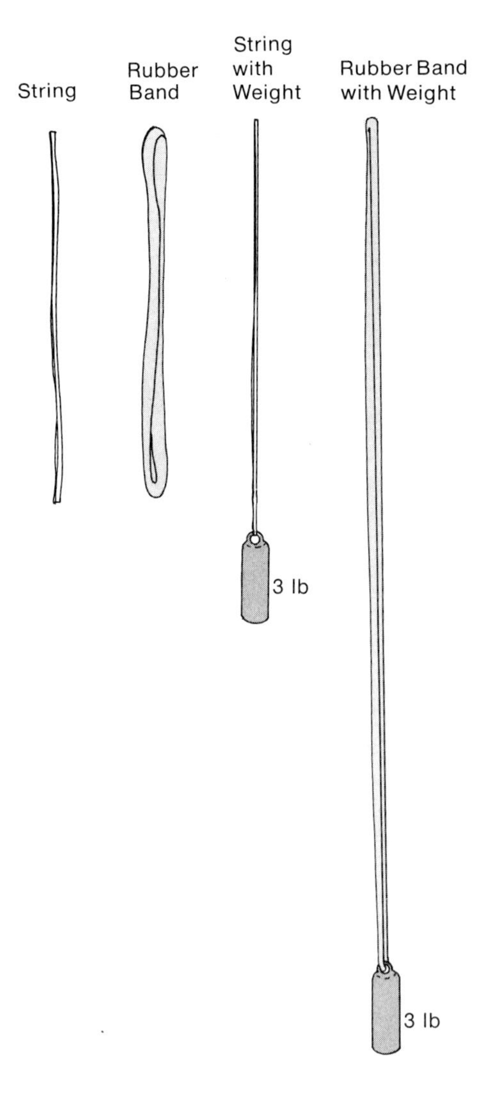

when the outside force is removed. Rubber is elastic, brick is relatively inelastic, and steel is intermediate between the two. Part of the engineer's job is to calculate the maximum stress to which an object will be subjected under normal use and then to choose materials that will deform to just the proper degree for the task involved. We spoke about this problem in another context in Section 3.7 in discussing the design of a sledge hammer. Since force is transmitted more rapidly through a rigid object than through a flexible one, a sledge hammer has a steel head and a wooden handle. The steel distorts little under impact and thus imparts a sharp blow, whereas the wood is more elastic and bends under impact, thereby reducing the force delivered to the person's hand. Conversely, if the handle were too flexible—if, for example, it were made of rubber—the sledge would be relatively useless.

The ski is an excellent example of a device whose deformation must match its function nicely. On a straight downhill run, a skier's weight should be distributed evenly on both skis. If the skier shifts his or her weight so that more force is applied on one ski than on the other, that ski will bend a little, and, as it bends, it enables the skier to initiate a turn. If skis were built to be extremely rigid so that they did not bend when stressed, it would be almost impossible to make them turn. (Think of how hard it would be to steer a car if all four wheels were pointed straight ahead and locked in position.) Therefore a ski must be flexible. On the other hand, if the ski bent too easily and distorted every time it hit a slight bump in the snow, the skier would wobble around the hill, out of control. Thus, engineers must be careful to design skis with the proper stress-strain ratio; the ski must flex easily but not too easily. The balance in this choice is delicate, and different skis are manufactured for travel at different speeds. A beginner, who skis at low speeds and is apt to exert a small amount of force in a turn, will purchase a ski that flexes easily, whereas a downhill racer, who wants

Skis must flex precisely in order to work properly. The skier has shifted her weight onto the downhill ski to initiate the turn. Note how the downhill ski has flexed more than the uphill one. This curve in the ski causes it to turn. (Photo by Dan Sparks; skier is Connie Russell.)

maximum stability at high speeds and is willing to work hard to turn, will require stiff skis.

Serious errors would result if engineers considered only strength and elasticity in design. Imagine that you were asked to design a hammer. A hammer head must have high compressional strength and low elasticity so that when it strikes a nail, the nail moves while the material in the hammer remains rigid. Well, brick has high compressional strength and is relatively inelastic, so would a brick hammer head be satisfactory? Of course not! One heavy blow and a brick would shatter into hundreds of tiny pieces. Brick is **brittle;** it fractures easily on impact. If brittle materials are stressed, they do not survive much distortion. Instead, they fracture after a small amount of bending or stretching.

The opposite of brittleness is **ductility.** A ductile material is one that bends or deforms easily before it breaks apart. Most wire is highly ductile. Take a wire coat hanger and bend it or twist it. It does not break but simply remains permanently deformed. Of course, brick or stone does not behave this way at all; brick will fracture before it bends. Brick is brittle, and wire coat hangers are ductile.

Suppose we take a piece of flat, ductile steel such as the one shown in Figure 12–2 and bend it first one way, and then the other, and then back and forth many times. After a while, a small crack will appear; the crack will widen and lengthen with more bendings, and finally the sheet will break. The tendency of materials to fracture upon repeated stress is called **fatigue.** Anyone who has done mechanical work on old cars and trucks is familiar with fatigue failure. If an old pickup truck is driven over rough back-country roads for many years, a spring may break, a motor mount bracket may crack, or some part somewhere may fall off. After a piece of metal is flexed and distorted thousands and thousands of times, fatigue sets in and the part may fracture. While a broken spring in a pickup truck is a relatively minor problem, fatigue in airplane parts is a serious consideration. Recall that airplane wings sway up and down noticeably during flight. This movement tends to fatigue the metal, and if you flew a plane long enough, the metal would eventually crack and the wing would fall off, just as a truck spring breaks after years of hard service. In order to ensure the safety of airline passengers,

Figure 12–2. ***A,*** **A plain piece of sheet metal.** ***B,*** **After the metal has been bent many times it starts to crack, demonstrating fatigue failure.**

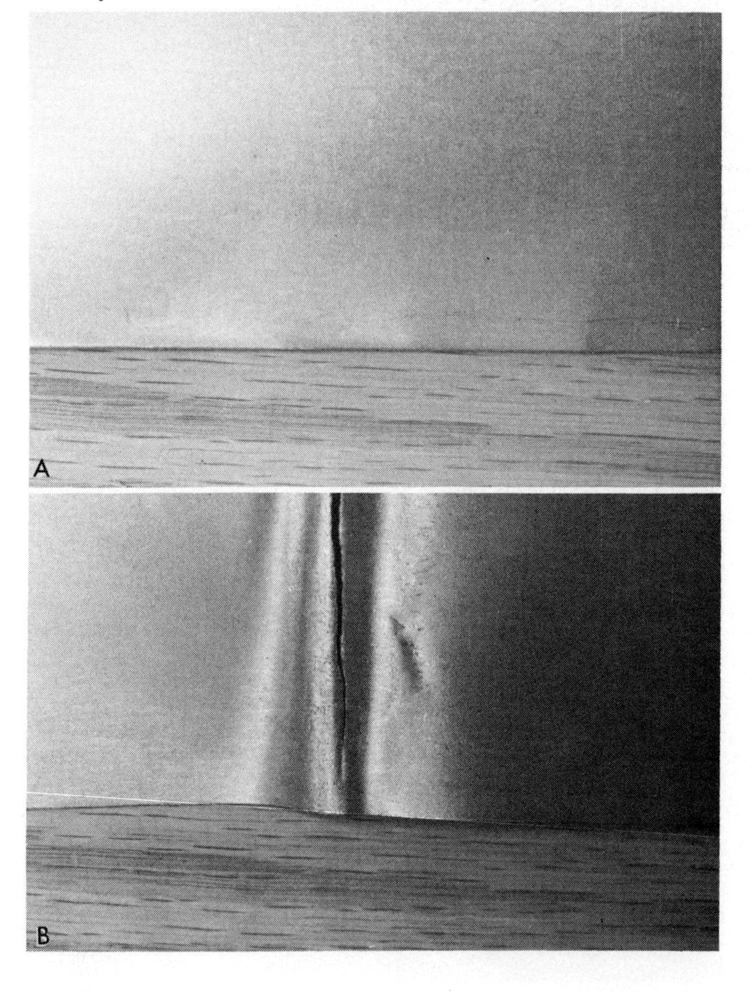

Airplane wings flex noticeably in flight. Eventually the metals fatigue, and the wings must be replaced. (Courtesy of Boeing Aircraft.)

Drill.

Jack.

Figure 12–9. Double-gear systems in which motion is transferred at right angles.

Figure 12–10. Train linkages.

A simple log bridge in the Himalayas in Northern India.

The simplest way to span a space is simply to place a long, straight, heavy log, board, or steel bar across the gap. The engineer's task is to calculate the maximum load that the structure must support and select some object strong enough to do the job. Wood beams and sometimes even stone slabs can be used for horizontal supports. Since logs and boulders generally are not found in the most convenient shapes or lengths, we must modify them, or manufacture our spans out of other material. Steel bars, for example, can be fabricated to virtually any length, but even steel does not solve all our engineering problems. You could manufacture a steel bar 1 km long, but then you would not be able to transport it from the mill to the construction site. Another problem is that a steel beam that is too long and heavy will sag under its own weight. Therefore we must learn how to make a beam that is both strong and light enough to support an external load in addition to its own weight.

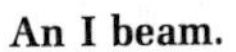

An I beam.

Beam construction supporting doorways in an adobe structure. Compare this construction with the arch shown on page 371.

To understand how strong, light beams are constructed, we must first study how a beam behaves when stressed. Look at the beam in Figure 12–11. The more weight that is placed on the beam, the greater will be the sag. The sag represents a deformation of the material, but not all parts of the beam deform in the same manner. Specifically, the top squeezes together and the bottom stretches. This necessarily means that some portion near the middle of the beam neither compresses nor expands, and the distortion is therefore greatest at the top and the bottom edges. As a result, *when a beam is carrying a load, the maximum compressive stress and strain are at the top of the beam, and the maximum tensile stress and strain are at the bottom. The least stress and strain are at the middle.* To help visualize these effects, think of a parade of Girl Scouts turning a corner. The girls in the inner files, like the top of the beam, must crowd together (compress) at the turn. Those at the outer file (like the bottom of the beam) will be stretched apart (and will have to hurry to cover the greater distance). But the middle file will be serenely undisturbed.

These observations can teach us how to design a beam that is light yet strong. The trick is to scoop some of the steel out of the middle where it is needed least. The result is a steel I-beam (see photograph). Since an I-beam is significantly lighter than a bar and almost as strong, it can support not only itself but a great deal of additional weight as well. It is also considerably cheaper, since it contains less material. For these reasons steel bars are almost never used by themselves for structural purposes, and I-beams are very common.

Steel plays an important role in all major construction today, for it is strong in tension and compression, elastic, and long-lasting. But steel is expensive, and in a great many applications concrete is the material of choice. Concrete is a mixture of cement and stone and, like most masonry products, has high compressive but low tensile strength. Nevertheless, today you can see concrete beams and bridges and overhanging concrete support members for large buildings. How can a material with low tensile strength be used in such applications? Actually a beam made of pure concrete would be unsuitable for any loadcarrying purpose. Since concrete is weak in tension, the bottom half of a loaded beam would crack, and the entire beam would fail. If we could somehow keep the bottom half of the beam from pulling apart, the beam could support a great deal of weight. As it turns out, this is easy to

Reinforced concrete.

Figure 12–11. Stress and strain in a beam.

do. Suppose we built a beam by setting steel rods in the wet concrete and then letting the mixture harden. Under load, the top half of such a beam resists crushing because of the compressive strength of the concrete, and the bottom half resists stretch because of the tensile strength of the steel rods. A composite structure of this type is called **reinforced concrete.** Thus any concrete beam, such as the type commonly used to support a highway bridge, is laced with steel rod to give it strength. Reinforced concrete is used in a great many applications. Think of a concrete highway. Weight from above forces it to sag, and frost from below forces it to buckle upward. Therefore, wire mesh is placed in the concrete to hold it rigid. Proper use of steel in cement and concrete enables designers to use this material in intricately shaped structures such as boat hulls. Cement ship hulls can be built by first forming a framework out of layers of strong wire, then plastering a specially formulated cement mixture over this mesh. For the cement hull to bend, twist, or otherwise distort, it must stretch all the wire in the structure, and if enough wire is in the hull, the boat becomes rigid and strong.

Figure 12–12. *A*, Two simple arches made of wire. *B*, A downward force causes an outward expansion.

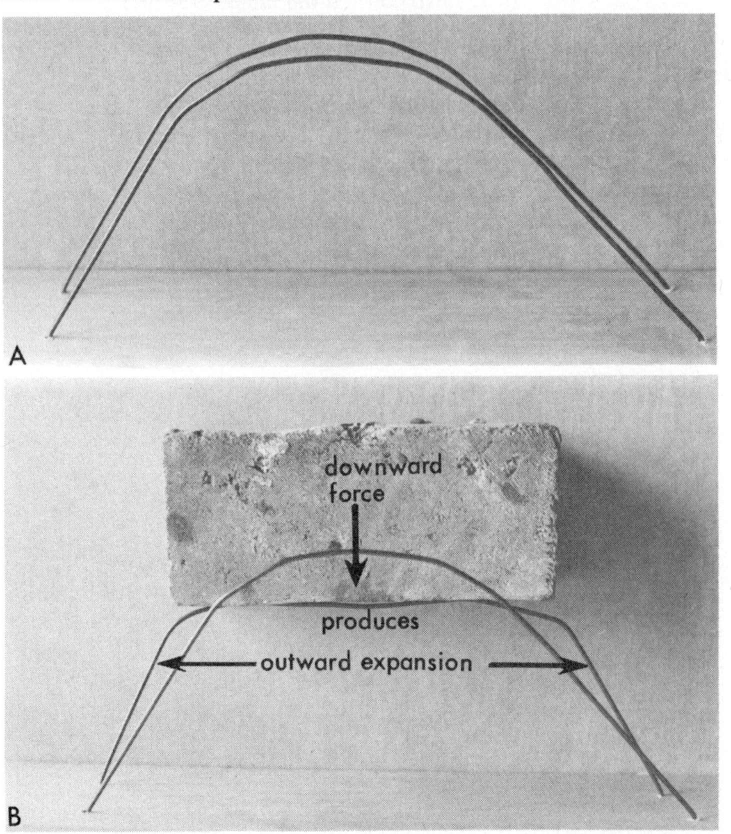

Although I-beams made of steel or reinforced concrete can support heavy loads over long spans and are much stronger than rods or bars, even the most carefully designed beams are limited. If any beam is made too long, it will sag under its own weight and be unable to support a load. Also, long beams are impractical because they are expensive to manufacture and to transport. For thousands of years engineers have known ways of designing structures that were stronger than single beams or rods. One of these forms is the **arch.**

The important difference between an arch and a beam is this: A loaded arch cannot sag downward unless the materials in it move *outward* first. This outward force is directed not only against the structural members of the arch itself but also against the point of attachment. To visualize this effect, consider the following two demonstrations. In the first, we have constructed two arches of thin, weak, metal rod and attached them both firmly to a block of wood (Fig. 12–12*A*). Now let us push down on one until it starts to collapse and leave the other alone for comparison. We can see in the second photograph (Fig. 12–12*B*) that as we push downward, the metal bends outward.

To perform the second demonstration, sit in an armchair, place each elbow on an arm of the chair, and clasp your hands together, thus forming a simple arch. Now have someone push down hard on the top of your arch. Since your bones are strong enough not to bend appreciably under the load, this arch will not fail like the thin metal rod. But if your friend pushes down harder, you will hear the sides of the armchair creak, and if the downward force is great enough and the chair is weak, the arms of the chair will break outward.

Thus, an arch can collapse only if the materials in it bend and move outward, or if the supports move apart. If an arch is properly built to resist these two types of outward movement, it becomes extremely strong. Roman engineers did not have steel to work with and had to build primarily with brick and stone. Since these materials have low tensile strength, it would be impossible to use masonry I-beams even if they could be manufactured. But brick and stone have tremendous compressional strength and are ideal for arches. Many ancient structures such as aqueducts and bridges were built of series of arches ultimately supported by the side of a mountain, as shown on the next page. Now suppose there is a large load on the center of one of the arches. The outward force on the loaded arch pushes against the adjacent arches. This force is directed outward again until the force is ultimately exerted against the sides of the mountain. For the arch to sag, some part of it must move outward, but to move in this manner either the masonry must compress or the mountains must move apart. Since neither condition is likely, the Roman arches were extremely strong, and many of them have stood for over 2000 years and remain strong to this day.

We have considered the engineering involved in the *design* of an arch; now let us think about the engineering of its *construction*. An arch has no strength until it is whole; an overhanging mass of stone and cement cannot support itself and is highly unstable. The two sides must mutually lean against each other in order for the structure to stand. Therefore the Romans had to build huge scaffolding to support the arches as they were being built. These scaffolds were made of wood and have long since been disassembled, but they must have been amazing by themselves, and the high arches that stand today are silent reminders of the wooden superstructures that must have been built first.

If we extend the sides of an arch laterally and curve them down to the ground, we get a structure called a **dome,** which is shaped roughly like a hemisphere. Domes are considerably stronger than arches. We can see in Figure 12–13 that whereas five arches made of slices of eggshells cannot support a single thin book, three eggshell

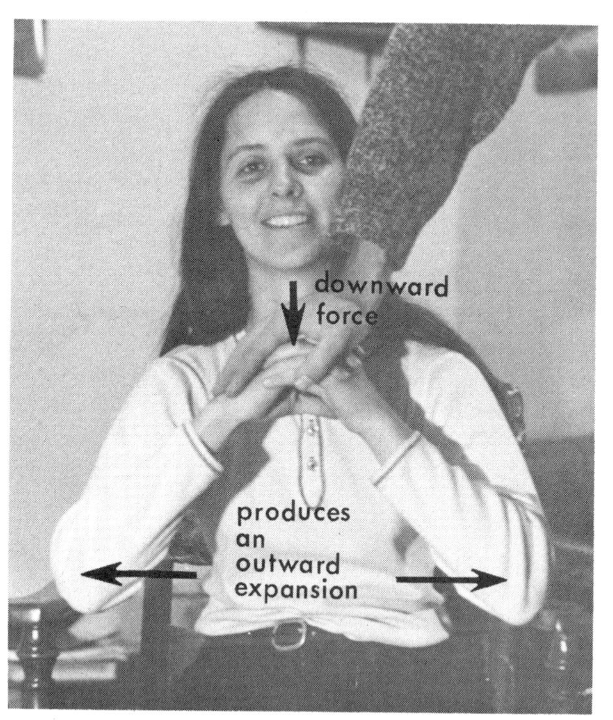

Try this experiment yourself. Form an arch with your arms as shown and have a friend push down at the top of your arch. You will feel your elbows push outward against the sides of the armchair as shown.

A simple arch made out of adobe bricks. Note that there is very little "cement" between the blocks, and that the "cement" is simply dried mud. The structure is supported by the inherent rigidity of the arch, not by adhesives.

The New River Gorge Bridge, world's longest arch (520 meters) under construction. An arch has no strength until it is complete. Therefore, temporary cables were strung above the structure to support it until construction was finished. At the stage of construction shown here, the center of the arch has just been fastened into place, and then the roadbed is to be added next. (Courtesy of the American Bridge Division, U.S. Steel.)

The Pont-du-Gard aqueduct, erected in the last quarter of the first century BC as part of a canal which brought water to Nimes. This is considered to be the most impressive of all the Roman monuments in France. Note that the outward forces are ultimately directed against the mountainsides. (Courtesy of the French Government Tourist Office.)

polluted when untreated sewage or chemical wastes are dumped into streams or lakes.

Pollution engineering is really short for "pollution control engineering," because the idea is to remove pollutants, not to add them. The pollution engineer must consider costs of buying, installing, and operating the equipment for the control of harmful impurities. Various other factors are also important, such as the noise that the equipment makes, the space it requires, and in some cases, the structural strength of the roof needed to support it.

The pollution engineer is not always asked to decide what is harmful, just as the civil engineer is not asked to predict how much traffic will cross a given river. The civil engineer can say, "Tell me how much traffic you expect and I will design a bridge and calculate its cost," or "Tell me how much money to spend for a bridge and I will design it and tell you how much traffic it can handle." In the same way, the pollution engineer can design equipment with a certain relationship between cost and benefit in mind, but as a rule, the more good it will do, the more expensive it will be.

Now let us be specific and look at the engineering of pollution control in gases, liquids, and solids, or in practical terms—air pollution engineering, wastewater engineering, and solid waste management.

Top view shows how fumes would pour from the smokestack of a steel furnace if pollution control devices were not installed. Bottom view shows operation with successful control. (Photo courtesy of Bethlehem Steel)

Air Pollution Engineering

It is easy to think of air pollution control as something one does to the source of the pollution—the engine or tailpipe of an automobile, or the smokestack of a power plant. That is, of course, a valid concept, but it is not the only one. One could also make cultural choices of many kinds that serve to reduce air pollution. Some of these are discussed in the sections of Chapter 4 that deal with energy sources. For example, solar energy is non-polluting and, of course, one could simply use *less* energy. But as we have said, the engineer does not usually make such choices.

The emission from a polluting source contains many harmless gases, such as nitrogen or oxygen, mixed with a much smaller concentration of pollutants. Typically, the volume of polluted matter in a contaminated air stream is in the range of 1/1000 to 1/10,000 of the total volume.

There are two general approaches for controlling pollution at the source: (a) the pollutants can be separated from the harmless gases and disposed of in some way, or (b) the pollutants can be somehow converted to harmless products which may then be released to the atmosphere.

Pollutants can be classified on the basis of their particle sizes. For purposes of pollution control, we will consider two major categories: (a) particulate matter, such as dusts and mists, whose particles are much larger than molecules, and (b) gases, which consist of molecules.

Particulate matter can be separated from a moving gas stream in a variety of ways that depend on the physical and chemical properties of the pollutants. For example, think of a household vacuum cleaner. Dust and dirt are drawn up from the floor in a stream of ordinary air. The air, now heavily laden with dust is sucked through a cleaner bag which is made of semiporous paper. Since dust particles are very much larger than gas molecules, the air passes through the filter bag while the dust is retained. Periodically, the bag becomes filled with dirt and the homemaker must either discard it or shake the refuse out and reuse the bag. Commercial air pollution control devices such as the ones shown in Figure 12–17 consist of large, semiporous bags that filter dust from a polluted air stream.

There are various mechanical collection devices that depend on the fact that particles are *heavier* than gas molecules. As a result, particles will settle faster and can be collected in a chamber that allows enough time for them to settle out. However, such methods are practical only for very large particles. More important than their settling rate is the fact that heavier particles have more *inertia*. As a result, if a gas stream that contains particulate pollutants is whirled around in a vortex (Fig. 12–18), the more massive pollutant particles may be spun out to the outer walls. These particles will then settle towards the bottom while clean gases will move upward and out the top of the collector. Such a device is called a **cyclone.**

Particles may also be removed from a gas stream by virtue of their be-

Figure 12–17. Typical bag filter employing reverse flow and mechanical shaking for cleaning. The figure shows the dusty gas being blown from the inlet toward the left and up. When the dusty gas reaches the six bags on the left, the gas goes into the bags while the dust remains on the outside (just like a vacuum cleaner running backward). The cleaned gas then comes out the tops of the bags and is discharged via the exhaust fan to the atmosphere. Meanwhile, the bags on the right, which have collected dust on their outer surfaces from the previous cycle, are being shaken and blown so that their dust falls to the bottom, where it can be removed. When the bags on the right are clean and those on the left are dusty, the air flow pattern is reversed. (From Stern: *Air Pollution.* 2nd ed. New York, Academic Press, 1968.)

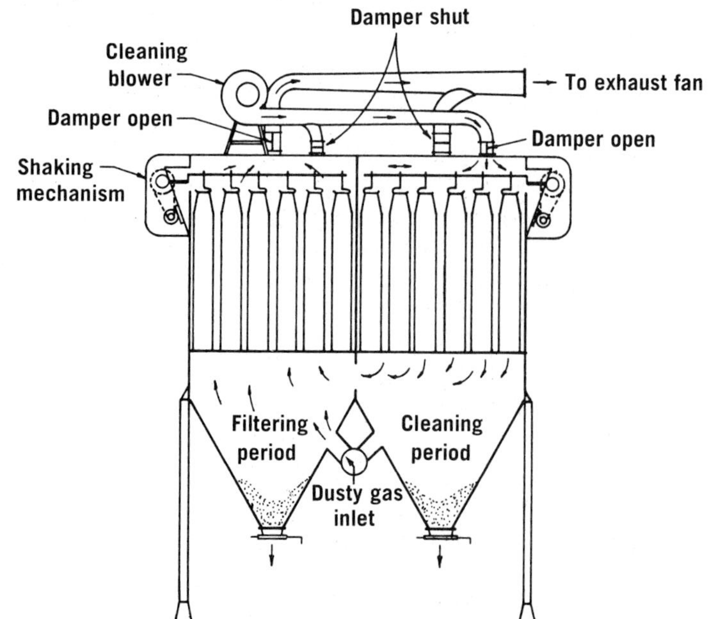

Figure 12–18. Basic cyclone collector. (From Walker: *Operating Principles of Air Pollution Control Equipment.* Bound Brook, N.J., Research-Cottrell, Inc., 1968.)

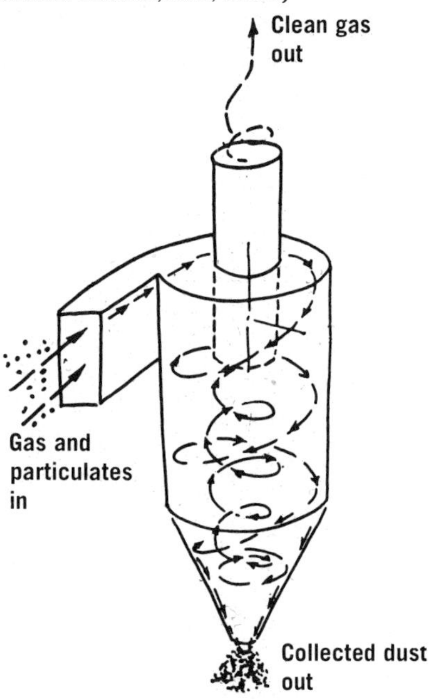

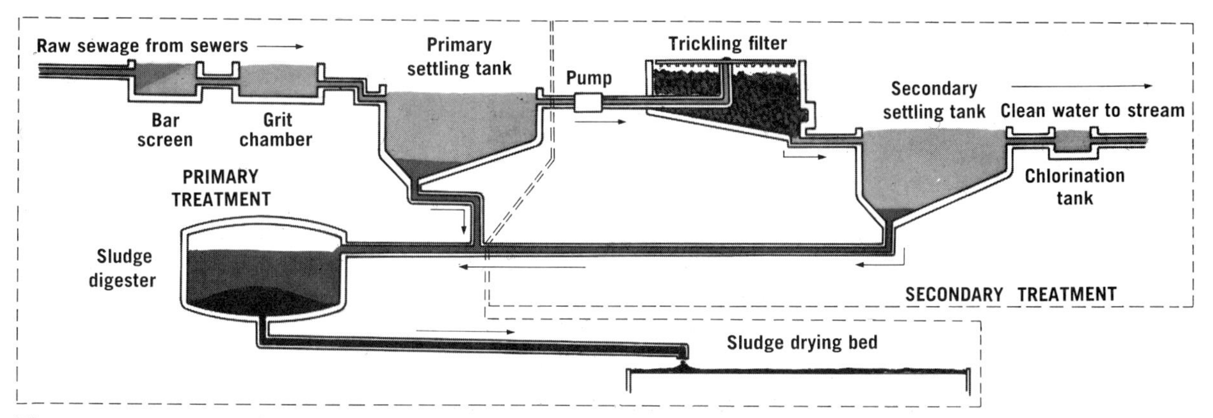

Figure 12–25. Sewage plant schematic, showing facilities for primary and secondary treatment. (From *The Living Waters,* U.S. Public Health Service Publication No. 382.)

Fig. 12–25), it first passes through a series of screens that remove large objects, such as rats or grapefruits, then through a grinding mechanism that reduces any remaining objects to a size small enough to be handled effectively during the rest of the treatment period. The next stage is a series of settling chambers, where the water is held long enough for some pollutants to sink to the bottom. This process first removes the heavy grit, such as sand that rainwater brings in from road surfaces, and then, more slowly, any other suspended solids—including organic nutrients—that can settle out in an hour or so. Up to this point the entire process, which is called primary treatment, has been relatively inexpensive but has not accomplished much. If the sewage is now discharged into a stream (as, unfortunately, is often the case), it does not look so bad because it bears no visible solids, but it is still a potent pollutant carrying a heavy load of microorganisms, many of them pathogenic, and considerable quantities of organic nutrients that will demand more oxygen as their decomposition continues.

Secondary treatment

All animals require oxygen for metabolism of food. Aquatic animals utilize the oxygen dissolved in the waters they inhabit. The solubility of oxygen in water is low (0.0084 g/L at 25° C). As a result, when water is rich in organic matter (such as sewage), organisms compete for oxygen, which is in short supply. Microorganisms reproduce much more rapidly than large animals such as fish, so they deplete the oxygen levels in the water and the fish die. Therefore, organic matter in water is a pollutant. In addition, many of the microorganisms carry disease.

The best way to reduce organic pollution in water is to supply plenty of oxygen, let the microorganisms consume the nutrients, then get rid of the microorganisms. One method of accomplishing this objective is the **activated sludge** process, shown schematically in Figure 12–26. Here the sewage, after primary treatment, is pumped into an aeration tank where it is mixed for several hours with air and with bacteria-laden sludge. Bacteria consume molecules of protein, fat, and carbohydrate. Protozoa consume bacteria. Each form of life plays its part in converting high-energy chemicals to low-energy ones. All the oxygen consumed at this stage is a substitute for oxygen that would otherwise be needed later when the waters are finally discharged to open streams and rivers. Therefore, this process constitutes a very significant purification.

The treated waters then flow to a sedimentation tank where the bacteria-laden solids settle out and are returned to the aerator. Some of the sludge must be removed to maintain steady-state conditions.

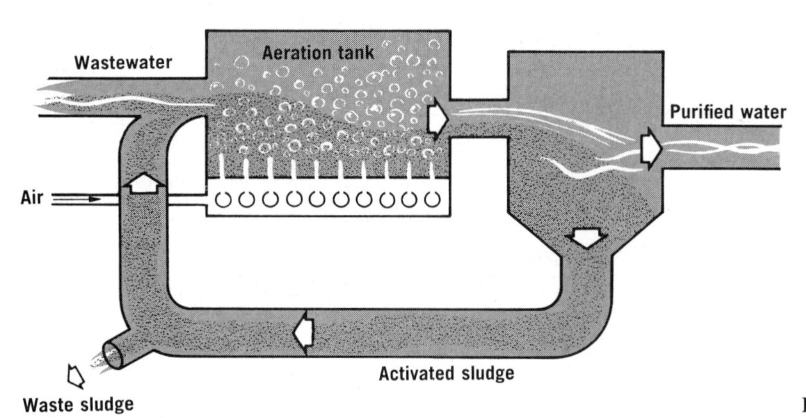

Figure 12–26. Activated sludge process.

The effluent from the biological action is still laden with bacteria, and so is not fit for discharge into open waters, let alone for drinking. Since the microorganisms have done their work, they may now be killed. The final step is therefore a disinfection process, usually chlorination. Chlorine gas, injected into the effluent 15 to 30 min before its final discharge, can kill more than 99 per cent of the harmful bacteria.

Let us now return to the sludge (Fig. 12–27). Each step in the biological consumption of this waterborne waste, from sewage nutrients to bacteria to protozoa and continuing to consumers of higher orders (such as worms), represents a degradation of energy, a consumption of oxygen, and a reduction in the mass of pollutant matter. Also, and perhaps most important from a practical point of view, the process brings about an increase in the average size of the pollutant particles. Look at Figure 12–23 to see how dramatic this change can be. Sugar is dissolved in water in the form of molecules which never settle out. Partially degraded starch and protein occur as colloidal particles approximately in the same size range as viruses. Bacteria are much larger, growing up to about 10 μm. Protozoa are gigantic by comparison; some amoeba reach diameters of 500 μm and thus are comparable in size to fine grains of beach sand. Some agglomeration also occurs in the metabolic processes of the protozoa, so that their excreta are usually larger than the particles of food they ingest. Finally, when the microorganisms die, their bodies stick together to form aggregates large enough to settle out in a reasonably short time. This entire process of making big particles out of little ones is of prime importance in any system of waste water treatment. The mushy mixture of living and dead organisms and their waste products at the bottom of a treatment tank constitutes the biologically active sludge. The final disposal of the sludge residue, whether by incineration, landfill, or other means, becomes a problem in the handling of solid wastes (Fig. 12–28).

Figure 12–27. Sewage sludge.

Figure 12–28. The Metropolitan Sanitary District of Greater Chicago transports its sewage sludge by barge and pipeline (above) to a 15,000 acre (6000 hectare) site in Fulton County, Illinois, where it is spread on agricultural areas that had been left in poor condition by strip-mining (below).

Another approach to biological purification of water uses the water hyacinth. These aquatic weeds, sometimes transported to new environments for decorative purposes, grow at an explosive rate in nutrient-rich waters. They have been considered to be pests because they interfere with fishing and navigation. However, their appetite for organic nutrients can be harnessed for water purification in a manner analogous to the use of bacteria. The hyacinth can then be harvested and used as a mineral and protein supplement to cattle feed, as a fertilizer for soil, or as a raw material for fermentation to a biogas fuel rich in methane. Since this method does not use bacteria, the treated water need not be chlorinated.

Tertiary or "Advanced" treatments

Although considerable purification is accomplished by the time wastewaters have passed through the primary and secondary stages, these treatments are still inadequate to deal with some complex aspects of water pollution. First of all, many pollutants in sanitary sewage are not removed. Inorganic ions, such as nitrates and phosphates, remain in the treated waters. If chlorination is incomplete, microorganisms will remain. In any case, chlorine will remain in some form or other, frequently as chlorinated organic matter which seriously impairs the taste of the water and which can even introduce new toxic substances.

Additionally, many pollutants originating from sources such as factories, mines, and agricultural runoffs cannot be handled by municipal sewage treatment plants at all. Some synthetic organic chemicals from industrial wastes not only resist the bacteria of the purification system but may also poison them. As a result, they nullify the biological oxidation which the bacteria would otherwise provide. There are also inorganic pollutants, including acids and metallic salts, as well as suspended soil particles from chemical and mining operations and from natural sources. Some of these materials occur as very fine particles from roadways, construction sites, or irrigation runoffs. These sediments are troublesome before they settle, because they reduce the penetration of sunlight, and afterwards, because they fill reservoirs, harbors, and stream channels with their silt.

The treatment methods available to cope with these troublesome wastes are often specific to the type of pollutant to be removed. In some instances the chemistry is rather complex. You might wonder whether there is any *one* method which works well for a large variety of pollutants that might find their way into your drinking water. The best choice would be adsorption. This method can even be used on an individual basis since it does not require any elaborate equipment to purify drinking water for one household. A cartridge of activated carbon inserted into the cold water line leading to your sink will do the trick.

Solid Waste Management

The reader will recognize that much of the effort in air and water purification goes toward *concentrating* the wastes. A small amount of dust in air or water may be dispersed in a large volume; after filtration, the dirt is reduced to a much smaller volume and is therefore easier to handle. But solid wastes are already concentrated, so what more can we do with them? There are three answers: (a) We can put them somewhere out of the way where they do no harm, or at least are not so noticeable, (b) we can concentrate them still more, and then dispose of the residue, or (c) we can recycle them.

An abandoned landfill in Southern Colorado has degenerated into an open dump.

About 80 per cent of the municipal refuse discarded in the United States in 1980 was deposited on land or on the ocean floor. The most primitive waste repository is the **open dump.** Waste is collected and, to save space and transportation costs, is compacted. The compacted waste is hauled to the dumping site, usually in the morning, and spread on the ground, further compaction sometimes being effected by bulldozing. Organic matter rots or is consumed by insects, by rats, or, if permitted, by hogs. Various salvaging operations may go on during the day. Bottles, rags, knick-knacks, and especially metal scraps are collected by junk dealers or by individuals for their own use. In some communities, the accumulation is set afire in the evening (or it may ignite spontaneously) to reduce the total volume and to expose more metal scrap for possible salvage. Of course, the organic degradation, the burning, and the salvaging are recycling operations. However, there are serious detrimental features to the open dump. Rats, fleas, and many types of microorganisms breed in and near exposed piles of trash; therefore, dumps are a potential source of disease. The fires, too, are uncontrolled and therefore always smoky and polluting. Rainfall that enters the dump may pollute nearby watercourses, and, of course, the dumps are ugly. Chemical dumps are particularly hazardous, as will be discussed shortly.

Ocean dumping is practiced by many coastal cities and represents little advantage over disposal on land. Barges carrying the refuse travel some distance from the harbor and discharge their loads into a natural trench or canyon on the ocean floor. In this way most of the trash is removed from sight, though not from communities of living organisms. Aquatic dumping areas are almost devoid of animals that live on the ocean floor (such as crabs and lob-

A botanical garden became the final layer of this completed landfill. (From Sanitary Landfill Facts. U.S. Department of Health, Education and Welfare, PHS.)

sters). Although plants and animals that live on the surface may survive in dump areas, they are affected by the unusual environment. For example, flounder caught in the former New York City dumping region had an off taste. Analysis of the stomach contents of these fish revealed that old adhesive bandages and cigarette filters constituted part of the animals' diet, and such dietary oddities may well have been the cause of the foul taste.

The **sanitary landfill** is far less disruptive to the environment than is uncontrolled dumping onto open land or into the ocean. A properly engineered landfill should be located on a site where rainwater, leaching through the refuse, will not pollute the groundwater. If such drainage cannot occur naturally, the site must be modified by regrading or piping to redirect the flow of water. After waste is brought to a landfill, it is further compacted with bulldozers or other heavy machinery. Large objects, such as furniture, are sometimes shredded. Each day, 15 to 30 cm of soil is pushed over the trash to exclude air, rodents, or vermin (see Fig. 12–29). In practice, however, the distinction between the sanitary landfill and the open dump is not always sharp. For example, a thin layer of earth may be an ineffective barrier against burrowing rats, flies developing from larvae, or gases evolving from decomposition.

The volume of solid wastes can be reduced by 80 to 90 per cent by **incineration.** The process, as applied to waste disposal, is more complex than simply setting fire to a mass of garbage in an open dump. A modern incinerator unit is currently used in Montreal, Canada. A crane removes refuse from a large storage pit and feeds it into the furnace at a constant rate. Burning occurs on a set of three inclined grates, which are agitated to ensure complete combustion and a constant movement of trash

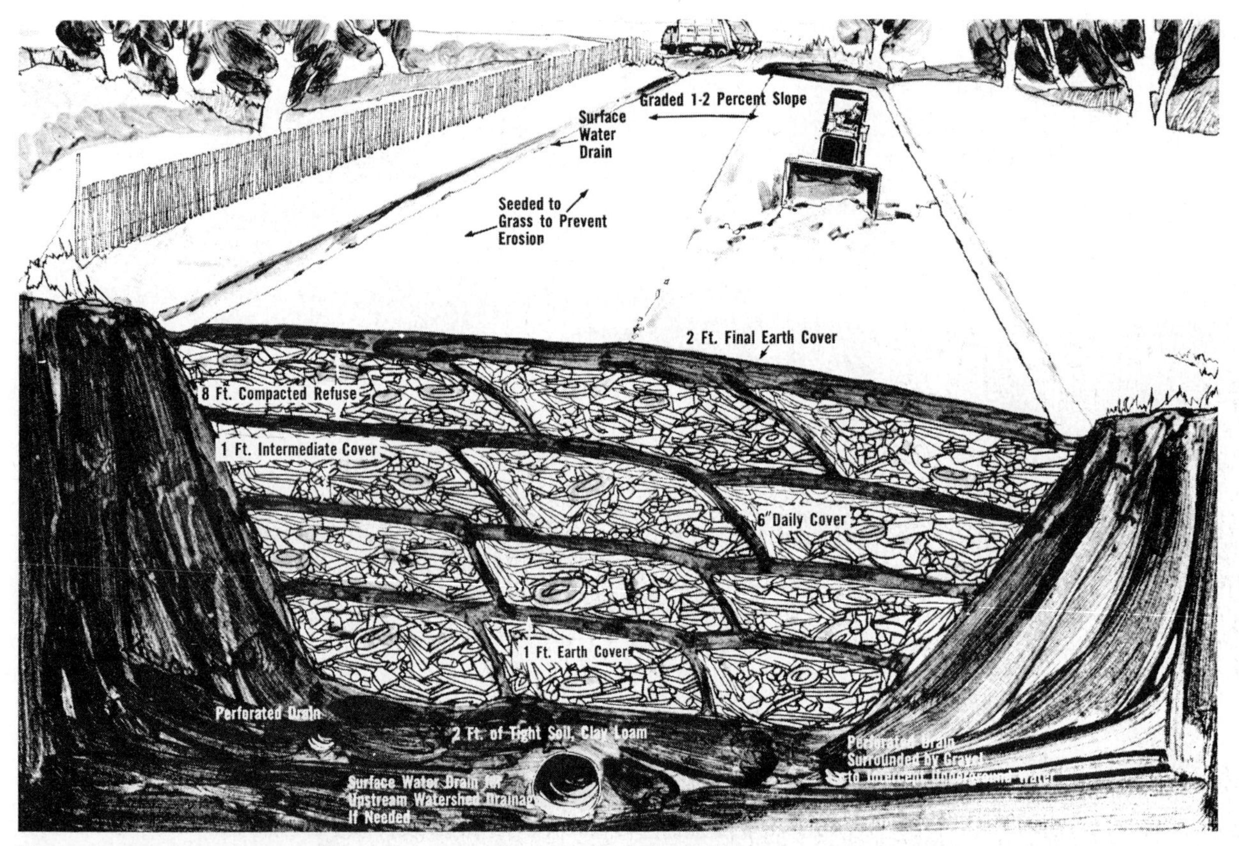

Figure 12–29. In ravines or valleys, the area method usually is best. Where the ravine is deep, refuse should be placed in lifts of six to 10 feet deep. Cover material may be obtained from the sides of the ravine. To minimize settlement problems, it's desirable to allow the first lift to settle for about a year. This is not always necessary, however, if the refuse has been adequately compacted. Succeeding lifts are constructed by trucking refuse over the first one to the head of the ravine. Surface and groundwater pollution can be avoided by intercepting and diverting water away from the fill area through diversion trenches or pipes, or by placing a layer of highly-permeable soil beneath the refuse to intercept water before it reaches the refuse. It's important to maintain the surface of completed lifts to prevent ponding and water seepage. (Courtesy of New York State Department of Environmental Conservation.)

into and ash out of the chamber. The ashes are ultimately removed by a conveyor belt and cooled; the metals are salvaged, and the remainder is removed to a sanitary landfill. The furnace heats the boilers and the resultant steam is sold to industry. Thus, the trash is used as an energy source. An auxiliary oil burner has been installed in the Montreal incinerator to ensure a constant supply of steam even if a crane were to break or the sanitation workers were to go on strike. Finally, the furnace gases are purified by an electrostatic precipitator.

At the present time, many industries and municipalities across the globe are burning trash as fuel. As mentioned in Chapter 3, large scale incineration is practiced in France. In the United States various cities and towns are incinerating garbage, and using the heat to produce steam for the generation of electricity.

Waste contains many valuable materials that can be recycled. Numerous recycling centers have been established throughout North America where aluminum or steel cans, glass bottles, cardboard, and old newspapers are collected and shipped to processing plants. Nevertheless, a great many people discard valuable raw materials in the trash. In several cities and towns in

North America, large municipal recycling plants have been built. In these places, unsorted garbage is collected, hauled to the refuse center, and then sorted automatically and efficiently. People need not go out of their way to separate trash and haul valuable items to collection centers. The facility that has been built in Franklin, Ohio is shown schematically in Figure 12–30. Large items like old swing sets and engine blocks are removed manually and the remaining refuse is fed into a specially designed hydropulper. (A hydropulper is a device that beats wood or scrap paper into fibers for manufacture of paper.) The fiber component of the

The Franklin, Ohio, recycling center. (Courtesy of Black Clawson Fibreclaim, Inc.)

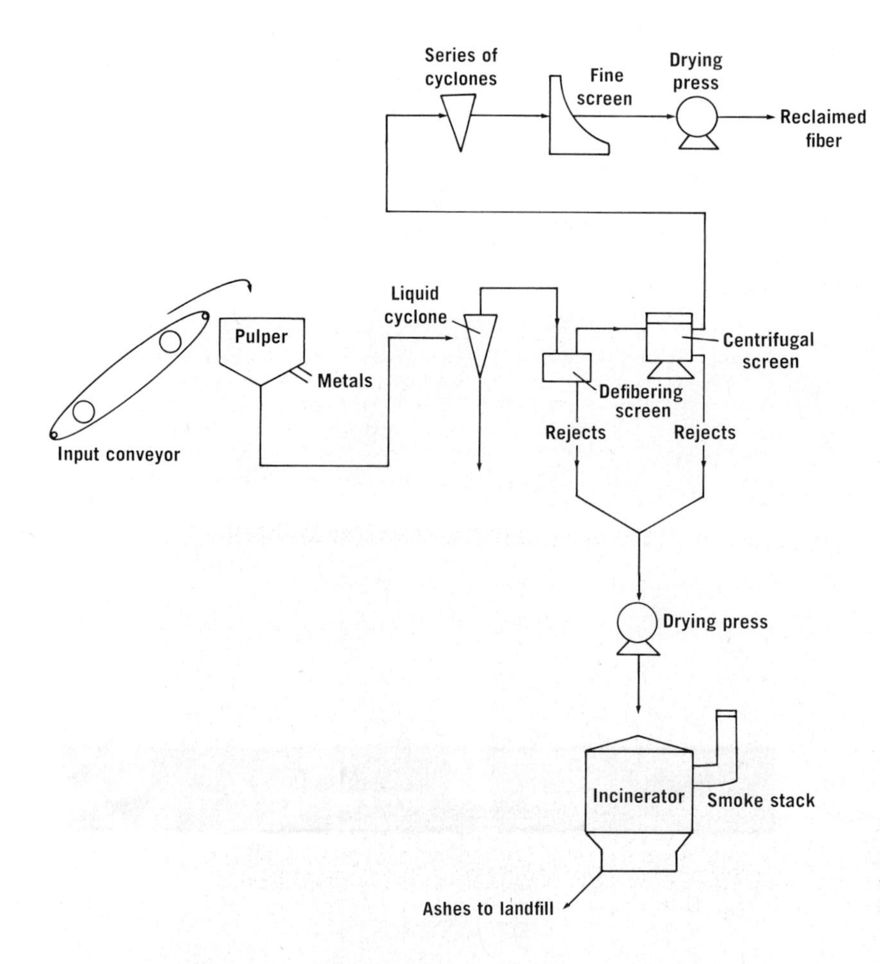

Figure 12–30. Schematic illustration of the Franklin, Ohio, recycling system.

Unfortunately, some of the air pollution problems (especially odors) associated with recycling systems have not been completely solved. Complaints from the surrounding communities have forced some plants to close down. Rising energy costs may cause them to reopen, however.

refuse is pulped, and brittle material such as glass and bones is pulverized, but hard solid objects are not affected. Anything that has resisted pulping and remains larger than 2.5 cm in diameter, such as large metal objects or rocks, is removed and washed. The iron is separated magnetically, and the other metals are separated manually for sale as scrap.

Meanwhile, the fiber slurry is pumped to a liquid cyclone, which separates the small, dense inorganic matter that passed through the screening. Glass, bones, small pieces of metal, especially aluminum from cans that break up in the pulper, and miscellaneous dirt, pebbles, and particles of sand are removed in this operation. The remaining slurry is washed again, and useful fibers are extracted and utilized for the manufacture of recycled paper. Organic rejects from the various screens and cyclones are considered to be non-recyclable and are dried and incinerated. The heat generated by the incineration step can be converted to salable steam or can be used to generate electricity.

As in other environmental questions, the decisions concerning the value of recovered energy or materials, the threat to human health or to life in the sea, and the desirability of an uncluttered landscape are not made by the engineer. Once the objectives are defined by social or political processes, it is up to the engineer to design workable systems at minimum cost.

Disposal of Chemical Wastes

Approximately 70,000 different chemical compounds are manufactured in the United States every year. Some of these are deadly poisons, some are mildly poisonous, others are suspected carcinogens* and many are harmless or beneficial to human health. Chemical manufacturing, like any other industry, produces wastes. Many of these chemical wastes are persistent in the environment and, in addition, are dangerous or even deadly poisonous. They can be destroyed or converted to harmless products by incineration or other costly chemical processes, but often the cheapest method is simply to pack the chemicals in steel drums and bury them somewhere. But steel drums, exposed to moist soil from the outside and often strong acids or bases from the inside, cannot remain intact indefinitely. They rust, corrode, and eventually leak, and the chemicals inside them seep into the soil and may travel through groundwater systems into rivers, streams, lakes, and reservoirs. However, corrosion and leakage is slow, so environmental disasters are often delayed for years. The Hooker Chemical Company in Niagara Falls, New York, began dumping 55-gallon drums of discarded chemicals into an abandoned canal sometime in the 1940's. In 1953, the company filled one of the dumpsites and sold the land to the city as a site for an elementary school and a playground. By the spring of 1978, many of the children who attended the school and many of the adults who lived nearby had suffered several different types of unusual effects. Epilepsy, liver malfunctions, miscarriages, skin sores, rectal bleeding, severe headaches, and birth defects were reported.

Investigators learned that the drums, buried decades before, were leaking. A study revealed that several other similar dumps were scattered about the city. No one is exactly sure what the ultimate damage may be, but many people have already suffered greatly, and the potential for even greater disasters exists. For example, an estimated 1000 kg of dioxin solution have been buried in the area. Dioxin is one of the most deadly poisons known; approximately 75 g (0.075 kg) dissolved in drinking water could kill one million people. At the present time, government experts believe that there may be 800 dangerous chemical dumps in the United States. No one is exactly sure how to find them all and how to remove the hazards.

A, Steel drums full of poisonous chemicals were buried near the city of Niagara Falls, N.Y. The landfill was then covered, leveled, and the property sold to the city as a site for a school playground. However, the drums rusted, and some of the liquids leached to the surface. Many children contacted strange and serious diseases. This photograph shows a pool of rainwater polluted with industrial chemicals from the dump beneath the surface. (Wide World Photos.) B, A school child's opinion of the problems in Niagara Falls, N.Y. (Wide World Photos.)

*A carcinogen is a compound that causes cancer. It is often difficult to assess carcinogenicity, for a person who is exposed to a carcinogenic chemical may not develop the disease until 20 or more years after the exposure.

CHAPTER OBJECTIVES

Note how different materials respond to different types of stress and why a material that is useful in one application may be inadequate in another. Know the working principle of an automobile engine. Review the operation of levers, gears, and pulleys. Study various structural members such as beams, arches, domes, and trusses, and understand why each one is strong.

Review the categories of pollution engineering. In air pollution control, pay special attention to the differences between conversion and separation methods, between gases and particles, and between control at the source and control at the point of exposure. In water purification, know which categories of pollutants are removed at the primary, secondary, and tertiary treatment stages. In solid waste treatment, note the degree to which the volume of waste is reduced by various methods, and study the advantages of recycling.

KEY WORDS

Engineering
Mechanical engineering
Electrical engineering
Civil engineering
Chemical engineering
Aeronautical engineering
Aerospace engineering
Environmental engineering
Nuclear power engineering
Stress
Tensile stress
Compressive stress
Shearing stress
Strain
Elasticity
Brittleness
Ductility
Fatigue
Hardness
Expansion joint
Alloy
Steel
Cylinder
Engine block
Piston
Piston ring
Cylinder head
Spark plug
Valve
Intake valve
Exhaust valve
Internal combustion
Crankshaft
Power stroke
Exhaust stroke
Intake stroke
Compression stroke
Ignition
Cam
Gear
Lever
Pulley
Fulcrum
Mechanical advantage
Drive gear
Working gear
Beam
Concrete
Reinforced concrete
Arch
Dome
Truss
Geodesic dome
Pollution engineering
Cyclone
Electrostatic precipitator
Scrubber
Activated carbon
Adsorption
Catalyst
Wastewater engineering
Distillation
Primary treatment (of sewage)
Secondary treatment (of sewage)
Tertiary, or advanced treatment (of sewage)
Open dump
Sanitary landfill
Incineration

FORMULAS TO KNOW

1. $\text{stress} = \dfrac{\text{force}}{\text{area}}$

2. $\text{mechanical advantage} = \dfrac{\text{output force}}{\text{input force}}$

TAKE-HOME EXPERIMENTS

1. **Hammers.** Go to hardware stores, construction sites, gas stations, etc., and list the number of distinctly different types of hammers that are in use. (Do not list different sizes or colors of the same general type of hammer; record only hammers with distinctly different shapes and functions.) Draw a picture of each type of hammer and explain the relationship between shape and function. (It should be easy to find 10 different types; with some effort you could find 30.)

2. **Expansion.** Locate a large bridge on a road that carries little traffic. Then locate the expansion joint in the bridge. Measure the distance between the two sides of the gap in the early morning or late evening and again during the hottest part of the day (in the early afternoon). (If there is any danger of being hit by an automobile while performing the measurement do not continue with this experiment.) Record the temperature at the time of each measurement. How many centi-

meters did the bridge expand? If it is convenient to measure the length of the bridge, express the expansion of the bridge material as follows:

$$\text{Per cent expansion per °C} = \frac{\text{expansion (cm)}}{\text{increase in temp. (°C)} \times \text{length of bridge (cm)}} \times 100\%$$

3. **Automobile engines.** Go to your local friendly gas station or automobile dealer and ask the mechanic if it would be possible to view an engine with the valve covers removed. Ask him to point out the valves, valve springs, rocker arms, and lifters. Ask him to start the engine while you watch the motion of the machinery. Describe what you see.

4. **Automobile jack.** Locate a conventional automobile bumper jack. (A hydraulic jack, scissors jack, or screw jack will not do.) Draw a picture of the mechanism, indicating the fulcrum, lever, and working portions. Calculate the mechanical advantage of the jack by measuring how far you must move the handle to lift a car a measured distance.

5. **Structures.** Using ice cream–bar sticks or wooden coffee stirrers, and glue, construct a truss similar to the one shown in the accompanying photograph. You should use 11 ice cream–bar sticks to construct the truss. (Try to use the same amount of glue on each joint.) Now construct four separate beams. Each one is built by gluing three bars together so that your beams are just as long as the truss. This is shown in the second photograph. Allow the beams and the truss to dry overnight. Now support the truss so it is held upright, and tie a loop of string in the center. Determine the strength of your truss by tying objects to the loop and gradually adding weight until the truss collapses. Support the four beams together as shown in the photograph and test their strength in the same manner as you tested the truss. Compare the two results. In this example you used 11 sticks for the truss and 12 bars for the 4 beams. Which structure supports a greater weight? Discuss your results.

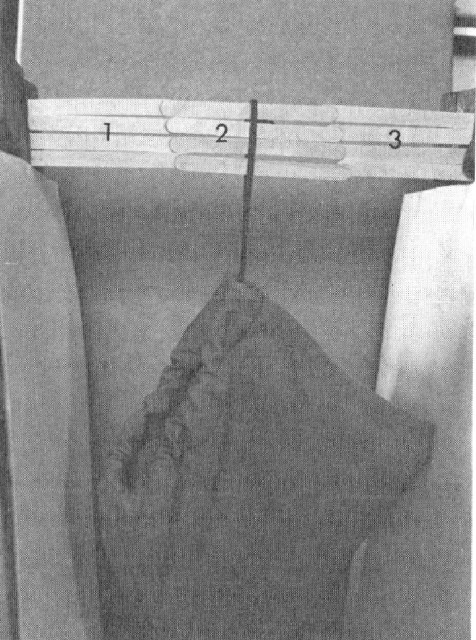

Top, Truss made from eleven sticks. *Bottom,* Beam made from three bars. Each bar was made from four ice-cream sticks, so that the masses of the two structures are about the same.

6. **Efficiency of a cigarette filter.*** Find the smoked butt of a filter cigarette. Carefully slice off the filter, using a razor blade or sharp knife. Now slice the filter in half, marking the tobacco end T and the mouth end M. Unwrap each half and estimate the relative shades of the brown colors as follows: Assume that the brown shade of the tobacco end is 100. Relative to this, estimate the shade of the mouth end. If you think it is three quarters as dark, call it 75, if it is 90 per cent as dark, call it 90; if it is half as dark, call it 50, etc. Better yet, ask a few of your friends to estimate the shades, but don't tell them what the T and M stand for. Now average the results. Calculate the efficiency of the filter, E, as follows:

$$E = \left(1 - \frac{M}{100}\right) \times 100\%$$

*The filter must be one of the type that is white before the cigarette is smoked. The usual material is cellulose.

Note that this calculation applies only to the efficiency of filtration of tarry particles whose color is visible. It does not apply to gases in cigarette smoke, such as carbon monoxide, which are not filtered at all.

7. **Water purification with activated carbon.** Food colors are usually available in small containers from which they can be dispensed in drops. Using such colors, prepare a set of lightly tinted solutions in ordinary drinking glasses, filled about three quarters full. Now stir a little activated carbon powder, of the type used for aquariums, into each glass. The carbon may be purchased from a pet shop, drugstore, or hobby shop. Place a saucer over each glass and allow the carbon to settle overnight. Note the effectiveness with which the colored impurities are removed.

Can you design a series of experiments to determine how much carbon is needed to remove a given amount of dye? Or to determine which dyes are easier or harder to remove?

PROBLEMS

1. **Definitions.** Define stress, strain, tensile stress; compressive stress, shearing stress.

*2. **Strength.** Nails have a high shear strength but can be pulled out of wood relatively easily. Suppose you were asked to build a wooden box designed to contain a great deal of weight. Would you construct it according to the plan in sketch *(a)* or sketch *(b)*? Explain.

3. **Stress and strain.** Which of the following objects are designed to be as rigid as possible, and which are purposely designed to flex: (a) baseball bat, (b) a gear in an automobile transmission, (c) a chisel for cutting steel, (d) a hand saw, (e) the tip of a fountain pen, (f) a gun barrel, (g) a frying pan, (h) a baseball, (i) the sole of a shoe, (j) a tennis racket? Defend your answers.

4. **Definitions.** If you are given an object that is fragile, are the materials in it likely to be brittle or ductile?

5. **Mechanical design.** Why are wood and brick unsuitable for use in the construction of a knife, a hammer, or an automobile driveshaft?

*6. **Mechanical design.** Diamond is very hard but brittle. Could you construct a useful drill bit entirely out of diamond? Explain. How would you construct a drill bit for drilling hard stone?

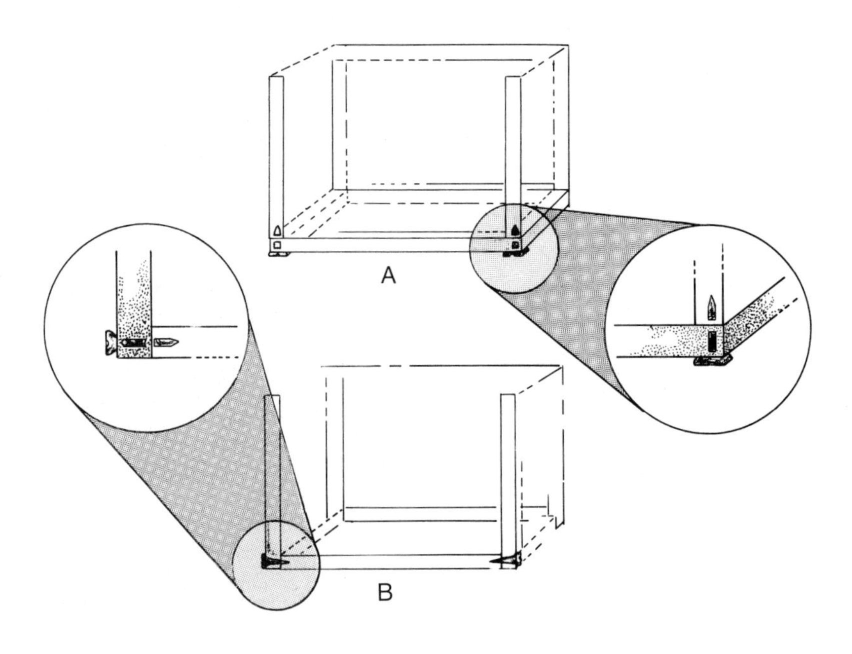

7. **Mechanical design.** List some factors that an engineer might consider before designing a knife; an automobile transmission; a bridge; an airplane.

8. **Materials.** Name a material that is elastic; one that has high compressive strength; one that has high tensile strength. Describe one use for each material.

9. **Materials.** Define elasticity. Is a rubber band elastic? What about a piece of steel? Explain.

*10. **Materials.** Give an example of a situation in which: (a) steel could be used and wood could not; (b) wood could be used and steel could not; (c) rubber could be used and steel could not; (d) steel could be used and rubber could not.

11. **Materials.** Automobile brake drums are frequently made of cast iron because this metal is resistant to wear by rubbing. But cast iron is brittle. If you were trying to remove a brake drum from your car but found that it was stuck on, would you try to pry it off with a screwdriver or tap it off with a hammer? Explain.

12. **Fatigue.** A nail in a piece of wood can help to support a house for hundreds of years without failing. Yet if you clamp one end of a nail in a vise and twist the other end back and forth, you can break a nail in half in a few minutes. Explain, and discuss the general nature of fatigue failure.

*13. **Design.** The wooden wagon wheels used in the last century were often rimmed with a steel "tire" as shown in the sketch. In order to fit the metal loop firmly around the wheel, wagoneers would build the iron loop smaller than the circumference of the wooden wheel. They would then stretch the metal, fit the stretched loop over the wheel, and let the metal spring back to shape for a tight fit. Think of an easy way to stretch such an iron loop without distorting it.

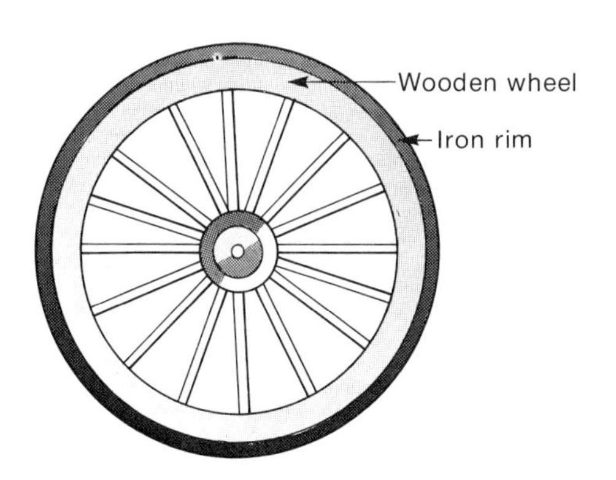

*Indicates more difficult problem.

*14. **Motion.** Referring to the mechanical transformations shown on page 356, which action is provided by (a) a shock absorber, (b) an automobile crankshaft, (c) the gears in a clock?

15. **Mechanical design.** Draw a picture of a simple crankshaft. What is the function of a crankshaft?

16. **Mechanical design.** Why is an automobile engine called an "internal combustion" engine?

17. **Automobile engines.** What is a cylinder; a cylinder head; a piston; a spark plug? What is the function of each?

18. **Automobile engines.** Explain what happens inside an automobile engine during the power, exhaust, intake, and compression strokes. During which parts of the cycle is the piston moving upward? Downward? At what point(s) in the cycle do the valves open and close, and when does the spark plug fire? How many valves are there in a four-cylinder engine?

*19. **Automobile engines.** What would happen if a small hole were burned in the face of one intake valve so that gases could leak through even when the valve was closed? Explain.

*20. **Automobile engines.** The piece of metal connecting the piston to the crankshaft is called the connecting rod. What would happen to a car if a connecting rod broke?

21. **Automobile engines.** Explain why a car with worn piston rings loses power.

*22. **Mechanical design.** In an automobile engine, each valve opens once for every complete rotation of the camshaft. Would it be possible to design a cam so that the valve opened twice for every complete rotation of the camshaft? Draw a picture of the cam needed in such a machine.

*Indicates more difficult problem.

*23. **Mechanical design.** In an automobile engine, a valve opens and then shuts again quickly. Draw a picture of a cam that would open a valve and hold it open for the duration of one half a revolution of the camshaft.

24. **Mechanical design.** Draw a picture of a gear system that would: (a) cause the working gear to rotate faster than the engine; (b) cause the working gear to rotate slower than the engine; (c) cause the working gear to rotate at the same speed as, but in the opposite direction to, the motor.

*25. **Mechanical design.** Imagine that you were designing an automatic bottle-capping machine. In order to do the job you need a device that moves up and down and presses the caps onto the bottles at regular intervals. However, the motor at your disposal powers a spinning shaft but does not provide up-and-down motion. Design two different linkage systems to convert rotational motion into a regular up-and-down motion.

26. **Levers.** Suppose you wished to exert a force of 2000 N against a piece of machinery to slide it across the floor. In order to do the job you decide to use a lever and position the fulcrum 0.25 m from the load. If you were capable of exerting a force of 400 N, how long would the lever have to be to enable you to move the machine?

27. **Mechanical advantage.** Suppose you had to lift a heavy iron ball 2 m in the air. You could either lift the ball outright, or roll it up a ramp. Which route would require more work? More applied force? Explain.

28. **Mechanical design.** The engine in a fairly large tractor is no bigger than the engine in an ordinary car, yet the tractor can pull much heavier loads than a car ever could. How can a tractor be built to have such a great pulling power with a small engine?

*29. **Bicycles.** Early bicycles were built without chains. The pedals were connected directly to the front axle. (a) How many times would the front wheel turn for every complete revolution of the pedals? (b) Is the rotational speed of the wheel (expressed in rpm) dependent on the size of the front wheel?

*Indicates more difficult problem.

(c) Does the size of the wheel in any way determine the forward speed of this bicycle? (d) These early bicycles had large front wheels. Do you think they would be more efficient for riding up hills or for riding on the level? Explain.

30. **Reinforced concrete.** What is the purpose of the steel in reinforced concrete?

*31. **Reinforced concrete.** If you were building a reinforced concrete beam, would you place your heaviest steel rod near the top, in the middle, or near the bottom of the beam? Explain.

*32. **Arches.** Modern highway engineers seldom build bridges over creeks or small gullies. Instead, they place circular pipes, called culverts, in the creek and build the road over the culvert. Is a culvert strengthened by packing dirt around it? Explain.

33. **Arches.** Why are arch bridges often built between two sides of a mountain?

34. **Trusses.** Show how a box can be strengthened by adding angle braces.

35. **Trusses.** Why is a truss stronger than a straight beam?

*36. **The strength of a circle.** The rim of a bicycle wheel has little strength. The spokes of the wheel have high tensile strength but little compressive strength. Explain why a bicycle wheel can support a large compressive load.

37. **Trusses.** (a) Builders generally use lumber 4 in or 6 in wide to construct peaked roofs, but need to use 10-in wide lumber for

*Indicates more difficult problem.

flat roofs of equal size. Why? (b) It is possible to build a peaked roof with 4-in lumber that is stronger than an equally sized roof made from 6-in lumber. Explain and draw a plan for the stronger roof.

38. **Air pollution control.** Suppose that you keep some animals in a cage in your room and you are disturbed by their odor. Comment on each of the following possible remedies, or some combination of them, for controlling the odor: (a) Spray a disinfectant into the air to kill germs. (b) Install a device that recirculates the room air through a bed of activated carbon. (c) Clean the cage every day. (d) Install an exhaust fan in the window to blow the bad air out. (e) Install a window air conditioning unit that recirculates and cools the room air. (f) Install an ozone-producing device. (g) Spray a pleasant scent into the room to make it smell better. (h) Light a gas burner in the room to incinerate the odors. (i) Keep an open tub of water in the room so that the odors will dissolve in the water.

39. **Air pollution control.** Distinguish between separation methods and conversion methods for source control of air pollution. What is the general principle of each type of method?

40. **Air pollution control.** Explain the air pollution control action of a cyclone; a settling chamber; a scrubber; activated carbon; an electrostatic precipitator; an incinerator.

*Indicates more difficult problem.

*41. **Water purification.** Biological treatment of wastewater reduces the mass of pollutant. Where does the lost matter go?

42. **Water purification.** Distinguish among primary, secondary, and tertiary types of wastewater treatment.

43. **Sewage.** In a combined piping system, some untreated sewage is dumped into the receiving watercourse during rainstorms. Is this procedure more acceptable than it would be in dry weather? Defend your answer.

44. **Sewage treatment.** What is activated carbon, and how does it help to purify water?

45. **Land disposal.** Explain the difference between an open dump and a sanitary landfill.

46. **Incineration.** List the advantages and disadvantages of incineration as a method of waste disposal.

47. **Solid waste management.** Suggest a scheme for a municipal refuse reclamation center that used different equipment than the Franklin, Ohio plant. Draw a flow sheet of your center and explain each operation.

48. **Chemical wastes.** Discuss some special problems involved in the disposal of hazardous chemical wastes. Suggest some solutions to the problems.

CHAPTER 13

The atmosphere is a changing and dynamic system whose movements affect our daily lives. The chapter opens with a discussion of the evolution of the modern atmosphere, followed by a description of its present composition and structure. It then proceeds to explain the global climate belts and the local factors that affect weather. The study of the past history of our atmosphere suggests that change may occur again in the future. In fact, the carbon dioxide concentration has increased measurably since the start of the Industrial Revolution, and many scientists are concerned that this and other changes may affect global climate.

OUR GEOLOGICAL ENVIRONMENT— THE ATMOSPHERE

13.1 EVOLUTION OF THE ATMOSPHERE

Most of the objects we have talked about so far in this book, such as railroad bridges or electric motors, can be measured conveniently in the same units that we use to describe ourselves—meters or kilograms. Other objects, such as atoms, are much smaller. Now we are about to talk about large bodies of matter such as our atmosphere, the oceans, and the Earth itself, and later we will study tremendously huge masses such as the Sun, our Solar System, and faraway galaxies. It is easy for the mind to become lost in the vastness of it all, and it is especially easy to think that massive objects are unmoving or unchangeable. Nothing is further from the truth. Often movement and change of geologically or astronomically sized objects are so complicated that we don't understand them well, or so slow that we can't measure them accurately on a human time scale, but the systems are dynamic nevertheless. Our atmosphere is an especially delicate and fluctuating system. Despite its large size, it is constantly in motion, as is obvious to anyone who has been outside on a windy day. But the movement of the winds is not the only changing aspect of the atmosphere. Its chemical composition can also be modified as, for example, by the introduction of pollutants. Perhaps we can all best appreciate the frailty of our modern atmosphere if we study its evolution.

Clouds. (Photo by Grant Lashbrook.)

As the solid Earth was being formed, gases were trapped within its core and gradually escaped to the surface through fissures in the rocks and volcanic eruptions. To the best of our knowledge, the primary constituents of the primitive Earth's atmosphere were probably nitrogen, ammonia, hydrogen, carbon dioxide, carbon monoxide, methane, and water vapor. Oxygen was present in trace quantities only. Most living creatures that we know today would be quickly poisoned by such a mixture. How was the modern atmosphere formed? Although some theorists believe that geological processes altered atmospheric composition, most scientists feel that living organisms and a favorable atmospheric environment evolved hand in hand. In the beginning, when there was little free gaseous

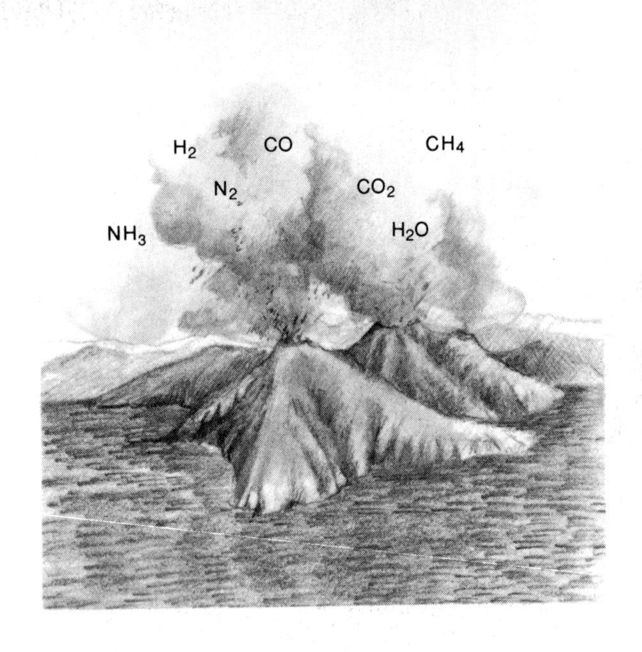

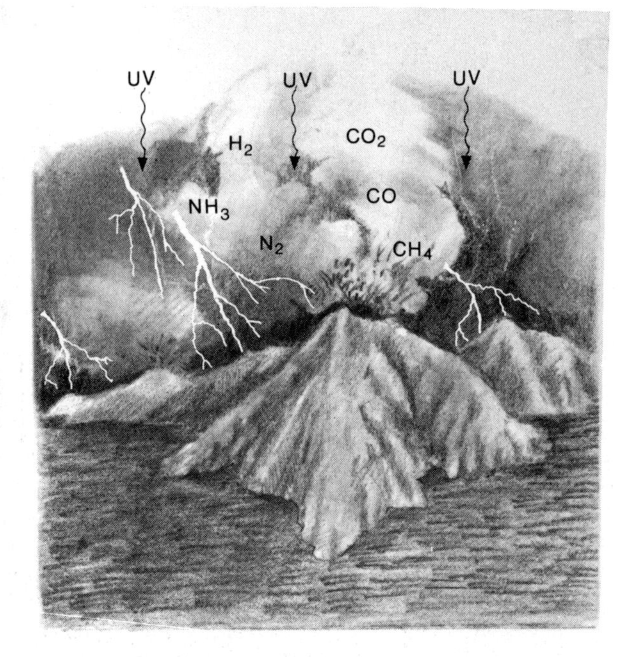

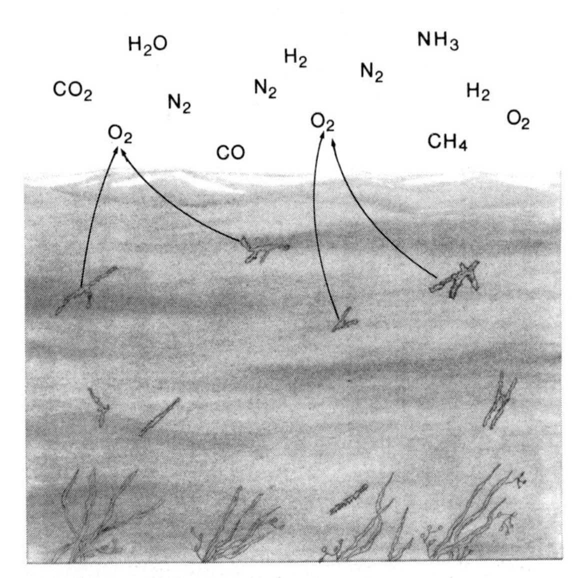

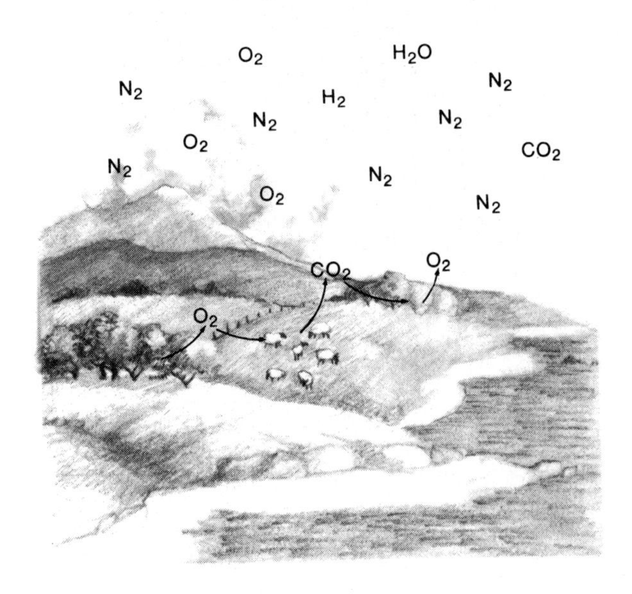

Evolution of the atmosphere.
A, **The primitive atmosphere was composed of gases released from volcanic eruptions.**
B, **The action of lightning and ultraviolet light on this atmosphere initiated a chain of reactions that led to the evolution of simple organisms. These microbes lived in the oceans.**
C, **As plants evolved, the composition of the atmosphere began to change. Oxygen, released during photosynthesis, began to accumulate.**
D, **The modern atmosphere is composed mainly of nitrogen and oxygen, with smaller concentrations of carbon dioxide, water, and other gases. The ratio of oxygen to carbon dioxide is maintained by dynamic exchange among plants and animals.**

molecular oxygen, there would be no ozone. Without a protective ozone layer, concentrated ultraviolet rays from the Sun could reach the Earth. Ironically, these rays, which could harm or destroy life today, were probably responsible for the formation of the first organic compounds and living cells. When energetic ultraviolet light struck the molecules of the primitive atmosphere, reactions were initiated that led to the synthesis of simple organic molecules. Somehow these organics combined to form both proteins and complex molecules that carry hereditary information. Then these large molecules joined together to form simple living organisms. (That is a simple sentence to learn or to write, but for such an event to occur by random combination of organic chemicals is nearly incomprehensibly improbable, and many millions or hundreds of millions of years elapsed between the time of formation of the first organic compounds and the evolution of the first living entity.) These earliest organisms lived in water, beneath a liquid blanket that filtered out the potentially lethal ultraviolet rays. Since there was no oxygen, they could not have metabolized their food as most organisms do today but must have lived by some **anaerobic** (without oxygen) process. These early anaerobes probably ate the organic molecules formed randomly by photochemical reactions. Up until this point, there was almost no free oxygen in the atmosphere and the organisms required none. (In fact, oxygen is poisonous to most anaerobes.) The next evolutionary step was a crucial one. Some types of plants evolved. Plants are able to synthesize their own complex organic molecules by combining simple organic molecules together in the presence of sunlight. Modern plants, such as grasses, trees, and algae, produce food according to the following equation:

$$\text{Carbon dioxide} + \text{water} \xrightarrow[\text{in the presence of chlorophyll}]{\text{sunlight}} \begin{matrix}\text{sugar}\\ \text{(glucose)}\end{matrix} + \text{oxygen} \qquad [13.1]$$

This process is known as **photosynthesis.** Notice that in Equation 13.1, carbon dioxide and water are combined in the presence of sunlight to form glucose (a sugar) and oxygen.

Oxygen-carbon cycle.

Most scientists feel that the excess oxygen released by the first plants accumulated slowly over the millennia until its concentration reached about 0.6 per cent of the atmosphere. Multicellular organisms require oxygen to survive and could have evolved only at this point. The emergence of various multicelled organisms about one billion years ago triggered an accelerated biological production of oxygen. The present oxygen level of about 20 per cent of the atmosphere was reached about 450 million years ago. While there have been some more or less severe oscillations since that time, an overall oxygen balance has always been maintained.

If the oxygen concentration in the atmosphere were to increase even by a few per cent, fires would burn uncontrollably across the planet; if the carbon dioxide concentration were to rise by a small amount, plant production would increase appreciably. Since these apocalyptic events have not occurred, the atmospheric oxygen must have been balanced to the needs of the biosphere during the long span of life on Earth. By what mechanism has this gaseous atmospheric balance been maintained? The answer appears to be that it is maintained by the living systems themselves. The existence of an effective internal balancing mechanism of the entire biosphere has led one scientist, J. E. Lovelock, to liken the biosphere to a living creature, which he calls *Gaia* (Greek for Earth).* He believes not only that the delicate oxygen–carbon dioxide balance is biologically maintained but also that the very presence of oxygen in large quantities in our atmosphere can be explained only by biological activity. If all life on Earth were to cease and the chemistry of our planet were to rely on abiological laws alone, oxygen would become a trace gas, and the atmosphere would once again be poisonous to complex plants and animals.

The concept of biological control over the physical environment warrants careful consideration. Lovelock

*J. E. Lovelock: "Gaia as seen through the atmosphere." Atmospheric Environment, 6:579, August, 1972.

The Earth consists of a delicately interconnected set of ecosystems. (Courtesy of NASA.)

Figure 13–4. Energy balance of the Earth. The sets of numbers in the dashed areas total 100 per cent.

for example if the ice cover grew, we would expect the surface to cool, and, alternatively, a decrease in albedo might cause a gradual warming trend.

Even though the Earth as a whole is not getting appreciably hotter or colder, there are marked temperature differences from season to season and from place to place.* Thus, temperate zones experience distinct summer and winter seasons, and the polar regions are always cooler than the equatorial ones. To understand the reasons behind these temperature differences, first consider what happens if we shine a flashlight onto a flat board. If we hold the light directly overhead and shine the beam vertically downward, the light illuminates a smaller area than it would if we shined the beam onto the board from an angle (see Fig. 13–5). Of the three positions shown in the figure, the one aimed at the shallowest angle illuminates the greatest area. Thus, the more we tilt the flashlight, the less concentrated is the light on the board, and the lower is the temperature of any point in the illuminated area. (Of course, we would observe the same results if we tilted the board instead of the flashlight.)

With this information in mind, let us consider what happens when light is beamed onto a spherical surface such as the Earth. We will hold the globe in a fixed vertical position and call the top and the bottom the Poles and the line that encircles the middle, the Equator. We see that if we shine a light perpendicular to the Equator, all the other sur-

*Small global climate changes have recently been observed. These are discussed further in Sections 13.8 and 13.9.

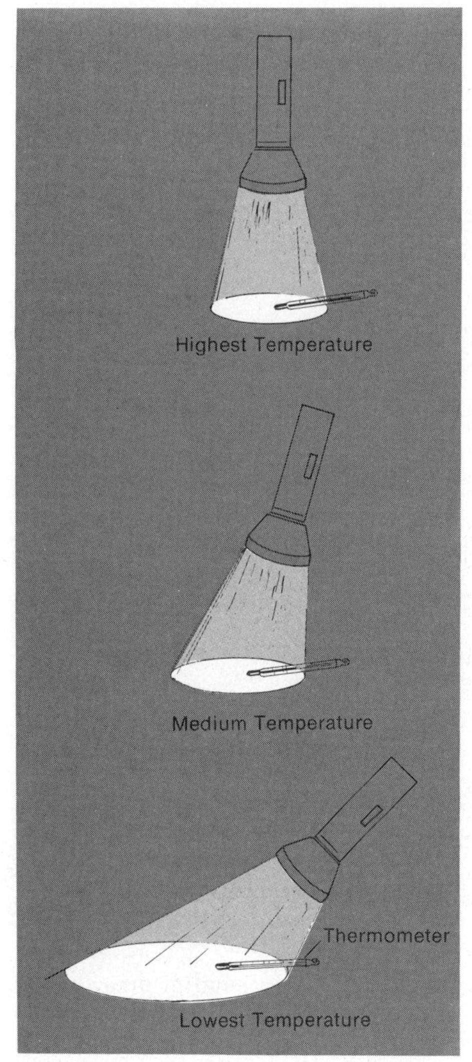

Figure 13–5. Intensity of light varies with angle of light source.

Light rays incident on a sphere.

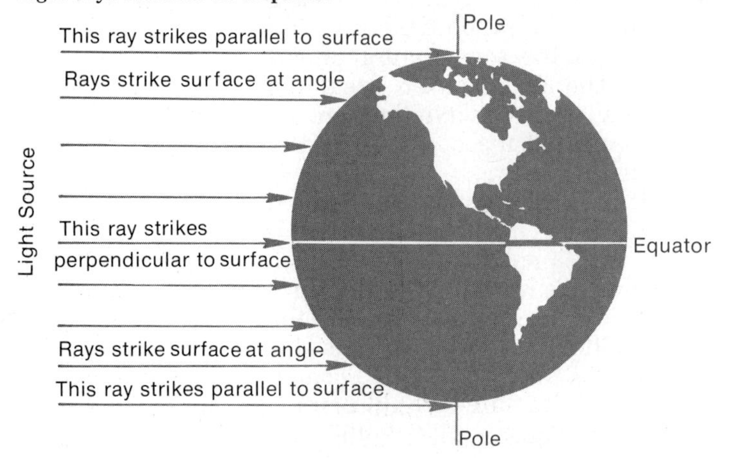

faces will receive light at an angle. Specifically, as we move toward the Poles, the surfaces are angled farther and farther from the perpendicular until at the Pole itself the surface of the sphere is actually parallel to the light. Thus the light intensity per unit area *decreases* as we move from the Equator to the Poles. At the Poles, the light is parallel to the surface, and no direct radiation strikes the area at all. A uniform light source shining perpendicular to the center of the globe delivers the most radiant energy to the Equator and the least to the Poles.

It is now obvious why the hottest climates on Earth are found near the Equator and why climates become progressively cooler as we move north or south from that line. This explanation accounts for general climatic regions but does not tell us why we experience summer and winter seasons in the higher latitudes. To understand these effects better, we must consider the Earth's rotation around an imaginary axis running through the North and South Poles. If this axis were perpendicular to the plane of the Earth's orbit, the Sun would always be directly above the Equator, and there would be no seasonal temperature variations. But in reality, the Earth's axis is tilted at an angle of 23½° with respect to the plane of its orbit. As a result of this tilt, the angle of incidence of the Sun's rays on the Earth changes as the planet moves around in its orbit. On June 21, the Earth is located so that the North Pole leans the full 23½° toward the Sun, as shown in Figure 13–6. This condition is called the **summer solstice.** The Sun strikes the Earth directly overhead at a location 23½° north of the Equator and not at the Equator itself. The northern latitudes receive more direct sun than the southern ones, and the North Pole, tilted toward the Sun, receives a continuous 24 hours of daylight. Polar regions are often called "lands of the midnight sun" because the Sun never sets in the summertime. While it is summer in the Northern Hemisphere, the South Pole is tilted away from the Sun and lies in continuous darkness, and June 21 marks the first day of winter in the Southern Hemisphere. Six months later, on December 22, the situ-

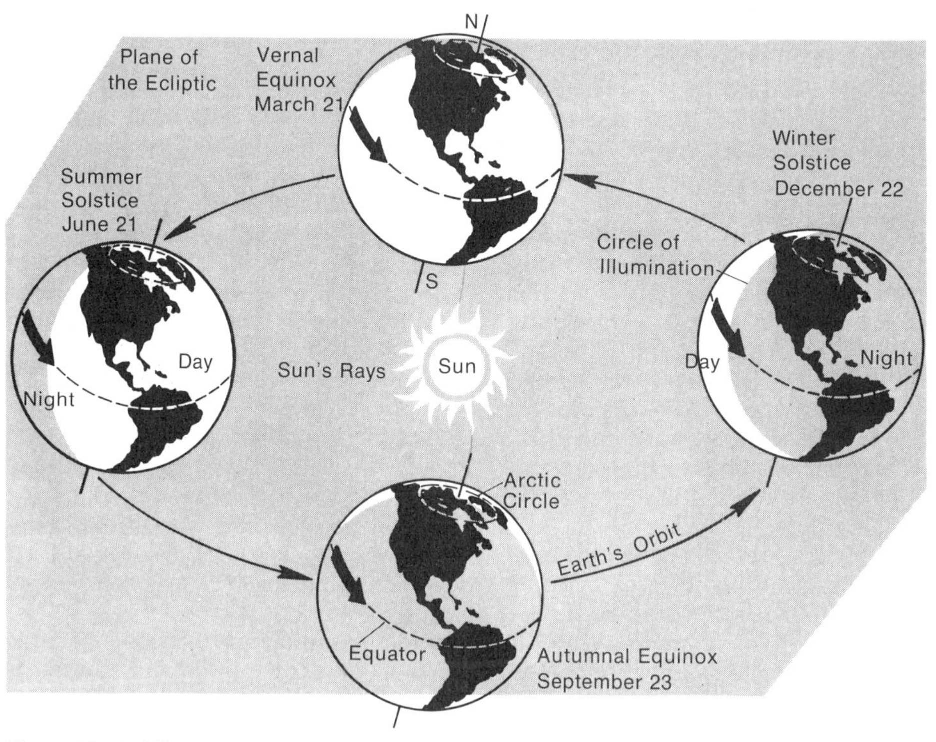

Figure 13–6. The seasons.

ation is reversed; the North Pole is tilted away from the Sun and lies in continuous darkness whereas the South Pole is bathed in constant light. It is summer in the Southern Hemisphere and winter in the north. What happens midway between these two extremes, on March 21 and September 23? Although the Earth is still tilted at 23½°, the tilt aims the North Pole neither toward nor away from the Sun but rather at right angles to it. Since no part of the Earth is angled toward or away from the Sun, the most direct light shines at the middle, that is, at the Equator, and the North and South Poles each receive equal periods of night and day. In fact, when the Earth is in either of these two positions, called the spring and autumn **equinoxes,** respectively, every portion of the globe receives 12 hours of daylight and 12 hours of darkness. This does *not* mean that all areas of the globe receive equal quantities of solar energy—locations on the Equator receive the most while the polar regions receive hardly any direct radiant energy at all.

In some years the solstices and equinoxes occur one day earlier or later than mentioned here. Thus the summer solstice sometimes occurs on June 22.

It is interesting to note that all areas of the globe receive the same total number of hours of sunlight every year. The North and South Poles receive their sunlight in dramatic opposition—6 months of continuous light and six months of darkness, while at the Equator each day is nearly 12 hours long throughout the year. However, once again, while the Poles receive the same number of hours of sunlight as do the equatorial regions, the sunlight reaches the Poles from a very acute (shallow) angle and therefore delivers much less total radiant energy.

Equinox is derived from the Latin words *equi* (equal) and *nox* (night). Thus the equinox is the period of equal nights.

13.4 ENERGY PROCESSES IN THE TROPOSPHERE—WIND AND RAIN

Wind

A steamship chugging across the ocean derives its power from the heat energy released when coal or oil is burned in the boilers. Where does the energy come from that powers a sailboat across the ocean? From the wind, of course. But wind isn't an energy *source* like coal or oil; it is more closely analogous to a working substance like the steam that drives a turbine. So the question remains, what energy source drives the winds?

The wind systems of our globe represent the functioning of a great natural heat engine that is similar in many respects to a mechanical heat engine. In the engine room of a steamship, fuel is used to boil water and heat the resultant steam. Since water vapor expands when it is heated, the heat energy is converted to kinetic energy of the moving steam. The moving steam then forces the blades of the turbine to rotate.

The power source of our natural wind systems is the Sun. When the Sun heats one part of the atmosphere more than another, this warm air expands and rises. Thus heat is converted to motion. As the light air rises, colder, denser air moves along the surface to take its place. This surface movement is **wind.** As we can see, wind systems operate much like convection currents in a room. Recall from our discussion of convection currents in Chapter 3 that if a heater is placed in one corner of a room, it will heat the air adjacent to it. The heated air expands, thus becoming less dense. This light air rises, displacing denser cool air downward until an air current is established. Wind systems are simply large convection currents that operate on local, continental, or global scales.

The wind powers this sailboat, but what energy source drives the wind?

Figure 13–7. Wind.

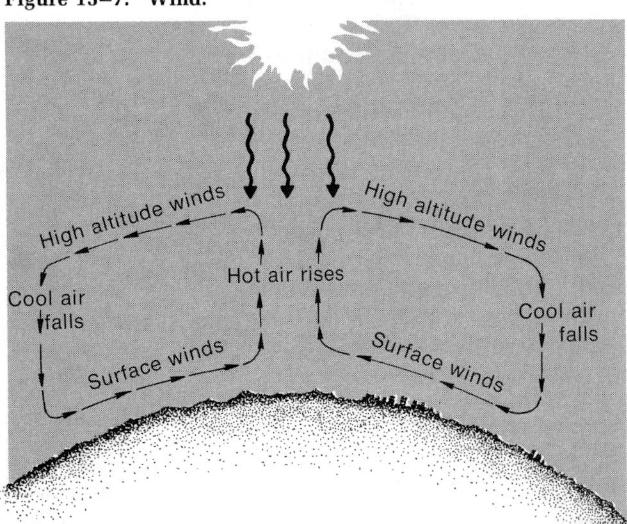

Consider, for example, the trade winds that blow steadily just north and south of the Equator. As we already learned, the sunlight is most intense at or near the Equator. As the air above the equator becomes hotter than the surrounding air, it rises and draws the cooler air in along the surface of the Earth, as shown in Figure 13–7. Thus, the Sun provides the energy for the movement of winds.

This picture of wind systems as being a straightforward and predictable convection cycle is, of course, greatly simplified. Wind systems are affected by a great many other forces, and some of these will be discussed later in this chapter.

Sail plane enthusiasts search for places where warm air is rising vertically to hold their craft aloft. (Photo by Jim Sharp.)

Rain

If you boil water on a stove, you can see a steamy mist above the kettle, and then higher still the mist seems to disappear into the air. Of course, the water molecules have not been lost. In the pan, water is in the liquid phase, and in the mist above the kettle the water exists as tiny droplets. These droplets then evaporate, and the water vapor mixes with air and becomes invisible. Air generally contains some water vapor. **Humidity** is a measure of the amount of water vapor in air. **Absolute humidity** is defined as the mass of water vapor contained in a given volume of air and is generally expressed in units such as g/m^3. But air cannot hold an unlimited quantity of water vapor. If you poured liquid water into a container of dry air, the water would start to evaporate; that is, some water molecules would leave the liquid and mix with the air molecules in the form of a gas. Of course, some molecules would go the other way, from gas to liquid. When the two opposing rates become equal, net evaporation stops, and the air is said to be *saturated* with moisture. The saturation quantity varies with temperature. Figure 13–8 shows that warm air can hold more water vapor than cold air. For example, a cubic meter of air can hold 23 g of water vapor at 25° C, but if the air is cooled to 12° C, it can hold only half that quantity, 11.5 g/m^3. The **relative humidity** is a measure of the amount of water vapor in the air compared to the saturation quantity at a given temperature.

> The **saturation quantity** of water vapor in air is often thought of as the maximum absolute humidity at a given temperature. This concept is correct as long as the air is in contact with liquid water and the two opposing processes of evaporation and condensation are going on at the same rate. However, if there are no liquid or solid surfaces on which the water vapor can condense, it is possible for the humidity to exceed the saturation level; this condition is called **supersaturation.**

Relative humidity (%)

$$= \frac{\text{actual quantity of water in a given volume of air}}{\text{saturation quantity at the same temperature}} \times 100\%$$

Figure 13–8. Maximum absolute humidity as a function of temperature.

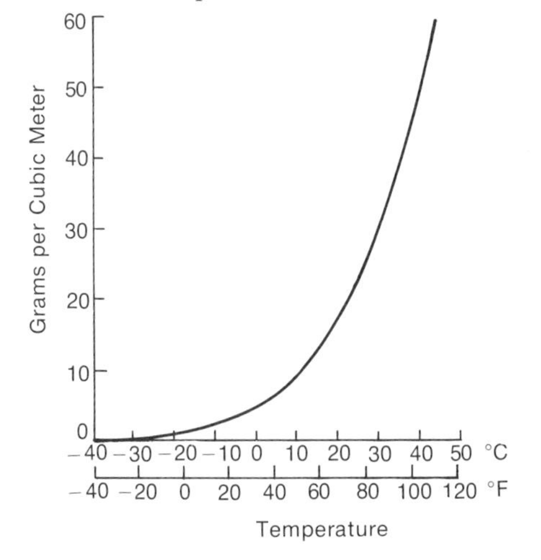

Now suppose that there are 11.5 g of water vapor per cubic meter in a parcel of air at 25° C. Since air at that temperature can hold 23 g/m^3 when saturated, it is carrying half of the saturation quantity, and the relative humidity is $\frac{11.5 \text{ g}}{23 \text{ g}} \times 100\% = 50\%$. As an experiment, let us take some of this air and cool it without adding or removing any water vapor. Since cold air can hold less water vapor than warm air, the relative humidity will rise even though the absolute humidity remains constant. If we cool the air to about 12° C, the relative humidity reaches 100 per cent because air at that temperature can hold only 11.5 g water per cubic meter. Any further cooling will cause the water to condense and form droplets.

You can observe how water condenses upon cooling by performing a very simple experiment. Heat some water on a stove until it is boiling rapidly. The clear air that lies just above the steamy mist will be hot and full of water vapor. Hold a drinking glass in this space and you will observe droplets of water condensing on the surface. The surface of the glass is cool, so it absorbs heat from the warm moist air that comes in contact with it. As the air cools, some of the water vapor condenses into liquid droplets. The same effect can be observed if you are inside a house on a cold day. If you breathe onto a window, droplets of water or crystals of ice will appear as your breath cools on the glass.

With this background we can easily understand how **dew** is formed. On a typical summer evening in a moist temperate zone, the air is liable to be warm and laden with water vapor.

Some readers will prefer to think of it the other way. Imagine a cool, comfortable room. Now someone turns up the thermostat, and the air starts to feel not only warm but also *dry*. The heat has not destroyed any water, so the absolute humidity has not changed, but the relative humidity, which is what we feel, has decreased.

Frost deposited on a window on a cold morning. (Courtesy of Jerome Wycoff.)

After the sun sets, the surfaces of various objects such as plants, houses, and windows begin to lose heat by radiation. In the early hours of the morning, when these surfaces are quite cool, water condenses from the warm moist air just as your breath condenses onto a window on a cold day. We call this condensation **dew.**

Clouds are also formed when warm, moisture-laden air is cooled. For example, when warm moist air from an ocean blows inland to a cold coast, the air cools, water condenses out, and low cloud formations known as **fog** are formed. Thus San Francisco (California), Seattle (Washington), and Vancouver (British Columbia) all experience foggy winters accompanied by rain and drizzle.

But cloud formation can occur in other ways as well. When air rises it expands, and when it expands, it cools at a rate of about 1° C for every rise of 1000 m. This effect is called **adiabatic cooling** (Fig. 13–9). Now imagine that a moist mass of air in a given region is moving toward the Equator. If the temperature of the air could remain constant, the water would remain in a vapor form indefinitely. However, as

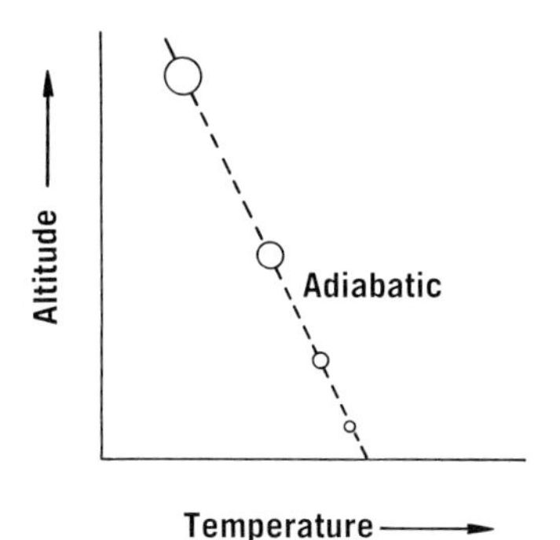

Figure 13–9. Adiabatic cooling.

Adiabatic means "without loss or gain of heat." To understand why air cools as it rises, let us imagine that we had a balloon filled with air and that this balloon was insulated so that no heat could be transferred in or out of it. We now move the balloon from the ground level higher and higher toward the upper atmosphere. As the altitude gets higher, the atmospheric pressure becomes lower, and our parcel of air expands. As it does so, it is pushing aside the air that surrounds it, and therefore it is doing mechanical work and expending energy. Since no energy (heat) flows into the parcel of air, the energy must come from its own internal heat energy, and the gas grows cooler.

this air moves into the tropics, it is heated and starts to rise upward and expand. This expansion causes it to cool adiabatically. If conditions are favorable, the air will cool so much that water vapor condenses out and clouds are formed. Thus cloud formation occurs most readily when moist air rises.

We can now understand a few simple relationships between barometric pressure and weather. When warm air rises, it expands and cools. The expansion makes it less dense, which means that it exerts less pressure and that the barometer reading in that region will be lower. But we already noted that cooling generally leads to cloud formation and, therefore, to a possibility of rain. Thus a falling barometer is a good indication that rain may soon follow. Alternatively, when cool air falls to the Earth, we would expect the barometric pressure to be high. Since air warms when falling, and since warm air can hold more moisture than cold air, clouds generally do not form under high pressure conditions. Instead, the warm air with low relative humidity will tend to absorb moisture from the earth. Thus a rising barometer generally predicts fair weather.

Of course, an understanding of this general correlation between barometric pressure and cloud formation does not instantly transform everyone into a seasoned weather forecaster. Many times the barometric pressure will drop and no rain will fall, or conversely, the pressure may rise amid cloudy skies. The temperature, rainfall, and wind patterns in a region are a result of many complex factors. Some of these are caused by local disturbances, others by global atmospheric patterns.

Climate is a description of long-term meteorological conditions. For example, we say that New York City has a temperate climate with moderate rainfall; one can always expect warm summers and cold winters in that city. **Weather,** on the other hand, is a description of relatively unpredictable short-term conditions. Storms, a heat wave, or a cold spell are all part of the weather in a given area.

13.5 GLOBAL WIND SYSTEMS AND CLIMATE

In general, the average temperature of the Earth is highest at the Equator and grows progressively lower as we approach the Poles. But the polar regions are not always cold, for a great many factors serve to influence local climates.

I (Jon) shall never forget the first time I crossed the Arctic Circle. We had been paddling north and living in our canoe for the past few weeks and were already accustomed to the isolation and solitude of a long wilderness journey. It was hot, and my partner Jock Jacober and I were lying on the top of the canoe, sunbathing and allowing the current of the mighty McKenzie River to carry us onward. Jock awoke to take a bearing and all of a sudden announced that we were north of the Arctic Circle and that we had crossed in swimsuits.

Arctic weather is strange. The sunlight reaches the polar regions at such an acute angle, even in summertime, that the quantity of radiation received is quite low. If the Sun were the only source of heat, these regions would be cold in summer and near absolute zero (−273° C) in winter, when no sunlight at all is received. Throughout the year, polar regions are considerably warmer than one would expect solely on the basis of the amount of sunlight received. On the other hand, measurements and calculations show that the equatorial regions of our planet receive so much radiant energy that they should be much hotter than they actually are. Thus heat must be carried in some way from the tropics to the Poles. As we shall see, winds and ocean currents are responsible for the transfer.

To understand global wind systems, consider for a moment what would happen if the Earth did not rotate about its axis. The intense sunlight at the Equator would heat the air there, causing it to rise. As the air rose, cooler air would move in from the polar regions to fill the partial vacuum, and a set of convection currents would be established, as shown in Figure 13–10. According to this model, in the Northern Hemisphere the predominant surface winds would blow southward, while in the upper atmosphere, warm air would move poleward. In the Southern Hemisphere the situation would be reversed.

Figure 13–10. Wind systems on a hypothetical non-rotating Earth.

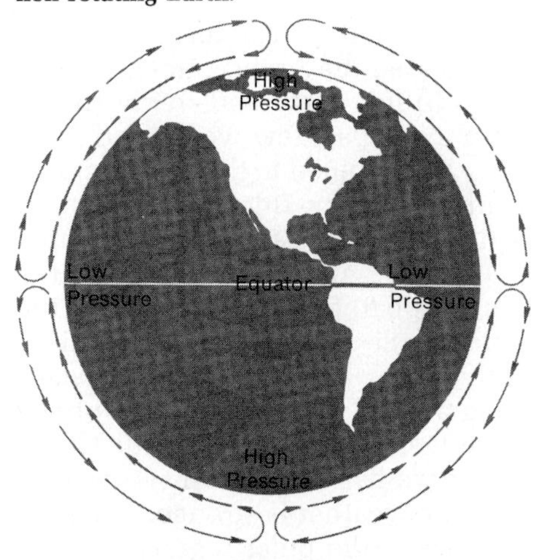

Surface winds would come from the north in the Northern Hemisphere and from the south in the Southern Hemisphere

Of course, our static model is too simple, because the Earth does rotate. To visualize the effect of this rotation, imagine what it would be like if there were a bowling alley on a moving train. Suppose that you were riding due north on the train and that you rolled your bowling ball directly down the center of the alley on a perfect path toward the strike zone. But just as the ball left your hand, the train reached a curve and started to turn toward the east (right). The ball continues to travel due north, but the target is moving away toward the right, so the ball appears to veer to the left, thereby missing the pins. The observed path, shown in Figure 13–11, results from the motion of the ball moving straight along an alley that is moving to the right. The bowling ball situation is an example of relative motion. To an observer on the train, the ball has moved off to the left regardless of its motion relative to some other frame of reference such as a compass.

What does this have to do with the wind? The circumference of the Earth is greatest at the Equator and smaller as we move toward the Poles. But all parts of the planet make one complete revolution every day. Thus, since a point on the Equator must travel farther than any other point on the Earth in 24 hours, the equatorial region moves faster. At the Equator, all objects move eastward with a velocity of about 1600 km/hr; at the Poles there is no eastward movement at all, and the velocity is 0 km/hr. Now, imagine a parcel of air located at the Equator. It is traveling eastward at 1600 km/hr and then gets heated and moves upward and starts to travel poleward. Let us say that this parcel moves north. As it starts, there are two components to the velocity, an eastward component and a northward component. At any distance north of the Equator it is traveling eastward *faster* than the Earth beneath it. Thus the motion of the air relative to the Earth is curved toward the east, or the right, as shown in Figure 13–12*A*.

Let us imagine what would happen if the situation were reversed and a parcel of air moved southward from the North Pole to the Equator. This air will be moving *slower* than air in tropical regions, and therefore it will lag behind

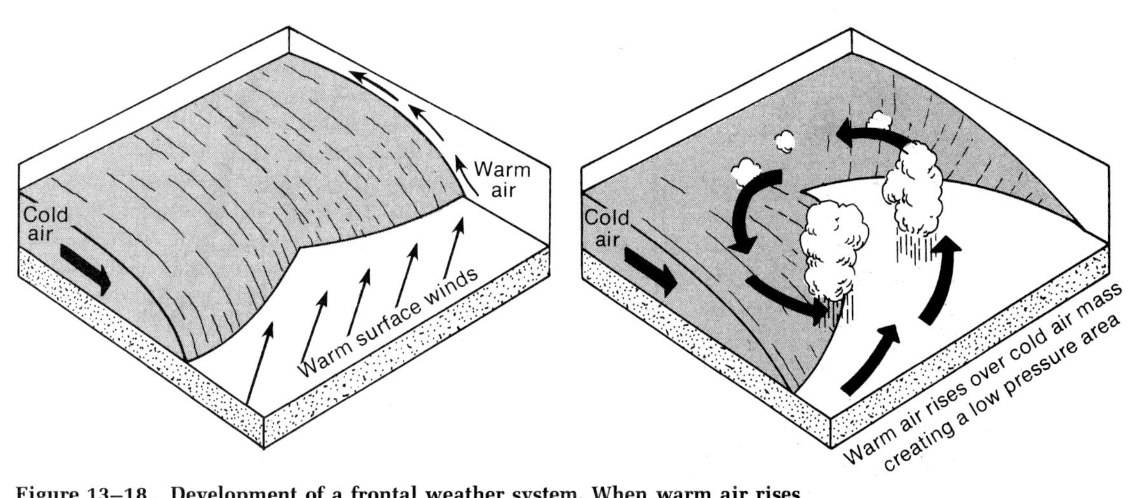

Figure 13–18. Development of a frontal weather system. When warm air rises over a cooler air mass, low pressure, winds, and rain or snow are likely.

Conversely, the air must fall on the downward side of the mountains. As it descends it is compressed and thereby heated. Since this warm, high-pressure air is unlikely to discharge moisture, a belt of dry climate, called a rain shadow, often exists on the lee side of major mountain ranges. Death Valley in California is a rain shadow desert.

Frontal Weather Systems

Air that lies over polar icecaps is frequently dry and cold, whereas air lying over tropical oceans is often warm and moist. An **air mass** is a large body of air that has approximately the same temperature and humidity throughout. Many weather patterns occur when different air masses collide. Imagine that a cold polar air mass traveling southward collides with a warm, moist, subtropical air mass traveling northeast, as shown in Figure 13–18. The cold air, being denser than the warm air, will tend to lie near the surface of the Earth, forcing the warmer, lighter air to rise as shown in the diagram. This rising air may then cool adiabatically, possibly leading to cloud formations and precipitation. Frontal weather patterns of this type are responsible for many of the storm systems that affect local weather. Figure 13–19 shows a series of actual weather maps illustrating the daily movement of a frontal system in the western United States during January, 1979. As you can see, a storm developed when the two opposing air masses collided.

Once again, it is important to understand that weather prediction is complex. An air parcel may rise and then for any of a wide variety of reasons, precipitation may not occur. Storm fronts sometimes seem to build, and then suddenly dissipate. Weather forecasters use sophisticated ground instruments, computer analysis, and accurate data from specially designed weather satellites, yet they still achieve only about 80 per cent accuracy in their predictions.

13.8 OUR CHANGING CLIMATE

After studying the orderly processes that control global wind systems, one might imagine that the average worldwide climate must be constant from year to year. But extreme changes occur over large spans of time. Thus, what is now the temperate zone in North America has experienced both tropical warmth and the cold of the Ice Ages in the distant past. One hundred fifty million years ago giant dinosaurs wallowed in hot, humid swamps, while only 25,000 years ago wooly mam-

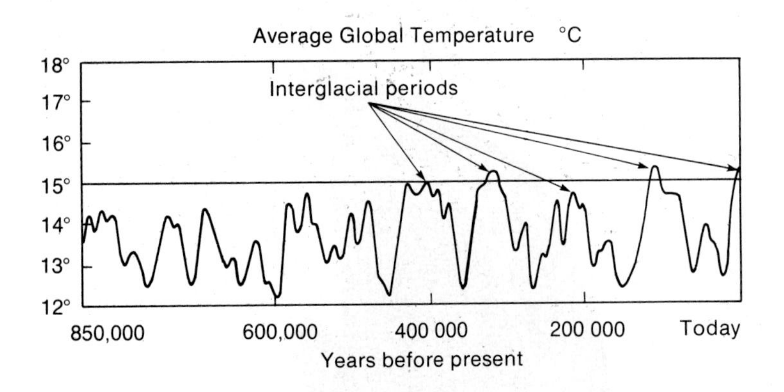

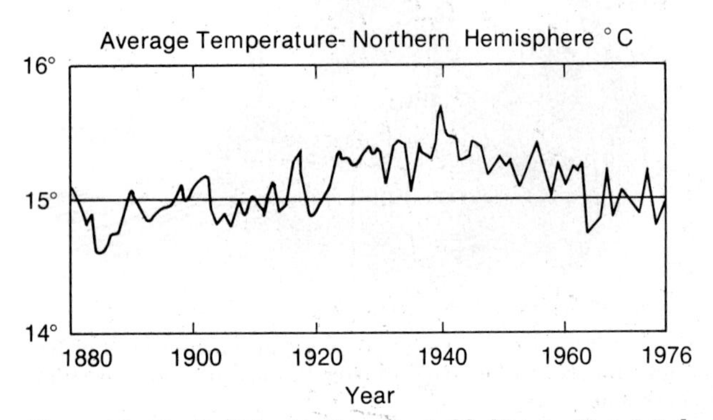

Figure 13–20. Past fluctuations in world climate. (Reprinted with permission from Walter Orr Roberts and Henry Lansford: *The Climate Mandate.* San Francisco, W. H. Freeman and Co., 1979, p. 31.)

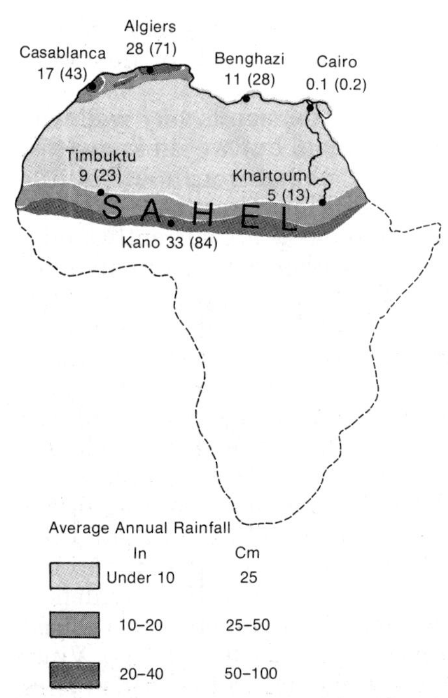

Rainfall map of northern Africa, showing the Sahara Desert and the approximate extent of the Sahel region. The numbers at the cities refer to their average rainfall in inches per year (numbers in parentheses are in cm/yr). No details are given below the shaded areas; the dashed outline shows only the shape of the African continent.

it usually means that the last killing frost occurs a week later in the spring and a week earlier in the fall than it did previously. Thus a seemingly insignificant change in average temperature becomes quite significant when it reduces the growing season by 2 weeks. Even frost-resistant plants grow much more slowly if spring and fall temperatures are cold. In recent years a 1° C cooling trend was blamed for a 25 per cent decline in hay production in Iceland.

Small temperature fluctuations also initiate a chain of processes that may seriously affect weather patterns. Monsoon behavior in particular seems delicately controlled by global weather. Because the Earth has cooled in recent years, the polar and Greenland ice and snow cover increased by nearly 12 per cent during the decade of 1965 to 1975. In turn, as the ice cover has increased, the cold arctic air mass has grown and moved southward a little bit. A small southward movement of cold air may interrupt the monsoons and seriously affect human populations.

To understand how this cold air affects a monsoon system, recall that the summer monsoons in southern Asia and Africa arise because continents warm more quickly than does the sea and that this warm air rises, drawing moisture-laden sea air inland to the low-pressure zone. But if cold air blows across the continent, the land will not heat so quickly, and the wind and rain patterns will be disrupted.

This calamity has occurred in several places. South of the Sahara Desert lies a semi-arid region known as the **Sahel.** This area has traditionally been a region of moderate rainfall, where nomads tended herds of cattle and always eked out a subsistence living. In the 6-year period from 1968 to 1974, cold arctic air moving into Africa intercepted the summer monsoons south of the Sahel and displaced the rain clouds southward, thereby depriving the Sahel of water. The result was a series of increasingly severe droughts. Many of the grasslands bordering the Sahara

The effects of drought in the Sahel region of North Africa. (Courtesy of Alain Nogues-Sygma.)

dried up, and the shifting sands of the desert advanced southward. In one location, the Sahara Desert extended southward nearly 50 km in a single year. Land that had supported cattle in the early 1960's supported nothing during the drought years. Approximately 50 million people lived in the Sahel in 1970, and of these, 10 million faced starvation during the drought. The situation was desperate. In 1974 it was written of one of the refugee camps, "More [nomads] arrive every day from the desert that has finally proven too much for them. They arrive without their animals. Mauritania had some eleven million head of cattle, . . . there are perhaps some two million cattle left. Even the camels have died. In the city of Boutilimit they saved five camels to haul up the water from the wells. The water level has fallen so far—it is now more than 200 feet deep—that the men are too weak to haul up the buckets. If the monsoons continue to fail, the future of the Sahel people is indeed bleak. They are caught between the Sahara on the north and political barriers to migration to the south, so there is nowhere to go."

The drought lifted late in 1974, and grasses and brush once again sprouted in the Sahel, but only 3 years later drought conditions returned. Climatologists have been wondering, "Was the severe drought of the early 1970's an isolated event, or an indication of bad times to come?"

In India the monsoons arrived on schedule in the late 1960's and early

Harvesting wheat by hand in northern India.

1970's, and agricultural productivity was high. In 1972, the polar air mass descended and cooled the continent slightly. This cooling caused the rains to arrive late and withdraw early. Many grain crops suffered, yields decreased, and famine was prevalent. The 1973 and 1974 seasons showed some improvement. Good times returned again in the mid 1970's, but in 1978 the monsoon was late in the northern part of the country.

Monsoon failure is not particulary unusual in India, and a few bad years can hardly be called a trend. But it is distressing to realize that in the early 1900's global temperatures were low and monsoon failures occurred once every three or four years. As the global temperature rose, the monsoons arrived much more regularly (one failure in 20 years), and as temperatures dropped again in the early 1970's another series of droughts occurred. If drought conditions are indeed closely linked to small temperature changes, the human race may be in a grave situation.

During the time period between 1900 and 1950, human development accelerated rapidly. This era witnessed an abnormally favorable global climate that led to high agricultural productivity. In addition, significant technological and medical advances supported the rapid growth of the human population. People's use of land for agriculture and water for drinking and irrigation approached a limit. Development continued in the 1960's even as the climate began to deteriorate, until at the present we are in a precarious position. Dryland farming extends right to the edge of most of the world's deserts; mountainside pastures creep up the slopes of the major mountain ranges; grains are grown in northern Canada and Russia nearly into the Arctic; and farmers are already pushing into the great jungle basins. There is limited room for further expansion. Deserts cannot be farmed without water and there just is not enough fresh water nearby to irrigate the deserts of the world. Some planners talk about desalinating ocean water for irrigation, but this type of project requires a great deal of energy, and energy is currently in short supply also. There are vast, untamed areas of jungles in Africa, South America, and Asia, but jungles are ecologically unique, for the jungle soils tend to contain little organic matter. If the trees are removed and the soil is plowed and planted to grain, it often hardens and becomes infertile within a short period of time. Of course, farms cannot extend poleward unless a global warming trend occurs. Yet, even with all the agricultural development, nearly half of the human population is undernourished and millions are literally starving. The problem that causes great concern is this: food production and population have been pushed to the limit during an unusual period of particularly mild climate. If the climate should change appreciably, farms in many regions of the world could fail. In fact, many climatologists believe that either a cooling or a significant warming might alter rainfall patterns across the globe and disrupt agriculture. As noted previously, a decline in temperature might have been responsible for drought and famine in parts of Africa and Asia. Approximately 5000 years ago, the Northern Hemisphere was

This author (Jon) visited India during the summer of 1978. Newspaper articles carried accounts of impending grain shortages due to drought, but then in August the monsoon rains finally arrived in earnest. Within a few weeks massive floods ravaged the lands. Entire sections of the city of New Delhi were under water, and an untold number of people were rendered homeless. Many of the previously drought-stricken fields were flooded and completely destroyed. The tragedy of the floods goes far beyond this season's rains. True, the monsoon downpours were unusually heavy. But in past decades heavy rains have caused far less flooding. Part of the problem stems from improper agriculture high in the Himalayas. In recent years, farmers in the mountain regions have cut nearly all the timber from many steep hillsides and have allowed their sheep and goats to overgraze the grasslands. As a result, there is little vegetation left to retain the water. When rain falls in the Himalayas, relatively little is absorbed by the sparse plant cover. Therefore, great quantities of water run rapidly into streams and rivers. Mud slides are common, and lowland valleys become much more susceptible to floods than they have been in the past. This is one of many instances when an agricultural disaster has resulted partly from bad weather and partly from poor use and conservation of soil resources.

much warmer than it is now. During that time grass grew in the Sahara, but little rain fell in parts of the Great Plains in the United States and sand dunes blew across the now fertile fields and ranches of eastern Colorado and western Nebraska. It is quite likely that if a warming trend were to be reestablished, the agricultural productivity of North America might be adversely affected.

13.9 NATURAL FACTORS AND CHANGE OF CLIMATE

World planners would like to be able to predict future changes of climate with greater accuracy. There would be immediate and significant advantages to such a worldwide prediction. For example, drought-resistant grains produce lower yields in normal years than high-yield corn, wheat, or rice, but in dry years the high-yielding crops may wither and die completely. If farmers knew what rainfall patterns to expect, they could plant the seeds that would maximize their yield for that particular year. Unfortunately, our understanding of atmospheric systems is too limited to permit accurate predictions a year or even a season in advance. Before we can foretell future climate patterns, we must be able to understand the factors that are causing the current changes of climate, and as we shall see, we don't yet understand nearly enough.

A woman holds her starving child in the Sahel region of North Africa. (Courtesy of the Agency for International Development.)

Change of Climate and the Earth's Orbit

Many climatic variations occur in regular, periodic intervals, although the time period for these cycles differs widely. For example, drought conditions recur in North America approximately once every 22 years, as will be discussed in the next subsection. More dramatic climatic variations have much longer time scales. Thus, the temperature of the Earth is known to oscillate on 23,000-, 41,000-, and 100,000-year cycles. During the cooler portions of these cycles, huge glaciers have advanced across the continents. Many different theories have been proposed to explain the advance and retreat of ice-age glaciers. Some scientists believe that the heat output of the Sun may vary, but no experimental proof is available to support this theory. At the present time, scientists have established a link between variation in the Earth's orbital path around the Sun and the ice ages. As stated earlier, the Earth is now tilted at an angle of 23.5° from the plane of its orbit. This tilt is believed to oscillate between 22.1° and 24.5°, completing one cycle every 41,000 years. If the tilt increases, the polar regions will receive more sunlight in the summer and less in the winter; as the tilt decreases, the opposite effect will occur. This and other orbital variations have been shown to correlate with temperature changes on Earth. According to the best estimates based on this theory, another glacial period is expected to begin some time within the next few thousand years.

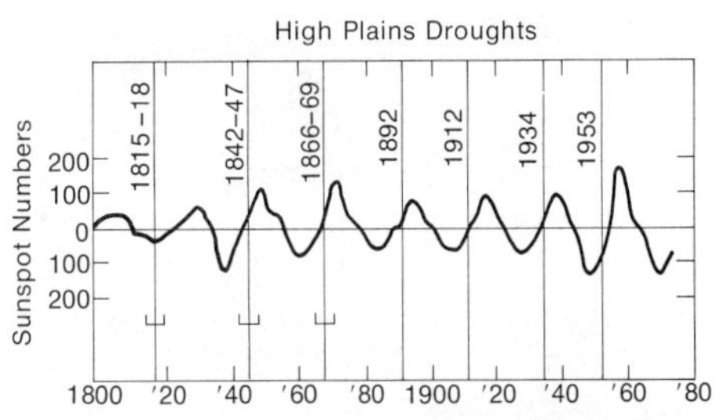

Figure 13–21. Relationship between sunspot cycle and drought in North America. (Courtesy of Dr. W. O. Roberts, University Corporation for Atmosphere Research, Boulder, Colorado, 80302.)

Figure 13–22. A slice of sequoia tree *(Sequoia gigantea)*. This tree began growing in 549 A.D. and was cut in 1891. Every year of growth is marked by a natural, circular ring known as a growth ring. The white numbers marked on the slice indicate 100-year intervals in the life of the tree. The rings in the central region of the tree are generally broader than those in the outer layers, because the tree grew more rapidly when it was young than it did at maturity. Local variations in width reflect the weather and rainfall for that year. Thus, scientists can study climatic variations in the region over a period of nearly 1350 years by measuring the widths of the rings. (Photograph courtesy of the American Museum of Natural History.)

Change of Climate and Sunspot Cycles

Since the days of early Greek astronomers, scientists have regularly observed large dark areas on the surface of the Sun. These visible aberrations, called **sunspots,** occur when one region of the Sun becomes cooler than the rest of the surface. The nature of sunspots is discussed further in Chapter 16; for now it suffices to know that (a) sunspots are associated with intense magnetic storms on the Sun; and (b) sunspot activity oscillates in distinct cycles. Early observations recorded that sunspot activity reached a maximum once every 10 to 11 years or so, dropped to a minimum, and then rose again. More refined measurements have shown that the magnetic polarity of the sunspot storms alternates. Taking this polarity shift into account, the true sunspot cycles occur with a 21- to 22-year interval. No one understands why these phenomena occur.

Many observers have noticed a statistical correspondence between drought on the North American plains and the sunspot cycle. As shown in Figure 13–21, sunspot minima have coincided with drought in North America at least since rainfall measurements have been recorded. Other researchers have shown that the correlation prevailed in prehistoric times as well. Trees are known to exhibit annual growth rings, as shown in Figure 13–22. If rainfall is adequate and weather is favorable, the tree will grow rapidly and the ring for that year will be broad, whereas in a drought year, the annual ring will be thin. By analyzing the tree ring thicknesses, researchers have shown that drought conditions have occurred in North America in a 22-year cycle since 1600. The close agreement shown in the data might lead one to say that sunspots *cause* drought in North America, but let us be careful. Note that this is only a statistical observation—it does not prove cause and effect. The relationship may be pure chance; perhaps the North American dry spells are influenced by some other unrelated phenomena that coincidentally cycles every 20 to 22 years. In order to prove that a relationship exists between sunspots and climate here on Earth, we must show *how* the relationship works.

Unfortunately such proof is hard to obtain. First, there is a problem in energy balance. A lot of energy is required to move global winds such as those that bring rain to North America. Yet the energy of the Sun appears to vary only minutely with changes in sunspot activity. Thus, if sunspots were to *cause* weather changes, a large mass of air would have to be moved by small differences in energy. Therefore scientists are not looking for a direct cause-and-effect relationship but rather for some sort of "trigger" mechanism. Perhaps the solar magnetic storms trigger a chemical reaction in the upper atmosphere. This chemical reaction may then release a great deal of energy and initiate global storm systems. It has been suggested that magnetic disturbances on the Sun may affect the formation of ozone in the mesosphere. Ozone is formed according to the following reactions:

$$O_2 + \text{photon} \rightarrow O + O$$

$$O + O_2 \rightarrow \underset{\text{ozone}}{O_3}$$

Ozone, once formed, absorbs radiation to decompose according to the reaction

$$O_3 + \text{photon} \rightarrow O_2 + O$$

Thus the photochemical reactions in the upper atmosphere affect the quantity and frequency of radiation reaching the troposphere. A trigger mechanism can be envisioned in which sunspots affect ozone formation. In turn, the ozone regulates the amount of heat received and held by the Earth and thus affects the patterns of wind circulation. At present this explanation is only a working hypothesis, and scientists are now gathering data that might prove or disprove it.

Polar Ice As a Trigger Mechanism

The Arctic Ocean is a particularly delicate geological system. As we noted earlier, polar regions do not receive nearly enough sunlight to maintain present temperatures. Instead they depend on heat carried northward by winds and ocean currents. The flow of heat northward by ocean currents is inhibited by the fact that the Arctic Ocean is largely landlocked (Fig. 13–23). Therefore, warm water carried northward from the Atlantic or Pacific ocean must pass through a few narrow straits to reach the Arctic. If a warm current were to shift slightly, it might miss an opening, be deflected, and fail to bring as much heat northward as it does at present. Thus, the heat balance of the northern polar region is delicately interconnected with the movement of ocean waters. However, the temperature of the arctic region is delicately balanced for other reasons as well. There is very little land surface in the Arctic. Owing to the extreme cold, the polar seas are permanently frozen into a formation called the **Polar Ice Cap.** The polar ice is subjected to two different environments. Above, the arctic air is generally cold, most often well below 0° C. But the underside of the ice

Figure 13–23. The Arctic Ocean.

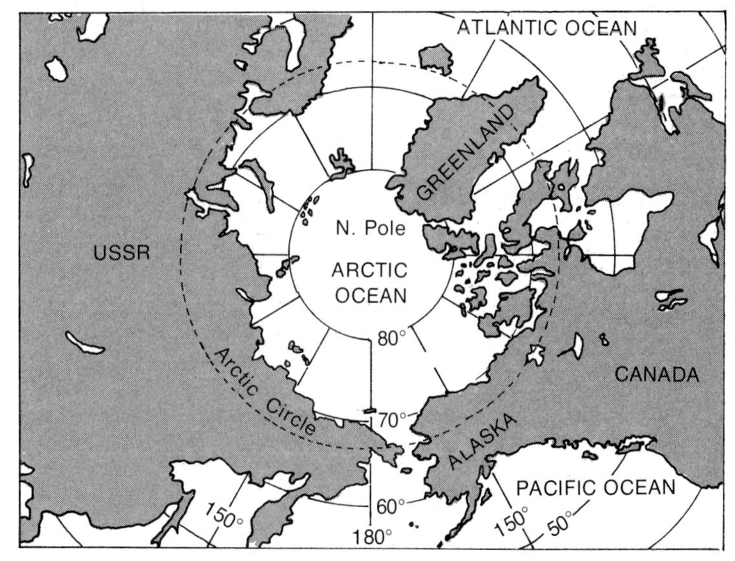

is in contact with warmer ocean water. Since ice is a good insulator, the temperature below the ice remains much warmer than the temperature above, and therefore the Polar Ice Cap is only about 2 to 4 m thick. Owing to its relative thinness, the Polar Ice Cap can either grow larger or melt back fairly quickly. Now, ice has an extremely high albedo, reflecting most of the radiation received from the Sun. Let's imagine that for some reason that we don't clearly understand, the winds and ocean currents moving to the Arctic shift very slightly so as to carry less heat northward than they did in previous years. The colder climate causes the Ice Cap to grow slightly. But as the Ice Cap grows, so does the polar albedo, and more heat is reflected back to space. Thus, the ice reflects sunlight and causes the Arctic to become colder still. In turn, colder times cause more ice to form. By this feedback mechanism a small shift in a circulation pattern may cause a large shift in polar climate. The delicacy of global systems becomes apparent when we realize that a cooler polar climate may affect monsoons in Africa and Asia.

13.10 HUMAN ACTIVITIES AND CHANGE OF CLIMATE

Recently, many people have grown concerned that human activity may be altering climate appreciably. It is already known that the climate in large urban centers is measurably different from that in outlying regions (see Table 13–1). Cities are generally warmer, cloudier, and wetter, and receive less sunshine and wind as compared with nearby rural regions. There are many reasons for these differences. For one, huge quantities of fuels are burned in urban regions, and the heat produced is sufficient to alter air temperatures measurably. Furthermore, the tall buildings block the wind and retain the warm air in the city centers. There are probably several reasons why cities experience increased rainfall and fog. Water mists from the cooling facilities of electric generators and other industrial facilities collect over the cities. Various air pollutants, such as aerosol particles, may serve as nuclei for water condensation, thereby inducing precipitation. Additionally, there is a relationship between thermal effects and

TABLE 13–1. AVERAGE CHANGES IN CLIMATIC ELEMENTS CAUSED BY URBANIZATION

Element	Comparison with Rural Environment
Cloudiness:	
cover	5 to 10% more
fog—winter	100% more
fog—summer	30% more
Precipitation, total	5 to 10% more
Relative humidity:	
winter	2% lower
summer	8% lower
Radiation:	
global	15 to 20% less
duration of sunshine	5 to 15% less
Temperature:	
annual mean	0.5 to 1.0°C higher
winter minimum (average)	1.0 to 2.0°C higher
Wind speed:	
annual mean	20 to 30% lower
extreme gusts	10 to 20% lower
calms	5 to 20% more

New York City. The climate in large urban centers is measurably different from that in outlying rural districts.

precipitation. If the air in the city is warmed sufficiently, it will rise, and air from surrounding regions will be drawn in, as shown in Figure 13–24. This pattern is similar to that of rising air over the Equator, or to the monsoon system, and often leads to precipitation.

Cities cover only a tiny fraction of the surface of the Earth, and the local weather changes just described do not affect world climate appreciably. However, there is growing concern that various types of industrial pollution may cause global changes in climate. Some of these are listed in the following discussion.

Absorption of Radiation—Carbon Dioxide and Water

If there were no atmosphere, the view from the Earth would be much like that which the astronauts see from the Moon–a terrain where starkly bright surfaces contrast with deep shadows, and a black sky from which the Sun glares and the stars shine but do not twinkle. The atmosphere protects us by serving as a light-scattering and heat-mediating blanket. As shown in Figure 13–4, about half of the incident radiation from the Sun passes through the atmosphere to the Earth; the rest is reflected or absorbed in the atmosphere. The energy absorbed by the Earth is eventually reemitted to the atmosphere as infrared radiation. A large portion of this infrared energy is reabsorbed by the atmosphere and is, in effect, conserved, with the result that the surface of the Earth is warmer than it would otherwise be.

Some molecules in the atmosphere absorb infrared radiation, and others do not. Oxygen and nitrogen, which together compose almost 99 per cent of the total composition of dry air at ground level, do not absorb infrared. On the other hand, molecules of water, carbon dioxide, and ozone do absorb infrared. Water plays the major role in absorbing infrared because it is so abundant. Carbon dioxide has been studied extensively because we are nearly certain that human activities are altering the carbon dioxide concentration in the atmosphere. Ozone is also released into the lower atmosphere by industrial activity.

Figure 13–24. Heat effects over cities. The heat generated in urban regions causes the air to rise. Cooler air from the countryside is drawn in to form a convection current. The rising air often leads to low pressure and increased precipitation over cities.

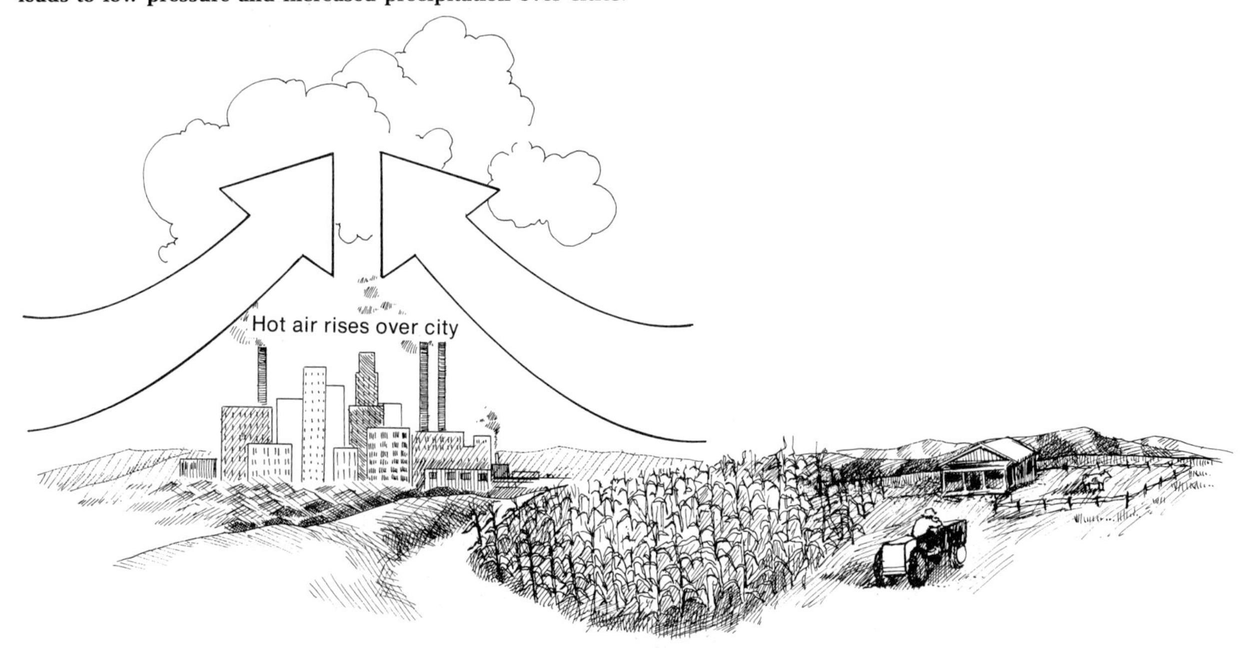

Carbon dioxide is released into the air whenever any organic matter is burned. For example, the carbon in coal burns according to the chemical equation

Carbon + oxygen → carbon dioxide (gas)

Similarly, wood burns completely according to the equation

Cellulose
(Contains carbon, hydrogen, and oxygen)
+ oxygen → carbon dioxide + water

The carbon dioxide released from the burning of fuels is sufficient to raise global atmospheric concentrations measurably.

Carbon dioxide is also cycled by natural processes. Growing plants convert carbon dioxide and water to sugars and oxygen during photosynthesis.

carbon dioxide + water → sugar + oxygen

Conversely, when a plant is burned or digested by some animal, the sugars react with oxygen to produce carbon dioxide and water with the release of energy:

sugar + oxygen → carbon dioxide + water

During the past 100 years, large areas of forests across the globe have been cut and converted to farmlands. The trees themselves are composed largely of carbon, hydrogen, and oxygen. When wood, branches, and leaves are burned, large quantities of carbon dioxide gas are released into the atmosphere. In addition, a forest floor consists of a thick, spongy layer of partly rotted leaves, needles, twigs, and other organic debris. In a healthy, undisturbed system, some of this material rots every year, while at the same time more falls from the trees, so that the total quantity of organic matter in the soil remains fairly constant. However, if the timber is cut, organic material rots faster than it is replenished. Thus, the balance is disrupted. Large quantities of organic matter decompose, and carbon dioxide gas is released. Some scientists beieve that more carbon dioxide is released from the destruction of organic matter in the soil than from the burning of fossil fuels, but not everyone agrees with this.

The most accurate measurements indicate that the carbon dioxide concentration in the atmosphere has increased from about 290 ppm in 1870 to 330 ppm in 1979 and that the rate of increase is accelerating.

Since carbon dioxide absorbs infrared, increased quantities of this gas will lead to global warming. Some scientists estimate that the carbon dioxide concentration will increase enough by the year 2040 to warm the Earth by as much as 2° to 3° C. It is impossible to predict the effects of such a temperature change on world climate. Growing seasons in the Northern Hemisphere may be prolonged by as much as 2 to 3 weeks, but as mentioned previously, a warming trend may also disrupt rainfall patterns. A significant global warming might also melt the polar icecap sufficiently to raise the ocean level, and flood coastal cities.

Dust

In 1815, a volcano erupted from the crater of Mount Tambora in Indonesia. It was the largest eruption in modern times; approximately 100 km^3 of ash and rock were ejected into the atmosphere and the top 1300 m of the mountain was completely blown away. The booming noise was so intense that on Java, nearly 500 km away, naval officers believed that pirates were shelling nearby coastal towns and sent warships to offer relief. Large quantities of dust from the volcano collected in the stratosphere and began to circle the Earth. One year later, in 1816, spring came late to the Northern Hemisphere. May was unusually cold, snow fell in northern New England in June, and frosts occurring in July and August virtually wiped out crops of corn and vegetables. Thousands starved and the year was

> The atmosphere of the planet Venus contains large concentrations of carbon dioxide. This carbon dioxide absorbs significant quantities of heat and is an important factor in raising the surface temperatures of the planet to approximately 500° C.

commonly called "eighteen hundred and froze to death." In several other instances abnormally cold seasons have followed major volcanic eruptions. Many scientists now believe that the high-level atmospheric dust from volcanos reflects significant quantities of sunlight back into space, thereby reducing temperatures on Earth.

What, then, of the dusts injected into the atmosphere by people? These materials, one component of air pollution, are composed primarily of smoke from the incomplete combustion of coal, oil, wood, and garbage and dust from agriculture. Of course, much of the larger particulate matter falls to the ground or is washed down by rain. There is some persistent introduction of small particles into the upper atmosphere, where they join the volcanic dust in increasing the Earth's albedo. However, this effect is as yet puny compared with that of volcanic dusts. The effect of pollutant particles in the lower atmosphere, where most of them are concentrated, is more complicated. Particles can absorb as well as reflect radiation, and the net heat effect of manmade dusts near the ground is not at all easy to interpret. There is therefore no convincing evidence that pollutant dusts in the lower atmosphere have any important effect on the Earth's temperature. However, the dust that settles to the ground is another matter. Most of us have seen how snow in the city can become dirty after a few days. If you live in a rural area where snowfall is common, spread a thin layer of ashes on a 1-m^2 section of snow on a warmish sunny winter day in late February or early March. By evening, you will notice that the snow under the ashes has melted faster than the snow nearby. The dark ash absorbs sunlight (lowers the snow's albedo) and causes the snow to melt. If increasingly larger quantities of dust from industrial facilities and agricultural activities were to settle on snow packs over wide areas, a change in global climate might possibly occur.

In fact it has been suggested that perhaps people should spread ashes on the North Polar Ice Cap, thereby increasing the ability of the region to absorb sunlight. It is theorized that this would cause some of the Ice Cap to melt, and thus the monsoon rains would return to the Sahel. If the reasoning is correct and the agricultural activity of the world could be raised by tampering with the arctic environment, the project might be worthwhile. However, the reasoning rests on a foundation of many incompletely understood theories. For instance, we are not at all sure that monsoon failures are directly related to the size of the Polar Ice Cap—that is just a working hypothesis. Even if we were sure of that relationship, we could not predict the effects of a global warming trend resulting from the melting of the polar ice. Perhaps weather patterns would shift so that rains would fall in India and drought would come to North America. We don't know. Global systems are so poorly understood that there is a significant risk in tampering with them.

Cerro Negro volcano (Nicaragua) blanketed the countryside and the city of Leon (17 miles away) with ash from October 23 to December 7, 1968. (From *Science and Public Affairs,* April, 1973.)

Depletion of the Ozone Layer

The Sun emits light over a wide range of wavelengths, including infrared, visible, and ultraviolet. It is the ultraviolet radiation which, having high energy, tans our skin. Heavier doses of ultraviolet can cause burns and can increase the chances of skin cancer or even of genetic mutations which may lead to birth defects. If more of the ultraviolet light that reaches our upper atmosphere were to penetrate to the surface of the Earth, the risks of such damages would increase.

Plants, too, might be adversely affected, and preliminary data suggest that the growth of some food crops is retarded by high doses of ultraviolet light. Fortunately, the high-energy ultraviolet photons are removed in the upper atmosphere by a series of photochemical reactions involving molecular oxygen and ozone. As mentioned in Chapter 9, (pages 269–270), ozone catalyzes the conversion of harmful ultraviolet rays to warming infrared radiation.

There has been recent concern that some air pollutants are thinning out the protective ozone barrier. Two pollutants of particular interest are the nitrogen oxides and the chlorofluoromethanes.

Nitrogen oxide (NO) is released in the exhaust of automobiles and of jet aircraft. When released from terrestrial vehicles, this compound helps produce smog, which irritates our eyes and endangers our health. Released in the upper atmosphere by high-flying airplanes, however, nitrogen oxide removes ozone by the following reactions

$$NO + O_3 \rightarrow NO_2 + O_2$$

$$NO_2 + O \rightarrow NO + O_2$$

The ozone that is thus destroyed is no longer available for absorbing ultraviolet. Notice that nitrogen oxide is a catalyst in this reaction and is not consumed. Therefore, even a small amount of this compound can destroy a large quantity of ozone. Additionally, since upper-level stratospheric air layers do not mix efficiently with air near the surface of the Earth, nitrogen compounds that are released into the upper atmosphere remain there for many years. Most conventional airplanes fly below the ozone layer, and their emissions do not directly affect it. However, supersonic transport aircraft fly high enough to release nitrogen oxide directly into the ozone layer. The possible danger of these emissions at these altitudes is one reason that environmentalists oppose the construction of SST's.

Nitrogen oxide and other reactive compounds are also produced by atomic bomb explosions. In particular, high-altitude explosion of nuclear weapons not only releases harmful radioactive wastes but also produces NO, which removes ozone. There is some evidence that a global nuclear war would destroy a significant portion of the ozone layer, and the resultant increase of ultraviolet light represents yet another hazard of nuclear warfare.

Another category of pollutants affecting the ozone layer is the chlorofluoromethanes. These compounds, which contain covalently bonded C, Cl, and F atoms, are chemically inert in the lower atmosphere and do not affect living systems. Partly for this reason they have been used as propellants in aerosol cans. Their function is simply to provide the pressure that propels the liquid out as a fine mist. However, quantities of the chlorofluoromethanes have been moving up to the ozone layer of the upper atmosphere. There they readily dissociate and by a series of chemical reactions cause the destruction of atmospheric ozone. Since ozone absorbs ultraviolet photons, any heavy concentration of these compounds in the upper atmosphere could conceivably allow large amounts of harmful ultraviolet light to reach the life-supporting layers of the Earth.

In December of 1978, the Environmental Protection Agency in the United States banned many uses of the chlorofluoromethanes. However, these materials are stable in the atmosphere and the environmental problems that they cause are expected to continue and even increase for decades. The World Meteorological Organization has estimated that 5 per cent of the ozone in the upper atmosphere will be destroyed by the year 2000, and depletion will reach 15 per cent a few decades into the twenty-first century. A 15 per cent reduction in the ozone will mean a 30 per cent increase in ultraviolet radiation to the Earth's surface, but no one really knows how this will affect biological systems. Additionally, a 10° C rise in the temperature in the upper stratosphere is expected, although, once again, no one really knows how this will affect life on Earth.

Those who favor new developments such as spray deodorants and SST's assume that the human inventiveness that produced them will also find ways to prevent or undo any adverse effects. (In scientific jargon, such a cure is called a "technological fix.") Environmentalists, on the other hand, take the position that global effects are so complex that we do not understand them well enough to dare to tamper with them and that, in any case, each "technological fix" will only lead to a new set of problems.

Perhaps human beings are significantly altering their own climate, or perhaps we will learn how to alter temperature and rainfall patterns in the future. But it may just be that global forces are so great and complex that we will primarily be observers of the weather that affects our very existence.

CHAPTER OBJECTIVES

Understand how the atmosphere evolved and why major disruptions to the world's ecosystems may affect atmospheric composition. Know how the Earth's atmosphere is structured. Review the Earth's energy balance, general climate patterns, and seasonal changes. Understand how wind, rain, and global wind patterns are formed. Study the role of oceans in world climate. The chapter briefly discusses movement of air masses and how they affect local weather. Finally, know what factors may cause climate to change and know how changing climates affect people's lives.

KEY WORDS

Anaerobic
Photosynthesis
Gaia
Barometric pressure
Troposphere
Stratosphere
Mesosphere
Thermosphere
Steady state
Albedo
Solstice
Equinox
Humidity
Absolute humidity
Relative humidity
Saturation quantity
Dew
Fog
Adiabatic cooling
Climate
Weather
Coriolis effect
Doldrums
Horse latitude
Trade winds
Ocean currents
Gyres
Sea breeze
Monsoon
Air mass
Sahel
Polar Ice Cap

TAKE-HOME EXPERIMENTS

1. **Weather.** Measure the temperature, barometric pressure, wind direction, and wind velocity in the morning, noon, and evening every day for 10 days. If you do not have an instrument for measuring wind velocity, you may describe it verbally. Use the following scale (adapted from the Beaufort Scale for sailing vessels) as an aid.

General Description	*Wind Velocity in km/hr*
Calm	Less than 1
Light breeze (you can feel it on your face; but there is little movement of trees and grasses)	7–10
Moderate breeze (trees sway noticeably and grasses wave)	10–35
Strong breeze (windy day—hats blow off; people remark, "It sure is windy today")	35–75
Gale (debris flies about in air, trees bend dramatically, large whitecaps appear even on small lakes and ponds)	75–125
Hurricane	125 and up

Record also the amount of cloud cover, precipitation, and other relevant noticeable factors. At the end of 10 days, review your data and see if you can observe any correlations or significant trends. For example, in some regions of the world a rising barometer and a northeast wind will nearly always bring cold weather and clear skies. Now try to predict the weather one day ahead every day for the next 10 days. How accurate are your predictions?

2. **Albedo.** On a bright sunny day record the temperature 2 cm above the surface of (a) a grassy field, (b) a tar roadway, (c) a lake or pond, (d) a bare gravelly or sandy field. The measurements should be performed as nearly simultaneously as possible so that the Sun's angle of incidence on the Earth will not have changed appreciably during the time span of your measurements. Make all the measurements either in direct sunlight or all in the shade, but do not compare sunlight measurements with those taken in the shade. Now record the temperatures of the soil and water 2 cm and then 10 cm under the various surfaces. (It may be impossible to dig under a tar roadway, so omit this measurement.) Compare your data and discuss the albedos and heat storage capabilities of the various media.

3. **Climate and growth.** Take a shovelful of fertile soil, mix it thoroughly, divide the soil into two equal portions, and place the portions in two different bowls or clay pots. Now plant ten seeds in each pot. You can use any type of seed as long as all 20 seeds are of the same variety and come from the same source. Choose two different rooms or locations that each receive fairly equal quantities of sunlight but that are maintained at different temperatures, and place one planter in each room. Water both samples equally. Measure the heights of the seedlings after two weeks. Comment on the effect of climate on seed germination.

Some plants are more sensitive to temperature differences than others. To learn about the temperature sensitivity of different plants, have each student in the class perform the experiment with a different type of seed. Compare your results.

4. **Weather.** Collect the weather maps from the daily paper for 10 days. Explain the symbols and see if you can predict the weather in your region for the next few days.

PROBLEMS

1. **Primitive atmosphere.** How did the primitive atmosphere differ from our atmosphere today?

2. **Primitive atmosphere.** Humans could not survive in the Earth's primitive atmosphere, yet life as we know it could not have evolved in the present one. Explain and discuss.

3. **Primitive life.** It is stated in Section 13.1 that the first living entity probably ate organic molecules. Where did these molecules come from? Would you guess that the first organisms also ate other living organisms? Defend your answer.

4. **Atmosphere.** Explain how plants help to maintain an atmosphere that can support animal life.

5. **Atmosphere.** List the primary layers of the atmosphere. Discuss the physical properties of each.

*6. **Atmosphere.** Imagine that enough matter vanished from the Earth's core so that the mass of the Earth were reduced to half its present value. In what ways do you think the atmosphere would change? Would the normal pressure at sea level be affected? Would the thickness of the atmosphere change? Would more molecules be lost to outer space? Explain.

7. **Atmosphere.** An astronaut out on a spacewalk must wear protective clothing as a shield against the Sun's rays, but the same person is likely to relax in a bathing suit in the sunlight down on Earth. Explain.

8. **Atmosphere.** Climbers find that while they are on high mountains they must wear dark glasses to protect their eyes and also that they get suntans or even burns even when the temperature is below freezing. Explain.

9. **Thermosphere.** The temperatures are quite high in the thermosphere, but little heat is stored there. Explain.

*Indicates more difficult problem.

10. **Albedo.** As the winter ends, the snow generally starts to melt around trees, twigs, and rocks. The line of melting radiates outward from these objects. The snow in open areas melts last. Explain.

11. **Albedo.** Refer to Figure 13–4. (a) What per cent of the incident solar energy is received by the Earth? (b) Does the Earth's surface receive any additional energy? If so, from what source(s)? (c) Is the amount of energy emitted by the Earth greater, less, or the same as that which it receives from incident solar radiation? Explain.

*12. **Sunlight and climate.** If the Earth were flat instead of spherical, would different regions experience different climates or similar ones? Assume that the flat Earth were tilted 23½° with respect to the plane of its orbit.

13. **Seasons.** How does the tilt of the Earth affect climate in the temperate and polar regions? Discuss.

14. **Climate.** If the North Pole receives the same number of hours of sunlight as do the equatorial regions, why is it so much colder at the Pole?

*15. **Seasons.** At the summer solstice, the North Pole is tilted toward the Sun and therefore is closer to it than is the South Pole. Is the summer weather in the Northern Hemisphere warm because this region is closer to the Sun, or is some other factor responsible? Explain.

16. **Condensation.** Explain why frost forms on the inside of a refrigerator (assuming it is an old-fashioned one and not a modern frost-free unit). Would more frost tend to form in (a) summer or winter, and (b) in a dry desert region or a humid one? Explain.

17. **Condensation.** Which of the following conditions will produce frost? Which will produce dew? Explain. (a) A constant temperature throughout the day. (b) A warm summer day followed by a cool night. (c) A cool fall afternoon followed by a freezing temperature at night.

*Indicates more difficult problem.

18. **Barometer and weather.** Explain why a falling barometer is a good indication that cloudy weather may soon follow.

*19. **Earth's spin.** If you were firing a long-range rocket and aimed it due north at a target due north of your launching pad, would you score a hit or a miss? What would happen if you fired due west at a target located due west? Explain.

20. **Winds.** How are the winds analogous to a heat engine? What is the energy source that powers the wind?

21. **Winds and the Earth's spin.** If the wind is blowing southward in the Northern Hemisphere, will the Earth's spin cause it to veer east or west? If the wind is moving south in the Southern Hemisphere which way will it veer? Justify your answer.

22. **Trade winds.** What is a trade wind? Why are they so predictable?

23. **Doldrums.** Why is the doldrum region relatively calm and rainy? Why are the horse latitudes calm and dry?

*24. **Doldrums.** Would the exact location of the doldrum low-pressure area be likely to change from month to month? From year to year? Explain.

25. **Trade winds.** Sailors traveling in the Northern Hemisphere expect to incur predictable winds from the northeast between about 5° N and 30° N latitudes. Should airplane pilots expect northeast trade winds while flying at high altitudes in the same region? Explain.

26. **Air currents.** Why doesn't the air that is heated at the Equator continue to rise forever?

27. **Oceans and climate.** Discuss the effect of the oceans on world climate. Would it be correct to say that coastal regions are always warmer than inland areas? Explain.

*28. **Water and climate.** Would a large inland lake be likely to affect the climate of the land surrounding it? Deep lakes seldom freeze completely in winter, whereas shallow ones do. Would a deep lake have a greater or a lesser effect on weather than a shallow one? Explain.

*Indicates more difficult problem.

29. **Sea breezes.** Would sea breezes be more likely to be strong on an overcast day or on a bright sunny one? Explain.

30. **Weather and climate.** Describe the difference between weather and climate. Which is more predictable?

31. **Monsoons.** What is a monsoon? How are they formed? At what time of the year will monsoons generally bring rain?

32. **Monsoons.** Explain how arctic air moving south can cause the monsoon rainfall patterns to change.

33. **Weather.** Describe four different weather conditions that may cause air to rise, resulting in precipitation.

34. **Weather.** What is an air mass? Describe what would be likely to happen if a polar air mass collided with a humid subtropical air mass.

35. **Weather.** Study the weather map shown below and predict the weather in Salt Lake City, Chicago, and New York City two days after this map was drawn. Defend your prediction.

36. **Changing climate.** Discuss the problems inherent in trying to determine whether world climate is changing.

37. **World climate.** Explain why a 2° C drop in global temperatures would be alarming.

38. **Changing climate.** In 1974 there was an unusually dry summer on the south coast of Alaska. The warm ocean air moving northward was intercepted by a south-moving cold front, and the rain fell into the ocean before it reached the land. Compare this weather pattern with the monsoon behavior in Africa and Asia. Does this evidence prove that the Earth is experiencing a global cooling trend, or may the two factors be functioning independently of each other? Is there enough data available to prove that a definite trend is occurring? Explain.

*Indicates more difficult problem.

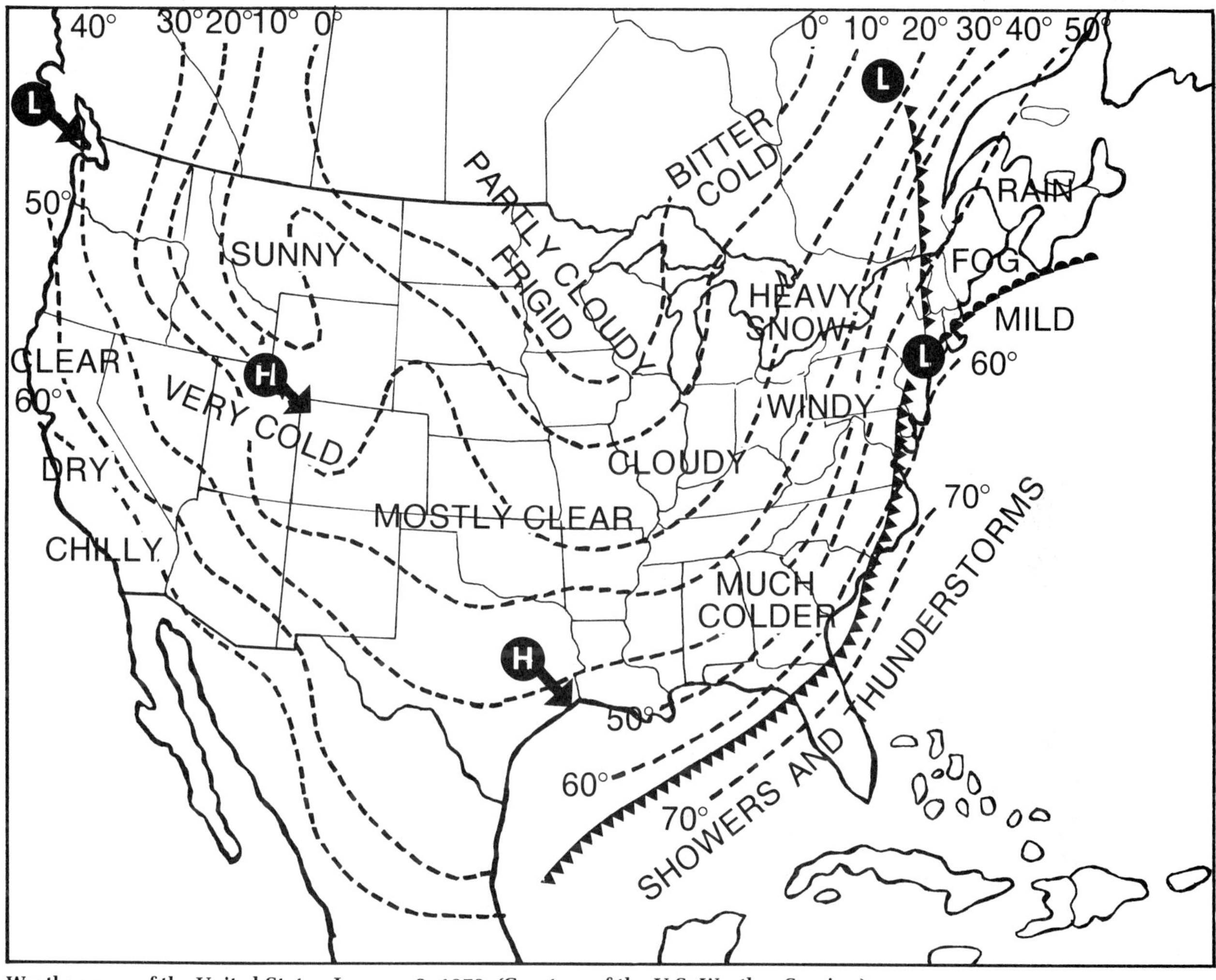

Weather map of the United States, January 2, 1979. (Courtesy of the U.S. Weather Service.)

39. **Climate and the human condition.** Explain how the 70 years of warm weather between 1880 and 1950 may ultimately be a source of a great deal of human misery.

40. **Climate change.** Name four factors that may cause climate to change. How many of these factors are at least partially controlled by people? Discuss.

41. **Sunspots and weather.** Discuss some questions that must be answered before we can *prove* that sunspots do or do not cause drought in North America.

42. **Polar Ice Cap.** Explain why the Polar Ice Cap is a delicate system that may magnify a small climatic change initiated by other phenomena.

43. **Local weather conditions.** Cities are generally warmer than the surrounding countryside. One reason is that concrete, stone, and tar store heat better than soil and trees do. In addition, great quantities of fuels are burned in a city, releasing considerable heat. The temperature differences are greatest in the early evening, after the sun has set. Predict the direction of local winds near cities. Would fog and rain be more likely to occur over the city or the countryside? Explain.

44. **Climate.** Discuss four ways in which people may be changing world climate. In each instance, explain what types of activities are causing the potential disruption, and what is the mechanism whereby climate may be changed.

45. **Climate.** Imagine that you must determine whether some particular climatic effect, such as increased fog or rainfall in a given area, is caused by human activity. Which of the following experimental method(s) would you rely on? Defend your choices. (a) Compare current data with those of previous years, when population and industrial activity were less. (b) Compare the effects during weekdays, when industrial activity is higher, with those on weekends, when it is low. (c) Compare effects during different seasons of the year. (d) Compare effects just before and after the switch to or from daylight-saving time, to see whether there is a sharp one-hour shift in the data. (e) Compare effects in areas where populations and industrial activities differ.

46. **Ozone layer.** What factors might conceivably deplete the ozone layer? How would each factor operate? What are the possible results of such depletion?

CHAPTER 14

Ancient people were certainly aware that dynamic movements occurred occasionally within the Earth's crust. We can surmise that even those who had never experienced an earthquake or seen a volcanic eruption had heard stories or legends retelling accounts of these events. In the early 1900's, a few geologists published theories suggesting that the continents themselves are drifting slowly across the surface of the globe. This idea was largely rejected at the time, but now it forms the basis for much of modern geology. The chapter opens with a discussion of the internal structure of the Earth and its magnetic field, and then proceeds to introduce the rock cycle and the theory of plate tectonics. Earthquakes, volcanoes, and mountain building are explained in terms of general tectonic theory. As mountains are slowly pushed upward by subterranean forces, they are simultaneously broken down by weathering, and the small fragments are carried away by erosion. The chapter ends with a discussion of our mineral wealth, ores, fuels, and soils.

OUR GEOLOGICAL ENVIRONMENT— THE EARTH

14.1 INTRODUCTION

Imagine yourself on a rocky beach, walking toward the surf. You can see, hear, and feel the wind and the water. If you talked in textbook language, you could say that you sensed the motion of your gaseous and liquid environment. But you do not see the cliffs move, and the Earth doesn't shake under your feet. That is to say, the solid earth seems to be a firm base beneath you, over which you walk, the winds blow, and the waves break. However, this apparent rigidity is deceptive—the Earth's crust is actually dynamic, not static. Continents drift across the ocean, mountains rise and fall, rocks flow or are pushed from place to place. These movements escape most casual observations because they are generally slow, although occasionally volcanic eruptions, earthquakes, and other types of rapid movement do occur.

There are two types of movement of solid material that affect our environment. Mountain-building, continental migration, erosion, and other movements of large masses of materials are powered by natural energy sources of far greater magnitude than any that humans can harness. These phenomena will be discussed in this chapter. The second type of movement, to be discussed in the next chapter, is initiated by human beings and involves comparatively tiny amounts of energy and relatively insignificant masses of material. We refer here mainly to mining and farming. Yet we find that these activities, which are insignificant on a scale of global energy, are vitally important on a human scale. Farmers generally dig up less than 1 m of a planet with a radius of 6,400,000 m, and miners probe only a few kilometers downward at most, yet the impoverishment of soil or the depletion of mineral reserves has major technological, political, environmental, and economic consequences. Therefore, we will study transformations that occur on widely varying energy scales, from the movement of continents to the displacement of relatively small quantities of minerals and topsoils.

14.2 THE STRUCTURE OF THE EARTH

Ancient philosophers theorized that the Earth was hollow, rather like a tennis ball, with a thin outer shell and a void in the center. This belief persisted in some circles even up to modern times. In the 1960's the Congress of the United States was considering legislation to finance the drilling of a test well under the ocean in an effort to penetrate the Earth's crust and sample the rock beneath it. Several concerned people wrote letters telling their senators and representatives that if such a hole were bored it would unplug the stop, so to speak, and all the oceans' water would drain away into the middle of the Earth. No scientists believe this theory anymore. We now know that the Earth is composed of several distinct layers of different kinds of solid or liquid matter. To understand why this layered structure exists, we must first remember that there is an appreciable quantity of naturally radioactive elements within the Earth. When a radioactive atom breaks apart, a small amount of energy is released as heat. If this heat is released near the surface of the globe, it will quickly be radiated off into space. On the other hand, heat energy produced deep within the interior of our planet cannot escape so easily, and remains trapped. Even though the quantity of heat released per day is small, geological time spans are large. Hundreds of millions of years after the Earth first became solid, this radiogenic heat gradually accumulated until the interior of the planet became so hot that rocks began to melt. Now, if you have a mass of molten rock, the denser material will settle to the bottom, while less dense materials float to the top. This is exactly what happened in the Earth. The dense elements, such as iron and nickel, gravitated toward the center. These were surrounded by a mantle of lighter rock and a surface crust that is generally of a comparatively low density. Most of the radioactive materials floated toward the surface layers with the lighter rock. As the radioactive materials moved closer to the surface, much of the heat was radiated out to space, and the Earth cooled somewhat. The present structure of the Earth, shown in Figure 14–1, consists of an inner solid **core** of iron and nickel, surrounded by an outer core of molten iron and nickel.

Figure 14–1. The structure of the Earth. A, Crust; B, asthenosphere; C, mantle (solid); D, outer core, probably liquid iron and nickel; E, inner core, probably solid iron and nickel.

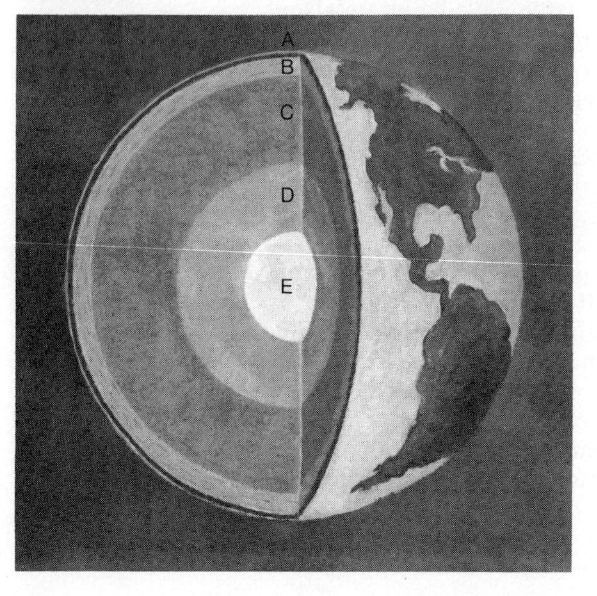

A large solid layer called the **mantle** surrounds the core. This zone contains over 80 per cent of the volume of the Earth, but because it is less dense than the core, it contains a smaller proportion of the mass. The uppermost boundary of the mantle contains a region approximately 200 km thick, called the **asthenosphere.** The asthenosphere is unique in that it is nearly hot enough to be molten, but not quite. As a result it is semifluid and plastic—vaguely similar to Silly Putty or road tar. Pockets of molten liquid exist here and there, and some of this material is occasionally forced upwards to form volcanic eruptions. The Earth is capped with a thin **crust,** the surface on which we live. This crust rides on the semifluid asthenosphere, and as we shall see in later sections, the fluids flow slowly, causing the crust to shift and distort.

We have told a fine and fascinating story, but how do we know that it is true? Of course it is only a theory, for no one has observed the formation of the Earth, but we are fairly confident that it is reasonably accurate. To understand how scientists can develop a picture of something without actually seeing it, let us consider how we know that the internal structure of the Earth is in fact layered as shown in Figure 14–1. No one has drilled a hole to the center of the Earth! One of the most powerful methods used in analyzing the Earth's interior is the study of earthquake waves. We have already learned that if a vibration is established in a medium, the speed of the resulting wave will be characteristic of the medium. Thus, if a bell is rung in air, a sound wave will travel outward with a velocity of about 331 m/sec. A sound wave is also generated if the bell is rung under water, but since water is denser than air, the sound will travel faster—1500 m/sec. Now what would happen if one person rang a bell under water while an observer listened for the sound on shore? The sound wave

Figure 14–5. Sedimentation in a river.

depths. In the Grand Canyon these layers were exposed a mile deep as the Colorado River gradually cut its way into a raised sedimentary plateau, and we can see the strata. As we shall note in later sections, horizontal layers of sedimentary rock may also be uplifted, twisted, bent, or broken as mountains rise and collapse.

Rock and soil may also undergo geologic change—**metamorphism**—by processes other than erosion and sedimentation. As an example, clay, a naturally occurring type of soil, is soft and pliable, but if it is heated it can be converted to a hard, strong solid. Thus, clay dishes and sculptures are molded when the material is soft and then hardened in a type of oven called a kiln. A similar process may occur naturally. Suppose, for example, that hot magma came in close contact with a natural clay deposit. The heat from the magma would harden the clay. Many other types of heat-hardening processes occur in the Earth. Thus, if limestone is subjected to heat and pressure, it will be converted to marble. Note that in the two examples given here, the minerals aren't melted. The heat and pressure alter the texture or chemical composition (or both) of the affected material and generally increase its hardness. The resulting product is called **metamorphic rock.**

A sedimentary rock formation in Garfield County, Utah. Note how the rock has been formed in horizontal layers. (Courtesy of U.S. Geological Society; photographer, C. B. Hunt.)

Mineral matter is slowly but continuously being changed from one form to another. Igneous rocks are broken apart to form sediments and then depending on conditions, may be converted to sedimentary or metamorphic rock. Similarly, metamorphic rock may erode and be deposited as sediments. In addition, surface rocks of all types are

A marble quarry. (Courtesy of Jerome Wycoff.)

sometimes slowly forced downward by geological actions into the hot plastic asthenosphere. Once within this layer, rock will melt, mix with other minerals, and undergo physical and chemical changes. This material may return to the surface millions or hundreds of millions of years later as newly formed igneous rocks. Thus, crustal material is formed, altered, and removed in a slow but continuous cycle (Fig. 14–6).

Figure 14–6. The rock cycle.

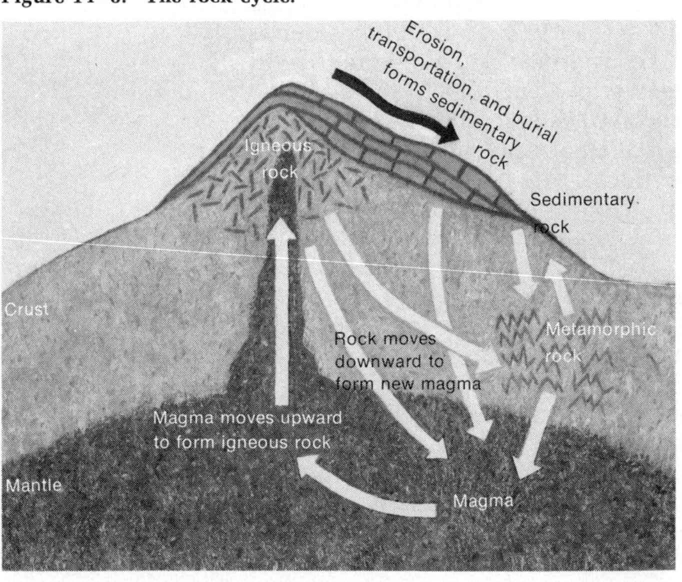

14.5 CONTINENTS AND CONTINENTAL MOVEMENT—PLATE TECTONICS

For most practical purposes we may safely assume that the Earth's crust is a rigid mass of rock lying on the surface of our planet. Thus we expect that the distance between any two cities in the world will remain constant from year to year, and that the continents will always lie in the same relationship to each other as they now do. However, the continents are not immobile and rigidly fixed in position. On the contrary, large land masses have moved considerably over the ages and continue to move at the present time. Of course, the continents travel slowly—only a few centimeters per year—but over the millennia they have traveled thousands of kilometers. Vast expanses of rock, millions of cubic kilometers in volume, are drifting slowly over the surface of the Earth. Sometimes they pull away from each other, leaving vast trenches or rifts; in other places they collide, causing the Earth's crust to crumple and wrinkle to form great mountain ranges. This concept, called the theory of **continental drift,** was at first looked upon by many geologists as being preposterous. How could the continents move about—did they plow through mantle rock like a ship moving through the sea? Since the time of those early arguments a great deal of evidence has been accumulated that demonstrates convincingly that the continents are, in fact, moving. These lines of evidence are summarized in the following paragraphs.

1. Look at a map of the world as shown in Figure 14–7A. If we cut out the continents and try to piece them together as part of a jigsaw puzzle, we find that they fit together amazingly well, as shown in Figure 14–7B. From this evidence alone early scientists deduced that perhaps there once existed one or perhaps two large supercontinents. The supercontinent(s) then broke apart, and the pieces slowly drifted away from each other to their present position.

2. Many mineral deposits on the Earth are concentrated in geographical

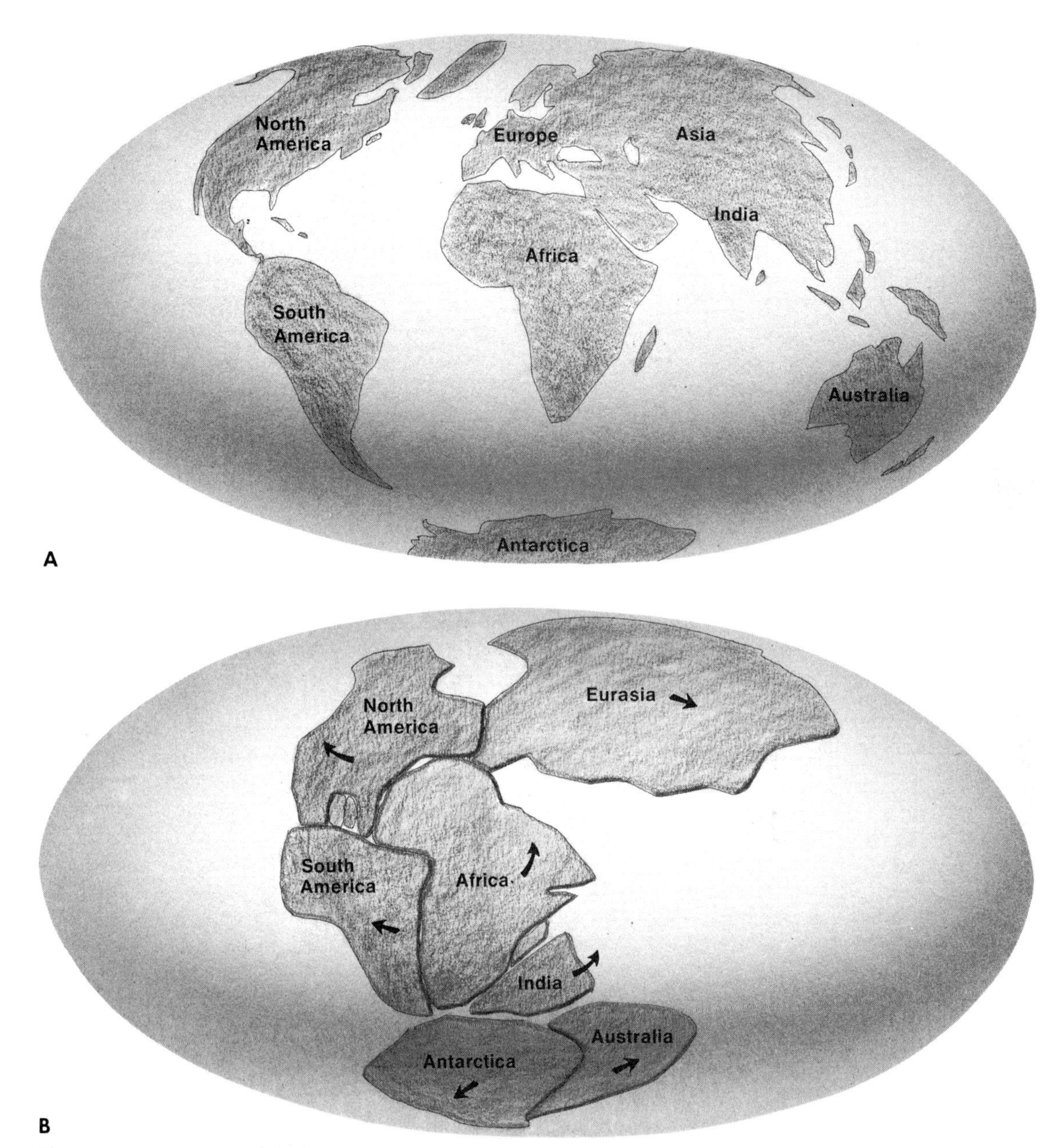

Figure 14–7. Continental drift.

strips, or belts, on the various continents. Such beltlike formations of tin deposits, for example, are shown in Figure 14–8. As seen on the map, many of these belts appear to end abruptly at the ocean. But if we fit the continents together, many tin belts line up. Belts of coal seams, salt deposits, and gypsum concentrations also seem to disappear into the ocean but align with each other when continents are pieced together. It is believed that these belts were formed many millions of years ago on a primordial supercontinent by individual processes such as sedimentation in large river valleys, or by the movement of large masses of ore-bearing magma through massive fissures in

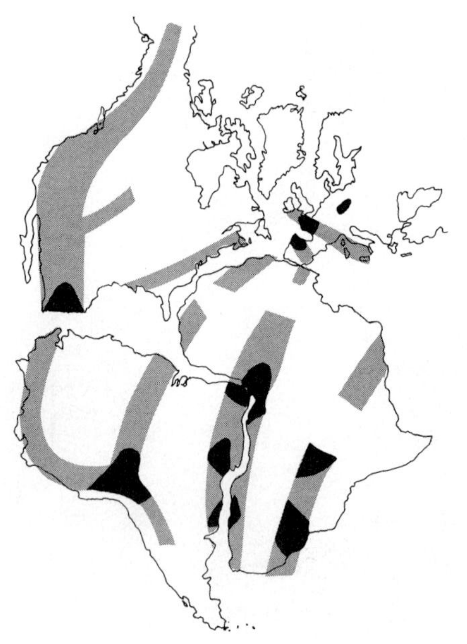

Figure 14–8. Tin belts of the world.

the Earth's crust. When the supercontinent broke up, the belts separated into the patterns we now observe.

3. Recall from Section 14.3 that tiny pieces of magnetic sediment floating down a stream will tend to align themselves with the magnetic North and South Poles as they settle. As these sediments coalesce to form rock, millions of tiny magnetic fingers pointing north are cemented into a fixed position. Thus, scientists can study ancient sedimentary rocks and determine where the magnetic North Pole was in relation to the rocks at the time of formation. Now let us say that there was a thick deposit of sedimentary rock. The bottom layer will be the oldest and may have been formed tens or even hundreds of millions of years before the uppermost sediments were laid down. If the magnetic North Pole and the continents had both been stationary, all the magnetic needles of all the rock layers would point in the same direction. But in fact the magnetic pointers shift direction from age to age, indicating that either the magnetic North Pole or the continents, or both, must have moved some time in the past. How can we tell which event occurred?

Geologists have studied rock magnetism all over the world. Rocks found in Europe that are about 100 million years old show that the magnetic North Pole lay somewhat east of its present location. However, North American rocks of the same age point to a different location for magnetic north (Fig. 14–9). But of course this cannot be—the magnetic North Pole can be in only one place at a time. However, if we move the continents closer together, the magnetic pointers from both regions would aim toward the same point. Thus we believe that the continents must have been touching each other at some ancient time and have drifted apart through the ages.

4. The geological evidence for continental drift is compelling enough to substantiate the theory, but strong supporting biological evidence has been collected as well. In 1908, the great British explorer and adventurer Sir Ernest Shackleton discovered coal deposits and fossils of tropical plants in Antarctica. You can explain this discovery by assuming either (a) that Antarctica was originally north of its present position and has since drifted south, or (b) that Antarctica has been stationary and the Earth's climate has changed drastically during the past 200 million years. Scientists could not distinguish between these two possibili-

Figure 14–9. Magnetic North Pole 100 million years ago, as deduced from European and American analyses. + = Present North Pole. ● = North Pole 100 million years ago (deduced from study of American rocks). ⊙ North Pole 100 million years ago (deduced from study of European rocks).

ties for about 60 years after Shackleton's initial discovery, until other fossil-hunting expeditions came to the South Pole. These researchers found fossil bones of various reptiles and amphibians that were virtually identical to bones found in South Africa. It is conceivable that plant seeds could have floated from one continent to another, but it is preposterous to imagine that several species of slow, wallowing, freshwater swamp-dwellers had swum 3800 km from South Africa across the tempestuous southern ocean to land and thrive in Antarctica. The only plausible explanation is that Antarctica was once connected to Africa.

There have been a great number of similar fossil discoveries in other parts of the world. Thus the early ancestors of the Australian kangaroo either swam from their evolutionary birthplace in South America across the Pacific to Australia, or walked across an ancient land bridge. Similarly, certain fossil amphibian bones are found both in the southern United States and in central Europe, but nowhere else. This observation can only mean that Europe and North America were once part of a single continent.

Scientists now believe that the Earth's crust is separated into six to eight huge chunks, called **tectonic plates.** Each of these plates may contain continental land masses or sections of the ocean floor, or combinations of ocean and continent. For example, the eastern part of the Pacific Ocean floor is generally believed to be several huge plates that are moving eastward and colliding with other plates that contain half of the Atlantic Ocean floor and North and South America and are moving toward the west. The belief that the crust is separated into great moving chunks floating, as it were, on the soft puttylike asthenosphere has given rise to the science of **plate tectonics.**

Estimates of the speed of the continental drifts vary somewhat. Most probably North and South America are now drifting away from Europe, Asia, and Africa at about 2 cm per year, and other land masses are believed to be moving at speeds varying between 1 and 15 cm per year.

Although there is almost universal agreement that the tectonic plates are moving with respect to one another, no one really understands the entire process in detail. To illustrate the types of questions that remain unanswered, consider the following two problems:

"I THOUGHT CONTINENTAL DRIFT WAS MUCH SLOWER."

From *Am. Sci.,* Sept.–Oct., 1972.

Problem 1. Since the Earth's crust is a continuous and complete shell, one part can move with respect to another only if the surface pulls apart in some places and buckles or squeezes together in others. What happens at these centers of separation and collision?

Shortly after World War II, oceanographers found that a distinct and sharp mountain range extends the whole length of the floor of the Atlantic

> Movement of a few centimeters per year may seem slow, but that depends on the time scale used as a reference. At a rate of 5 cm per year, a continent will move 2000 km in 40 million years, which is not long by geological reckoning.

Ocean from north to south, as shown in Figure 14–10. This mountain range is now called the **mid-Atlantic ridge.** It is peculiar because right in the middle of it lies a deep rift—somewhat like a steep valley that cuts the ridge in half. This rift is believed to be the boundary between one large plate moving in a westerly direction and another one traveling away from it towards the east. As these segments of the Earth's crust separate, soft plastic rock from the asthenosphere oozes upward through the crust along the ridgeline. These minerals cool and harden to replace material that is drifting away. The regions of the ocean floor that are near the mid-Atlantic ridge are therefore composed entirely of newly formed igneous rock (Fig. 14–11).

The mid-Atlantic ridge forms the eastern boundary for the great American plates. As you can see in Figure 14–12, the American plates include part of the Atlantic Ocean floor on the eastern end and extend westward to include Greenland, nearly all of North and South America, and parts of eastern Siberia. These huge masses drift slowly westward and collide with the Pacific Ocean plates as shown in the drawing. Thus, the western segments of the plates are subject to mammoth collision stresses. Think of it; entire continents slowly smashing into each other! Naturally, such collisions must cause the deformation of materials somewhere.

Geologists believe that the thick American plates have slid up and over the oceanic plates in certain places. As a result, the western segments of the American plates have risen into the air, forming large mountains such as the Andes and various coastal ranges along the west coast of the American continents. At the same time, the tremen-

Figure 14–10. Locations of mid-ocean ridges and oceanic trenches. Heavy lines indicate trenches, and double lines indicate ridges. Note the fracture zones offsetting the ridges. The double-dashed line in Africa represents The East African Rift. (After Isacks et al., 1968, and Le Pichon, 1968.)

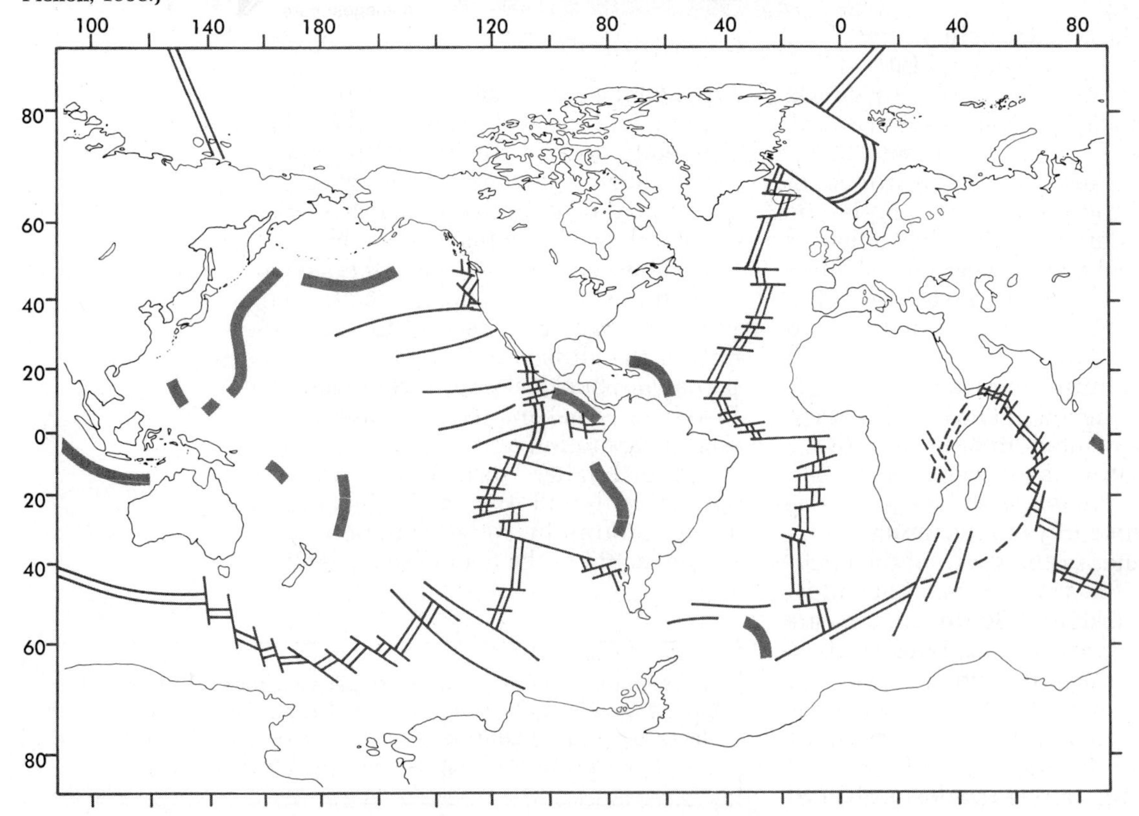

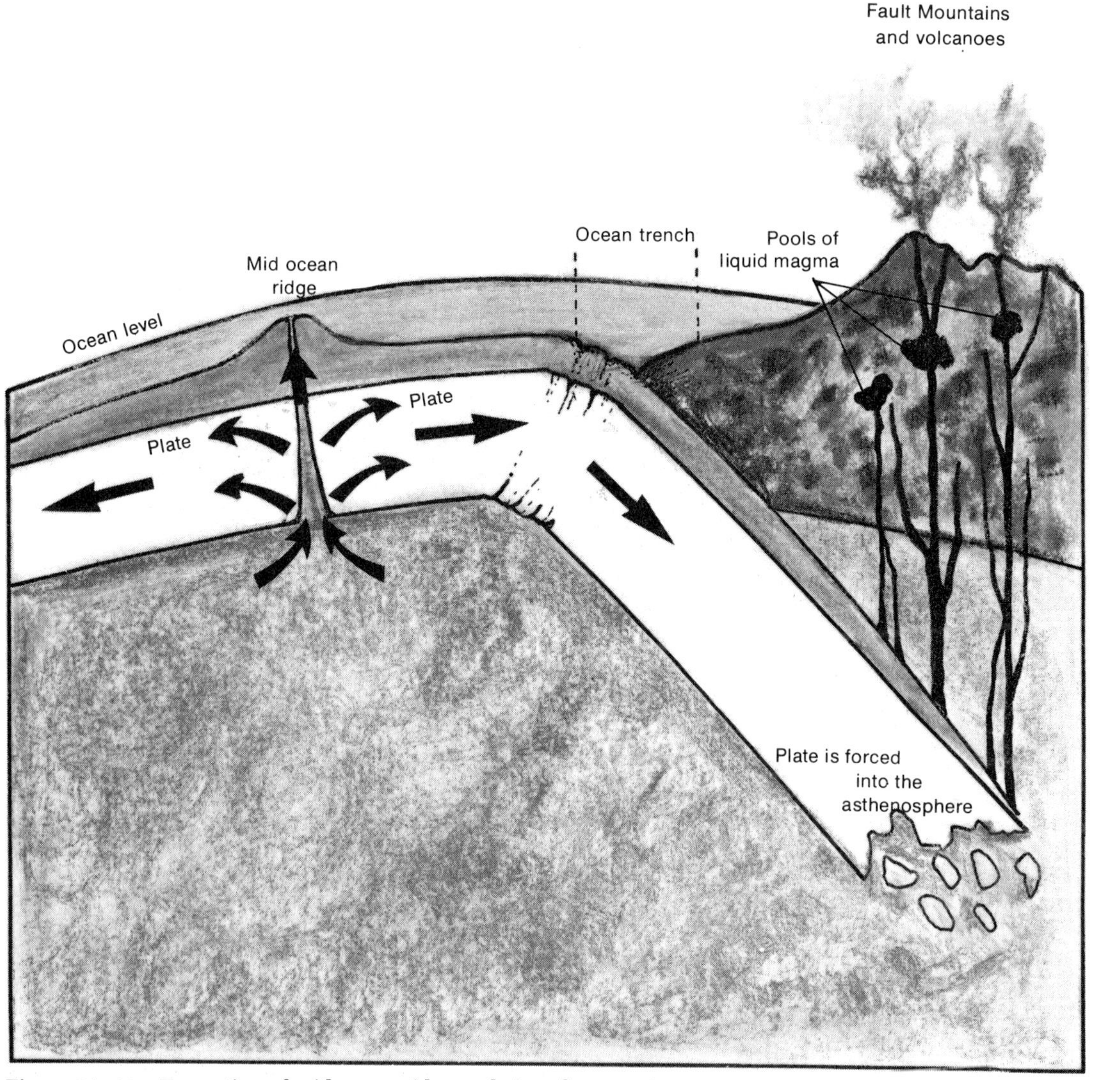

Figure 14–11. Formation of mid-ocean ridge and rise of mountains.

dous weight of the continental plates has forced segments of the oceanic plates to sink deep within the interior of the mantle. This process is called **subduction.** As the oceanic plates have been pushed downward, a deep trench has formed under the sea just west of the Andes. Geologists believe that the oceanic plates are being pushed so far downward that they are sinking into the asthenosphere, where rock is heated and slowly melted.

Thus, in summary, on the eastern boundary of the American plates, rock is moving upward from the mantle to the surface at the mid-Atlantic ridge. But if rock is oozing upward along one boundary, material must be forced downward at another. At the western edge of the American plates, the collision forces matter from the oceanic plates downward and back into the asthenosphere to complete the cycle.

However, not all plate movements can be explained in such a satisfying manner. For example, the African plate appears to be moving eastward away from the mid-Atlantic ridge, but there are no apparent places where neighboring plates are being forced downward.

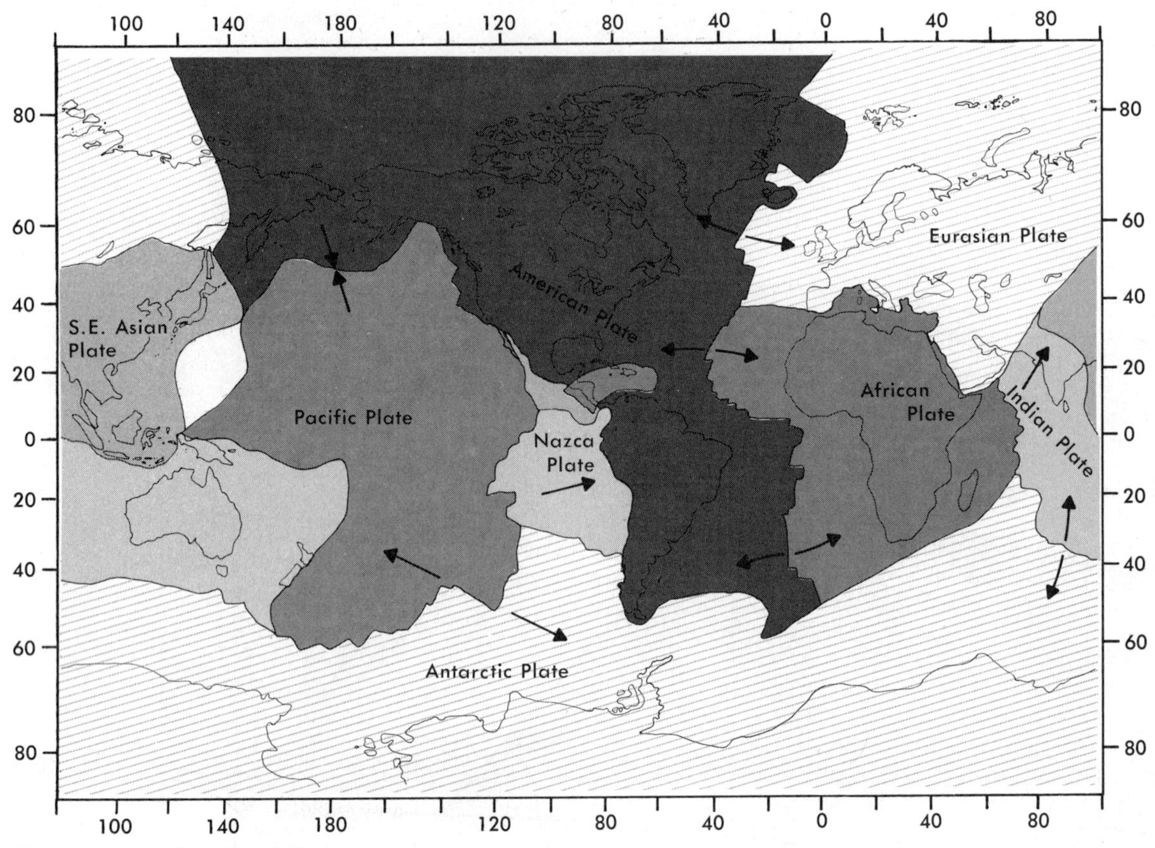

Figure 14–12. Tectonic plates.

Material flowing upward from the mantle must be balanced by crustal minerals being forced back downward, but geologists are not sure how this balance is achieved. Or, as another example, India is believed to be traveling northward and colliding with Eurasia (Fig. 14–13). Measurements indicate that the two continents collided 40 million years ago, and since the initial impact, India has continued to push northward for a distance of approximately 2000 km. Neither plate has been forced downward. Instead, they both have buckled upward and formed the Himalayan mountain range. But this buckling, by itself, cannot account for the material that must have been displaced as India traveled its full 2000 km. Imagine that you could roll the Himalayas flat with a giant rolling pin. India would be pushed back southward, but it wouldn't move as much as 2000 km. What has happened to the land that must have been displaced as India has moved northward into Eurasia? No one knows for sure. Some geologists theorize that Eurasia has spread apart, much as a block of wood or plastic might be deformed when hit with a sledge hammer.

Problem 2. What causes the plates to move, anyway? The crust is less dense than the asthenosphere; thus, the tectonic plates may be visualized as "floating" along the surface of the globe. One theory states that the asthenosphere may be heated unevenly, causing large convection currents to be established, as shown in Figure 14–14. The continents may then ride along these convection currents much as icebergs are carried long distances as they float on ocean currents. However, there are many incompletely answered questions in the development of this theory. For example, the crust is not a uniform layer but is thin under the oceans and much thicker under the continents. If this is true, the convection currents must rise and fall to fit these subterranean contours. Convection currents can in fact follow complex contours. This action is analogous to wind systems that pass over mountain ranges. The discovery of continental roots, therefore, does not rule out the existence of these currents. However, it indicates that motions of the mantle must necessarily be complex.

The slow motion of tectonic plates has significantly shaped the surface of the Earth. As mentioned earlier, the American plates have collided with oceanic plates to the west. The continental plates have risen, forming the Andes and the western mountains of North America. In turn, these mountains have influenced weather patterns considerably. Both the deserts and the snow-fed rivers that exist along the west coast of the American continent have all been formed indirectly by the slow creep of the continents themselves. Similarly, the Himalayan range was formed from the collision of the Indian subcontinent with Eurasia. Just south of the Himalayas lie the fertile monsoon-soaked plains of the Ganges River. But the mountains are a barrier that blocks the northward motion of the monsoon, and as a result, the high Tibetan Plateau is dry and semi-arid. The

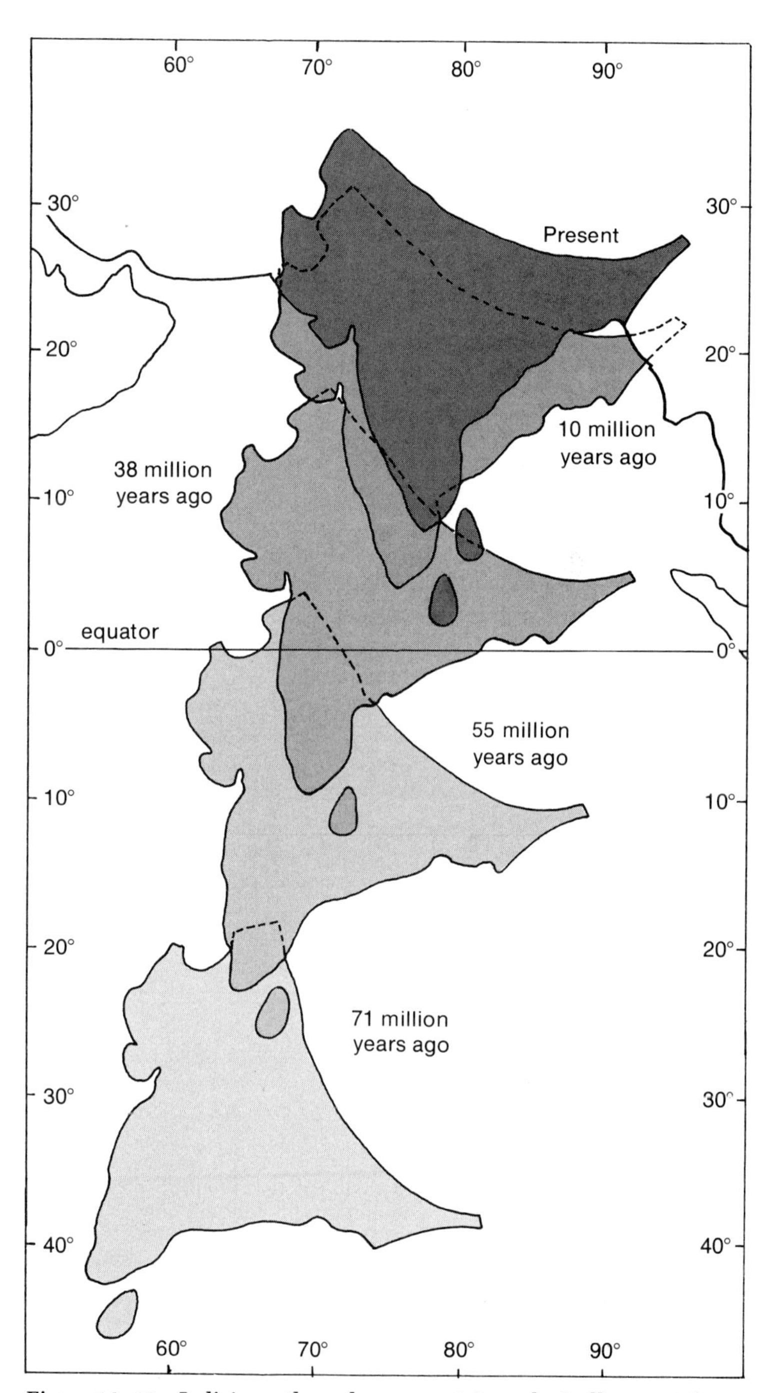

Figure 14–13. India's northward movement. In geologically recent times, the Indian subcontinent has collided with the Asian continent, creating the Himalayan mountain range.

Figure 14–14. One theory suggests that convection currents exist in the mantle and that the continents ride on these currents.

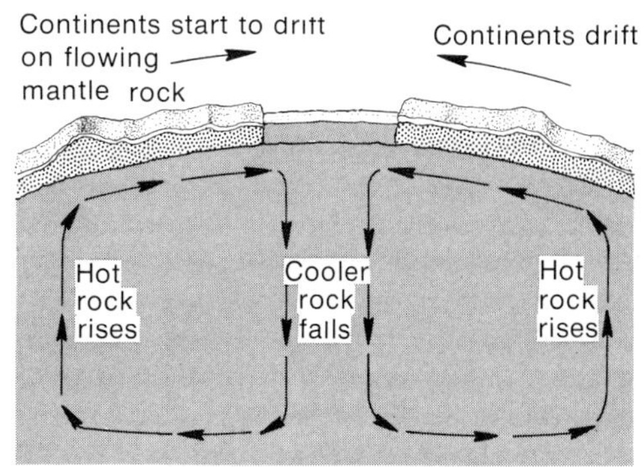

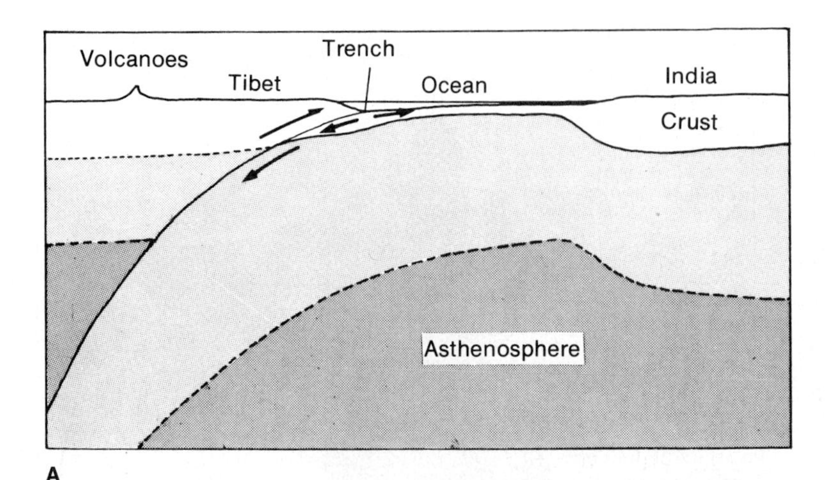

Formation of the Himalayas.
A, Geological condition as the Indian subcontinent approached Asia (about 20 million years ago.)
B, As India collided with Asia, land masses buckled upward to form the Himalayan mountains.

The Tibetan Plateau. National borders do not always follow geographical separations. The valley and mountain in this photograph now lie in northern India, although they are part of the Tibetan Plateau.

Local horsemen tying down their loads in a village high in the Himalayas in northern India.

dry and inhospitable Gobi Desert lies North of Tibet. The western part of the Gobi is surrounded on three sides by peaks 5000 m high. Here, fierce dry winds have piled waves of sand dunes 150 km long and 3 to 5 km apart from each other. North of the Gobi, there is a giant rift in the Eurasian continent. Part of the rift is filled with water, creating the deepest fresh water lake in the world, Lake Baikal, which is over 1800 m deep.

Another great rift system has been observed in east Africa. Many geophysicists believe that the African continent is cracking and splitting apart. Several million years ago, the Okavango River, flowing out of the Angolian highlands, emptied into the Indian Ocean; now it spreads out into the sands of the Kalahari Desert in a giant fresh water delta and marsh system hundreds of kilometers inland. Ninety-five per cent of the water evaporates into the air, and only a small stream flows out of the basin. Geologists believe that the rifting continent has lifted in places, blocking the Okavango's path to the sea and damming it to form the inland delta.

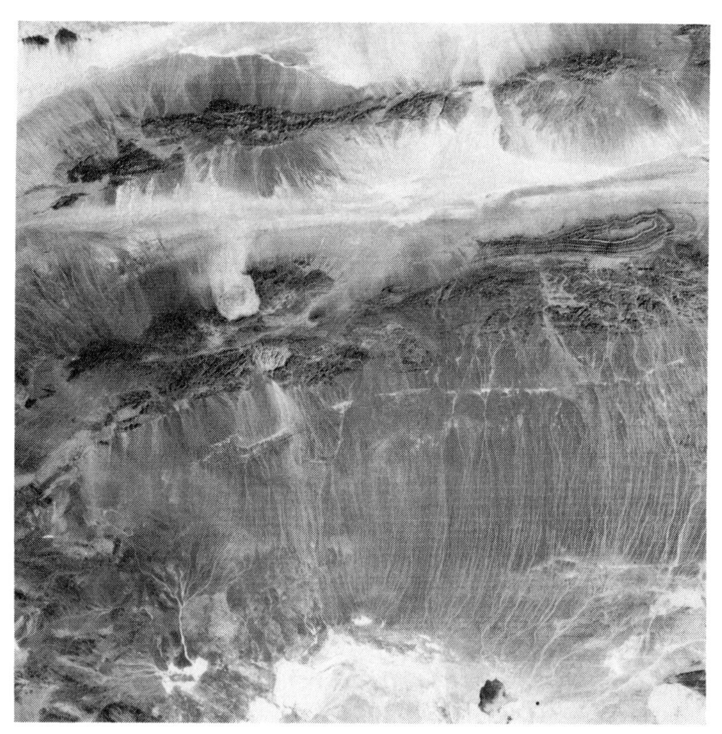

Satellite view of a portion of the Gobi Desert. Note the succession of parallel ridges formed by movement of wind and water. Courtesy of NASA Landstat.)

A satellite photograph of the Okavango delta. At one time, the Okavango River flowed into the sea, but then the Earth's crust split, rose, and dammed the river. Now the water spreads out, forming a large marsh that protrudes into the desert. (Courtesy of NASA Landstat.)

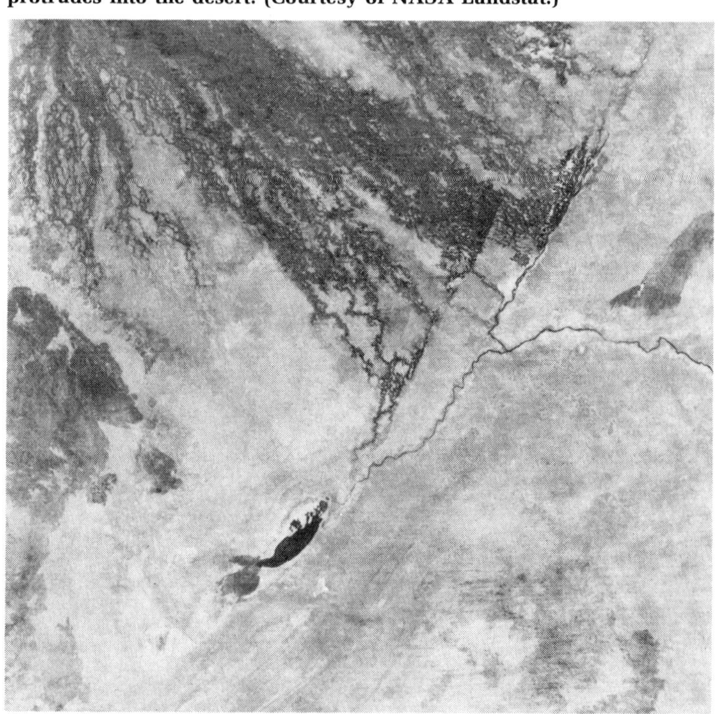

Impala approaching a waterhole in the Okavango delta region of southern Africa. (Photo by N. Myres, Bruce Coleman, Inc.)

14.6 EARTHQUAKES AND VOLCANOES

Earthquakes

In most parts of the Earth, the crust is whole and solid and is held together firmly. In some places, especially at the intersections of tectonic plates, there are weak points in the rock structure known as **faults.** Try to imagine the forces that operate on a fault formation. On one hand a large segment of land—perhaps a whole continent—is being pushed in a given direction. But other forces oppose this movement. Another continent may be pushing in the opposite direction, or alternatively, the frictional forces between the rock of adjacent tectonic plates may hold the continent stationary. Under certain conditions the tectonic plates will slowly slip past each other, creeping almost imperceptibly at a rate of a few centimeters a year. But sometimes the plates are held motionless even while they are being pushed. When this happens, tremendous stresses build up. Years and years may elapse without motion, until suddenly the stress becomes so great that it overcomes the friction, and rocks on either side of the fault move rapidly with respect to each other. The ground shakes, and the result is known as an **earthquake.**

From our knowledge of plate tectonics we can predict that earthquakes are not likely to occur randomly but are most frequent at the intersections of plates. Thus, there are distinct regions of earthquake activity on the face of the globe, as shown on the map in Figure 14–15.*

During some earthquakes, the land on one side of the fault may slide up and over, while the other side drops under as tectonic plates converge. In other cases, the plates may move in opposite horizontal directions. Both patterns are shown in Figure 14–16. The **San Andreas fault** in California is an example of an earthquake center of primarily horizontal movement. This major fault system stretches from the Gulf of California northward beyond San Francisco and out to sea. It is thought that this fault is caused by the collision of the North American continent with part of the Pacific Ocean floor.

Sometimes horizontal movement can be slow, gradual, and relatively

* It is possible for earthquakes to occur in other regions as well. Local geological conditions may cause fault formation and earthquakes, but most of the large ones occur in predictable regions.

This distortion of railroad tracks occurred during an earthquake, when segments of land slid horizontally past each other. (Courtesy of U.S. Geological Society.)

A section of Huaras, Peru, after the 1970 earthquake. (Courtesy of U.S. Geological Society).

non-violent. Such motion is known as **fault creep.** In several locations in California, buildings have been unintentionally located so that they straddle the great San Andreas fault right where creep is occurring. Slowly, the two pieces of earth slide past each other. Many tiny shakes and quakes occur, but none is severe enough to topple the buildings. However, as the earth on

Figure 14–15. Centers of earthquake activity.

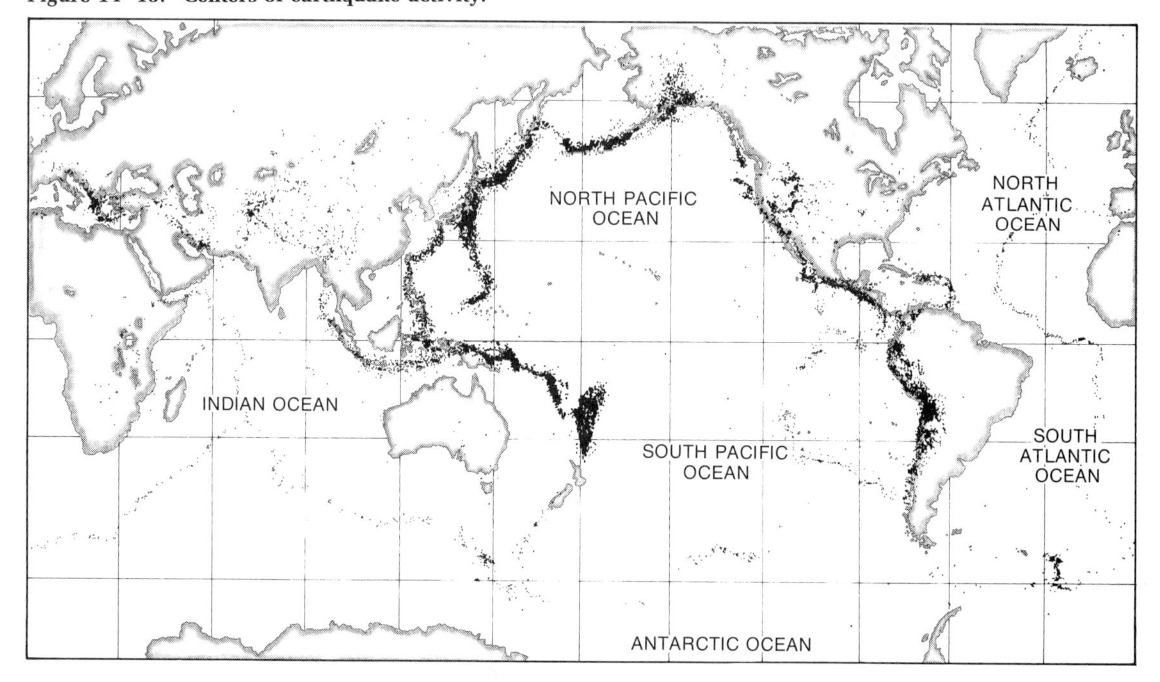

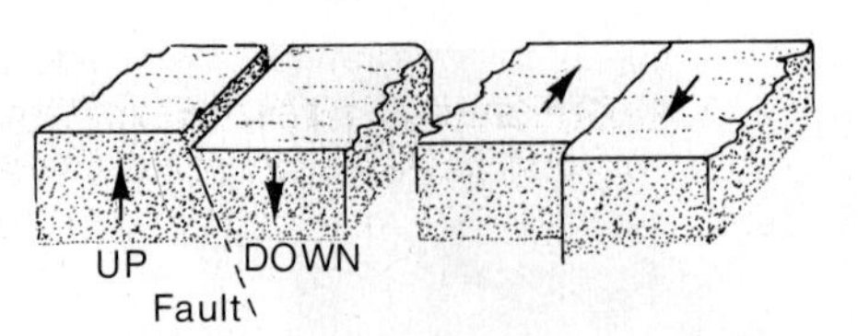

Figure 14–16. Earthquakes.

each side of the fault moves, it cracks the foundation until straight walls fracture and break apart.

Such gradual slippage can destroy a few buildings along the fault, but since there is no serious sudden movement, nearby buildings are not harmed. But if tectonic pressures build up too severely, sections of the Earth may move suddenly, resulting in a disastrous earthquake. For example, if part of a tectonic plate flows along at a rate

Historically and prehistorically active faults in San Francisco Bay region.

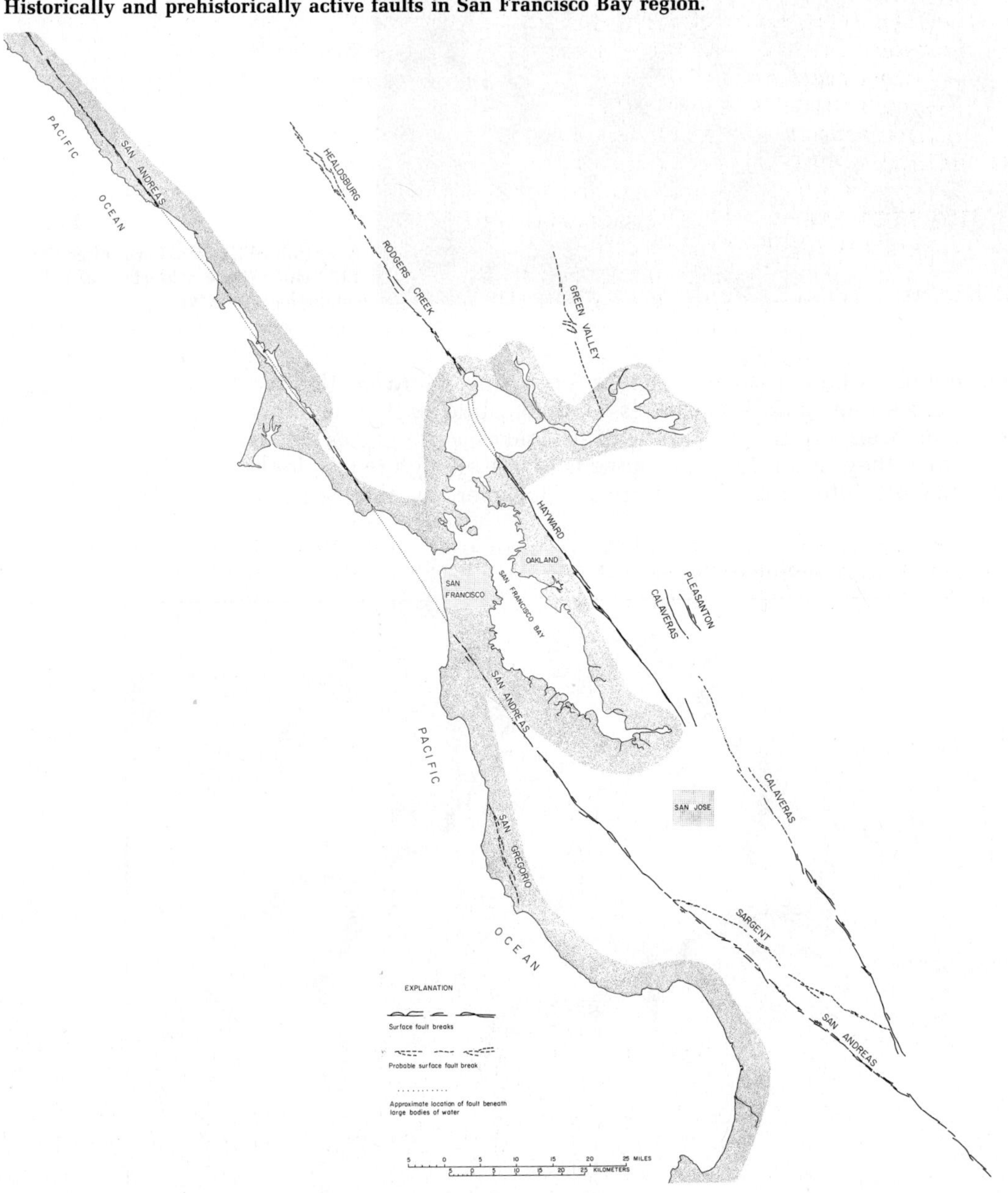

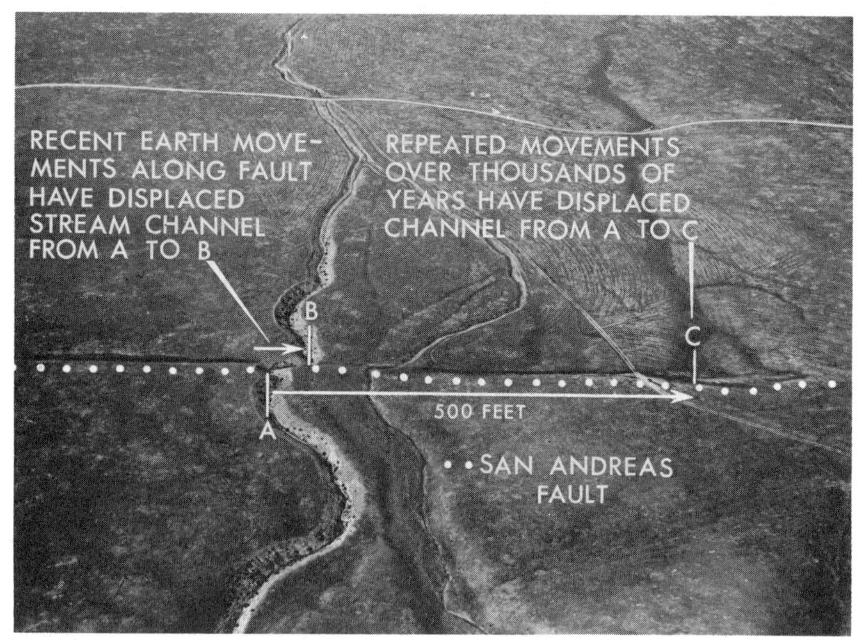

Horizontal movement of land along San Andreas fault. (Courtesy of U.S. Geological Society.)

of 5 cm a year, and another part is held rigid by frictional forces, the rock may stretch like a giant rubber band. Tremendous forces are involved. The slow stretch may accumulate for 100 years or more, when suddenly rock surfaces break loose and an earthquake occurs. A 5-cm stretch per year for 100 years would result in a total displacement of 5 m. In 1906, sections of rock near San Francisco jumped 4½ to 6 m in a matter of seconds and then abruptly came to a halt. Buildings were split and separated. Of course, in the city of San Francisco itself, disaster struck. The rapidly shifting rock caused the soil above it to move and settle. Many buildings whose foundations were anchored in soil toppled immediately. As buildings fell and underground gas lines were cut by

California earthquake, 1906. The wrecked Hibernia Bank building in San Francisco. (Photo by W. C. Mendenhall. Courtesy of U.S. Department of the Interior Geological Survey.)

moving earth, great fires were started. The fires spread throughout the city, causing widespread destruction that actually was more devastating than the effects of the quake itself.

Earthquakes are probably the most devastating of all natural phenomena. They generally strike without forewarning, destroying homes, apartment buildings, and sometimes even entire cities. In many regions of the world, lumber is scarce and people build their houses out of dried mud bricks called adobe. The roofs of these buildings are generally constructed of red clay tile. Adobe tile buildings are easily toppled by earthquakes, and millions of people have died in recent years when the heavy mud blocks have collapsed. Several summers ago, this author (Jon) was in Huaras, Peru, in the Andes mountains. Huaras is located in an extremely active earthquake zone, and entire towns have been destroyed in the region in recent decades. I asked a construction worker why no one built with wood, or used steel and reinforced concrete, so the buildings could withstand quakes. He shook his head and told me that everyone knew that their houses would fall in the event of an earthquake, and that many people would die, but local residents simply could not afford other construction materials. People simply hope that they will be lucky enough to be working in the fields if and when the next earthquake strikes.

Workers building an adobe house in an earthquake-prone region in South America. The men know that the house is vulnerable to earthquake activity but do not have the money to purchase other building materials.

If scientists could predict earthquake activity, people could be evacuated from unsafe buildings just before a potential disaster. Chinese geophysicists initiated a massive research program directed toward earthquake prediction. In late January, 1975, these scientists noted unusual motions of the subsurface rock layers near the city of Haichang and ordered a massive evacuation of the region. The evacuation was completed on the morning of February 4, and in the early evening of the same day, a large earthquake occurred. Houses, apartments, and factories were destroyed, but there were very few deaths.

Immediately after that success, many geologists optimistically hoped that a new era of quake prediction had begun. But, in 1976, Chinese geophysicists failed to predict an earthquake in Tangshan that killed approximately 650,000 people, and in many other regions of the world scientists have been unable to make accurate forecasts.

Some of the general principles of earthquake prediction are relatively well understood. If segments of the Earth's crust have moved significantly along one region of a large fault system but other regions have remained stationary, then the rock that has not moved will be stressed, as mentioned previously. These stressed regions are likely to crack, fracture, and move in the near future. As an example, earthquake activity has caused the rock to shift all along the coast of Alaska, with the exception of the gap regions shown in Figure 14–17. Geologists have concluded that the stress must be high in this gap region and earthquake probability likely. On February 28, 1979, a large earthquake struck the eastern border of the gap located near the city of Valdez. Many scientists feel that a quake is now likely in the Valdez area. There is significant environmental concern because Valdez is the southern terminal of the Alaskan pipeline. Huge storage tanks hold great quantities of crude oil, loaded supertankers are sailing southward out of the port, and, of course, oil is flowing through the pipeline itself. When will

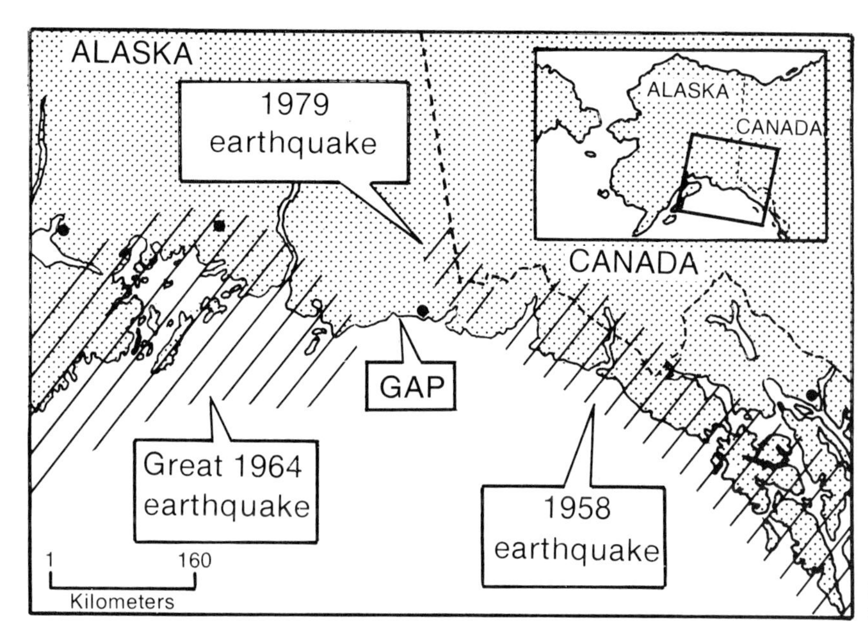

Figure 14–17. Recent earthquake activity on the south coast of Alaska.

the quake occur? In the spring of 1979, geologist William McCann, who has studied the region, stated, "These patterns indicate that a quake may occur in about 20 years. But, in fact, it may be much longer. It could be another 20 to 40 years. But we would not be at all surprised if it were tomorrow."

After an earthquake has occurred along an active earthquake zone, tectonic stresses will start to build up again. Several decades or even a century later, another quake is likely in the same region. According to this reckoning, southern California, the San Francisco Bay area, central Japan, central Chile, Taiwan, the west coast of Sumatra, and parts of the west coast of Mexico are all threatened by major disasters in the near future. But what is meant by near? A week? A month? Ten years? Another century? No one knows for sure. Of course, it would be impractical to evacuate Los Angeles in anticipation of a quake that may strike in 25 years!

Many scientists have theorized that a large quake is preceded by many small ones. As an analogy, if you try to break a stick by bending it slowly, you may hear a few small cracking sounds just before the final snap. However, an analysis of data shows that only about half of the major earthquakes in recent years were preceded by small shocks. Other scientists have concluded that fault creep is a natural means of relieving stress. They say that if rock surfaces slide by each other gradually, severe stress will not build up, and an earthquake will not occur. Therefore, a quake is not likely to occur in active creep zones, and the danger points are those which lie along known faults but are presently immobile. However, others disagree and argue that fault creep, like small quakes, is simply a signal that should warn us of impending disaster. Until scientists are able to answer these and other complex questions, earthquake prediction will not be reliable.

Volcanoes

Perhaps the most spectacular and rapid geological event occurring on Earth is a volcanic eruption, which occurs when hot molten magma moves upward through fissures in the rocks and escapes as fiery lava on the surface. The eruption is generally accompanied by the release of large quantities of steam and other gases. Sometimes

A, A relatively mild volcanic eruption (Mount Ngauruhoe, New Zealand, 2290 m. In many parts of the world, such eruptions do not interfere with nearby human activities, such as farming. (Photo by Lionel Green.) *B,* A violent eruption of Mount Vesuvius. Mount Vesuvius erupted in the year 79 A.D. At that time its lava, ashes, and fumes destroyed the nearby cities of Pompeii and Herculaneum. (Photo by Frederic Lewis, Inc.)

magma is ejected in relatively calm lava flows, while in other instances, violently explosive eruptions occur. Mauna Loa, a towering mountain that rises above the sea to form the second highest peak on the island of Hawaii, has erupted in modern times, but the non-violence of these events has enabled people to work and farm only kilometers from the volcanic crater. When the mountain becomes active, masses of molten rock flow smoothly out of a central crater and down the sides of the mountain until they cool and solidify. These frequent gentle lava flows have gradually accumulated to form the mountain, which rises 4500 m from the ocean floor to the surface of the sea and another 4200 m above that. From ocean floor to summit, Mauna Loa is about as tall as Mount Everest.

Not all volcanoes are so gentle, however. In the early 1800's the island of Krakatoa in Indonesia was a landmark for clipper ships that carried tea and other freight from India. The mountain on the center of the island was conical, covered with trees, and rose nearly 800 m above sea level. On August 26, 1883, a huge volcanic explosion rocked the island. The crew of a ship sailing offshore witnessed an immense cloud of dust, ash, and steam that darkened the horizon. Lightning storms and intense squalls developed as the sailors headed out to sea to escape the violence. On the next day four more great explosions rocked the island, and when the dust had cleared away, the island of Krakatoa and its 800 m mountain had disappeared. A few tiny islets remained on what had been the rim of the former island, but the rest was gone. It is believed that a crack appeared in the crust of the Earth and approximately 20 km^3 of volcanic material shot skyward. As the exploding lava shot into the air, a huge hole appeared in the center of the island, and when the lava flow subsided, the mountain had collapsed into this hole and disappeared into the basin under the sea (see Fig. 14–18).

All volcanic eruptions occur when molten magma forms in the interior of the Earth and moves up to the surface through fissures in the rock. The violence of the eruption is controlled by factors such as the chemical composition of magma, its temperature, the shape and size of the fissures, and the quantity of gas in the fluid mixture. If the lava is thick and viscous and if large amounts of gas are trapped in the molten rock, eruptions are likely to be violent. The viscous lava will not flow easily and is prevented from moving upward until the gaseous pressure pushes it out with explosive violence. On the other hand, the magma of a gentle volcano such as Mauna Loa is more fluid and contains comparatively less steam. The fluid lava moves upward and out of rock fissures easily, and, as there is little steam, extreme pressures never develop.

Volcanoes have played a vital role in the evolution of planetary atmospheres and of life itself. When solid planets such as Earth, Venus, and Mars were originally formed, various gases were trapped in the rocky interiors. Many of these gases, compounds of hydrogen, carbon, nitrogen, oxygen, and sulfur, were released during volcanic eruptions. As discussed in the previous chapter, the volcanic gases accumulated to form an atmosphere on each planet, and on Earth, some of them combined to form amino acids, proteins, and living organisms.

Figure 14–18. The collapse of a mountain.

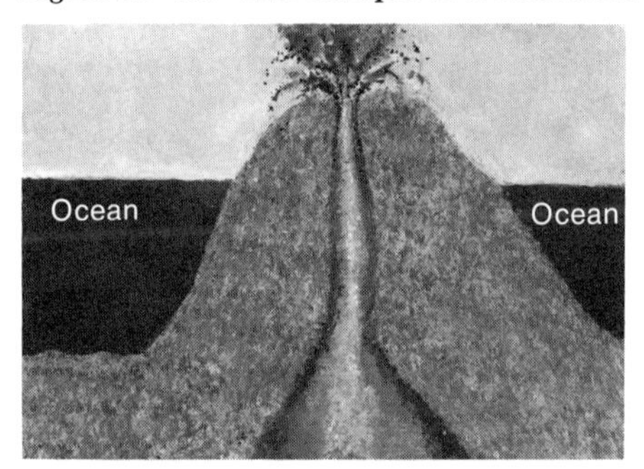

A Volcano erupts

B Crater widens

C Mountain falls inward on itself

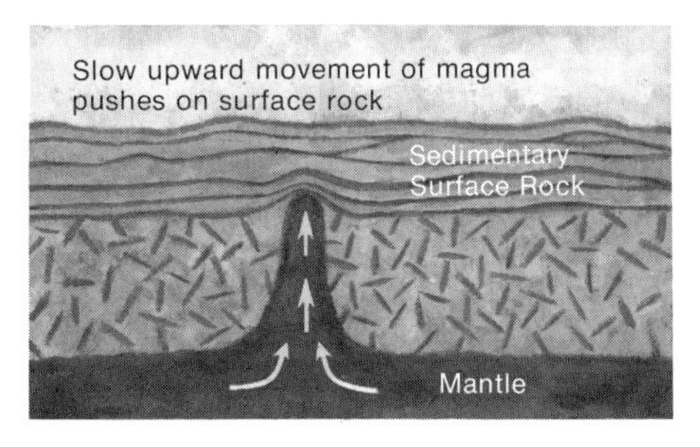

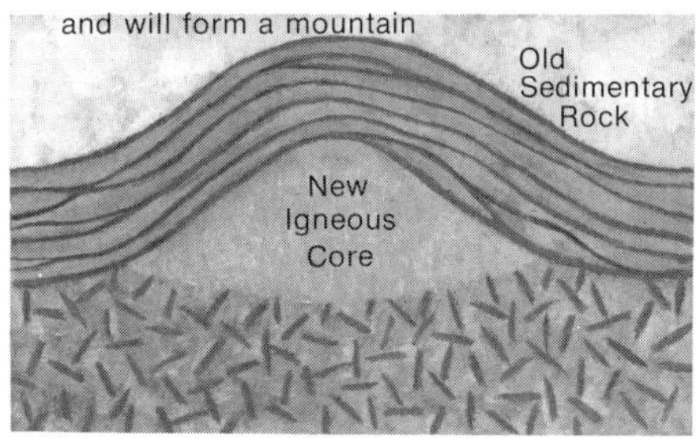

Sometimes magma intrusions do not erupt into a volcano but slowly push upwards against surface rocks to form mountains.

14.7 WEATHERING AND EROSION

Millions or tens of millions of years are required for rock to form, distort, and rise upward to become a mountain range. During this time the rock is exposed to many different kinds of surface forces. These forces, acting collectively, remove small pieces of rock and carry them downslope. The wearing away and removal of material from the Earth's surface occurs in two stages. First, the rock is broken into small fragments by various chemical and mechanical processes. The deterioration of rock into small pieces is called **weathering.** The small bits of rock and soil are then carried away by the action of running water, glacial ice, winds, and waves. This movement of material is called **erosion.**

Chemical Weathering

Air and water, especially when carrying impurities, may be corrosive and therefore can react with many types of rocks and minerals. For example, pure iron is a hard strong metal. But there are no natural deposits of pure iron near the surface of the Earth.

A section of Carlsbad Cavern, New Mexico. These passageways and huge rooms were formed as underground streams weathered the rock formations and eroded sections away. (Courtesy of U.S. Geological Society.)

As the Earth's crust was being formed, any iron in contact with atmospheric oxygen reacted to form loose flaky compounds called iron oxides, which are chemically equivalent to rust. The conversion of a hard abrasion-resistant material (iron) to a softer flaky one (rust) is an example of weathering.

Water is another chemically active substance. Many minerals dissolve to some extent in pure water; a few, such as sodium chloride (used commonly as table salt), are highly soluble. But water never exists in nature in its purest state. Even distilled water contains dissolved air, which includes two important reactive components—oxygen (O_2) and carbon dioxide (CO_2). Dissolved oxygen is an oxidizing agent; thus a nail rusts when it is under water. Dissolved carbon dioxide reacts with water to form an acidic solution. Thus rainwater is slightly acidic and therefore slightly corrosive. This solution is capable of dissolving many types of rocks and therefore carries mineral matter to the ocean. Other corrosive impurities may enter water systems from a large variety of sources. For example, sulfur compounds present in polluted air or in certain natural rock formations dissolve in water to form strongly acidic solutions. In many industrial regions of the world atmospheric pollutants have mixed with airborne water droplets to such an extent that the rainfall is acidic enough to kill fish in small streams and ponds and corrode statues and buildings. Salt from ocean spray, oxides of nitrogen from combustion or lightning, and many other substances may all dissolve in water and enhance its corrosiveness.

Mechanical Weathering

Rocks can also be broken apart by purely mechanical processes such as expansion and abrasion. Most liquids contract when cooled and shrink even more when they freeze. Water is anomalous—it expands when it freezes. Thus if water drips into a crack in the rock and then freezes, the resultant expansion will act to push the rock apart. If you ever climb in a high mountain range in the spring or early summer, when water freezes at night and thaws during the day, be careful; mountains come alive with falling rocks. You can stand in a narrow valley and listen as the debris tumbles off the high cliffs.

Plant roots also can crack rocks by expansion. If a little bit of soil collects in a fissure in solid rock, a seed may fall there and start to grow. The roots will then work their way down into the rock. As the plant grows and the roots expand, they push the rock apart just as ice does.

Have you ever walked along a stream bed or ocean beach and looked at the rocks lying in or near the water? If you have, you might have noticed that many are rounded or smooth. They have been broken down and abraded by the action of moving water. Pure water, by itself, has little abrasive power, but when water is moving rapidly it picks up bits and pieces of silt and sand. When these small particles are hurled against the rocks, the solid material is gradually ground away. During storms and floods, fist-sized stones or even large boulders are pushed by the violent water, and as they tumble along and rub against each other, small bits are broken off and ground into sand. Over long periods of time the erosive action of streams or rivers can reshape huge land masses. In Utah and Arizona, the Colorado River has dug tremendous trenches below the level of uplifted plains to form the Grand Canyon and its tributaries. Ocean waves are also abrasive. They can carve away significant portions of a sandstone cliff in a single winter storm.

The roots of this tree have cracked this large boulder apart. Root action is a powerful weathering agent. (Photo by Grant Lashbrook.)

Rapidly moving water is a powerful force that erodes mountains and hillsides.

Ocean waves break rocks into small fragments (weathering) and carry the small particles away (erosion).

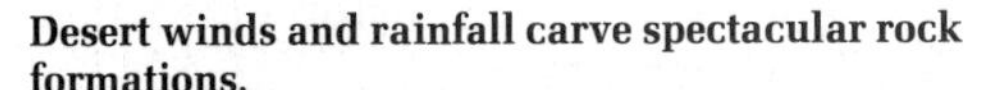

Desert winds and rainfall carve spectacular rock formations.

wind. If purely gaseous air blows against a rocky mountainside it will have little effect. But if small pieces of dust, silt, and sand are suspended in the air and are blown against the rocks by wind action, they will chip away at the solid material. In desert regions, where there is little running water, erosion by wind is particularly significant and produces spectacular land formations.

In high mountains and near polar regions, the snow that falls in winter never melts completely during the summer months and therefore accumulates from year to year. As the snow is compressed by the layers of material above it, it gradually turns to ice. When the ice builds to considerable thickness it becomes quite massive and moves slowly downslope. Such a formation is known as a **glacier.** Huge glacial deposits of ice exist in many parts of the Earth. In Greenland the ice layer is 3000 m thick, while in Antarctica the ice cap measures 4000 m in certain locations. Mountain glaciers are much smaller, sometimes being as thin as 60 to 90 m. When ice near the bottom of a glacier is subjected to the weight of thousands of tons of ice above, it takes on unusual properties and flows slowly, like a semifluid plastic. For this reason, large glaciers travel downslope toward the sea, floating, as it were, on a layer of cold, fluid material. Glaciers are particularly powerful and grind the rocks beneath them. As the glacier flows downhill, it picks up pieces of rock and soil, small stones, and even huge boulders weighing many tons. When this solid material is dragged seaward, it carves huge valleys and shapes mountains or even continents.

Erosion

Once rock has been weathered, small pieces of it can be carried away by some moving substance, such as running water, wind, or glacial ice. Erosion is the process whereby weathered material is transported. Bare soil is particularly vulnerable to erosion. If the vegetation is cut from a hillside, then even a single rainstorm will carry large quantities of earth downhill. Mil-

with inorganic sediment and compressed for hundreds of thousands of years, a small coal deposit will develop. However, most modern swamps are poor coal producers. It is estimated that a layer of compressed organic debris 12 m thick is required to produce a 1-m layer of coal. For a layer this large to accumulate, conditions must be favorable and stable in a region for a great many years. Coal deposits probably are being formed today in many areas, notably in the Ganges River delta in India, but the process is extremely slow—much, much slower than the exploitation of existing reserves. Therefore, since we cannot expect formation of new deposits to keep pace with use, we have all the more reason to conserve our present reserves.

Oil and gas are also organic deposits, but we think that these fuels were formed from tiny marine microorganisms rather than from the debris of large plants. As microscopic sea creatures settled to the bottom of the ocean and were later covered with mineral sediment, tiny droplets of body oils were squeezed out of each organism. If the rock formation was favorable, this oil was trapped into large deposits and altered chemically by heat and pressure until petroleum was formed.

Farming in rich soil.

14.9 SOIL

Rock is a poor medium to support the growth of plants. Plants need a continuous supply of minerals, water, and sunlight. Although an organism growing on rock may be exposed to adequate sunlight, the minerals are generally bound chemically into the structure of the rock and are not readily accessible, and water runs off the surface and is gone soon after a rainstorm has passed. When rock is cracked and broken into tiny pieces by various weathering processes, the resultant material becomes sand, silt, or clay, depending on the size of the various particles. These inorganic mixtures are also unsatisfactory for maintaining a healthy and diverse plant community. True soil, which does support vigorous plant growth, is an intimate mixture of pulverized rock and organic debris. The organic matter contains many nutrients necessary for plant growth. For example, plants need nitrogen for the synthesis of protein and therefore cannot grow without an adequate supply. Although nitrogen is plentiful in the air, it exists as the gaseous element N_2, and most plants cannot convert N_2 to protein. Instead, plants need certain nitrogen compounds, such as ammonia or nitrates, found in soil and water. Pure silica sand, SiO_2, contains no nitrogen, and thus, without a source of this essential nutrient in a usable form, most plants cannot grow. However, fertile soil contains available nitrogen compounds as part of the organic component. These materials are introduced to soil by a variety of processes. Some bacteria, including those that live on the roots of peas, beans, and alfalfa, have the ability to utilize free nitrogen and convert it to usable nitrogen compounds. These organisms therefore represent an important asset to a plant community. Once nitrogen is incorporated into proteins and introduced into the soil, it can be recycled many times, as shown in Figure 14–20. For example, rotting leaves and animal urine contain ammonia, NH_3. The nitrogen in ammonia is bound in a chemical form that is readily assimilated by almost all plants for the synthesis of protein.

In addition to being a rich source of vital nutrients, soil plays an important role in the regulation of essential plant processes. Plants need soil with properly regulated nutrients, density, moisture, salinity, and acidity. Soil conditions have traditionally been regulated by the **humus,** a very complex mixture of compounds resulting from the decomposition of plant tissue. A given piece of tissue, such as a leaf or a stalk of grass, is considered to be humus rather than debris when it has decomposed sufficiently in the soil system so that it is no longer recognizable. Compared to inorganic soil, humic soil is physically lighter, it holds moisture better, and it is more effectively balanced against rapid changes of acidity. Additionally, certain chemicals present in humus aid the transfer and retention of nutrients. For example, calcium ions, Ca^{2+}, can exist in water solutions from which they are available to plants. However, atmospheric carbon dioxide reacts with water to form carbonate ion, CO_3^{2-}, which reacts with calcium in water to form the sparingly soluble compound, calcium carbonate, $CaCO_3$.

$$Ca^{2+} + CO_3^{2-} \rightarrow CaCO_3$$

Calcium ion + carbonate ion →

calcium carbonate

Plant roots cannot absorb calcium efficiently from calcium carbonate. However, calcium ions may also react with certain organic compounds, called **chelates,** in the humus to form organic calcium complexes which will be denoted as calcium^{+2}-chelate. Plant roots can readily absorb the calcium from

Figure 14–20. Pathways whereby nitrogen is removed from and returned to the soil (nitrogen cycle).

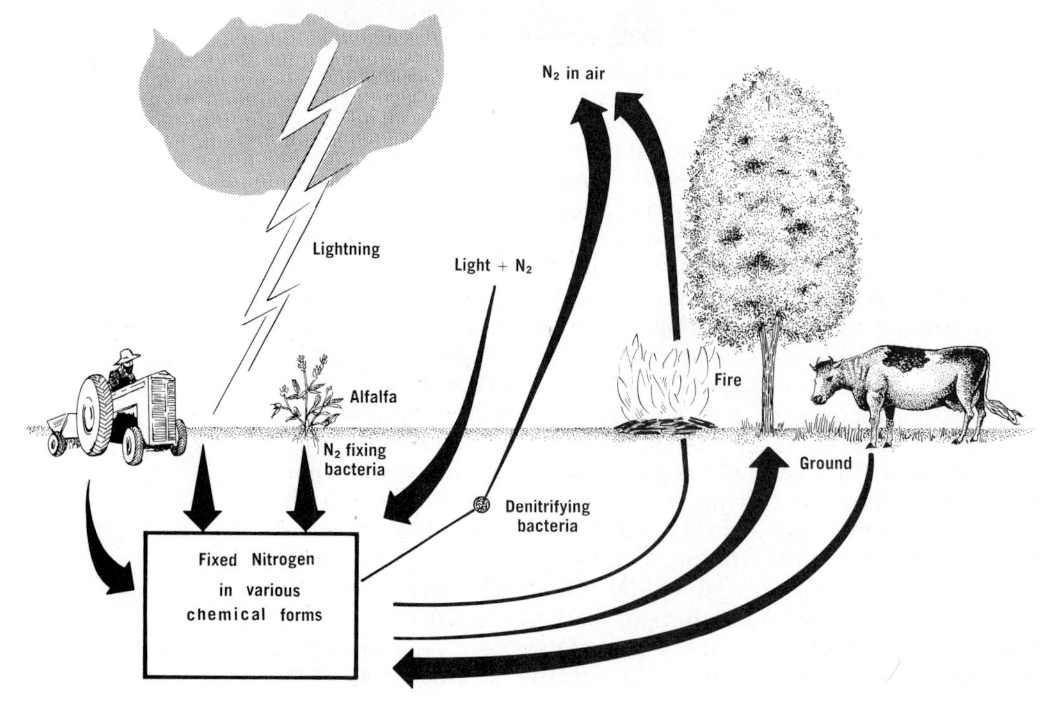

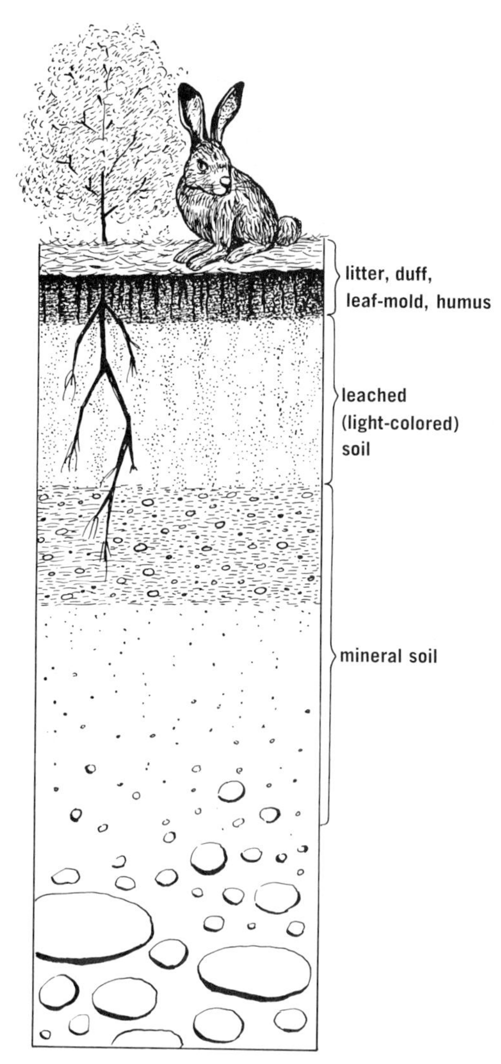

Cross-section of forest soil.

Cross-section of forest soil.

these organic complexes. Thus, two possible fates of calcium in the soil are

Calcium + carbonate →

calcium carbonate
(relatively inaccessible to plants)

Calcium + chelate →

calcium^{+2}-chelate
(relatively accessible to plants)

Thus, the organic components of the soil tend to react with various ions and retain them in a form that is easily absorbed by plant roots and utilized in the growing systems.

We will see in the next chapter that depletion of humus by shortsighted agricultural practices is threatening the

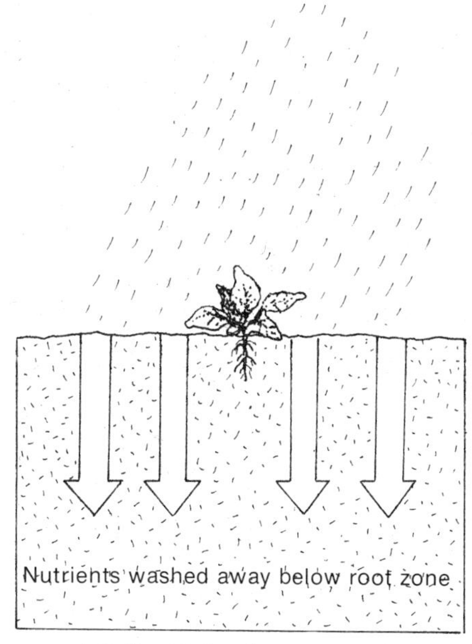

***A* Soil with low humus content**

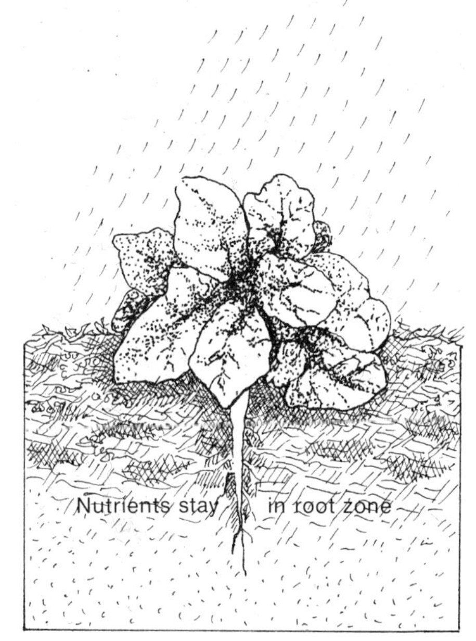

***B* Soil with high humus content**

Humus helps retain nutrients in the soil.

productivity of billions of hectares of fertile farmland.

14.10 EPILOGUE

Geology covers a wide range of topics, from the formation and shaping of the Earth's crust and the long-term cycling of mineral matter, to the development and chemistry of soil. Some geological events, such as earthquakes and volcanoes, occur quite rapidly, while others, such as continental drift, are so slow that they are barely measurable. The net result of all the changes is that our Earth is filled with beauty and diversity, and much of it is a pleasant and hospitable place for life.

CHAPTER OBJECTIVES

Understand the following:

The structure of the Earth.

The Earth's magnetism.

The rock cycle.

Plate tectonics, continental drift and how drift has been a driving force for the creation of many major land forms of the Earth.

Earthquakes and volcanoes and the relationships between these phenomena and continental drift.

The difference between weathering and erosion and the major types of forces that are responsible for each of these processes.

How mineral and fossil fuel deposits were formed.

The nature of soil, and how it differs from finely ground sand.

KEY WORDS

Core (of the Earth)
Mantle
Asthenosphere
Crust
Seismology
Magma
Lava
Igneous rock
Sediments
Sedimentary rock
Metamorphism
Metamorphic rock
Continental drift
Tectonic plates
Plate tectonics
Subduction
Mid-Atlantic ridge
Earthquake
Fault
Fault creep
Volcano
Weathering
Erosion
Placer deposits
Coal
Soil
Humus

TAKE-HOME EXPERIMENTS

1. **Flow.** There are several readily available materials that appear to be solid but tend to flow slowly as a liquid. In this respect their behavior is analogous to that of the material in the plastic layer of the Earth's mantle. Two such solids are road tar and Silly Putty, a commercial product available in many toy stores. Take some tar or Silly Putty and place it in a small pan so that you have a layer about 5 cm thick. Now place one penny on the Silly Putty near one end of the pan, and a stack of seven pennies on the putty near the other end. (Glue the seven pennies together so that the stack doesn't fall over.) Observe what happens after 5 minutes, 5 days, 2 weeks. Discuss.

2. **Weathering and erosion.** Find a place near your home or school where you can observe the effects of weathering and erosion. Describe what is happening, and, if possible, photograph the site. What agent (wind, ice, water, etc.) is causing the breakdown and removal of material? Collect samples of the rock or soil as it appears before being perturbed, and then collect samples of the sediment that is being carried away. Compare the textures of the two materials. In your example is the weathering or erosion directly harmful to humans and their activities? Discuss.

3. **Sand and soil.** Fold two pieces of filter paper as shown in the accompanying sketch, and place one in each of two funnels. Fill one funnel with dry sand and another with dry

How to make a filter.

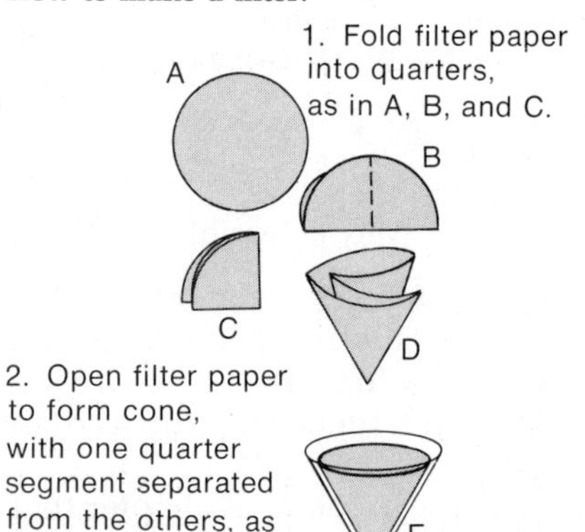

ENVIRONMENTAL GEOLOGY

15.1 THE LIVING EARTH—ECOSYSTEMS

No machine can perform as many different functions as a living organism. Animals and plants, unlike machines, can feed and repair themselves, adjust to a changing environment, and reproduce. These abilities depend on complex interactions among the separate parts of the organism. Each mammal, for instance, is far more than an independent collection of brain, heart, liver, stomach, and other organs. What affects one part of the body affects its entirety.

Even with all its built-in mechanisms of life, however, an individual plant or animal cannot exist as an isolated individual. It is dependent upon its physical and biological environment for survival. It must utilize some source of energy (food or light), ingest water and nutrients, dispose of wastes, and maintain a favorable temperature.

Plants and animals occurring together, plus that part of their physical environment with which they interact, constitute an **ecosystem.** An ecosystem is defined to be nearly self-contained, so that the matter which flows into and out of it is small compared to the quantities that are internally recycled in a continuous exchange of the essentials of life. The dynamics of the flow of energy and materials in a given geological environment, as well as the adaptation made by the plants and animals to find a place within the environment, constitute the subject matter of the **ecology** of natural systems.

Ecosystems vary widely with respect to size, location, weather patterns, and the types of animals and plants included. A watershed in New Hampshire, a Syrian desert, the Arctic Ice Cap, and Lake Michigan are all distinct ecosystems. Common to them all is a set of processes. All plants and animals need energy to survive. Green-leafed plants are able to utilize some of the energy in sunlight and transform it into chemical energy. This process is known as **photosynthesis.**

$$\text{Carbon dioxide} + \text{water} + \text{sunlight} \xrightarrow{\text{plants}} \text{sugar} + \text{oxygen}$$

Alpine ecosystem, San Juan mountains, Colorado.

Short-grass prairie ecosystem in North America.

Animals and some plants cannot obtain chemical energy from sunlight directly. Rather they eat plants or other animals and use the energy stored in their tissues. This process is called **respiration.**

$$\text{Sugar} + \text{oxygen} \xrightarrow[\text{animals}]{\text{plants and}} \text{water} + \text{carbon dioxide} + \text{energy}$$

Energy alone is insufficient to support life. Imagine, for example, that some aquatic plants such as algae were sealed into a sterilized jar of pure water and exposed to adequate sunlight. The process of photosynthesis, which utilizes the atmospheric carbon dioxide and releases oxygen, would not be balanced by the plants' own respiration, and soon the plants would starve for lack of carbon dioxide. If the experi-

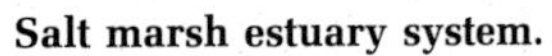

Salt marsh estuary system.

menter maintained the proper atmosphere through some gas-supply and exhaust lines, the plants still would not survive. They would starve for lack of the chemicals necessary for life. Suppose, then, that the experimenter fertilized the jar with the proper inorganic chemicals, which had been sterilized to ensure that no additional living organisms entered the system. The plants would grow, and the cells that died in the normal processes of life would accumulate. Soon there would be no more room to introduce new fertilizer, and, unless the jar were enlarged, the fertilization would have to be stopped and the algae would die. The jar might be stabilized indefinitely, however, if some plant-consumer, a snail for example, were introduced, and the pure water were replaced by pond water to supply inorganic nutrients and decay organisms. Assuming an initially balanced ratio of snails to algae, the jar would now perhaps become a balanced, stable ecosystem, in which the nutrients would be continuously recycled. The algae use water, carbon dioxide, sunlight, and dissolved nutrients to support life and build tissue. Oxygen is one major waste product of algae and at the same time is an essential requirement of snails and other aquatic animals.

In general, plants produce more food than they need. This overproduction allows animals to eat parts of the plants, thus obtaining energy-rich sugars and other compounds. These compounds, in turn, are broken down during respiration, a process that uses oxygen and releases carbon dioxide. Other animal waste products, such as urine, though relatively energy-poor, are consumed by microorganisms in the pond water. The waste products of the microorganisms are even simpler molecules that can be reused by the algae as a source of raw materials. The consumption of dead tissue by aquatic microorganisms is essential both as a means of recycling raw materials and for waste disposal. The interaction among the various living species permits the community of the jar to survive indefinitely. In fact, biology laboratories have sealed aquariums in which life has survived for a decade or

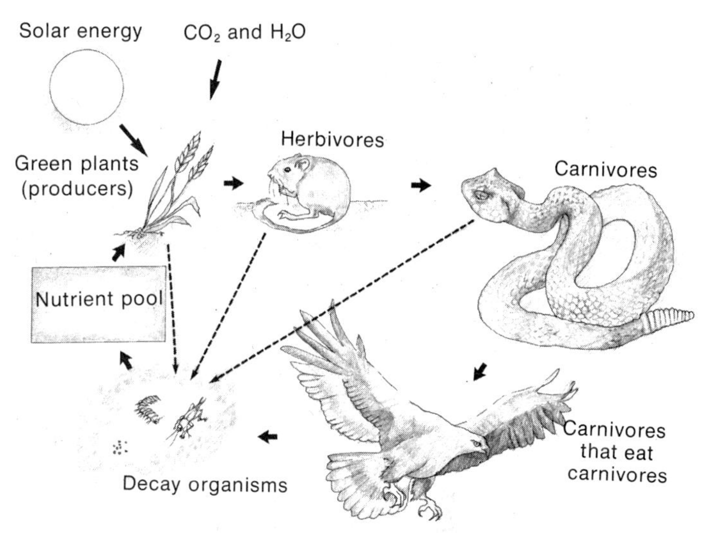

Figure 15–1. Simplified model of a terrestrial ecosystem.

more. We would like to stress that the picture presented of this cycle has been greatly simplified. Cycles that occur in nature are so complicated that they are not fully understood today.

The Earth itself can be considered to be a sealed jar, for although it receives a continuous supply of energy from outside, it exchanges very little matter with the rest of the Universe. Thus, for all practical purposes, life started on this planet with a fixed supply of raw materials. There are finite quantities of each of the known elements. The chemical form and physical location of each element can be changed, but the quantity cannot.

This statement does not apply to radioactive elements, which are discussed separately in Chapter 10.

The substances produced by living organisms are widely varied. First, there are wastes associated with the act of living. Plants produce more oxygen than their life processes require; animals exhale carbon dioxide. However, organisms themselves can be viewed as products. A tree produces leaves, twigs, a trunk; a lion produces bones, a mane, a tail. All these parts of an organism, indeed the entire organism, when it is either living or dead, is a product that can be consumed by other organisms.

Over long periods of time, waste products must be recycled efficiently for ecosystems to survive. Thus, if many trees in a forest die from some disease epidemic, the populations of decay organisms will flourish and consume the dead wood. Once most of the organic material has been decomposed, the populations of decay organisms will decline. Similarly, if rainfall is adequate, and the grasses in a prairie-grassland system grow to be strong and healthy, the populations of such grazing animals as grasshoppers, mice, or bison will increase; however, during times of drought, when there is little food, many of the animals will migrate, die, or fail to reproduce rapidly. Mature ecosystems are generally balanced so that nutrients are all recycled. Of course, this balance is sometimes disrupted. For example, formations of coal deposits are the remains of ancient swamp systems that did not rot completely. In addition, flood, drought, fire, and population explosions often temporarily disrupt the normal balance of ecosystems.

A sluglike nudibranch crawling over encrusting sponges, which are also inhabited by sea anemones. (Photo by Harold Wes Pratt.)

Oxygen, nitrogen, carbon dioxide, water, and mineral substances are all constantly recycled in ecosystems throughout the Earth. Let us consider the cycling of minerals such as phosphorus, calcium, sodium, and potassium in a particular watershed in New Hampshire.* One area that was studied extensively includes a ring of mountains and the enclosed valley. Rain is the area's only significant source of water; the only important exit for flowing water in this watershed is through a single stream, because the geology of the area is such that seepage is negligible. In such a system the total input of minerals is limited to two processes: the rain deposits some mineral matter, and weathering of rocks frees some minerals from the Earth's crust. This gain is partially balanced by losses.

In the particular watershed that was studied, it appeared that the stream outflow removed fewer minerals than weathering and rainwater were bringing in. However, the net gain for the ecosystem was very small compared to the requirements of all the life forms in the valley. This means that the valley life was dependent on mineral recycling, for the influx of new material was too slow to support a healthy forest. In fact, all ecosystems depend upon the ability of each individual incoming inorganic ion to undergo countless transformations from soil to plant tissue, from plant tissue into the organic wastes or on to animal tissue, and then to the wastes, back to the soil, and around again and again before being washed out of the system. Therefore, input and output rates bear little relationship to the quantity of inorganic matter in the private pool of any given ecosystem.

---

*For the details of this example, refer to Chapter 4 of *The Ecosystem Concept in Natural Resource Management* by G. N. Van Dyne (ed.). New York, Academic Press, 1969.

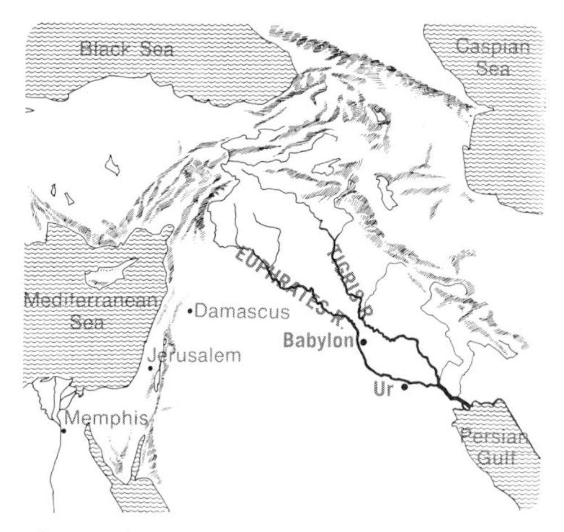

The Fertile Crescent.

Tigris-Euphrates valley gave birth to several great civilizations. We know that highly sophisticated systems of letters, mathematics, law, and astronomy originated in this area. Obviously, then, men had the time and energy to educate themselves and to philosophize. We can deduce that the food supply must have been adequate. Today much of this region is barren, semidesert, badly eroded, and desolate. Archeologists dig up ancient irrigation canals, old hoes, and grinding stones in the middle of the desert. What must have happened?

Part of the story starts at the source of the great rivers in the Armenian highlands. The forests were cleared to make way for pastures, vineyards, and wheat fields. But croplands, especially if poorly managed, cannot hold the soil and the moisture year after year as well as natural forests or grasslands can. As a result, large water run-offs such as those from the spring rains or melting mountain snows tended to flow down the hillsides rather than to soak into the ground. These uncontrolled waters became spring floods. As a protective measure, canals were dug in the valley to drain the fields in the spring and to irrigate them in the summer and fall. Later, devastating wars resulted in the abandonment of the canals and croplands. The neglected canals turned to marsh, and the formation of marshes shrunk the rivers, and the diminished rivers could no longer be used to irrigate other areas of land. The water table sank, so that the yields per hectare today are less than the yields 4000 years ago.

The American Prairie

Although the United States is now the greatest exporter of food of any nation in the world, soil depletion has occurred and continues to occur in this country too. The early European settlers found millions of hectares of virgin land in America. The eastern coast, where they first arrived, was so heavily forested that even by the mid-eighteenth century, a mariner approaching the shore could detect the fragrance of the pine trees about 300 km from land. The task of clearing land, pulling stumps, and planting crops was arduous. Especially in New England, long winters and rocky hillsides contributed to the difficulty of farming. It was natural that families should be lured by the West, for here, beyond the Mississippi, lay expanses of prairie as far as the eye could see. Deep, rich topsoil and rockless, treeless expanses promised easy plowing, sowing, and reaping. In 1889 the Oklahoma Territory was opened for homesteading. A few weeks later the population of white people there rose from almost nil to close to 60,000. By 1900 there were 390,000—a people living off the wealth of the soil. In 1924 a thick cloud of dust blew over the East Coast and into the Atlantic Ocean. This dust had been the topsoil of Oklahoma (see Fig. 15–4).

For each of the earlier examples we have incomplete records of weather patterns and cannot be sure of what factors caused the soil depletion. But in the American **Dust Bowl** we know that poor agricultural practices, coupled with natural drought, were responsible for the disaster. As we learned in Chapter 13, drought recurs in the North American plains about once every 20 to 22 years. The natural prairies on which the bison grazed were resistant to this drought. This resistance arose out of the diversity of the grassland system. Both annual and perennial plants grow

Dust storm. (Photo by Arthur Rothstein from Edward Steichen [(ed.)]: *The Bitter Years: 1935–1941*. New York, Doubleday, 1962.)

in the prairie. The perennial grasses and bushes live continuously from year to year and grow deep roots to absorb moisture from lower levels of the subsoil. Annuals, on the other hand, grow from seed in the springtime, flower, then die during the hot summer months. During dry years there is so little water that many annuals die. However, the perennials, which use water

Figure 15–4. Diversity promotes stability.

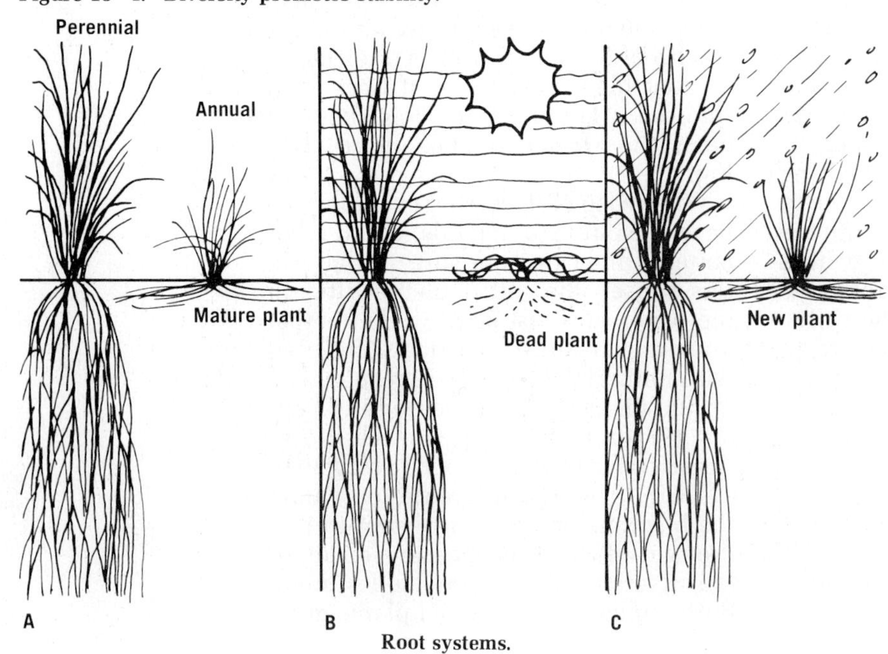

Root systems.

deep underground, are able to live; in doing so, they hold the soil and protect it from blowing away with the dry summer winds. In years of high rainfall, the annuals sprout quickly, fill in bare spots and, with their extensive surface root systems, prevent soil erosion from water run-off. Survival of both types of grasses is ensured by minimization of root competition because the different plants have root systems that reach different depths. In addition, not all species flower at the same time of the year, so that the seasons of maximum growth and consequent maximum water consumption differ.

Practices of the new settlers upset this naturally balanced and resistant system. They killed the bison to make room for cattle, then killed the wolves and coyotes to prevent predation of the herds. Moreover, they often permitted their cattle to overgraze. In overgrazed land, the plants, especially the annuals, become so sparse that they cannot reseed themselves. The land itself, therefore, becomes very susceptible to soil erosion during heavy rains. In addition, the water runs off the land instead of seeping in, resulting in a lower water table. Because the perennial plants depend upon the underground water levels, depletion of the water table means death for all prairie grasses. The whole process is further accelerated as the grazing cattle pack the earth down with their hooves and block the natural seepage of air and water through the soil.

The introduction of the plow to the prairie had an even more severe effect because the first step in turning a prairie into a farm is to plow the soil in preparation for seeding. At this point, of course, the soil is vulnerable, since the perennial grasses, which normally hold the soil during drought, have already been killed.

If the spring rains fail to arrive, the new seeds won't grow and the soil will dry up and blow away. As an emergency measure during droughts, farmers often practice **dust-mulching.** By chopping a few centimeters of the surface soil into fine granules, a thin layer of dust is formed. This dust layer aids the capillary action whereby underground water is brought to the surface. Thus the soil remains moist just below the dust, and the seeds sprout. However, before labeling dust-mulching a success, one must examine several other factors. Fertile soil is more than pulverized rock. Recall from Chapter 14 that topsoil contains large quantities of humus. Humus is formed and decomposed in a continuous cycle. When a leaf falls to the earth, it starts to rot and is gradually converted to humus. As the rotting process continues, the "organic" matter is eventually oxidized completely to form carbon dioxide and water. In most natural ecosystems, the formation and decomposition of humus are balanced, so that the total quantity of "organic" matter remains relatively constant from year to year. Dust-mulching brings much of the previously underground "organic" material to the surface. Once on the surface, this "organic" matter reacts with the oxygen of the air (oxidizes)

"Organic" originally meant "derived from a living organism." According to this definition, composted straw, manure, offal from a slaughterhouse, and bone meal would all be considered to be organic materials. After it was shown in a series of discoveries from 1828 to 1845 that some components of these substances could also be synthesized from non-living sources, "organic" came to refer to compounds containing C—C or C—H bonds, with or without other atoms.

By this new definition, composted straw, manure, and slaughterhouse offal are all complex mixtures of many different organic compounds (with a few inorganic ones in the mixture, too), but bone meal, which consists mostly of calcium salts and other minerals and contains little carbon and hydrogen, is largely inorganic.

Very recently, in usages such as "organic foods" and "organic gardening," the word has recaptured some of its old meaning and has added new overtones. In these contexts "organic" implies a relationship to, or a derivation from, living systems that are unadulterated by human technology. Special emphasis is given to the absence of synthetic additives that are foreign to natural food webs. Thus, DDT-sprayed beans are not organic, but sea salt qualifies. In this context, therefore, "organic" may be briefly defined as "naturally constituted." Thus, an "organic" gardener would include pulverized phosphate rock as well as bone meal in a list of "organic" materials.

To avoid confusion among the various definitions of the word *organic*, the following convention will be used: organic means containing carbon-hydrogen or carbon-carbon bonds, and "organic" (with quotation marks) will be taken to mean naturally constituted.

much more rapidly than it would have had it remained underground. As a result, humus deteriorates faster than it is replaced, and the fertility of the soil is diminished. Of course, the farmer can replace lost "organic" matter by spreading manure or other soil conditioners, but the fact is that millions of hectares of previously fertile farmland have been ruined because the farmers have not refertilized adequately.

On the other hand, if, after plowing, the spring rains are too heavy, the soil may easily wash away before the seeds have an opportunity to grow. Even after seeds have sprouted, the practice of pulling weeds between the rows leaves some soil susceptible to erosion by heavy rains.

The preceding discussion is relevant to the events in Oklahoma. Over a period of 20 to 35 years the soil fertility slowly decreased. Incomplete refertilization and loss of soil from wind and water erosion took their toll. Finally, when a prolonged drought struck, the seeds failed to sprout and a summer wind blew large quantities of topsoil over 1500 km eastward into the Atlantic Ocean.

The droughts that killed the Oklahoma farms had no lasting effect on those prairies left untouched by humans. In fact, these virgin lands are still fertile. In a few thousand years, perhaps, the wind-scarred Dust Bowl will regain its fully fertility.

In spite of all these past disasters, and in spite of our current understanding of soil chemistry, many North American farmers continue to endanger their most valuable resource, the soil. One hundred years ago the area that is now North and South Dakota, eastern Montana, and southern Saskatchewan was buffalo prairie; now it is cattle and wheat country. Currently, it is common to plow fields, leave them idle during the spring and early summer, then plant winter wheat in the late summer or early fall. The practice of leaving soil exposed to spring rains and summer heat has rapidly accelerated the decomposition of humus. As a result, soil fertility has declined. In 1979,

Soil resources are also destroyed by industrial development. The South Platte River Basin shown here is potentially one of the richest agricultural regions in Colorado, yet much of the farmland has been preempted by commerical interests.

Bottling plant capable of filling 1000 bottles per minute.

led to a tripling of energy consumption in the bottling industry. Today, 1.7 kilowatt hours of electricity, enough to light a 100-W bulb for 17 hr, is needed to manufacture and transport *one* 12-oz throwaway bottle.* Glass from a no-deposit, no-return bottle can be recycled, but it must be transported to the recycling plant, crushed, sorted according to color, remelted, and reprocessed. Overall, more energy is needed to recycle glass from a no-deposit bottle than is needed to manufacture one from virgin materials. It is therefore obvious that raising the deposit for glass bottles and selling only returnable ones would be environmentally more sound than the present utilization of throwaways.

In the 1940's some beer and soft drink manufacturers shifted partially to the use of steel cans as containers. Cans are lighter, easier to ship, and less susceptible to breakage than glass. But steel cans are hard to open, so in the late 1950's aluminum cans appeared on the market, and soon thereafter "flip-tops" were added. Aluminum cans require even more energy to manufacture than glass bottles do. But because they are cheaper to handle *for the beverage bottlers and shippers,* they have been marketed extensively in recent years. Since aluminum can be remelted efficiently, considerable quantities of energy could be saved if aluminum cans were recycled. However, despite active recycling campaigns, only about 20 per cent of the aluminum cans sold in the United States are returned.

Many environmental groups have mounted advertising campaigns to educate people about the problems of beverage containers, and numerous recycling centers have been established throughout North America. These campaigns, dependent mainly on voluntary cooperation, have met with only limited success. In 1972 the state of Oregon initiated a more comprehensive program to outlaw throwaway containers. The Oregon bottle bill banned flip-top cans and placed a mandatory 2- to 5-cent deposit on all beverage containers. Within the first year, the total quantity of roadside litter was reduced by 23 per cent, and the energy conserved amounted to enough fuel to heat 11,000 housing units for an entire year. Bottle bills have been enacted in Ver-

In Ecuador (South America), a bottle of beer costs about the equivalent of 40¢ in United States currency. The deposit on the bottle, however, is three times the price of the beer. Thus, an empty bottle is worth about $1.20 (in United States currency), and people simply do not discard them.

*Bruce Hanon: *System Energy and Recycling, A Study of the Beverage Industry.* Center for Advanced Computation Document #23, University of Illinois Press, 1973.

Energy is conserved when aluminum is recycled.

mont and Maine, but similar laws have been defeated by voters in Colorado, Michigan, Massachusetts, and Montana.

15.5 ENVIRONMENTAL GEOLOGY—AN OVERVIEW

Perhaps the primary limiting resource in the world today is fuel. If we had enough energy, most of the problems discussed in this chapter could be overcome easily. For example, modern farming is closely linked to availability of fossil fuels. Not only do tractors and other farm machinery consume gasoline, but also a great deal of fuel is needed for the manufacture of fertilizers. In fact, in regions of advanced agricultural technology, more than 1 Calorie of fuel energy is used to raise 1 Calorie of food. This use of fossil fuels has enabled farmers to achieve spectacular yields of food per hectare of land. No doubt, if more energy were available, these yields could be even higher. For example, artificial soil conditioners could be manufactured, or plants could be grown in carefully controlled greenhouse environments. Furthermore, energy could be used to desalinate (remove the salt from) sea water, thereby producing fresh water that could irrigate deserts and help grow still more food. Of course, cheaply available energy would enable us to solve other problems as well—we could, for example, process low-grade ores and power advanced pollution-control systems.

However, as we discussed earlier (Chap. 4), our coal, oil, gas, and uranium reserves are limited, and therefore we cannot expect to use them to irrigate large expanses of desert and to extract iron and other metals from sea water or other low-grade sources. Because our energy future is so uncertain, the least we can do now is to conserve our natural resources as prudently as possible.

"Admit it. Now that they're starting to recycle this stuff, aren't you glad I didn't throw it out?" (From *Saturday Review of Literature,* July 3, 1971. By Joseph Farris.)

CHAPTER OBJECTIVES

Understand what an ecosystem is and how it functions. Recall how short-sighted agricultural practices have led to the depletion of soil.

Consider the factors that determine the availability of ores and fertilizers.

Understand the theory of recycling and its relationship to economic and social problems.

KEY WORDS

Ecosystem
Photosynthesis
Respiration
Nutrient cycle
Dust bowl
Dust-mulching
Ore
Mineral reserves
Acid mine drainage
Strip mining
Recycling

FORMULAS TO KNOW

These aren't mathematical formulas, but they are important chemical equations.

1. Carbon dioxide + water + sunlight $\xrightarrow{\text{photosynthesis}}$ sugar + oxygen

2. Sugar + oxygen $\xrightarrow{\text{respiration}}$ carbon dioxide + water + energy

TAKE-HOME EXPERIMENTS

1. **Sand and soil.** For this experiment you will need a small shovelful of *dry* sand or sandy gravel. Mix one portion of the sand with an approximately equal weight of *dry* rotten leaves, coffee grounds, grass clippings, or other organic matter. Place about 100 g of the unmixed portion of sand in one small dish and 100 g of the sand-organic mixture in the other. Add about 20 mL of water to each, and then weigh both dishes accurately. Place them side by side on a table and weigh them every half-hour for several hours. Does the weight change? Why? Which sample loses water faster? Why? Discuss the implications of this experiment for agricultural practice.

2. **Recycled paper.** In this experiment we will manufacture recycled paper from old newspaper. Cut a square of newspaper approximately 30 cm on a side and shred it into small pieces. Fill a large bowl ¼ full of water, add the shredded paper, and let the mixture soak for an hour or two. Beat the mixture vigorously with an electric mixer or hand-operated egg beater until the paper breaks up into fibers and the mixture appears creamy and homogeneous. Next, dissolve two heaping tablespoons of starch or wallpaper paste in ½ L of warm water, add this solution to the creamy slurry, and stir. Take a piece of fine window screen and dip it into the

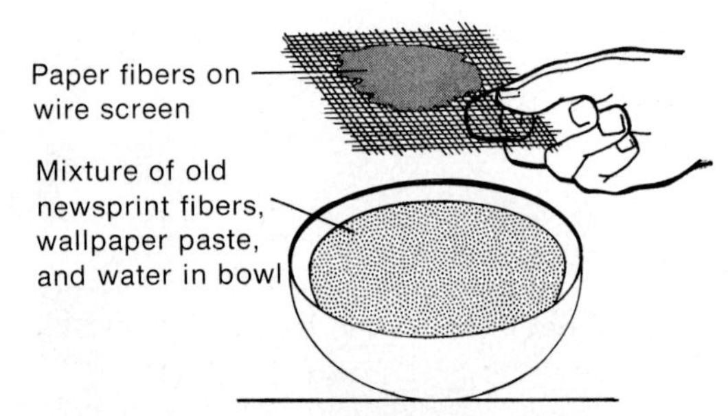

Recycling: Making new paper from old.

solution. Lift the screen out horizontally, as shown in the sketch. If you have done this correctly there will be a fine layer of paper fibers on the screen. Stir up the contents of the bowl and redip the screen carefully as many times as is needed to build up a layer about ¼ cm thick.

This layer must now be pressed and dried. To do this, place a cloth towel on a tabletop and lay the screen over the towel so that the fiber layer is facing upward. Cover the fibers with a piece of thin plastic (a plastic bag is fine). Now squeeze down evenly on the plastic, using a block of wood for a press. Most of the water should be squeezed from between the fibers, through the screen, and on to the cloth towel. Set the screen out to dry for a day or two, peel off the newly fabricated recycled paper, and write a letter to a friend!

PROBLEMS

1. **Energy.** Classify each of the following substances as energy-rich or energy-poor with specific reference to its ability to serve as a food or fuel: sand, butter, paper, fur, ice, marble, and paraffin wax.

*2. **Energy.** Organisms have evolved to obtain energy from foods or from the process of photosynthesis. Would it have been possible for life forms to evolve that obtain their energy by some other process, such as rolling down hills? Defend your answer.

3. **Nutrient cycles.** We speak about nutrient cycles and energy flow. Explain why the concepts of nutrient *flow* and energy *cycle* are not useful.

*4. **Nutrient cycles.** Give three examples supporting the observation that nutrient cycling has not been 100 per cent effective over geological time.

5. **Ecosystems.** What is an ecosystem? Discuss the energy and nutrient balance in an ecosystem. Name or describe three specific ecosystems.

6. **Ecosystems.** Could a large city be considered a balanced ecosystem? Defend your answer.

7. **Agricultural ecosystems.** Explain why agriculture is more disruptive to natural ecosystems than are hunting and gathering of food.

8. **Agriculture.** Why do most modern farmers purchase fertilizer whereas some ancient farming communities existed for centuries without using outside sources of fertilizer?

*9. **Destruction of ecosystems.** A common logging practice in the United States today is **clearcutting,** the removal of all trees and bushes in a single logging operation. Conservation groups attack clearcut-

*Indicates more difficult problem.

ting because it destroys wilderness recreation areas. Will clearcutting affect people other than those who enjoy wilderness? Explain.

10. **Longevity of agriculture.** If a given land area is farmed for many years, does its productivity necessarily decrease? Justify your answer.

11. **Stability.** Explain how ecosystem diversity promotes stability.

12. **Dust Bowl.** Some people contend that the loss of the topsoil in the American Dust Bowl in the 1930's was due primarily to natural causes, while others contend that farming practices were to blame. Which position do you feel is more accurate? Defend your answer.

13. **Mineral reserves.** Explain why energy is an important factor in calculating future mineral reserves.

*14. **Mineral reserves.** Petroleum is generally burned as a fuel, but in many applications the chemical compounds in the oil are used for the manufacture of plastics and other materials. Explain why petroleum cannot be economically recycled after it is burned, but if it is used for the synthesis of plastics it can be recycled many times.

*15. **Depletion of mineral resources.** A noted environmental scientist reported that the world tin reserves may be depleted in 1990. In making this prediction, he assumed that (a) mining technology and world economic activity will remain constant, (b) consumption levels and population will remain constant, and (c) no new deposits will be discovered. Comment on the validity of these three assumptions. Do you feel that the assumptions are valid? If so, defend your conclusion. If not, propose three assumptions that you feel have greater validity.

16. **Recycling.** Does automobile recycling really conserve iron, or energy? Discuss.

17. **Recycling.** Sand and bauxite, which are the raw materials for glass and aluminum, respectively, are plentiful in the Earth's crust. If we are in no danger of depleting these resources in the near future, why should we concern ourselves with recycling glass bottles and aluminum cans?

*18. **Recycling.** As mentioned in the text, broken or obsolete items can be repaired, broken down for the extraction of materials, or discarded. Which route is most conservative of raw materials and energy for each of the following items? (a) a 1948-model passenger car that doesn't run; (b) a one-year-old passenger car that doesn't run; (c) an ocean liner grounded on a sandbar and broken in two; (d) an ocean liner sunk in the central ocean; (e) last year's telephone directory; (f) an automobile battery that won't produce current because the owner of the car left his lights on all day; (g) an empty fountain pen ink cartridge?

*19. **Planned obsolescence.** An old timer complains that years ago a man could store canned milk in the creek for 3 years before the can would rust through, but now a can will only last 1 year in the creek. Would you agree with the old man that cans should be made to be more durable? What about automobiles? Explain any differences.

*20. **Recycling.** During World War II, when rubber was scarce in the United States, someone suggested that industry should develop a process to scrape rubber off curves on roadways because that is where most tire wear occurs and then re-form the reclaimed material into new tires. What do you think of this suggestion? Explain.

21. **Beverage containers.** Outline some economic and technical problems of the beverage container business.

*22. **Recycling municipal trash.** A person lives in a sparsely populated canyon in the Northern Rocky Mountains. His household trash is disposed of in the following manner: papers are used to start the morning fire in the potbellied stove; food wastes are either fed to livestock or composted. Ashes are incorporated into the compost mixture; metal cans are cleaned, cut open, and used to line storage bins to make them rodent-resistant; glass bottles are saved to store food; miscellaneous refuse is hauled to a sanitary landfill. Comment on this system. Can you think of situations where this system would be undesirable? Do you think that it is likely that many people will adopt this system?

*23. **Industrial salvage.** Manufacture of felt from fur scraps is a marginally profitable enterprise. One factory operates as follows: Fur scraps are first decomposed by heating them in a vat with dilute sulfuric acid. The useful fibers are extracted, and the remaining liquid, which consists of water, sulfuric acid, and decomposed animal skin, is dumped un-

*Indicates more difficult problem.

treated into a river. The cost of purifying the effluent would drive this particular business bankrupt. Discuss the overall environmental impact of this fur-scrap recycling center.

*24. **Industrial salvage.** When animals are slaughtered for human consumption, various waste products are produced. These include fat and bones from cattle, chicken feathers and entrails, blood, and unused fish parts. These wastes, when discarded, are a large source of water pollution. Some factories, called **rendering plants,** recycle these materials by converting them to tallow (which is used to make soap) and to animal feed products. However, many rendering plants discharge odorous pollutants into the atmosphere. Discuss the overall environmental impact of these rendering plants.

*25. **Beverage containers.** In 1976 voters in Colorado were asked to decide whether or not to levy a mandatory tax on non-returnable cans and bottles. The beverage industry strongly opposed the law. In one brochure published by a major beer manufacturer it was stated:

*Indicates more difficult problem.

Claim: Amendment #8 [the proposed bottle law] would conserve energy and resources.

Fact: Any savings in coal consumption resulting from the law would be offset by an increase in the consumption of gasoline, natural gas and water.

Returnable bottles are heavier than nonreturnable cans. Manufacturing their heavy, durable carrying cases would require an increase in energy consumption.

Bottles would also require twice as much space as cans. Trucks would have to make at least twice as many trips to haul refillable containers, to say nothing of the extra trips to pick up empties, resulting in increased gasoline consumption.

Washing re-usable bottles requires five times more water than cans. Heating the water for sterilization and removing the detergents that are used means increased energy consumption.

Examine, these statements critically. Have all the facts been presented fully and accurately, or do you feel that the brochure states the case incompletely? Is it reasonable or misleading? Defend your position.

*26. **Recycling and the Second Law of Thermodynamics.** Referring to a discussion of the difficulty in recovering ores from ocean sediments, Professor Peter Frank of the Department of Biology of the University of Oregon wrote, "The Second Law of Thermodynamics comes in with a vengeance. . . ." Explain what he meant.

CHAPTER 16

Astronomy is one of the oldest scientific endeavors, yet it remains extremely active in modern times. This chapter contains some material that was first understood in the fifteenth and sixteenth centuries, and other information that was learned in the fall of 1979. Before 1957, when the Russians launched the first Sputnik, our knowledge of our neighborhood in space was based entirely on studies conducted from the surface of the Earth or from high-altitude balloons. All of these experiments were necessarily limited, for not only does our own atmosphere distort any ground-based observations, but the objects under study are very far away. In recent years, thousands of spacecraft have been launched. Some of the more spectacular of these have landed astronauts on the Moon, analyzed samples of Martian soil, and taken high-resolution photographs of Jupiter and Saturn. Other less highly publicized spacecraft have provided information about the Sun, dust particles in space, background radiation, and myriads of other phenomena.

Our study of the Solar System includes discussions of planetary and lunar motion, followed by a summary of the present theories on the formation of the Solar System. The structure of the Sun, the nine planets, the comets, asteroids, and meteoroids is then introduced.

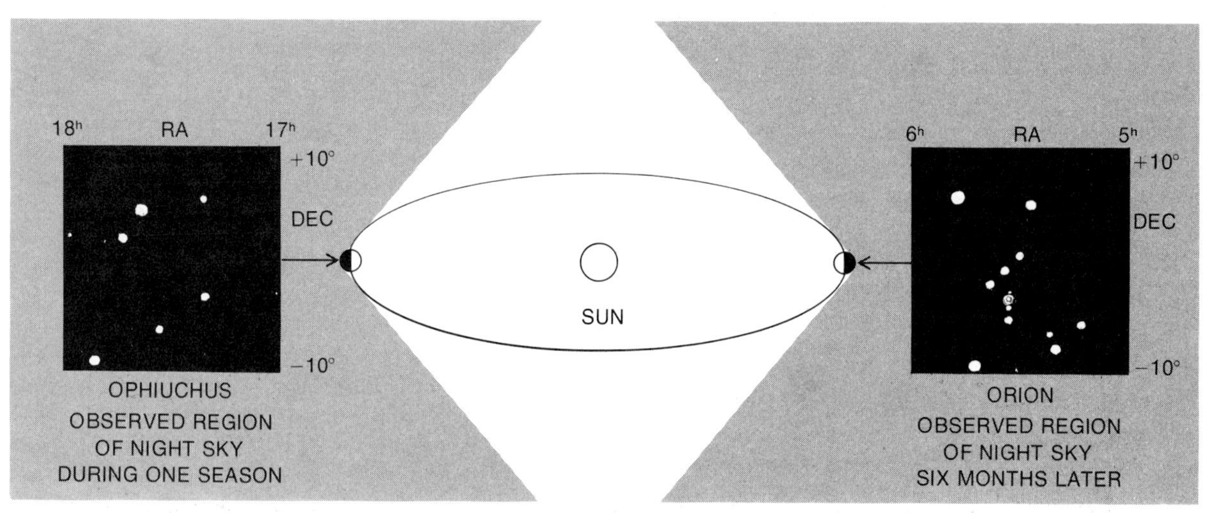

Figure 16–3. Why the night sky changes with the seasons. (From Pasachoff, Jay M.: *Contemporary Astronomy.* Second edition. Philadelphia, Saunders College Publishing, 1981.)

axy, and the galaxy itself is whizzing along, drawing our Sun and planets through the void of intergalactic space.

16.3 THE MOTION OF THE MOON

Phases of the Moon

Even the most casual observer of the Moon has seen that it appears to change shape on a regular basis. If on one evening the Moon is circular and bright, we say that it is **full.** A few evenings later, part of the disc will be darkened. As the days progress, the dark portion will grow until only a tiny sliver of moonlight, called a **crescent,** is left, and finally, about 15 days after the Moon was full, it becomes invisible. We call this day the time of the **new moon.** The day after the new moon, the thin crescent reappears. As the nights go by, the visible portion of the Moon gets bigger and bigger until the cycle is complete and the Moon is full again. Further observation reveals that when the Moon is full, it rises approximately at sunset and on each successive evening will rise about 53 min later so that in 7 days it will rise in the middle of the night. In about 29½ days the cycle is complete, and the next full moon rises on schedule in the early evening.

To understand the phases of the Moon we must first realize that the Moon does not emit its own light but simply reflects light from the Sun.

An ellipse is a closed curve. Inside of each ellipse are two imaginary points called the foci. The sum of the distances from the foci to the edge of the curve is always the same for any point on that curve. To draw an ellipse, put two nails in a board and stretch a string between them as shown. Then move a pencil as shown, always keeping the string taut.

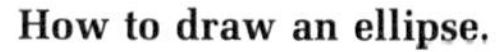

How to draw an ellipse.

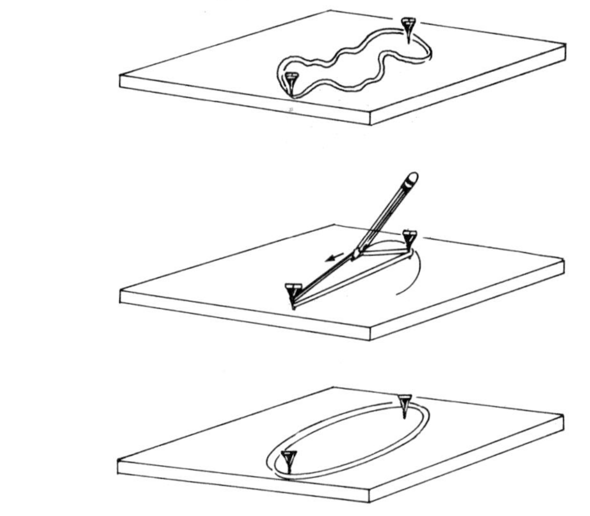

The idea that the Sun and not the Earth is the center of the Solar System was proposed by Nicolaus Copernicus in the early sixteenth century. He was not able to detect the parallax shift of the stars but based his reasoning on the fact that the motions of the planets could be explained much more simply if the Sun were the center of the Solar System. Copernicus was ridiculed by many of his contemporaries, and his idea did not gain wide popularity until many years after his death.

The early Greek thinkers had assumed that planetary bodies moved around each other in circular orbits. This theory was disproved by another great early astronomer named Johannes Kepler (1571–1630). Kepler studied Copernicus' work and received it enthusiastically. However, after many careful measurements, Kepler realized that the Earth and other planets do not move about the Sun in perfectly circular orbits but rather that planetary orbits are elliptical.

The concept of a heliocentric Solar System was initially proposed by Copernicus and supported by Kepler and Galileo. But old ideas die hard. In 1633 Galileo was taken before a high court of the Church and asked to recant his belief that the Sun and not the Earth was the center of the Solar System. Galileo bowed to the pressure of the Church rather than face imprisonment and torture, but his ideas were widely accepted soon after his death.

"Heliocentric" is derived from *Helios* (Greek for the Sun) as the *center* of the Solar System. The element helium is so named because its spectrum was discovered in the rays of the Sun's outer atmosphere during an eclipse.

Thus the amount of moonlight received depends on the relative positions of the Sun, the Moon, and an observer on the Earth. The Earth revolves around the Sun in a flat planar orbit, as if the two were positioned on an imaginary table top. The Moon's orbit around the Earth is tilted with respect to this plane so that generally the Moon, the Sun, and the Earth do not lie in a straight line (Fig. 16–4). As the Moon orbits, half of the sphere facing the Sun is continuously illuminated. If the Moon is positioned directly behind the Earth, we see the entire sunlit area, and the Moon appears to be full. However, if the Moon is between the Earth and the Sun, the sunlit side is facing away from us, and we cannot see the dark shadowy surface that faces the Earth. The Moon is then invisible to us, and we say that it is **new.** Midway between these two extremes, when the Moon is located 90° from the line between the Earth and the Sun, half of the illuminated half is visible, and we say that the Moon is quartered. The Moon passes through one complete cycle, from new to first quarter to full to third quarter and back to new again, with each complete revolution around the Earth. As stated earlier, the lunar cycle repeats every 29½ days.

But why does the Moon rise at a different time each day? Since the Moon travels in a complete circle about the Earth with respect to the stars once every 27⅓ days, that means that it travels 360° in 27.3 days, or 360°/27.3 days = 13.2°/day. Let us say that today the Moon rises at 6 P.M. Twenty-four hours later, the Earth will have rotated once, but in the meantime the Moon will have moved 13.2° across the sky so that the Earth must rotate a little bit extra in order to "catch up" with its satellite. (It takes the Earth approximately 53 min to rotate 13.2°.) Thus the timing of the moonrise depends on the Moon's position above a point on the Earth, and this also changes in a regular cyclic pattern.

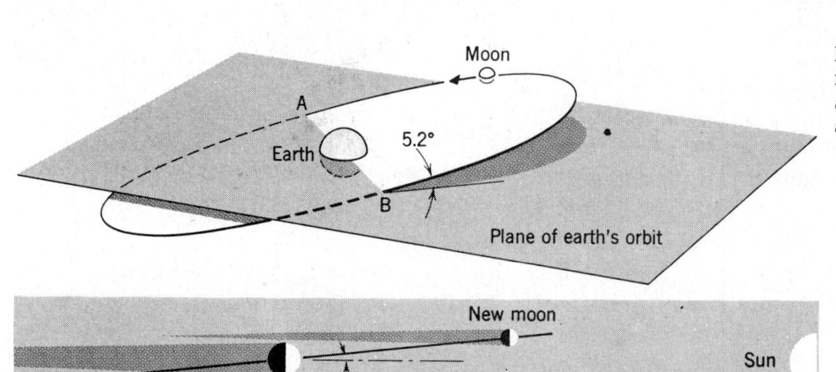

Figure 16–4. The Sun and the Earth lie in one plane, while the Moon's orbit around the Earth lies in another. (Scales are exaggerated for emphasis.)

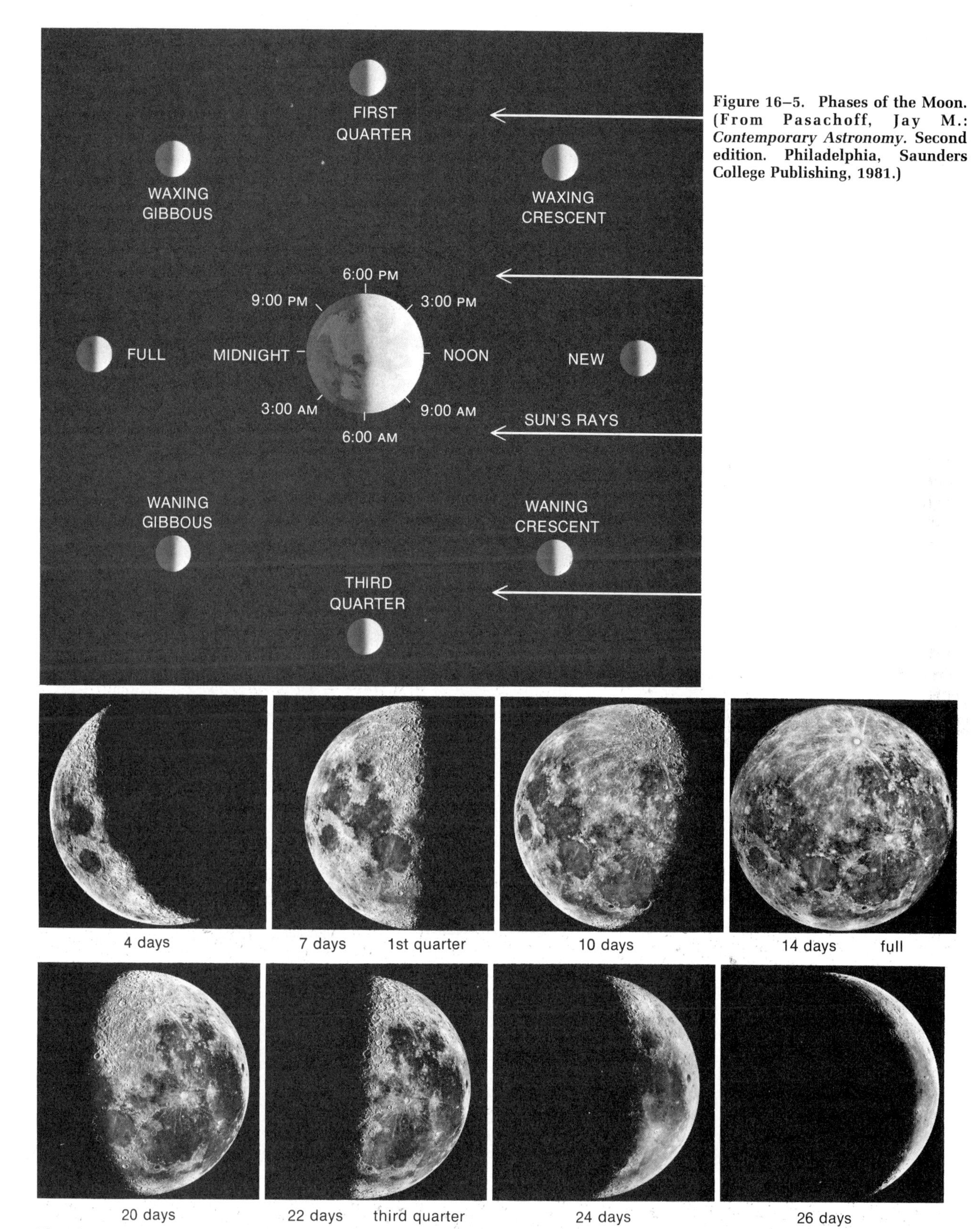

Figure 16–5. Phases of the Moon. (From Pasachoff, Jay M.: *Contemporary Astronomy.* Second edition. Philadelphia, Saunders College Publishing, 1981.)

The phases of the Moon. Astronomical telescopes invert images, as seen here. (Lick Observatory photograph)

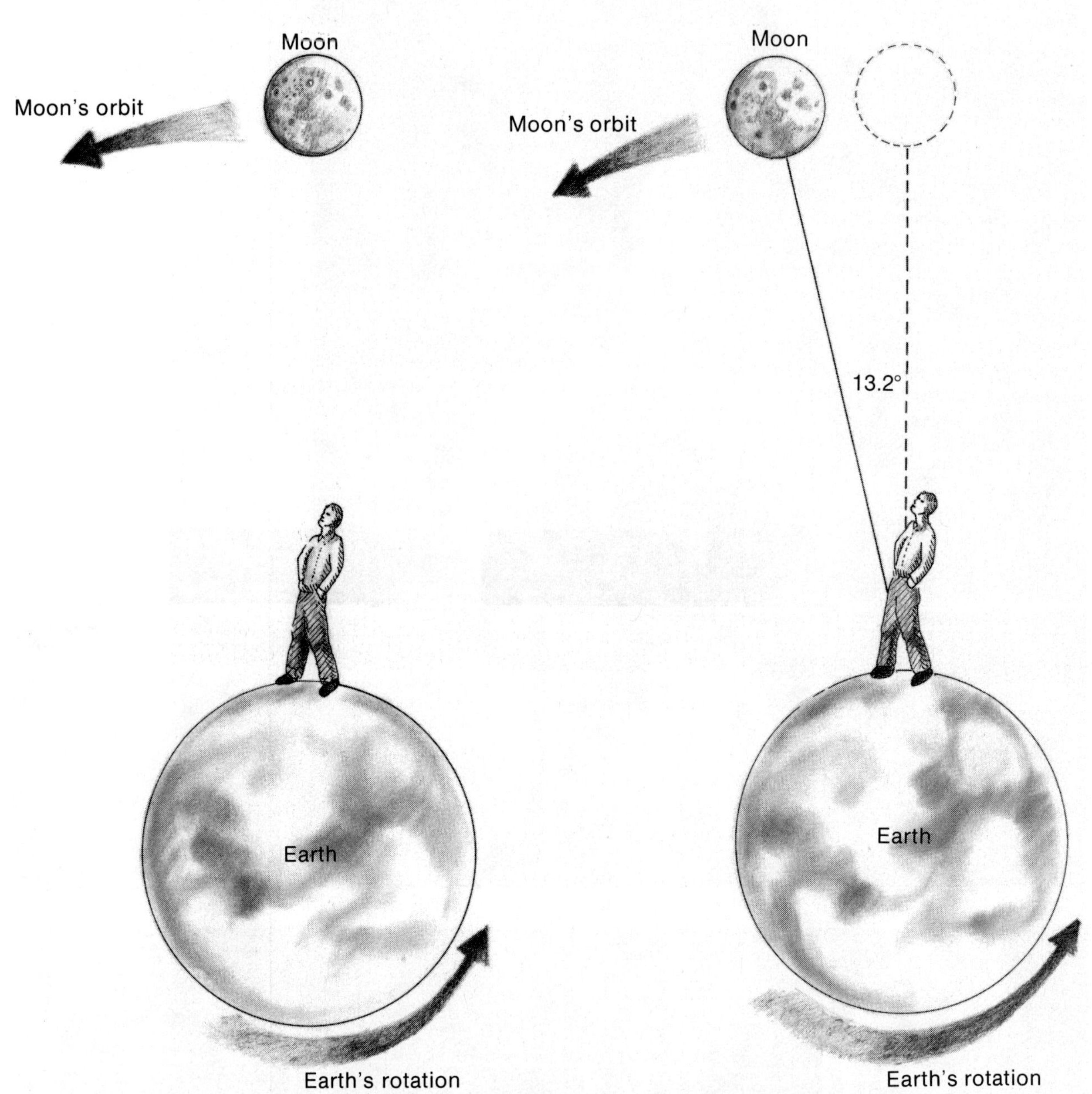

Figure 16–6. The Moon moves 13.2° every day. *A,* The Moon is directly above an observer on Earth. *B,* One day later, the Earth has completed one complete rotation, but the Moon has traveled 13.2°. The Earth must now travel for another 53 minutes before the observer is directly under it again.

A solar eclipse.

Eclipses of the Sun and the Moon

We mentioned earlier that the Moon's orbit is tilted with respect to the plane of the Earth's orbit about the Sun. But two planes tilted with respect to each other must necessarily intersect, as shown in the adjacent drawing. Therefore, as the Moon orbits, it must pass through the Earth-Sun plane twice during each revolution. These points are called the **nodes** of the orbit. If we draw a line between the Sun and the Earth we see that normally the nodes of the Moon's orbit do not fall on that line.

Two planes intersect in a straight line.

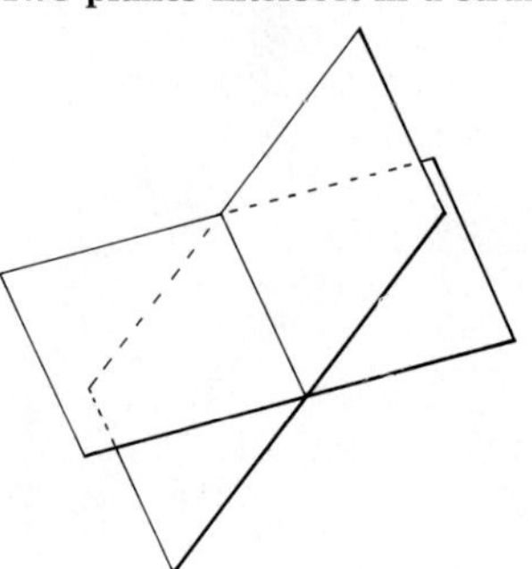

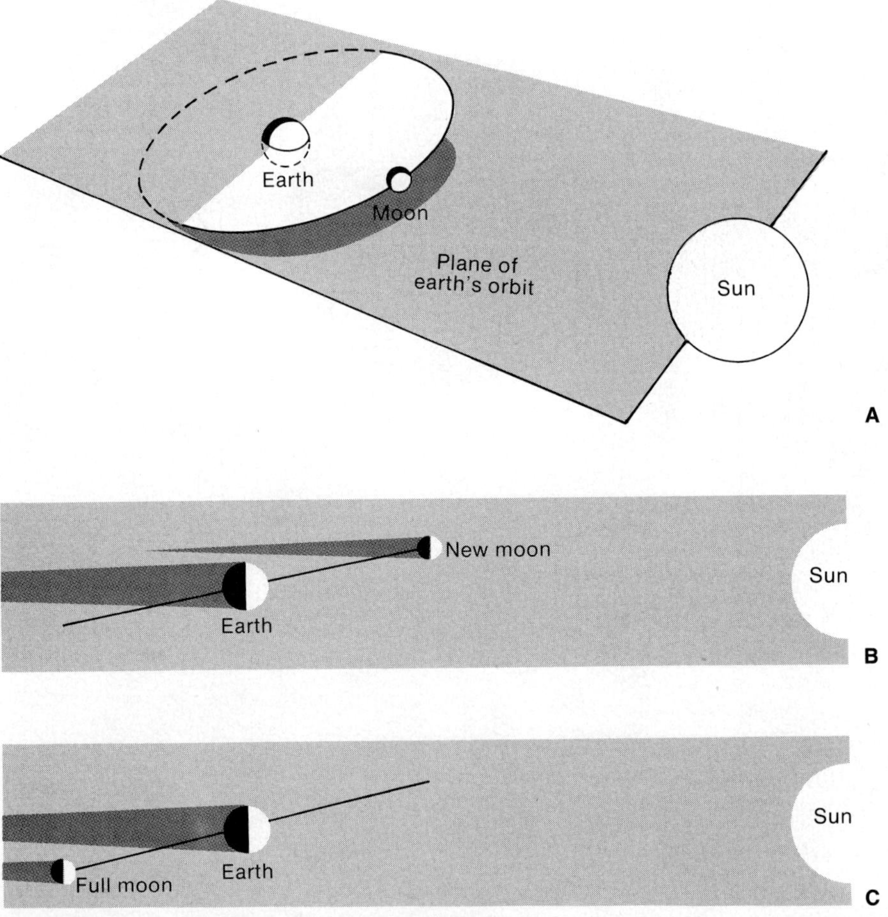

Figure 16–7. Eclipses of the Sun and Moon. The Sun and the Earth lie in one plane while the Moon's orbit around the Earth lies in another. (Scales are exaggerated for emphasis.) Legend continued on next page.
***A,* Normally the Moon lies out of the plane of the Earth-Sun orbit . . .**
***B,* so at new moon the Moon's shadow misses the Earth . . .**
***C,* and at full moon the Earth's shadow misses the Moon.**

However, as shown in Figure 16–7, the nodes of the Moon's orbit do line up with the Sun twice every year. Suppose that there is a full moon at one of these special times. The Moon will be positioned behind the Earth, but now instead of lying above or below its orbital plane, it is directly behind the Earth–in its shadow. The Moon becomes temporarily invisible, and we say that it has been **eclipsed.**

What happens, now, if there is a new Moon at the time when the lunar orbital nodes line up with the Sun? The Moon's shadow will fall onto the Earth, thereby blocking out, or eclipsing the Sun. Observers of a total solar eclipse report that as the Moon slides totally in front of the Sun, an unnatural darkness descends, and the Earth becomes still and quiet. Birds seem to become confused, return to their nests, and cease their singing. While the eclipse is total, the Sun itself is hidden, but the outer solar atmosphere or **corona,** normally invisible owing to the Sun's brilliance, appears as a halo around the black Moon.

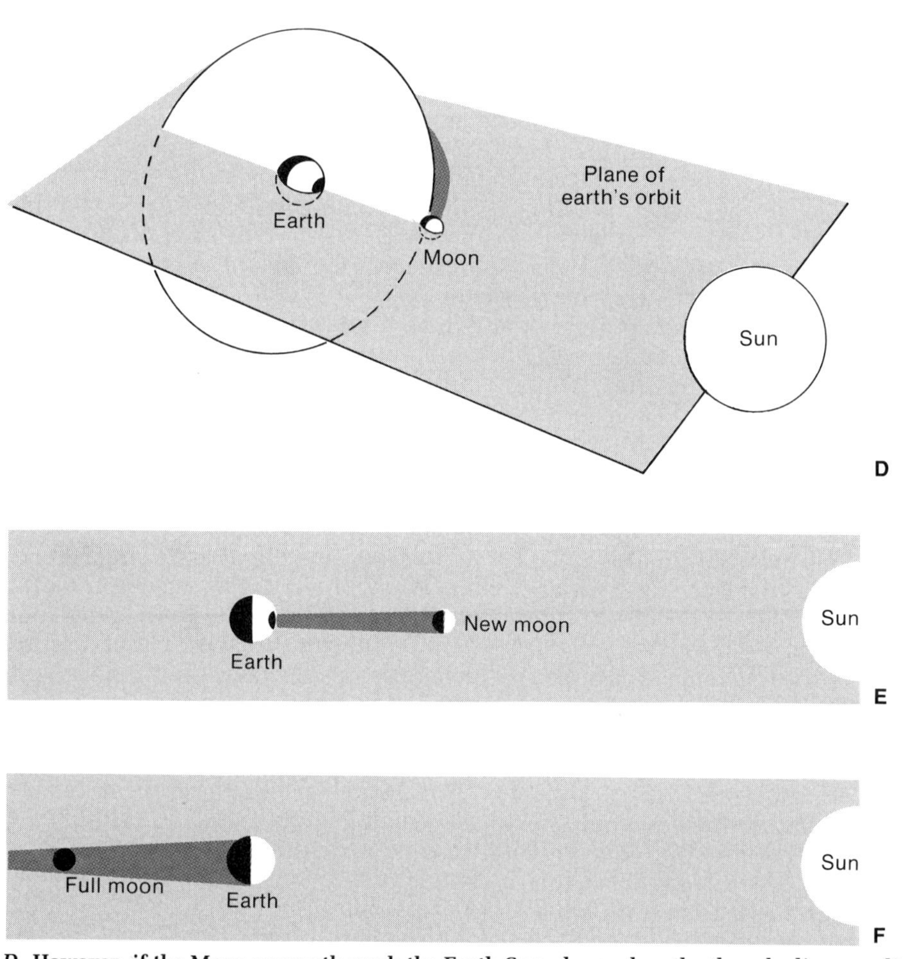

D, However, if the Moon passes through the Earth-Sun plane when the three bodies are aligned properly, then an eclipse will occur.
E, An eclipse of the Sun occurs when the Moon is directly between the Sun and the Earth, and the Moon's shadow is cast on the Earth.
F, An eclipse of the Moon occurs when the Earth's shadow is cast on the Moon.

The Tides

As you study a subject such as the tides, reading a book while seated in a comfortable library chair, it becomes easy to lose touch with the natural power and majesty of the phenomenon. Instead of memorizing information about tidal systems, imagine that you are working on a fishing boat on the coast of southeastern Alaska. You would soon notice that the level of the ocean rises and falls in a cycle of approximately 12 hours. Thus, if the water were low at noon, it would reach maximum height at about six o'clock and be low again near midnight. These vertical displacements are called the **tides.**

When the tide rises in the open bays, the water must rush in toward land. Off the coast of southeastern Alaska, which is dotted with thousands of islands, channels, fjords, and river mouths, this incoming water is funneled around the irregular coast in distinct **tidal currents.** A tidal current is simply a flow of ocean water that is caused by the tides. If such a flow moves at a rate of two knots eastward on a rising tide, it will reverse itself when the tide starts to fall and move with an approximate velocity of two knots westward. Since fish tend to move with the tides, you as a fisherman would try to place your net when the tidal conditions were optimal. Let us say, for example, that in a certain location it was best to set the net at low tide and let the fish move into it as the waters rise and the currents flow. You would soon find out that low tide does not recur at the same time each day. If today's low tide occurred at 4:43 A.M., tomorrow's might not occur until 5:29 A.M., and the next day's would be still later, until eventually low tide would not occur until noon. What this means to you on the fishing boat is that you go to work at different times each day, sometimes waking before dawn and at other times sleeping until late in the morning. If you were observant, you would notice that each day the tides were delayed approximately 40 to 50 min, or about the same amount of time that the moonrise is delayed from day to day.

A fishing boat leaves her home port and sails off to the fishing grounds. (Photo by Paul Synder.)

Living on your fishing boat, you would also notice that the tides are not constant in intensity. Some days high tide is higher than it is on other days. For example, the high tide might be 5.5 m above the fixed tidal reference point one day, while the next day it might be 5.8 m, and three days later the morning tide may be only 5.0 m high. Similarly, the height of the low tide also varies. When the difference between high and low tides reaches a maximum, the tidal currents are naturally most intense. In some regions these currents become so great at these times that nets and fishing lines are swept away, and it becomes impossible to fish effectively. So that is a good time to repair your gear or relax at beach parties, digging clams and lying fat and lazy on shore. After living the life of a fisherman for awhile, you could not help but notice that these beach parties generally occur when the Moon is full or new. In other words, the tidal cycles seem to be linked with the phases of the Moon.

Consider the Earth-Moon system as shown in Figure 16–8. For simplicity imagine a situation in which the Earth is completely surrounded with water. At any one instant of time, one section of this giant ocean, (marked A in the figure), will lie just under the Moon, while all other regions are further away. Since gravitational force is greater for objects that are closer together, the part of the ocean closest to the Moon will be attracted with the

A

B

Tides in the Bay of Fundy. *A,* Low tide. *B,* High tide. (Courtesy of National Film Board of Canada.)

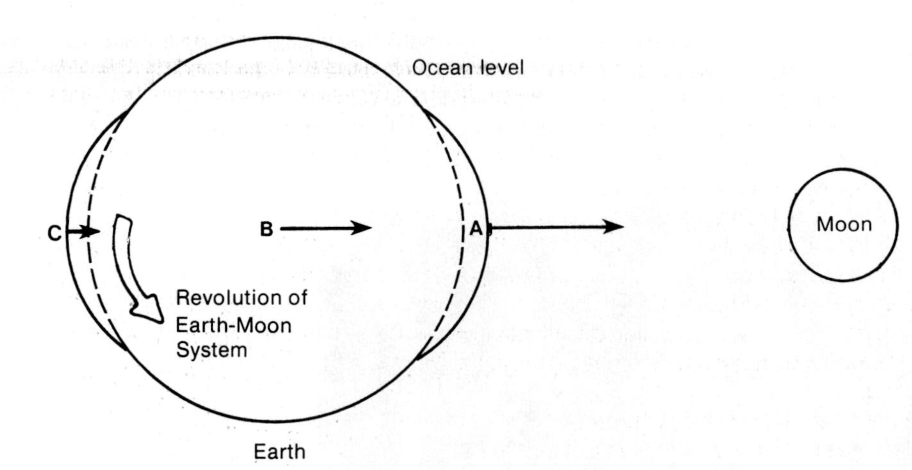

Figure 16–8. Schematic view of tide formation. (Magnitudes and sizes are exaggerated for emphasis.)

greatest force. The ocean bulges outward, resulting in high tide. Following this reasoning it is easy to explain why the high tide appears later every day. An observer on the Earth located just under the Moon at noon of one day will see that the gravitational pull of the Moon causes the ocean to bulge and the tide to rise. Twenty-four hours later the Earth has made one revolution, but because the Moon has traveled some distance during that time, the Earth must spin a little extra for the observer to be located under the Moon. Thus the tide will reach a maximum a little later each day. Just as moonrise and moonset vary with the solar day, so do the tides.

But now our simple explanation runs into trouble. A given point on the Earth passes directly under a given point on the Moon approximately once every 24 hours, but the period between successive high tides is only 12 hours. The tide is high not only when you are directly under the Moon but also when you are 180° away (see Figure 16–8). In order to understand this concept, we must consider the Earth-Moon orbital system. We normally visualize the Moon to be in orbit around the Earth. Of course, this is true, but at the same time the Earth is in orbit around the Moon. It is, in a sense, as if the two partners are locked together like dancers spinning around in each other's arms. Recall from our discussion in Chapter 2, that an orbiting satellite is falling around the body that it is attracted to. Thus, an astronaut in a space station is accelerated towards the Earth but never hits because the craft has a rapid horizontal velocity. This horizontal velocity carries the astronaut around the Earth so a crash is avoided. Following this reasoning, we see that the Earth is continuously falling around the Moon. Now refer to Figure 16–8 again and look at the three points A, B, and C. The point closest to the Moon, A, will be attracted to the Moon with the greatest force, as mentioned previously. Point C will be attracted with the least force. As the Earth falls towards the Moon, point A falls fastest (has the greatest acceleration). Therefore it will bulge outward and produce a high tide at point A. The center of the Earth, B, falls slower than point A, but faster than the surface of the ocean at C. As a result the ocean is left behind a little, so a bulge is formed. This bulge is the high tide 180° away from the Moon. Thus the tides rise and fall two times.

To explain why the tidal bulges are greatest during the periods of new and full moon, we must include the effect of the Sun's gravitational field as well. If there were no Moon at all, the Sun's gravitational field would cause tides twice a day. Since the Sun is so much farther away than the Moon, these solar tides would be smaller than the lunar ones. When the Moon is new or full, the gravitational fields of the Sun and the Moon enhance each other, and we experience a large tidal difference. When the Moon is 90° out of line with the Earth and the Sun, the effect of the

Sun's gravitation does not reinforce that of the Moon. Since the lunar tides are greater than the solar ones, the tides still follow the Moon, but their strength is reduced.

16.4 THE FORMATION AND STRUCTURE OF THE SOLAR SYSTEM

There are several conflicting theories that attempt to explain the origin of our Solar System and of the planet Earth. According to the most widely accepted of these ideas, our galaxy once contained many clouds of gas and frozen dust.* These clouds were nothing like clouds we see in our own atmosphere. For one, they were extremely diffuse, and would be considered to be a good vacuum by terrestrial standards. Second, they were composed mainly of light elements and are believed to have been approximately 75 per cent hydrogen, 24 per cent helium, and 1 per cent other elements. Approximately five billion years ago, billions of years after the galaxy itself had taken form, the cloud that was to become our Solar System began to contract. This diffuse mass was originally rotating quite slowly. The material in the cloud was quite cold, with temperatures perhaps as low as −270° C. At these extremely low temperatures, particles move about so slowly that even a very slight force will be able to affect them appreciably.

*At the present time, many diffuse clouds of gas and dust remain, and some of these appear to be contracting to form new stars or solar systems.

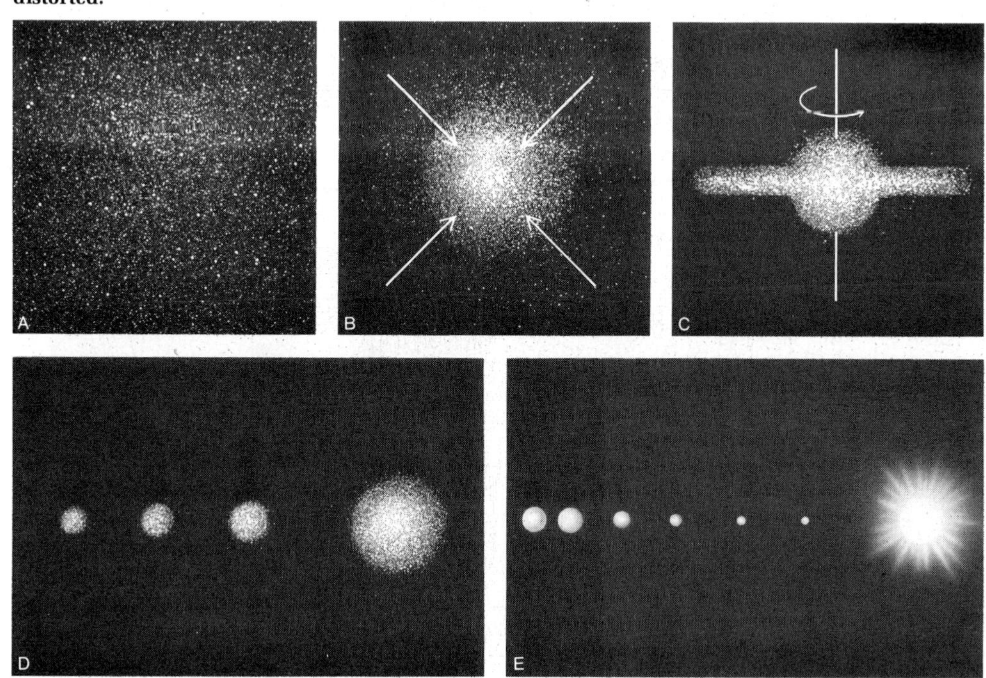

Figure 16–9. Formation of the Solar System. (From Pasachoff, Jay M.: *Contemporary Astronomy*. Second edition. Philadelphia, Saunders College Publishing, 1981.)

A. The solar system was originally a diffuse cloud of dust and gas.

B. This dust and gas began to coalesce under its internal gravitation.

C. The shrinking mass began to rotate and was distorted.

D. The mass broke up into a discrete protosun orbited by large planets composed primarily of hydrogen and helium.

E. The sun heated up until fusion temperatures were reached. The heat from the sun then drove most of the hydrogen and helium away from the closest planets, leaving small, solid cores behind. The massive outer planets remain mostly composed of hydrogen and helium.

Some scientists believe that the slight gravitational attractions among the dust and gas particles themselves caused the cloud to condense slowly into a spherical structure (Fig. 16–9A and B). Or, alternatively, perhaps a star exploded in a nearby region of space and the shock effect triggered the condensation. As the condensation continued, more and more matter gravitated toward the center of this newly formed sphere. Therefore, the density and pressure began to increase within the cloud. As atoms were pulled inward, they accelerated under the influence of the gravitational field. Some of the energy from the collapse was converted into heat, and the temperature of the gas and dust began to rise. This shrinking ball began to rotate more and more rapidly as it contracted.

As the rotation accelerated, the matter at the outer fringes of the ball started to move quite rapidly, thereby orbiting the contracting core. Thus, the ball distorted to form a body shaped something like that shown in Figure 16–9C. The center of this cloud then coalesced into a large mass that is called the **protosun,** meaning the "earliest form of the Sun." The outer section separated into discrete orbiting masses that were the **protoplanets,** and eventually they evolved into the planets. The individual clouds then continued to condense, and as they condensed they grew hotter.

Within the protosun itself, the gravitational attraction was very great, and the gases pulled inward rapidly until intense pressures and temperatures were reached. The highest temperature was found in the very center of the protosun, where atoms were accelerating inward at the fastest rate. As the contraction progressed, the temperature continued to rise. Eventually, when the critical temperature of ten million degrees Celsius was reached, collisions between hydrogen nuclei were so intense that nuclear fusion reactions were started. Hydrogen fused into helium, great quantities of energy were released, and the Sun was born. Amazing!

At the same time, the smaller protoplanets were also coalescing and heating. However, none of them was massive enough to generate sufficient heat during the contraction to initiate fusion reactions. Therefore, after their formation, the protoplanets began to cool gradually.

Most of the mass of the Solar System is concentrated in the Sun. Nine major planets orbit the Sun: Mercury, Venus, Earth, Mars, Jupiter, Saturn, Uranus, Neptune, and Pluto. Some of the planets have one or more satellites of their own orbiting about them. For example, 1 moon orbits the Earth, there are 2 orbiting Mars, and 14 known satellites revolve about Jupiter. In addition to the planetary systems, other bodies such as asteroids, meteoroids, and comets orbit about the Sun. Figure 16–10 is a pictorial representation of the entire system.

Since all the planets were originally formed from a single fairly homogeneous cloud of dust and gas, it seems

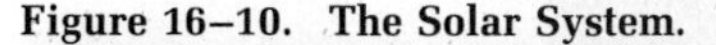
Figure 16–10. The Solar System.

probable that all were originally composed of the same elements in roughly the same proportions—75 per cent hydrogen, 24 per cent helium, and 1 per cent other elements. So, imagine that there were nine primordial blobs of interstellar matter. In the beginning, they all had roughly the same composition, but some were more massive than others, and, of course, each one orbited at a different distance from the Sun. Gradually, the planets began to evolve. Matter was pulled inward by gravitation, radioactive compounds were trapped within the rocky cores, and the spheres were heated by the Sun. As the evolution continued, rocks melted and some gases were boiled off into space, while others were released into the atmospheres during volcanic eruptions. The rates of all these reactions and changes were partly controlled by the surface and internal temperature of each planet and by the strength of the gravitational field. Thus, the mass and distance from the Sun were crucial in determining the evolution of each planet. At the present time, no two are alike. For example, Venus is hot and rocky with surface temperatures high enough to melt tin or lead. As we know, the Earth is temperate, and covered with great forests, prairies and oceans, while the surface of Jupiter is a vast sea of liquid hydrogen.

The four planets closest to the Sun—Mercury, Venus, Earth, and Mars—are all relatively small, dense, and rocky. They are called the **terrestrial,** or Earth-like planets. The next four—Jupiter, Saturn, Uranus, and Neptune—are much larger, more massive, and less dense, being composed mainly of hydrogen and helium. The composition of Pluto is not known with certainty.

Scientists believe that all the terrestrial planets were once considerably larger and more massive than they are today. For example, Earth may have been 1,000 times more massive than it is at present. As these planetary bodies were heated by the Sun, most of the hydrogen and helium may have been gradually boiled off into outer space. Or, perhaps, the slow pressure from the solar wind blew the primordial atmosphere away. Another theory proposes that a colossal solar explosion, a kind of super solar wind, sent a shock wave into space and expelled most of the gases from the inner planets, leaving behind four barren, rocky, lifeless spheres.* But the proto-forms of Jupiter, Saturn, Uranus, and Neptune were farther away from the Sun and would therefore have been less severely affected by high solar temperatures or energetic explosions. Also, they were considerably more massive, so the light atoms were held more tightly by the gravitational fields. For these reasons, the hydrogen and helium remained on these planets, and they are still composed mainly of light elements. The furthermost planet from the Sun, Pluto, is about as dense as Saturn, but it is much smaller.

16.5 THE SUN

Ancient Greek scientists and philosophers believed that the Sun was a perfect, symmetrical, homogeneous sphere, unblemished in any way. This belief was first questioned by Galileo in the seventeenth century. While studying the Sun with the aid of a telescope, he noted occasional dark spots appearing on its surface. Many critics disagreed with Galileo, although they refused to look through his telescope. They argued instead on philosophical grounds, claiming that if Galileo questioned the perfect symmetry of the Sun he was simultaneously questioning the perfection of God, and this was heresy of the highest order. We now have a great deal of evidence to show that the Sun is in fact a complex heterogeneous sphere. Some of the evidence has been obtained visually, from frequent observations of dark spots and granular structures on the surface of the Sun and from huge flares of hot gas that occa-

*Such solar blasts are believed to occur commonly during the early life of stars the size of our Sun. We believe that the output of the Sun will be constant for a few billion years to come. Stellar evolution will be discussed in more detail in the next chapter.

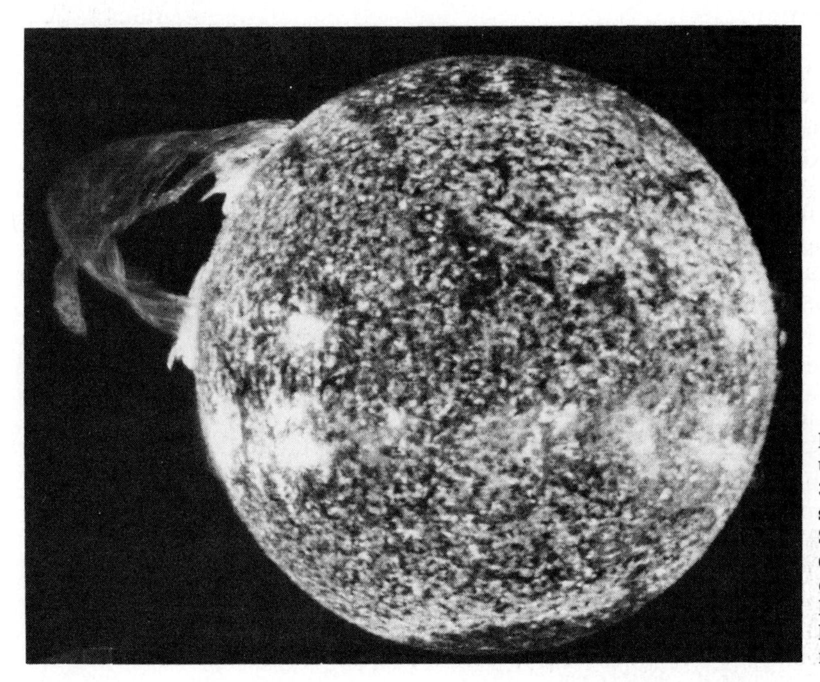

Figure 16–11. A view of the Sun in the ultraviolet radiation of ionized helium at 304 Å, photographed with the Naval Research Laboratory's instrument aboard Skylab, shows a prominence that has erupted into space. It is 40 times the size of the Earth. (From Pasachoff, Jay M., and Kutner, Marc L.: *University Astronomy.* Philadelphia, Saunders College Publishing, 1978.)

sionally shoot outward from its surface. Yet our visual information represents only a small part of the solar data that have been collected. Astronomers also study many other forms of electromagnetic emissions: radio, infrared, ultraviolet, X-rays, and gamma rays. Additionally, much of what we now deduce about the unseen internal structure of the Sun has been inferred by calculating how matter must behave under the conditions of the solar environment. Of course, such inferences are uncertain, and many solar phenomena remain poorly understood.

Although nearly 70 elements have been detected in the Sun's atmosphere, most exist in trace quantities only. The main ingredient is hydrogen, which alone counts for nearly 75 per cent of the total matter. Helium, second in abundance, makes up close to 24 per cent of the total, and the sum of all the other elements accounts for slightly more than 1 per cent.

Never look directly at the Sun either with the naked eye or with a conventional telescope to see its surface structure, for severe damage to your eyes will result. Studies of the Sun require the use of special filters to block out most of the intense light. Normal sunglasses, and even two Polaroid lenses set at right angles to each other are not safe. Exposed film is also not recommended.

The central core of the Sun is extremely hot and dense, reaching temperatures of over 15 million degrees Celsius at a pressure of one billion atmospheres. What happens to the hydrogen and helium? Recall (Section 8.10) that individual gaseous atoms cannot remain electrically neutral at these extreme conditions. Interatomic collisions are so intense and so frequent that the electrons are simply knocked out of their atoms. As a result, there exists a homogeneous mixture of hydrogen and helium nuclei surrounded by a rapidly moving sea of electrons. Such a mixture is called a **plasma.** Suppose that within this plasma two hydrogen nuclei approach each other on a collision course. Their thermal energies are very great, and some can overcome their mutual electrical nuclear repulsions and fuse together to form helium. This nuclear fusion releases energy, as is discussed in Chapter 10. Eventually the Sun's hydrogen will be largely converted to helium, and when that happens, some billions of years in the future, the Sun will change drastically.

A great deal of energy is released from the core during the fusion reaction. This energy is carried radially outward by energetic photons. However, radiation cannot pass from the core directly through the body of the Sun to the surface. The photons are absorbed by many particles along their route, reemitted, and finally are absorbed again in a region just under the surface. Energy is carried outward from there by convection. The structure of the Sun is shown in Figure 16–12.

At the visible surface of the Sun, called the **photosphere,** light and heat are radiated out to space. Typically the temperature may be 5800° C with a pressure only one-tenth that of air at the Earth's surface. The part of the Sun that we see is an extremely diffuse region of glowing gaseous hydrogen and helium. Close examination of the photosphere reveals that it has a granular structure, as shown in Figure 16–11. The bright spots are regions where hot gases are rising upward, and the dark spots are cooler areas of descending gas. Thus we have visual evidence that convection carries energy to the surface of the Sun.

The solar fusion reaction results in the conversion of hydrogen to helium, according to the following reactions:

$$\underset{\text{(proton)}}{{}^{1}_{1}\text{H}} + \underset{\text{(proton)}}{{}^{1}_{1}\text{H}} \rightarrow \underset{\text{(deuteron)}}{{}^{2}_{1}\text{D}} + \underset{\text{(positron)}}{{}^{0}_{+1}\text{e}} + \text{energy}$$

followed by

$$\underset{\text{(proton)}}{{}^{1}_{1}\text{H}} + \underset{\text{(deuteron)}}{{}^{2}_{1}\text{D}} \rightarrow \underset{\text{(helium-3 nucleus)}}{{}^{3}_{2}\text{He}} + \text{energy}$$

followed by

$$\underset{\text{(helium-3 nucleus)}}{{}^{3}_{2}\text{He}} + \underset{\text{(helium-3 nucleus)}}{{}^{3}_{2}\text{He}} \rightarrow \underset{\text{(helium-4 nucleus)}}{{}^{4}_{2}\text{He}} + \underset{\text{(proton)}}{2\,{}^{1}_{1}\text{H}} + \text{energy}$$

Figure 16–12. The structure of the Sun. (From Pasachoff, Jay M.: *Contemporary Astronomy.* Second edition. Philadelphia, Saunders College Publishing, 1981.)

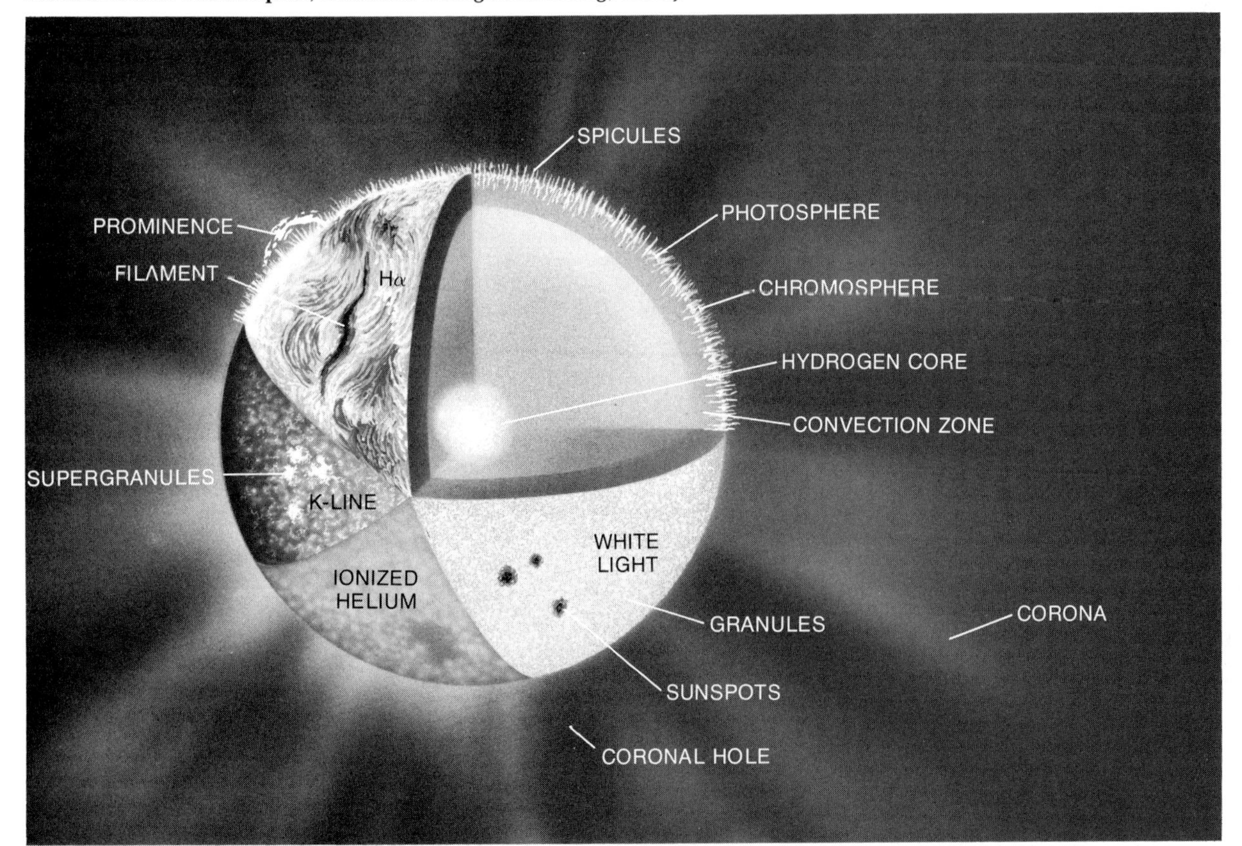

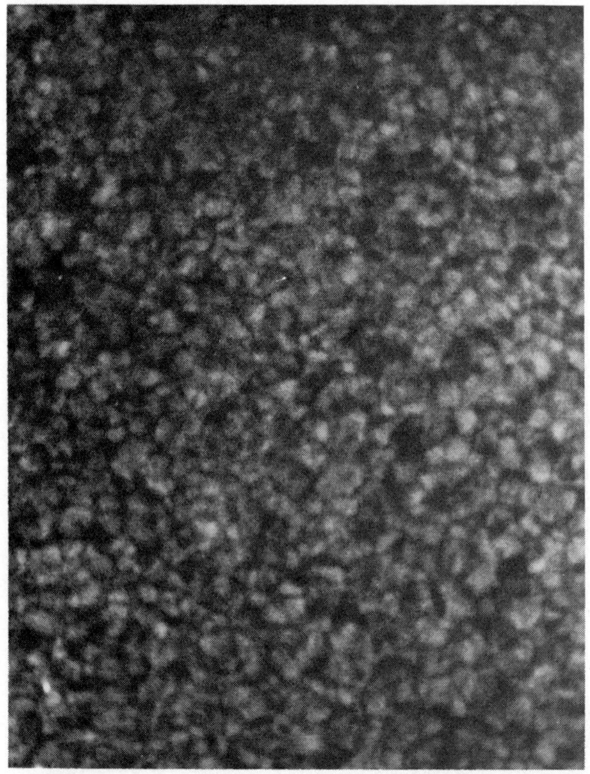

A segment of the Sun's surface, highly magnified, showing the granulated structure. (Hale Observatories.)

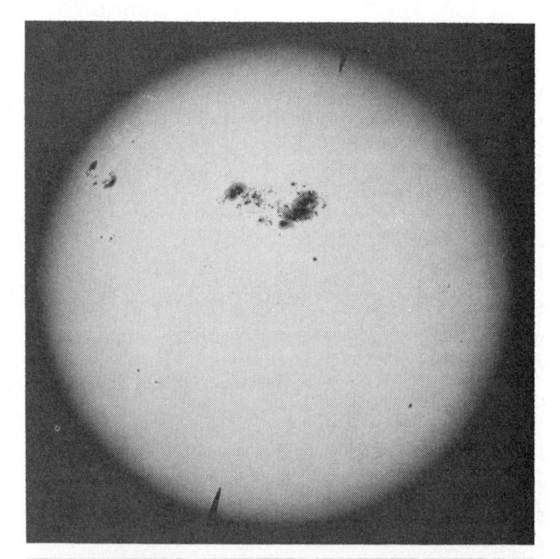

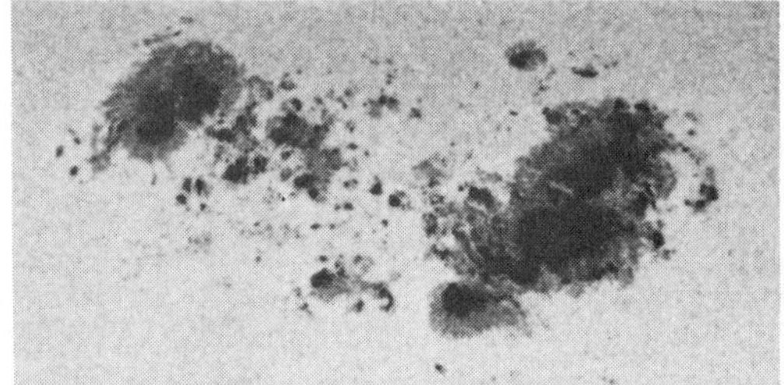

The sunspot of April 7, 1947. (Hale Observatories.)

A solar prominence. (From Pasachoff, Jay M., and Kutner, Marc L.: *University Astronomy.* Philadelphia, Saunders College Publishing, 1978. Big Bear Solar Observatory, California Institute of Technology.)

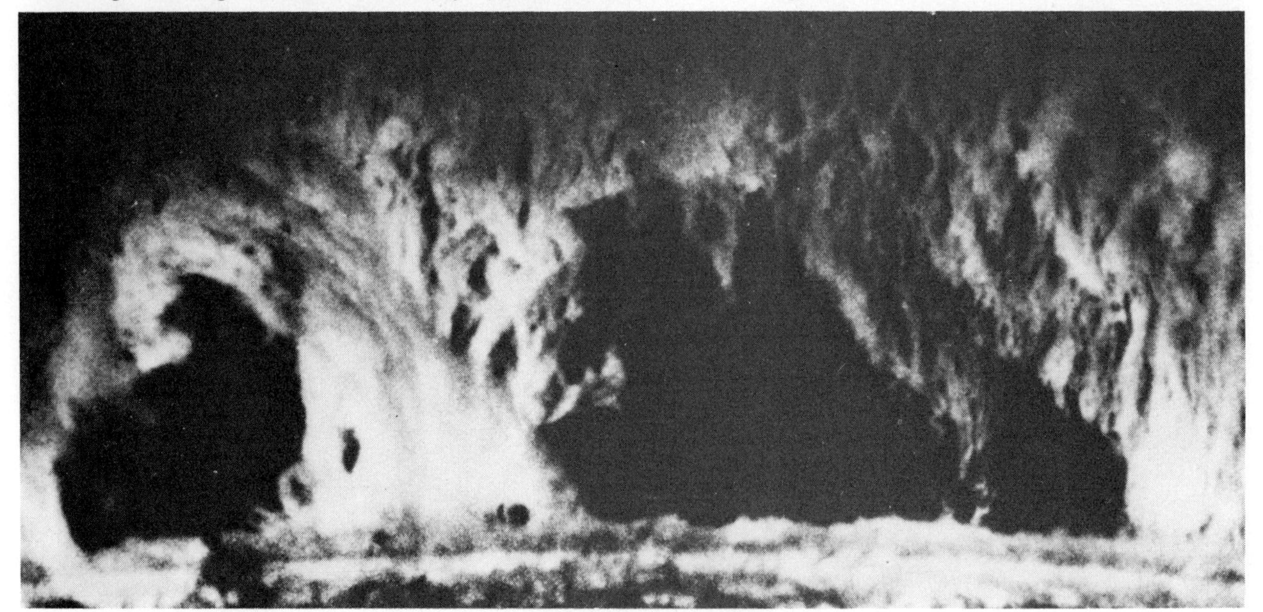

Large dark spots called **sunspots** also appear regularly on the surface of the Sun. These are the same phenomena observed by Galileo over 350 years ago. A single sunspot may be small and last for only a few days, or it may be as large as 150,000 km in diameter and remain visible for several months. From spectral analysis we now know that sunspots are simply regions of the Sun that are a thousand degrees cooler than the gases around them. Because they are cooler, they radiate less energy and hence appear dark by comparison with the rest of the photosphere. No one is able to predict exactly when or where a particular sunspot will appear or how long it will last, but we are learning to predict when sunspot activity will be most intense. Curiously, they become more frequent on a 22-year cycle, as was discussed in Chapter 13.*

Since we know that heat normally flows from a hot body to a cooler one, it would seem logical to suppose that a large, cool region of gas would be heated quickly and disappear. Yet, we have observed that sunspots are relatively long-lived. Sunspot formation is associated with the presence of intense magnetic fields on the Sun. Astronomers believe that these strong magnetic fields restrict the solar turbulence and somehow inhibit the transfer of heat from hot regions into the nearby sunspots.

Large **flares** of hot gas sometimes explode from amid a group of sunspots. Gases accelerate upward and outward, attaining velocities often in excess of 900 km/hr, and shock waves smash through the solar atmosphere. Truly the Sun is not a static, homogeneous, symmetrical sphere such as the Greek philosophers envisioned. Sometimes these flares are powerful enough to have direct effects here on Earth; they initiate reactions that can interrupt radio communication and are associated with auroral displays in our polar regions. Also, as we noted previously, such solar activity may affect terrestrial climate, but no definite relationship has been proved.

*Sunspots become most intense every 11 years, but since the magnetic polarity of the disturbances reverses itself every other sunspot cycle, one complete cycle occurs only once every 22 years.

COMPARISON OF SOME VERY HOT TEMPERATURES

Surface of the Sun	6000 K
Nuclear fission bomb	100,000 K
Sun's corona	1,000,000 K
Core of the Sun	18,000,000 K
Hydrogen bomb (nuclear fusion bomb)	100,000,000 K
Core of hottest stars	2,000,000,000 K

The Sun is not bounded by a sharply defined surface. Rather, its gaseous regions extend far out into space. Above the photosphere lies a turbulent, diffuse, gaseous layer called the **chromosphere.** The chromosphere is normally very difficult to observe from here on Earth. Farther out, beyond the chromosphere, there exists an even more diffuse region called the **corona.** The corona can be observed as a beautiful halo around the Sun during a full solar eclipse. It consists of an energetic stream of electrons, protons, and ions flying out into space at high velocities. Yet, this brilliant halo is extremely diffuse, less than one billionth of the density of the Earth's atmosphere. Beyond the corona itself, the corona particles continue to travel out into space even more diffusely. This stream of particles is called the **solar wind.** It surrounds the Earth and extends outward toward the far reaches of the Solar System.

16.6 THE MOON

Before the exploration of space that was conducted in the 1960's, the study of the Moon and nearby planets had been a great deal more difficult than the study of the Sun. As we learned in the preceding section, scientists are able to study the Sun and other stars through the interpretation of spectral data. But the Moon and the planets do not emit their own light—they primarily reflect the rays of the Sun. Therefore if we analyze the spectrum of moonlight, we get

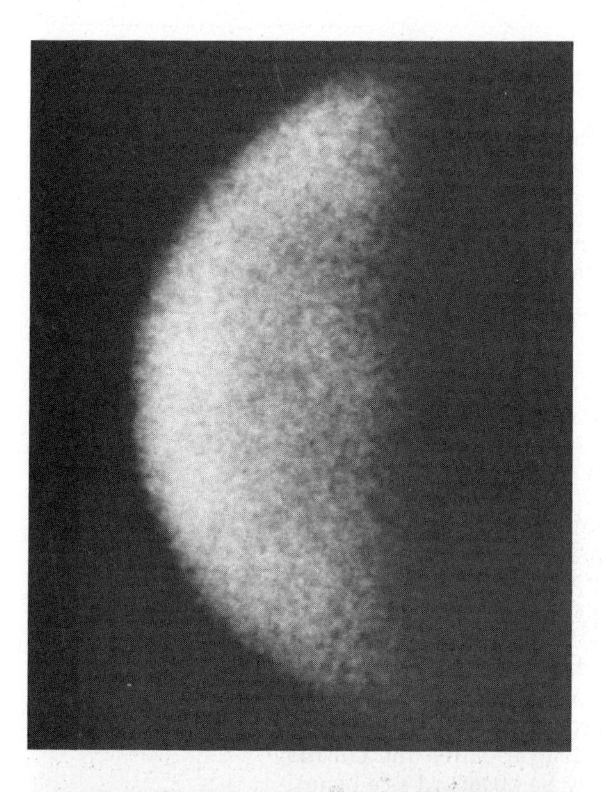

Spacecraft have greatly increased our knowledge of the Moon and the planets. Shown above is one of the best photographs of the planet Mercury taken from Earth. The photograph below was taken by the Mariner 10 spacecraft and shows considerably more detail. (Photos courtesy of Hale Observatories and NASA.)

something close to a solar spectrum and thus learn little about the Moon. We can study the nature of some regions of planetary atmospheres by observing the frequencies of sunlight that are absorbed, but this information tells us nothing about the nature of the surfaces of the planets. Unfortunately, even Earth-bound studies of the surface detail must always be limited. Let us say, for example, that it were possible to build an optically perfect telescope as large as we wanted. No matter how effective our telescope was, we would still be unable to see the details of the surface of another planet. The problem arises because the Earth's atmosphere is turbulent and heterogeneous. Light entering this atmosphere is refracted unevenly. This effect produces an inherent blurring in any observation of a distant object, thus limiting the resolution of any terrestrial telescope. This problem was unsolvable until it became possible to build rockets to carry telescopic and photographic equipment above our own atmosphere.

The first Russian Sputnik was launched into orbit around the Earth in 1957. Since that time, thousands of research rockets have been fired into space. Many have carried not only telescopic and photographic equipment but other types of scientific instrumentation as well. These instruments have recorded data about planetary temperatures, the strengths of magnetic and gravitational fields, the chemical composition of planetary atmospheres, the nature of atomic particles in interplanetary space, and much more. Astronauts have landed on the Moon, carried out a variety of experiments, and returned to Earth with valuable samples of lunar rock and soil. As a result of all this exploration, our knowledge of our Solar System has expanded at an extremely rapid rate. Certainly lunar and planetary astronomy are among the fastest growing scientific fields today as we continue to receive information from laboratories in space.

The Moon is close enough so that its gross surface features are detectable by telescope. Its mountain ranges, smooth flat plains (called seas or **maria**), and thousands of craters have been well known since the time Galileo first observed them in the 1600's. Before the Apollo space program, however, we really knew very little about the geology of the Moon. Now we know much more, but many unanswered questions remain. The two most significant puzzles are the following:

First, how was the Moon formed, and how did it begin to orbit the Earth?

Second, what is the geological history of the Moon; was it once hot and molten like the Earth, and if so, does it still have a molten core?

The student who may be interested in a clear introduction to the physics of rocket flight should refer to Chapter 4, "Of Capture and Escape" in Isaac Asimov: *Asimov on Physics*. New York, Avon Books, 1976. The problems involved in orbiting, flying past, or landing a spacecraft on a heavenly body are all discussed.

Figure 16–13. In order to show the whole Moon, but still show the detail that does not show up well at full moon, the Lick Observatory has put together this composite of first and third quarters. Note the dark maria and the lighter, heavily cratered highlands. Two young craters, Copernicus and Kepler, can be seen to have rays of light (that is, lighter than the background) material emanating from them. (From Pasachoff, Jay M., and Kutner, Marc L.: *University Astronomy*. Philadelphia, Saunders College Publishing, 1978.)

Perhaps the single most significant discovery of the Apollo program was that the entire surface of the Moon is covered with different types of igneous rock. Since igneous rock is formed only when lava cools, it became clear that at least the surface was once hot and liquid. The next logical question arose: How was it heated? Recall that the Earth is heated by radioactive decay within its interior. A celestial body may also be heated by intense meteor bombardment. When a piece of rock flying through space is attracted to a large body such as the Moon, it accelerates downward and lands with considerable kinetic energy. Upon impact, this kinetic energy is converted to heat. If a continuous rain of large meteors strikes a planet or satellite, the heat produced may be sufficient to melt its surface entirely. Is it reasonable to believe that such an intense rain of debris ever occurred? Most astronomers feel that early in the formation of the Solar System, as the clouds of dust and gas were beginning to condense, a great quantity of rock and small chunks of matter must have been flying through space. If these were attracted by a larger body such as the Moon, a continuous meteor shower could have occurred.

The question now at hand is: Was the moon heated by internal radioactivity or by external bombardment? Theoretical geologists have calculated that it would take roughly one billion years for radioactive decay inside the Moon to build up enough heat to melt the rock. Analysis of lunar rock showed that the oldest igneous rocks were crystallized from molten lava when the Moon was a mere 400 million years old. Thus, since there was insufficient time for the rock to have been melted by radioactive decay, at least some of the melting of the Moon was caused by meteor bombardment. Perhaps considerable heat was also generated as the original nebula condensed during the formation of the Moon itself. Further study of lunar geology has given us a partial picture of the rest of its history, but there are still large gaps in our knowledge, and scientists are still debating the relative merits of various theories. A brief history of the Moon is outlined below.

1. There is still significant dispute about the origin of the Moon. When the first Apollo data were analyzed, scientists believed that the chemical composition of the Moon was considerably different from that of the Earth. This view was supported by the observation that the Moon is considerably less dense than the Earth. Using this data, many astronomers speculated that the Moon was formed in some remote region of the Solar System and then captured by the gravitational field of the Earth at some later time. However, after the samples were studied in more detail, lunar geologists concluded that the chemical differences between the Moon and the Earth are not that great after all. Moreover, other experiments indicated that the Moon, like the Earth, probably has a metallic core. According to the most widely held theory at the present time, the Earth and the Moon were probably formed simultaneously from a single cloud of dust and gas. As this cloud condensed, a high concentration of heavy elements gravitated towards the center of this sphere to form the Earth, while the outer ring, which became the Moon, was made up of minerals with a lower density.

2. We believe that the Moon formed about 4.6 billion years ago. A few hundred million years after its formation, the surface of the Moon grew hot enough to melt. Probably some of the heat required to melt the surface was generated during the condensation of the protomoon, while most of the rest was supplied by an intense meteor bombardment. Later the Moon cooled and solidified again.

3. During the time period from about 4.2 billion years ago to 3.9 billion years ago, a second gigantic series of meteor showers rained down upon the Moon. Billions of meteors, some small, and others as large as the state of Rhode Island, smashed into the surface and gouged out most of the craters that we see today.

4. At the same time that the meteor shower was marking the surface, the lunar interior was being heated by radioactive decay. Huge subterranean lava

A

B

C

A, The surface of the Moon, showing numerous craters and mountain ranges.
B, Close-up photo of flat lunar plain with mountain range in background.
C, Astronaut James B. Irwin on the surface of the Moon. Lunar car and module in background. Behind that lies Hadley Delta, 4000 m high. (All Moon photos courtesy of NASA.)

A

B

A, Eugene Cernan riding on the Lunar Rover during the Apollo 17 mission. The mountain in the background is the east end of the South Massif. B, Drawing by Alan Dunn; Copyright © 1971 *The New Yorker Magazine, Inc.* (From Pasachoff, Jay M.: *Contemporary Astronomy.* 2nd edition. Philadelphia, Saunders College Publishing, 1981.)

beds were formed. About 3.8 billion years ago some of this molten material flowed upward through the surface crust to form many active volcanoes. Smooth lava flows covered vast regions of the Moon, forming what is now called the lunar maria, or seas. (The use of the word seas is a misnomer; on the contrary, these regions are dry, barren, flat expanses of rock.) This volcanic activity lasted approximately 700 million years and ended about three billion years ago.

5. Because the Moon is small, the heat produced by radioactive decay was quickly dissipated into space, so that the Moon soon cooled considerably and now lies geologically quiet and inactive. Seismographs left on the lunar surface by Apollo astronauts indicate that the energy released by moonquakes is only one billionth to one trillionth as much as is released by earthquakes here on our planet. Seismic data indicate that the core of the Moon is probably molten, or if it is not, it is at least hot enough to be soft and plastic. However, the cool, solid upper mantle and crustal layers are thick enough to inhibit appreciable seismic activity. Meteor bombardment of the Moon has continued throughout this history of geologic dormancy, although the intense rain of meteors that once occurred has never returned. The craters produced by these later collisions have remained intact and can be seen today.

The lunar experiments tell us a great deal about the history of our own planet. If the Moon was subject to intense meteor bombardment four billion years ago, the Earth, being larger and exerting a greater gravitational force, must have attracted more debris and thus must also have been melted at the same time. We can imagine that the Earth also cooled, only to have been reheated by its own internal radioactivity. Since the Earth is so much larger than the Moon, it has not cooled so rapidly, and as a result the core continues to be molten and the mantle is hot and geologically active to this day. Most of the original rocks of the Earth's crust have long since been pushed down into the mantle by tectonic activity, to be

TABLE 16–1. PARTS OF THE SOLAR SYSTEM

Noun	Adjective	Greek gods, and other references
Mercury	Mercurial	Mercury orbits the Sun more rapidly than any other planet and was therefore named after the speedy messenger of the gods. Mercury is also the god of commerce, thievery, eloquence, and science, and the symbol for the Western Union Telegraph Co.
Venus	Venusian Cytherean	Venus is the brightest and most beautiful star in the sky and was named for the goddess of love and beauty.
Earth	terrestrial earthly	Latin *terra* = Earth.
Mars	Martian	The planet Mars is slightly red in color. Perhaps the red color suggested blood, but in any case Mars was named after the god of war (e.g., martial music).
Jupiter	Jovian	King of the gods (the biggest). Jovial (merry) disposition.
Saturn	Saturnian	Saturn was the farthest planet from Earth that was known to the ancients. It was named after the god of agriculture. Saturnine (gloomy) disposition.
Uranus	Uranian	Son and husband of the goddess of Earth. Note that the name for the element uranium is derived from the same root as Uranus.
Neptune	Neptunian	God of the sea. Element neptunium.
Pluto	Plutonian, Plutonic	God of the underworld. Element plutonium.
Sun	solar	Latin *sol* = Sun.
Earth's Moon	lunar	Lunatic (too much moonlight).
Everything but the Earth	extraterrestrial	

remelted and reformed in a continuous and dynamic process, and other ancient landforms have been altered or destroyed by erosion. Thus, the first 1.5 billion years of the Earth's history have been lost. But the Moon, cold and lifeless, has preserved a record of its history and has allowed us to probe more deeply into the origins of the Earth.

16.7 MERCURY—A PLANET THE SIZE OF THE MOON

Our studies of lunar geology have taught us much about the state of our Solar System several billion years ago. But to complete the picture, really to understand what conditions were like throughout our local region of space,

HOW IS THE GEOLOGICAL HISTORY OF THE MOON AND THE PLANETS DEDUCED?

Considerable information about the geological history of a moon or planet can be deduced by studying the number and type of meteor craters. If there are two regions, and one is marked by a series of meteor craters while the other is smooth and level, we can deduce that both regions were once covered with craters, for external bombardment would affect the entire planet equally. At a later date some of these craters must have been obliterated by volcanic or tectonic activity or through extensive erosion. Thus, the cratered region is geologically older, and the smooth region would have been formed by geological processes. If a few scattered craters appear in the smooth area, and if smaller craters lie inside larger ones, it seems reasonable to believe that a second, later era of meteor bombardment followed the first.

This chronology serves as a rough guide to the sequence of events, but doesn't date the various time periods. In order to

(continued on next page)

establish lunar chronology, astronauts have collected samples of rock from various representative areas on the Moon and brought them back to laboratories on Earth. These have been dated by studying patterns of radioactive decay.

No one has yet retrieved samples of rock and soil from any other celestial bodies for careful analysis here on Earth. However, the lunar chronology may be used to establish a general geological time scale for the Solar System. First, we assume that any significant period of meteor bombardment must have affected the Moon and nearby planets at the same time. Then, it is a simple matter to compare crater patterns on planets with those on the Moon. If the densities, sizes, and general shapes of the craters on a planet are similar to those on the Moon, we may deduce the age of the planetary rock from our knowledge of the Moon. This type of deductive reasoning is not foolproof, but at the moment it is the best we have.

we must expand our vision and study the geological history of the planets.

Mercury is the smallest planet with a radius less than four-tenths that of the Earth. It is also closest to the Sun, and therefore it orbits the Sun faster than any other planet. In fact, each Mercurial year is only 88 days. Mercury rotates on its axis rather slowly, so that it rotates only three times for each two complete revolutions around the Sun. Since it is so close to the Sun and its days are so long, we would expect its sunny side to become unbearably hot, while temperatures would plummet during the course of the long night. These extremes of temperature are enhanced by the fact that there is very little atmosphere on Mercury, so that there can be no wind to carry heat from one region to another. Studies of infrared and radio emissions indicate a daily high of about 500° C (hot enough to melt tin or lead) and nighttime lows of −150° C (nearly cold enough to liquefy oxygen if there were any on the planet).

Little was known about the surface of Mercury before the spring of 1974. At that time a sophisticated spacecraft called *Mariner 10* passed close to Mercury and began relaying information back to Earth. The first *Mariner 10* photographs revealed a cratered surface, similar in many respects to that of the Moon. The similarities in surface contours indicates that the geological histories of the two bodies must be similar. Thus, although many questions remain unanswered, most scientists agree that after its initial formation, Mercury was subject to a period of intense meteor bombardment, similar to the bombardment that occurred on the Moon. Perhaps the interior of the planet was once hot, but no one is sure, for there are no vast lava plains comparable to the lunar maria. The ancient meteor craters stand out sharply, unmarked by extensive erosion or tectonic leveling, for there has been little geological activity during the past few billion years.

Perhaps the most striking discovery of the Mariner probe was that Mercury has a small, but distinctly measurable magnetic field. We believe that the Earth's magnetic field results from the effect of its relatively rapid rotation of its iron core. The surprising

TABLE 16–2. THE PLANETS

Planet	Distance from the Sun (millions of kilometers)	Radius ÷ Earth's Radius	Mass ÷ Earth's Mass	Density (g/cm³)	Length of One Planetary Year* (days)
Mercury	58	0.38	0.055	5.4	88
Venus	108	0.95	0.81	5.2	225
Earth	150	1	1	5.5	365
Mars	229	0.53	0.11	3.9	687
Jupiter	778	11	318	1.3	4340
Saturn	1420	9.4	95	0.7	10,800
Uranus	2860	4.4	15	1.0	30,700
Neptune	4490	3.8	17	1.7	60,000
Pluto	5910	0.4	0.002	0.7	91,000

* Taken with respect to the stars.

The first-pass view of Mercury's northern limb shows a prominent scarp extending from the limb near the middle of the photograph. The photograph shows an area 580 km from side to side. (Courtesy of NASA.)

discovery of a magnetic field on Mercury, *which rotates slowly*, indicates that we do not understand the reasons for the existence of planetary magnetic fields as well as we had thought.

Since the surface of Mercury is so hot, and the gravitational field of the planet is so small, we would expect that any atmospheric gases would have vaporized into space long ago. Surprisingly, an atmosphere was detected on Mercury, and although it is only one trillionth as dense as that on Earth, even this small amount has puzzled scientists.

16.8 VENUS—A STUDY IN CONTRASTS

Of all the planets in our Solar System, Venus most closely resembles Earth with respect to size, density, and mean distance from the Sun. From this information alone, astronomers once believed that environmental conditions on Venus might be expected to be similar to those on Earth and thus that some form of life might be found there. However, until recently it was impossible to study the surface of Venus, for it is wrapped in a thick dense atmosphere and an opaque cloud cover. But now we are virtually certain that no life exists on Venus, for the environment there is excessively harsh. Temperatures on the planet are extremely high; the surface is nearly as hot as that of Mercury, and this heat would destroy any of the complex organic molecules necessary for life.

The atmosphere is dense and turbulent. It is composed of over 97 per cent carbon dioxide, and contains smaller concentrations of nitrogen, helium, neon, and other gases. Drops of concentrated sulfuric acid rain fall from sulfur-bearing clouds. Winds traveling over 300 km/hr at higher elevations blow the clouds around and cause severe lightning storms. A mysterious glow, the result of some sort of unexplained chemical reaction or lu-

Venus. Note that the solid surface of the planet is obscured by a turbulent cloud cover. (Courtesy of NASA Jet Propulsion Laboratory.)

minescence, has been detected by spacecraft.

One is immediately led to wonder why conditions on Venus should be so different from those on Earth. The search for an answer to this question brings us to a better understanding of the homeostatic balance of our own atmospheric environment. Recall from Chapter 13 that we stressed that the Earth's atmosphere is a delicately balanced system. Living organisms probably maintain the present concentration of oxygen and carbon dioxide in the air. But in turn, atmospheric gases regulate surface temperature by the way they absorb infrared radiation. Thus, carbon dioxide absorbs heat efficiently and serves to keep the Earth warm, whereas oxygen does not absorb infrared and permits the heat to escape into space. In sum, terrestrial plants and animals regulate not only the composition of our atmosphere but also (indirectly) surface temperatures. We are not quite sure how delicate this balance is, but some scientists feel that a single large-scale disruption of the present system could be irreversible. This conclusion is supported by current theories on the formation of the Venusian atmosphere. According to the most widely accepted theory, Venusian climate was once very much like that on Earth, only Venus, being slightly closer to the Sun, was originally slightly warmer. According to theory, this initial temperature difference markedly affected the carbon dioxide composition of the atmosphere.

Carbon dioxide is an interesting substance, intimately associated with the forms of life and the climatic processes on Earth. Its formula is CO_2, and its molecular structure is represented as O=C=O. At normal terrestrial temperatures and pressures it is a gas, under high pressure (as in a fire extin-

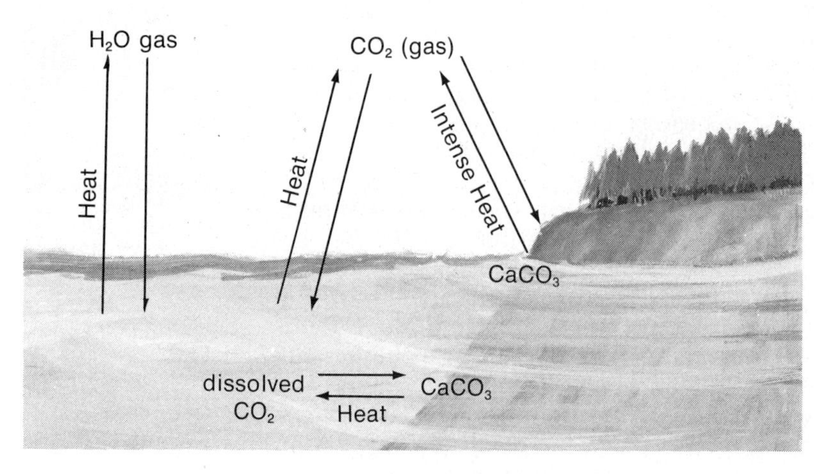

H_2O and CO_2 gases are good infrared absorbers and therefore trap the Sun's energy.

guisher tank) it is a liquid, and below −79° C it is a solid, known as dry ice. CO_2 dissolves readily in cold water, especially at high pressure, and reacts with various substances to form carbonates, such as calcium carbonate, $CaCO_3$, which is the main ingredient of limestone, marble, clamshells, and pearls. CO_2 can be released from a water solution by heat and from a carbonate by acid (or very high temperature).

Most of the carbon dioxide on Earth is held in limestone formations, a lesser amount is in solution in the sea, and only a small fraction exists free in the atmosphere. Most probably the carbon dioxide on Venus was at one time also bound in the water and rocks. But since Venus naturally receives more sunlight than does Earth, more of the bound carbon dioxide was released as a gas. The gaseous carbon dioxide then acted as an infrared absorber and caused further warming of the atmosphere. Conditions spiraled, and further warming led to the release of more carbon dioxide until the atmosphere reached its present state. It now contains 97 per cent carbon dioxide and is nearly 100 times as dense as that of the Earth. Thus, the atmosphere became a more and more effective insulator, and heat from the surface of the planet could not escape into space. Temperatures rose until finally an equilibrium temperature of about 450° C, hot enough to melt tin or lead, was reached.

Is it possible for a small temperature rise on Earth to initiate the chain reaction that once started on Venus? We don't know, but we learn again and again that natural systems may respond drastically to a small initial perturbation.

In 1975 a Soviet spacecraft landed on the surface of Venus. The intense heat and pressure rapidly destroyed the instruments aboard, but before the radio transmitter failed, a single photograph was sent back to Earth. This picture shows sharply angular rock, as can be seen in Figure 16–14*A*. A second Soviet craft soon landed 2000 km away and returned a photograph of a smooth landscape interspersed with sections of cooled lava or highly weathered rock (Fig. 16–14*B*). What a wealth of information is contained in just two photographs! The angular rocks must be geologically young, for they would be expected to erode rapidly in the harsh conditions of the Venusian atmosphere. The smooth landscape and weathered rock of the second landing site would necessarily be older. Thus, scientists were able to deduce from the evidence that there has been recent tectonic activity on Venus. In 1978, two United States Pioneer spacecraft used radar equipment to generate topographical maps of the plant. These data have supported earlier conclusions about geological activity, and have shown mountain ranges higher than the Himalayas, rifts or gorges many times larger than the Grand Canyon, and vast plains.

SOME REACTIONS OF CARBON DIOXIDE IN THE ENVIRONMENT

1. It dissolves in water, or can be released from a water solution by heat.

$$CO_2 \text{ (dissolved)} \underset{\text{cold}}{\overset{\text{heat}}{\rightleftharpoons}} CO_2 \text{ (gas)}$$

2. It reacts to form carbonates.

$$\underset{}{CO_2} + \underset{\text{hydrated lime}}{Ca(OH)_2} \rightarrow \underset{\substack{\text{calcium carbonate} \\ \text{(limestone)}}}{CaCO_3} + H_2O$$

3. It can be released from its carbonate by heat or acid.

$$CaCO_3 \xrightarrow{\text{heat}} \underset{\text{calcium oxide}}{CaO} + CO_2$$

$$CaCO_3 + \underset{\text{sulfuric acid}}{H_2SO_4} \rightarrow CaSO_4 + H_2O + CO_2$$

The third planet from the Sun is the Earth, the history and geology of which are discussed in Chapters 13 and 14.

Figure 16–14. *A,* The surface of Venus photographed from Venera 9. Notice the sharply angled rocks.
B, The surface of Venus 2000 km from the Venera 9 landing site, photographed by Venera 10. Note how much smoother the surface is. (Both from Pasachoff, Jay M.: *Contemporary Astronomy.* Second edition. Philadelphia, Saunders College Publishing, 1981.)

16.9 MARS—A SEARCH FOR EXTRATERRESTRIAL LIFE

Mars has captured the imagination of scientists and lay people alike, for early observations seemed to indicate that if extraterrestrial life existed within the Solar System, it would be found on that planet. Even today, after samples of Martian soil have been analyzed directly and no conclusive evidence of organic matter has been found, children still hide from imaginary Martians in their play and some scientists believe that perhaps we should look harder for microbes on this planet. Traditionally, there have been three main arguments that lead to the speculation that life may exist on Mars.

1. The gross physical features of Mars are comparable to those of Earth. It is both smaller and less dense than our planet, but the differences are not great. Mars is close enough to the Sun to receive appreciable quantities of solar radiation so that we would expect it to be reasonably warm. Of course, we learned in the last section that Venus is quite inhospitable despite its favorable size and position in the Solar System, so this argument by itself is not conclusive.

2. Unlike Venus, Mars is covered by a thin, nearly cloudless atmosphere that enables us to view its surface from telescopes mounted on Earth. Several hundred years ago it was noted that the Martian polar regions are white and that the white ground cover shrinks in summer and expands in winter. These changes strongly suggested that the white regions are ice caps. Moreover, if

Figure 16–15. *A*, This 100° view of the Martian surface was taken from the Viking 1 lander looking northeast at left and southeast at right. It shows a dune field with features similar to many seen in the deserts of Earth. From the shape of the peaks, it seems that the dunes move from upper left to lower right. The large boulder at the left is about 8 m from the lander and is 1 × 3 meters in size. The boom that supports Viking's weather station cuts through the center of the picture. (From Pasachoff, Jay M.: *Contemporary Astronomy*. Second edition. Philadelphia, Saunders College Publishing, 1981.)

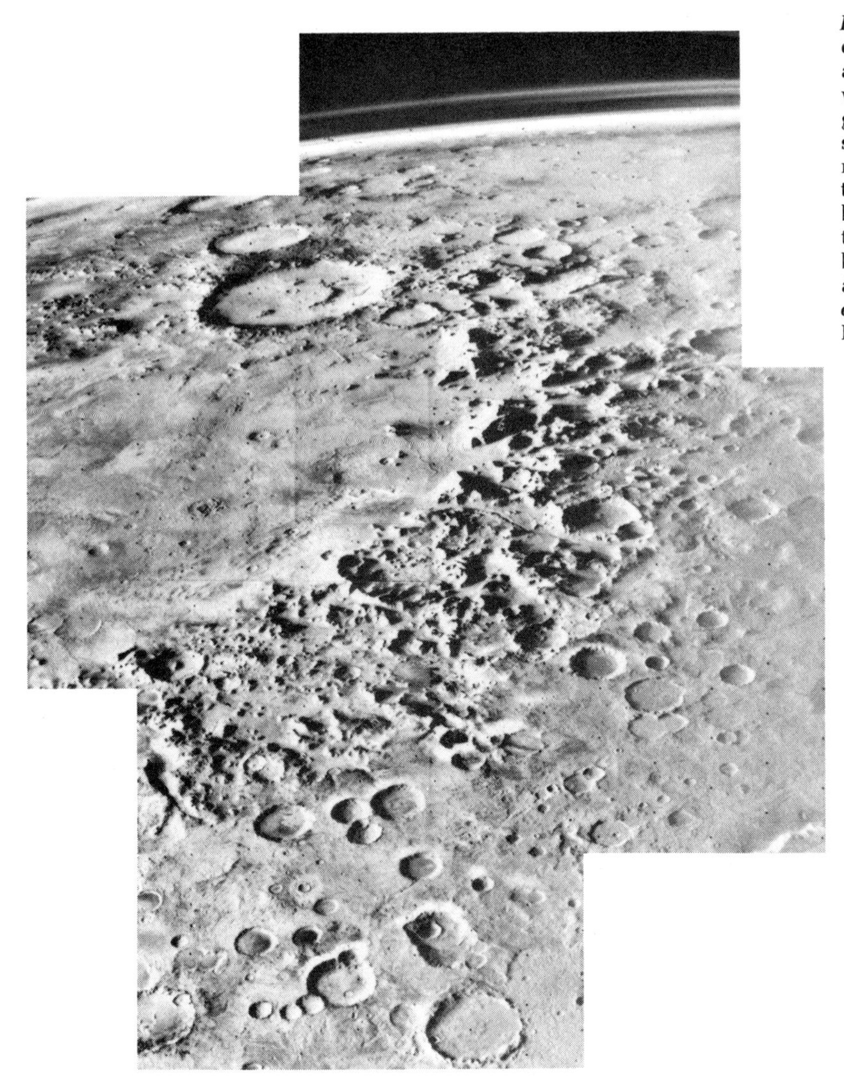

B, This oblique view from the Viking 1 orbiter shows Argyre, the smooth plain at left center. The Martian atmosphere was unusually clear when this photograph was taken, and craters can be seen nearly to the horizon. The brightness of the horizon results mainly from a thin haze. Detached layers of haze can be seen to extend from 25 to 40 km above the horizon, and may be crystals of carbon dioxide. (From Pasachoff, Jay M., and Kutner, Marc L.: *University Astronomy*. Philadelphia, Saunders College Publishing, 1978.)

Olympus Mons, the largest Martian volcano is nearly three times as high as Mt. Everest, and its crater is large enough to drop Manhattan Island into. (From Pasachoff, Jay M.: *Contemporary Astronomy.* Second edition. Philadelphia, Saunders College Publishing, 1981.)

16.10 JUPITER—A STAR THAT FAILED

Mercury, Venus, Earth, and Mars constitute a foursome called the **terrestrial planets.** They are all relatively small, with a solid mineral crust, and all orbit close to the Sun. Despite their differences, the four are composed of roughly the same elements and have experienced similar geological histories. As we shall see, the giant outer planets that we are about to study—Jupiter, Saturn, Uranus, and Neptune—are considerably different from the terrestrial group. Visualize once again the primordial dust cloud that was eventually to condense to form the Solar System. As the cloud shrank and broke apart, the protosun and all the protoplanets were originally composed mainly of hydrogen and helium. The Sun's gravitation was so great that it pulled its gases inward with enough force to initiate fusion reactions. On the other hand, the gravitational fields of the terrestrial planets were so weak that most of their light gases escaped and boiled off into space or were blown away by the solar wind. Jupiter is very much larger than any of the terrestrial planets, yet very much smaller than the Sun. Therefore, it is physically similar to neither.

As Jupiter was being formed, the inward condensation provided enough energy to heat the dust appreciably, but fusion temperatures were never reached. Yet the internal mass was sufficient for the gravitational forces to retain most of the original hydrogen and helium. Therefore, the chemical composition of Jupiter is much like that of the Sun, but its internal temperature and structure are very different. Many of the outer bodies of the Solar System, like the stars, contain mostly hydrogen and helium.

As shown in Figure 16–16, more than half the volume of Jupiter is a vast sea of liquid, molecular hydrogen, H_2. There is no hard, solid, rocky surface where an astronaut could land or walk about. An inner layer that is also composed of hydrogen lies beneath this outer hydrogen ocean. Within this mantle region temperatures are as high as 30,000° K, and pressures are as great as 100 million times the Earth's atmospheric pressure at sea level. Under these extreme conditions, hydrogen molecules are pulled apart to form atoms, and the atoms themselves are squeezed together so tightly that the electrons are "loosened" from their specific nuclei. The electrons become free to travel throughout the highly compressed array of hydrogen nuclei, much as electrons travel in conventional metals. As a result, the hydrogen assumes a metallic form. This material conducts electricity and is called **liquid metallic hydrogen.** Jupiter's core is a solid, rocky sphere about 20 times as massive as the Earth, and is probably composed of iron, nickel, and other metals and minerals.

Above the surface, the Jovian atmosphere contains a mixture of gases, liquid droplets, and crystalline parti-

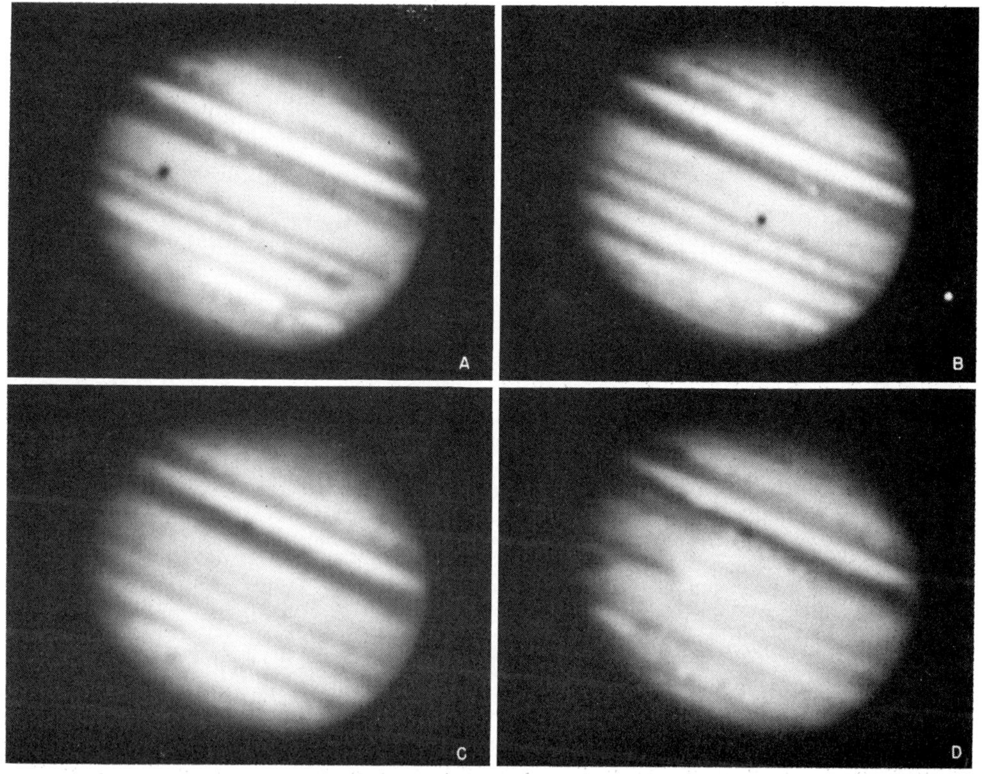

Jupiter, as seen through a 200-inch telescope. Note one of Jupiter's satellites in the lower right-hand corner and its shadow projected on the surface. (© California Institute of Technology and Carnegie Institution of Washington. The Palomar Observatory.)

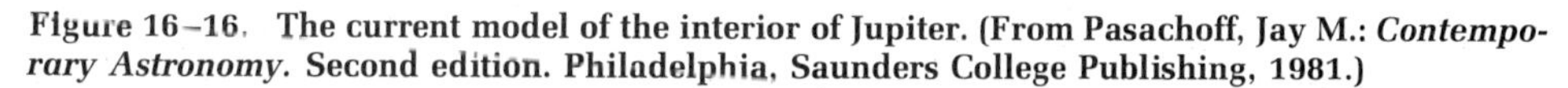
Figure 16–16. The current model of the interior of Jupiter. (From Pasachoff, Jay M.: *Contemporary Astronomy.* Second edition. Philadelphia, Saunders College Publishing, 1981.)

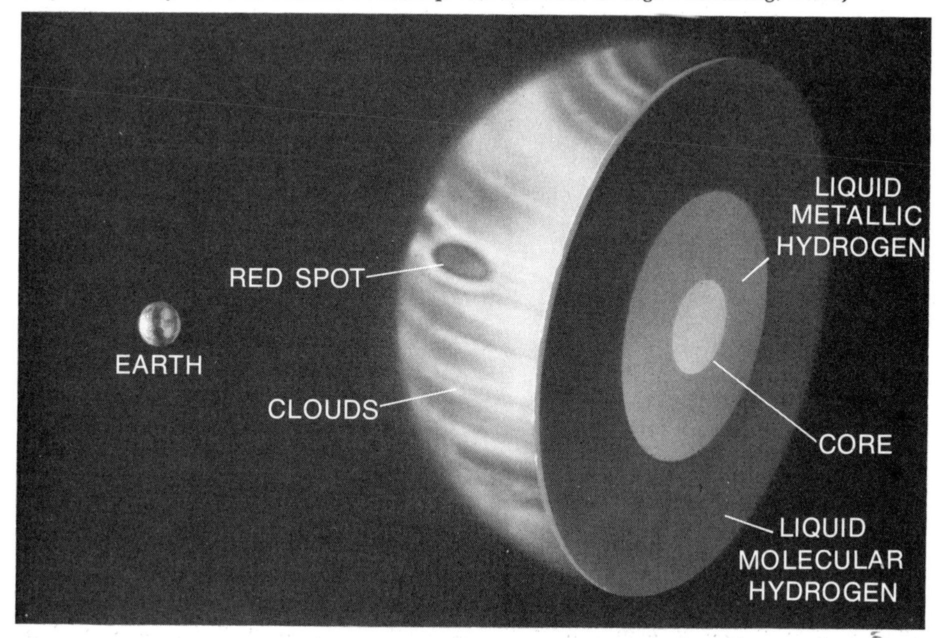

cles, consisting of hydrogen, helium, ammonia, methane, water, hydrogen sulfide, and other substances. This atmosphere is indeed a turbulent region. It is heated from above by the rays of the Sun and from below, to an even greater extent, by the interior of the planet. Moreover, the giant planet spins quite rapidly, rotating once approximately every ten hours. Recall from Chapter 13 that on Earth the wind systems are initiated by uneven heating of the atmosphere, which generates large convection cells that lift and lower massive quantities of gas. The

Voyager 1 took this photo of Jupiter on February 1, 1979, at a range of 32.7 million km. Scientists can now see different colors in clouds around the Great Red Spot, which imply that the clouds swirl around the spot at varying altitudes. Scientists also observe apparently regular spacing between the small white spots in the southern hemisphere and similar positioning of dark spots in the northern hemisphere. A major activity will be to understand the form and structure of the spots and how they may relate to interactions between the atmospheric composition and its motions. When scientists compare this image with the 6000 others already taken, they see many changes. The bright cloud in the equatorial region north of the Great Red Spot, for example, appears to be where bright clouds originate, then stream westward. On the other hand, the bright ovals south of the Great Red Spot were seen to form about 40 years ago and have remained much the same ever since. The Great Red Spot itself has been observed for hundreds of years, though never in the detail seen here. Objects as small as 600 km across can be seen in this image, the best resolution achieved of Jupiter. This photo was produced from three black-and-white images taken from blue, green, and orange filters and assembled by the Image Processing Lab at the Jet Propulsion Laboratory. The Voyager Project is managed for NASA's Office of Space Science by the Jet Propulsion Laboratory. (Courtesy of NASA.)

This photo of Jupiter was taken by Voyager 1 on March 1, 1979, at a distance of 5 million km. The photo shows Jupiter's Great Red Spot (*upper right*) and the turbulent region immediately to the west. At the middle right of the frame is one of several white ovals seen on Jupiter from Earth. The detail in every structure here is far better than has ever been seen from any telescopic observations. The Red Spot and the white oval both reveal intricate and involved structure. The smallest details that can be seen in this photo are about 95 km across. The Voyager Project is managed for NASA's Office of Space Science by the Jet Propulsion Laboratory. (Courtesy of NASA.)

motion of the air is then deflected by the effects of the rotation of the Earth, thus forming a complex pattern of wind systems. On Jupiter, atmospheric gases are heated even more intensely, and convection cells are established. The extremely rapid rotation of the planet then deflects any horizontal movement, generating turbulent wind systems. Great storms and changing weather patterns can be seen on the surface of Jupiter. Powerful jet streams travel at speeds of up to 500 km/hr in alternating bands from east to west and from west to east. Periodically, cloud systems are caught by the jet stream winds and dispersed or distorted. In one example, time-lapse photographs showed a series of clouds, each as large as North America, move along in a jet stream, strike a dark-ringed bright spot, bounce back, and move off again in the opposite direction at high speeds. Lightning storms and auroral displays have been observed.

Most of the recognizable storm systems appear to form, distort, and move on within a few hours or days, but some of them are surprisingly stable over long periods of time. Over 300 years ago, two European astronomers reported seeing a **Great Red Spot** on the surface of Jupiter, and although its shape and color has changed noticeably from year to year, the spot remains intact to this day. It is now believed to be a giant hurricane-like storm so large that if the Earth's crust were peeled off like a giant orange and laid flat, it would fit entirely within it. No one knows exactly why the Great Red Spot has retained its integrity over all these years. Hurricanes on Earth dissipate after a week or so, yet some combination of forces has maintained the integrity of the Great Red Spot for centuries.

Recall that Jupiter contains a me-

Artists drawing of the Voyager spacecraft in flight. (Courtesy of NASA Jet Propulsion Laboratory).

tallic core capable of conducting electricity, and that the planet itself rotates rapidly on its axis. These conditions combine to produce a powerful dynamo effect that produces an intense magnetic field that generates 400 million times as much energy as is produced by the Earth's magnetism. On Earth, charged particles from the solar wind and other cosmic sources are trapped by the magnetic field and forced to orbit around our planet in a broad, doughnut-shaped belt. The much stronger Jovian magnetism has trapped a proportionately larger quantity of high-energy particles, and the radiation levels surrounding Jupiter are the highest ever recorded in space. Strong electromagnetic interactions have been observed between Jupiter and one of its closest moons, Io. The surface of Io contains many ions, and it is believed that some of these are strongly accelerated by the Jovian magnetic field. Temperatures over 100 million degrees Celsius, hotter than the interior of the Sun, have been recorded within a high speed plasma near Io. However, comparatively little heat is contained in this cloud, because the ion density is very low. Thus, spacecraft can pass through the plasma without melting, even though no material could ever penetrate the core of a hot star without vaporizing nearly instantaneously.

The Moons of Jupiter

Recall that many fifteenth and sixteenth century astronomers believed that the Earth was the center of the Universe and that all the other heavenly bodies revolved around it. In 1610, Galileo discovered four tiny specks of light close to Jupiter. He noted that they distinctly orbited around Jupiter and correctly reasoned that they were satellites of the giant planet. This direct visual evidence that at least some objects did not orbit the Earth was the first concrete proof that the Earth was not the center of all motion in the Universe.

A total of 14 moons revolve around the planet Jupiter. A rocky ring, similar to the rings around Saturn, lies within the orbit of the closest moon, and according to current theory, this ring may be the remnants of a fifteenth satellite that was either torn apart by the gravitational field of Jupiter or was never able to coalesce (see Section 16.12 for a further discussion of the origin of planetary rings). Of these 14, the 4 that were originally discovered by Galileo have been most widely studied. The innermost Galilean moon, Io, is small, dense, and rocky, while the outermost, Callisto, is significantly less dense and is believed to consist largely of water ice. Thus, the Jovian moon system is reminiscent of the Solar System itself, for as we have seen, the inner four planets are much more dense than the five in orbit beyond.

These similarities imply that perhaps Jupiter and its moons were formed simultaneously, much as the Solar System itself was formed. Just as the Sun and the planets condensed out of a single nebula, it is possible that Jupiter and its moons condensed as sort of a mini–solar system of their own. As Jupiter coalesced, huge quantities of heat must have been generated by gravitational forces. This heat was sufficient to boil most of the lighter elements off the surface of Io, leaving behind a relatively dense sphere. The outer two Galilean moons, Ganymede and Callisto, retained more of their lighter elements and are now less dense.

Io

Io is a small satellite, only two-thirds the size of the Earth's Moon and just slightly more dense. Since it is too small to have retained the heat released by radioactive decay in its interior, some observers expected to see a cold, lifeless, cratered, lunar-like surface. Nothing could be further from the truth. Spectacular photographs transmitted from Voyager spacecraft showed clear images of volcanoes erupting on the surface of Io. (see Fig. 16–17). Huge masses of gas and rock were seen to be ejected over 200 km above the surface. These pictures provided the first evidence of currently active volcanism in

Figure 16–17. Volcanic explosion on Io. Voyager 1 acquired this image of Io on March 4, 1979. An enormous volcanic explosion can be seen silhouetted against dark space over Io's horizon. At this time solid material had been thrown up to an altitude of about 160 km. (Courtesy of NASA.)

the Solar System. A few weeks before the Voyager photographs were transmitted to Earth, two scientists hypothesized on theoretical grounds that tidal forces might possibly heat Io's interior enough to make the planet geologically active. To understand this concept, recall that the gravitational field of our own Moon is sufficiently strong to cause the rise and fall of the ocean tides on Earth. Similarly, the Earth's gravitation affects the Moon and may be partly responsible for many of the small moonquakes that have been reported on the lunar crust. Jupiter is more than 300 times more massive than the Earth, so the gravitational forces exerted on Io are correspondingly greater. In addition, the three nearby satellites, Europa, Ganymede and Callisto, are large enough to exert significant tidal forces on Io, but these forces pull in the opposite direction. This opposition of tidal effects has caused enough friction within the interior mantle of Io to generate the heat required for a nearly continuous volcanic action. The frequent lava flows have obliterated all ancient land forms, giving Io a smooth and nearly craterless crust.

Europa

Calculations show that the second of the Galilean moons, Europa, should also be subject to powerful tidal forces, but since Europa is further from Jupiter, the tidal influence should be significantly less. Although no active volcanoes were observed on Europa, the surface appears to be smooth and relatively craterless, indicating that some sort of geological activity has occurred in recent times. Perhaps the

This picture of Europa, the smallest Galilean satellite, was taken in the afternoon of March 4, 1979, from a distance of about 2 million km by Voyager 1. The bright areas are probably ice deposits, while the dark areas may be the rocky surface or areas with a patchier distribution of ice. The most unusual features are the systems of long linear structures which cross the surface in various directions. Some of these linear structures are over 1000 km long and about 200 or 300 km wide. They may be fractures or faults which have disrupted the surface. (Courtesy of NASA.)

planet has cooled considerably, or perhaps some volcanoes are currently active but were not erupting just at the time the spacecraft was passing by, or perhaps they were not detected because Voyager never flew close enough to Europa to record them. Even if there are no volcanoes, large lines or streaks observed on the surface are believed to be global fault systems or earthquake fractures resulting from tectonic movement.

Ganymede and Callisto

Both Ganymede and Callisto are believed to be large spheres composed of a mixture of rock and water ice. Two distinctly different types of terrain were observed on Ganymede; one is heavily cratered while the other is grooved and contains fewer craters. Astronomers believe that the heavily cratered regions are more than four billion years old, whereas the smooth regions are much newer, and have been formed by recent tectonic activity.

Callisto, the outermost Galilean moon, is heavily cratered and shows no grooved or smooth terrain. These data indicate that its surface crust is very old. The craters are shaped differently than those on Ganymede or on our own Moon, and some observers believe that a layer of ice is slowly moving or flowing across the surface.

The study of the moons of Jupiter has been rewarding indeed. Evidence of volcanism and tectonic movement support many theories of geologic activity on Earth and may aid in our understanding of our own planet. Furthermore, detailed studies of cratering rates on these distant moons will increase our understanding of events in the Solar System billions of years ago.

Ganymede is Jupiter's largest satellite with a radius of approximately 2600 km, about 1.5 times that of our Moon. Ganymede has a bulk density of only approximately 2.0 g/cm^3, almost half that of the Moon. Therefore, Ganymede is probably composed of a mixture of rock and ice. The long white filaments resemble rays associated with impacts on the lunar surface. (Courtesy of NASA.)

This picture of Callisto was taken by Voyager 1 on Tuesday, March 6, 1979, during Voyager's approach to Jupiter's outer large satellite. The spacecraft was 350,000 km from Callisto at the time and shows features about 7 km across on the surface. Callisto is a little smaller than Ganymede (about the size of the planet Mercury) and is apparently composed of a mixture of ice and rock. The darker color of Callisto suggests that the upper surface is "dirty ice" or water-rich rock frozen on Callisto's cold surface (approximately 120 K, or −243°F at the equator). Far more craters appear on the surface of Callisto than on the surface of Ganymede, leading scientists to believe that Callisto is quite old. Callisto possibly dates back to final accretional stages of planet formation 4 to 4.5 billion years ago. (Courtesy of NASA.)

16.11 SATURN

Saturn, the second largest planet, is similar in many respects to Jupiter. It has the lowest density of all the planets, so low in fact that the entire planet could float on water if we had a bathtub large enough to hold it. This low density implies that it, too, must be composed primarily of hydrogen and helium. Saturn's clouds and atmosphere have been analyzed by ground-based observers, as well as by instruments aboard Pioneer 11, which passed the planet in the fall of 1979. The data that have been processed to date indicate that the atmosphere is similar to that of Jupiter, with the exception that the mean temperature of Saturn is lower

Saturn's density is lower than that of water. (From Pasachoff, Jay M.: *Contemporary Astronomy.* 2nd edition. Philadelphia, Saunders College Publishing, 1981.)

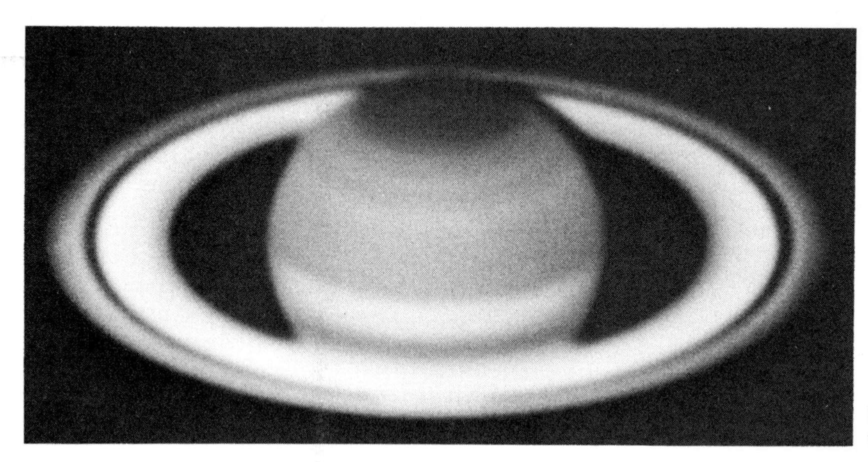

Figure 16–18. Saturn and ring system. (Hale Observatories.)

than that of her sister planet. Therefore, some substances that are gases on Jupiter are frozen solid on Saturn. Dense clouds cover the planet, and several distinct, storm systems have been photographed. As was expected, Pioneer detected a sizable planetary magnetic field.

Saturn is surrounded by a series of bright rings that are readily visible from Earth even through a small telescope (see Fig. 16–18). They appear to be extremely thin, perhaps no more than 10 km or maybe even 10 to 100 m thick, but they are quite wide. The rings are composed of many rough chunks of ice or rock whose diameters range from perhaps a few centimeters to a meter or so. According to current theory, these rings are believed to be the scattered remnants of a moon that was never formed or one that was formed and then ripped apart by the gravitational field of Saturn. Small objects, such as the page of this book or a human being, are held together by electrical attractions among the atoms and molecules. But large objects, such as the Sun, the planets, and their satellites, are held together mainly by gravitational forces. Now imagine what happens to a small satellite orbiting a larger central planet. The surface of the moon closest to the planet is attracted more strongly than the region further away, establishing a differential shear, called a tidal force. As mentioned earlier, the tidal forces between the Earth and Moon cause ocean movements on

Voyager I passed close to Saturn in November 1980. Three new moons were discovered as well as a great amount of additional detail on Saturn's ring and atmosphere.

View of Saturn taken by Pioneer during its flyby mission. The somewhat distorted shape of the planet is due to uneven spacing of scan lines by the instrument aboard the spacecraft and will be corrected by additional computer processing. (Courtesy of NASA.)

The moon Titan as seen for the first time by spacecraft. Taken by Pioneer on September 2, 1979. (Courtesy of NASA.)

the Earth and seismic rumblings on the Moon, whereas forces between Io and Jupiter are comparatively greater, causing the internal layers of rock in Io to move and heat up. If a satellite is too close to its planet, then the tidal forces can be greater than the internal forces of attraction and the satellite will be pulled apart. Thus, the rings of Saturn may be composed of the debris of a satellite that was too close to the mother planet to hold together.

16.12 URANUS AND NEPTUNE

Uranus and Neptune, both invisible to the naked eye from Earth, were unknown to the ancients. They are so distant that even today we know little about them. Uranus and Neptune are both quite large in size but low in density. Presumably they are similar in structure to Jupiter and Saturn, being composed primarily of hydrogen and helium and having a solid mineral core. In 1977, scientists discovered rings around Uranus, and the structure of these may be similar to the structure of the rings around Saturn.

16.13 PLUTO

Pluto, the outermost of the known planets, is quite small, roughly about the same size as the Earth. Spectroscopic studies of Pluto's surface indicate that methane ice exists on the planet. Therefore, temperatures must be extremely low, colder than −220° C. For many years astronomers believed that Pluto was dense and rocky, like the terrestrial planets. However, our understanding altered drastically in 1978 when a satellite was discovered orbiting this distant planet. Using mathematical laws discovered by Kepler and Newton in the 1600's, it is possible to calculate the relative masses of a planet and a satellite if we know the radius of the satellite's orbit and the time required for one complete rotation. Using

Small sections of the plates from which Tombaugh discovered Pluto. On February 18, 1930, Tombaugh noticed that one dot among many had moved between January 23, 1930 (*top*) and January 29, 1930 (*bottom*). Tombaugh used the astronomical technique of *blink comparison,* in which two photographs are optically superimposed and viewed one after the other. Objects that have moved become readily apparent. (From Pasachoff, Jay M.: *Contemporary Astronomy.* Second edition. Philadelphia, Saunders College Publishing, 1981. Lowell Observatory Photograph.)

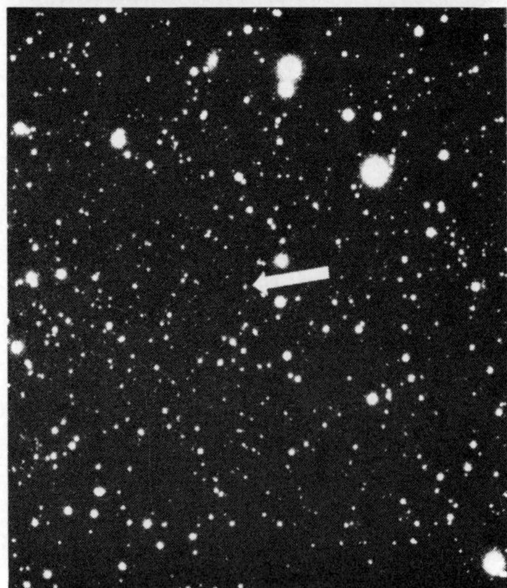

TABLE 16–3. COMPARISON OF THE NINE MAJOR PLANETS

Planet	Distance from Sun (millions of kilometers)	Mass (compared to mass of Earth = 1)	Density (compared to density of water = 1)	Composition of Planet	Density of Atmosphere (compared to Earth's atmosphere = 1)
Terrestrial Planets					
Mercury	58	0.06	5.4	Rocky with metallic core.	One trillionth
Venus	108	0.82	5.2		100
Earth	150	1	5.5		1
Mars	229	0.11	3.9		0.01
Giant Planets					
Jupiter	778	318	1.3	Liquid hydrogen surface with liquid metallic mantle and solid core.	Dense and turbulent
Saturn	1420	95	0.7	Hydrogen and helium outer layers with solid core.	Similar to Jupiter except that some compounds that are gases on Jupiter are frozen on the outer planets
Uranus	2860	15	1.0		
Neptune	4490	17	1.7		
Most Distant Planet					
Pluto	5910	0.002?	0.7	?	?

the best available data, the density of Pluto has been estimated to be about that of Saturn, indicating that it is composed of light elements.

16.14 COMETS, ASTEROIDS, AND METEOROIDS

The terrestrial planets are no longer subject to the intense bombardment from outer space that once generated enough heat to melt large volumes of crustal rock. But if you sit outside on almost any clear night watching the sky for a few hours, you may see a fiery streak called a **meteor,** or **shooting star,** descend toward Earth. Shooting stars appear when small bits of interplanetary solid matter, called **meteoroids** are caught by the Earth's gravity and accelerated through the atmosphere. Friction between the meteoroid and the atmosphere produces enough heat to melt the solid and emit a fiery glow. Most meteoroids are barely larger than a grain of sand when they enter the

Shooting star. (From Pasachoff, Jay M.: *Contemporary Astronomy: An Introduction.* Philadelphia, W.B. Saunders Co., 1977.)

atmosphere and are completely vaporized before they reach the Earth. If they are larger, say the size of a basketball, some of the original material falls to the ground. A fallen meteoroid is called a **meteorite.** Examination of fallen debris indicates that meteorites are roughly as old as the Solar System, approximately 4.6 billion years. Some meteorites have never been subjected to planetary heating and remelting, and scientists feel that these fragments represent the kind of primordial material that originally condensed out of the interspacial dust. Most meteorites are probably debris from non-planetary bodies that orbit the Sun and thus are our neighbors in the Solar System.

Between the orbits of Mars and Jupiter there is a large open space, in which eighteenth-century astronomers predicted on numerological grounds that a planet might be found. Instead of a full-sized planet, however, observers have found tens of thousands of smaller bodies orbiting in a wide ring. These bodies are called **asteroids.** The largest asteroid has a diameter of 770 km. Three others are about half the size, and most are far smaller. The orbit of a given asteroid is not permanently fixed, like that of a planet. If an asteroid passes too close to a nearby planet, it will, of course, be pulled towards it and fall onto the planet's surface. However, if an asteroid passes by a planet without getting too close, the gravitational force of the planet will pull the asteroid out of its current orbit and deflect it into a new orbit about the Sun. Thus a given asteroid may change its orbit frequently in an erratic manner. So imagine tens of thousands of small bodies racing through space in changing paths. It is not surprising that many of them should collide with each other. After a collision, the asteroids often break apart, and the small fragments and pieces of dust leave the collision site helter skelter at widely divergent angles. Some of these fragments cross the orbit of the Earth and are attracted by our gravitational field. These then fall through the atmosphere and are visible as shooting stars. Asteroids are not the only source of meteoroids. We will see later that when the Earth travels through the diffuse tail of a comet it attracts many small particles and intense meteor showers are visible.

What is the probability that a large fragment or even an entire asteroid will strike the Earth some day? Geological evidence indicates that such events have occurred in the past. For example, there is a large crater near Winslow, Arizona, approximately 1.5 km in diameter, that was formed by a falling meteorite which probably weighed about one million metric tons. This meteorite is believed to have landed in recent geological history, and the crater is perhaps no more than 50,000 years

Aerial view of the Winslow meteor crater.

old. Other curious circular basins exist on the surface of the Earth that may well be eroded remnants of large meteor craters. For example, in one region of the province of Quebec, Canada, there is a series of long thin lakes that were carved out by the glaciers during the Ice Age. In the center of these lies a single circular lake. The rock under this lake is cracked and fragmented as if it had been struck by a large heavy object. Since it is unreasonable to assume that a glacier rotated to form the circular lake, it may have been formed by impact from a large meteor. In addition, hundreds of other similar formations have been found, leading scientists to suspect that devastating meteorite impacts have occurred fairly frequently, and therefore one might expect another to land sometime within the next few thousand years.

Occasionally a fuzzy object appears in the sky, travels slowly around the Sun in an elongated elliptical orbit, and disappears again out into space. These objects are called **comets** after the Greek word for "longhaired" and have been considered to be powerful astrological omens. Despite their fiery appearance, comets are quite cold, and most of the light that we see is simply reflected sunlight. According to current theory, the head of a comet is probably a tenuous collection of rock and metallic particles coated with water, ammonia, methane, and carbon dioxide, all as frozen solids. As the comet approaches the Sun, solar radiation vaporizes its surface, and the force of the solar wind blows some of the lighter particles away from the head to form a long tail. As the comet orbits the Sun, the solar wind constantly blows the tail so that it always faces away from the Sun, as shown in Figure 16–20. Comet tails have been observed to be over 90 million miles long (almost as long as the distance from the Earth to the Sun). There is very little matter in a comet tail. By terrestrial standards this region would represent a good cold laboratory vacuum, yet viewed from a celestial perspective such an object looks like a hot, dense, fiery arrow. Some comets travel in very long cigar-shaped orbits that carry them well out into space, beyond even the orbit of

Isaac Asimov in his essay "The Rocks of Damocles" argues that the biblical flood of Noah may have been caused when a giant meteorite fell in the Persian Gulf, washing a devastating tidal wave up the Tigris-Euphrates Valley. He states, "It would be a supertsunami, a tidal wave to end all tidal waves, and it would scour much of the valley clean. The water would cover what was indeed 'all the world' to the inhabitants and drown countless numbers in its path.

"In support of this notion I would like to point out that the Bible speaks of more than rain. Genesis 7:11 says not only that 'the windows of Heaven were opened,' meaning that it rained, but also that 'the same day were all the fountains of the great deep broken up.' Meaning what? Meaning, it seems to me, that the water came in from the sea.

"Furthermore, Noah's ark lacked any motive power, either sails or oars, and simply drifted. Where did it drift? It came to rest on the mountains of Ararat in the Caucasian foothills northwest of the Tigris-Euphrates. But an ordinary river flood would have washed boats southeastward out to sea. Only a tidal wave of unprecedented scope would have carried the ark northwestward."

Figure 16–19. *A,* **Halley's Comet. Fourteen views made between April 26 and June 11, 1910.**

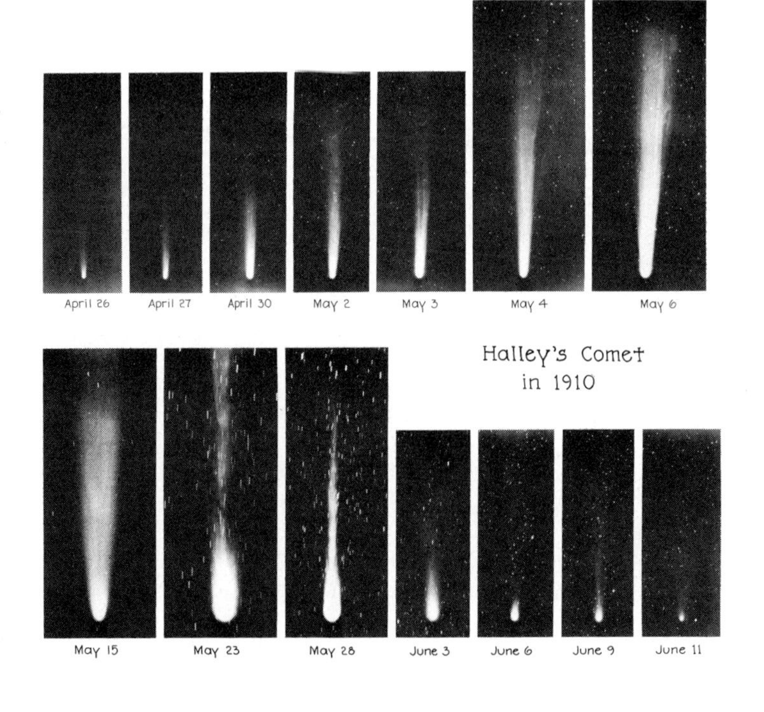

Comet West, a bright comet that was visible to pre-dawn observers in the Northern Hemisphere in 1976.

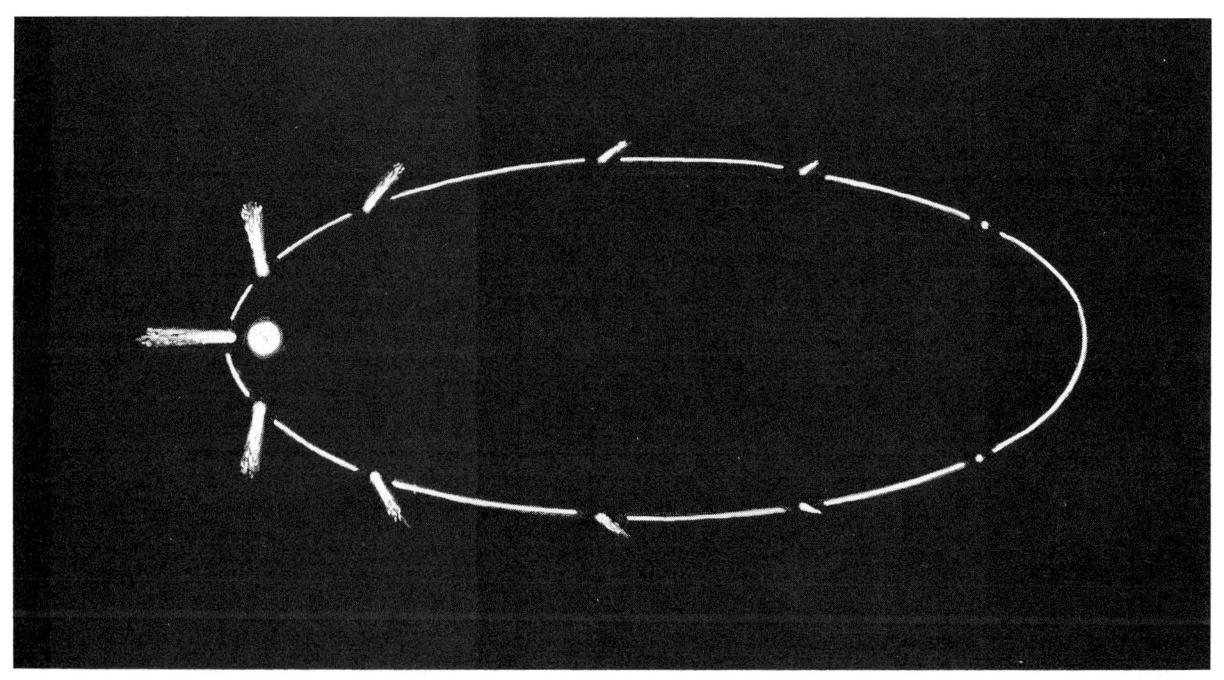

Figure 16–20. A comet's tail always points away from the Sun.

Pluto, the furthermost of the known planets.

Approximately 12 comets per year pass by the Earth on their orbits around the Sun, but most of these are too faint to be seen by the naked eye. Very few comets are visible enough to attract the attention of non-scientists.

> Comets have long been seen as omens.
>
> "When beggars die, there are no comets seen; the heavens themselves blaze forth the death of princes."
>
> Shakespeare, *Julius Caesar*

16.15 EPILOGUE

If we measure the size of the Solar System using any form of terrestrial standards, it appears to be quite large. After all, Pluto orbits with a mean distance of 5.6 billion kilometers from the Sun, and comets orbit farther out than that. But when we extend our vision outward into space, we find that a few billion kilometers is insignificant, for intergalactic distances are measured in billions of billions of kilometers. And our Sun is only one of billions of stars in a galaxy that is only one of millions of galaxies in the known universe.

CHAPTER OBJECTIVES

Understand the motion of the Earth and the Moon and be able to explain: (a) the phases of the Moon; (b) eclipses; (c) tides.

Understand the current theories for the formation of the Solar System.

Know the structure, composition, and geological history of the Sun, the Moon, and the nine planets: Mercury, Venus, Earth, Mars, Jupiter, Saturn, Uranus, Neptune, and Pluto. Familiarize yourself with other objects in the Solar System: meteoroids, asteroids, and comets.

KEY WORDS

Parallax
Ellipse
Revolve
Rotate
Heliocentric
Full moon
New moon
Crescent moon
Nodes of an orbit
Eclipse
Tide
Tidal current
Protosun
Planets
Photosphere
Sunspot
Solar flare
Chromosphere
Corona
Solar wind
Moon
Lunar maria
Mercury
Venus
Mars
Terrestrial planets
Jupiter
Liquid metallic hydrogen
The Great Red Spot
Saturn
Uranus
Neptune
Pluto
Shooting star
Meteoroid
Meteorite
Asteroid
Comet

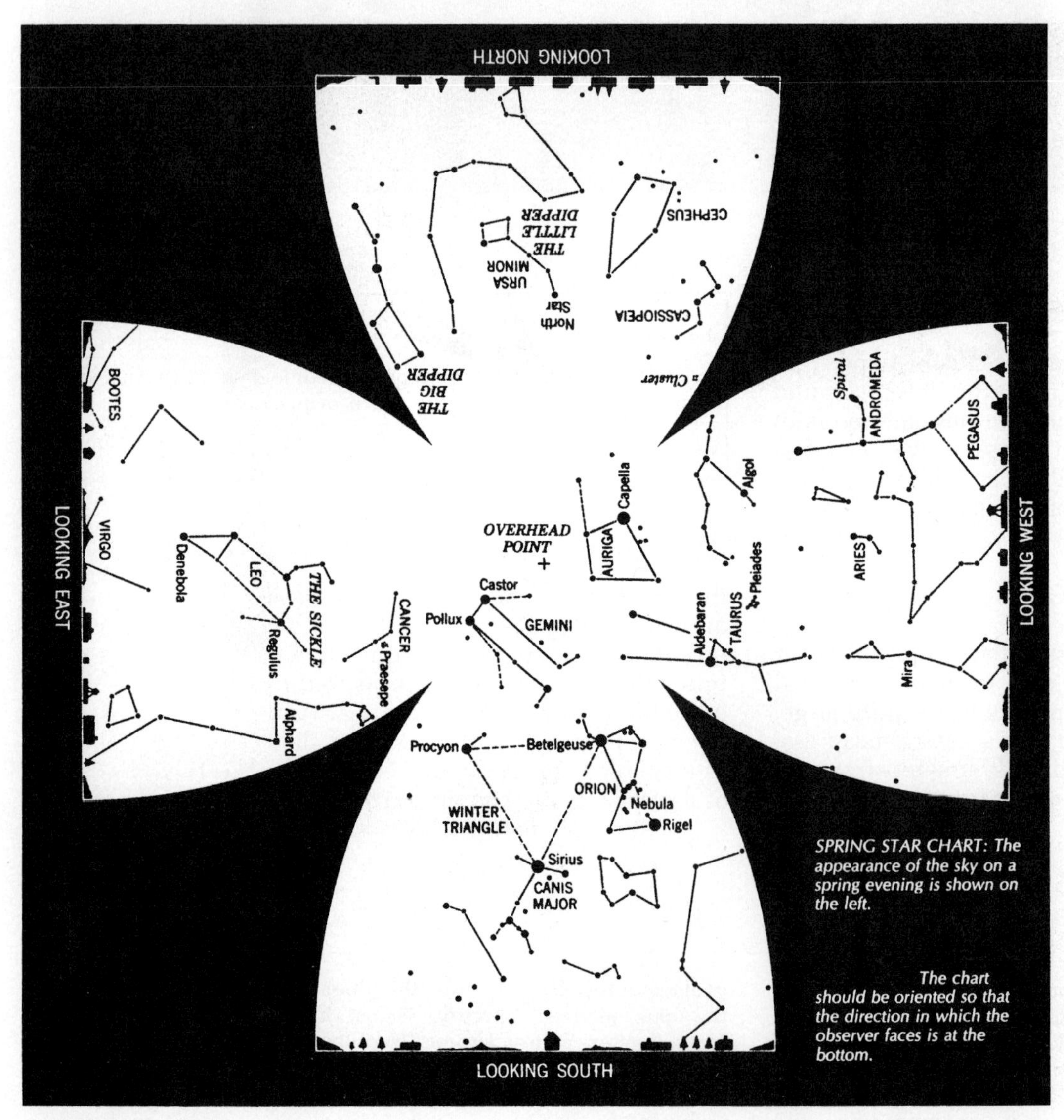

SPRING STAR CHART: The appearance of the sky on a spring evening is shown on the left.

The chart should be oriented so that the direction in which the observer faces is at the bottom.

A, **Spring star chart.**

TAKE-HOME EXPERIMENTS

1. **Stargazing.** Using the accompanying star charts as a guide, locate two constellations in the sky that appear in the early evening just after sunset. Go outside four hours later and locate them again. Have they moved with respect to your viewpoint from Earth? Have they moved relative to each other? Draw a rough sketch of what you see.

Locate the Big Dipper. Now draw an imaginary line from the two stars that form the end of the bowl and extend that line straight away from the bowl about five times the distance between the two stars. You will see a large star here, called the North Star. Does the North Star change positions with the others? The North Star appears stationary because it lies on the Earth's axis of rotation. Observe how the other stars appear to rotate around the North Star.

2. **Sunrise, sunset.** Using a compass to determine direction, carefully note where the Sun sets on the horizon. Does it set due west? Explain your observation. Predict where you would expect to see the Sun rise.

3. **Ellipse.** Draw an ellipse using the procedure found on page 523.

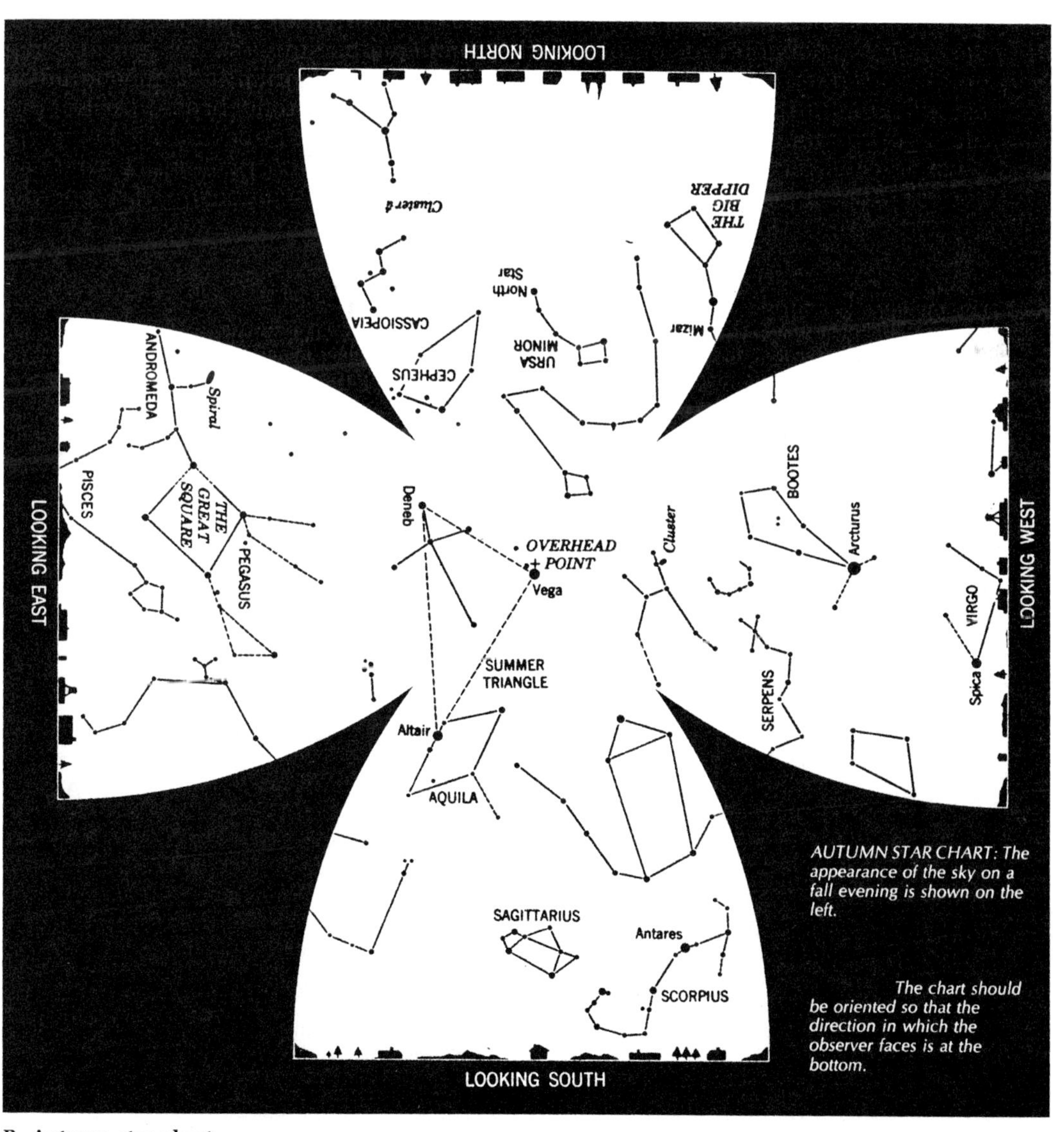

AUTUMN STAR CHART: The appearance of the sky on a fall evening is shown on the left.

The chart should be oriented so that the direction in which the observer faces is at the bottom.

B, Autumn star chart.

4. **Relative motion.** Following the procedure outlined on page 521, show that if the Earth and the Sun were the only objects in the Universe it would be impossible (and irrelevant) to tell whether the Sun orbits around the Earth or the Earth orbits around the Sun.

PROBLEMS

1. **Structure of the Solar System.** Explain why it was difficult for the ancients to prove that the Sun and not the Earth is the center of the Solar System.

2. **Parallax.** Explain what we mean by parallax. Show how distance can be measured by studying parallax.

*3. **Parallax.** Suppose that you are driving a car and the speedometer reads 80 km/hr. If a person sitting next to you looks at the speedometer at the same time he may read a different value, perhaps 70 km/hr. Explain how two people can look at the same instrument at the same time and read different values.

*4. **Parallax.** With rigidly fixed modern telescopes, astronomers can determine how far away some stars are by observing the parallactic shift as the Earth travels around the Sun. Using this technique, would it be easier to estimate distance to nearby stars or to distant stars, or would it be equally difficult for all stars? Defend your answer.

5. **Night sky.** Are the same stars visible in the sky on a winter night as on a summer night? Explain.

6. **Motion of the Earth.** The motion of the Earth relative to the center of the galaxy is composed of at least five different independent movements. Describe each one.

7. **Phases of the Moon.** How is the Moon positioned with respect to the Earth and the Sun when it is (a) full, (b) new, (c) crescent?

8. **Phases of the Moon.** Do the Sun, Earth, and Moon lie in a single plane? Explain.

9. **Lunar cycles.** Many societies use a lunar calendar instead of a solar one. In a lunar calendar, each month represents one full cycle of the Moon. How many days are there in a lunar month? If there are 12 months to a lunar year, will a lunar year be longer or shorter than a solar year? Explain.

*Indicates more difficult problem.

10. **Moon cycle.** Why does the Moon rise approximately 50 min later each day than it did the previous day?

11. **Eclipses of the Sun and Moon.** Draw a picture of the Sun, Earth, and Moon as they will be during an eclipse of the Sun. Draw a picture of the Sun, Earth, and Moon as they will appear during an eclipse of the Moon. Explain how these positions produce eclipses.

*12. **Tides.** Explain why high tide in a given region arrives approximately 50 min later every day.

*13. **Tides.** On the northwest coast of Alaska there are few roads, and many people travel mostly by boat. Imagine that someone lived in a shallow bay so that you could enter and leave only at high tide. If you visited that person and stopped in for a cup of coffee, how long would you have to wait before you left again? Could you plan to visit every Friday at 10 AM? Explain. Would it be easier to enter the bay when the moon was full, new, or quartered? Defend your answer.

14. **Tides.** Explain why there are approximately two high tides every day.

15. **Origin of the Solar System.** Briefly outline the modern theory that explains the origin of the Solar System.

16. **Evolution of the Solar System.** Explain why the protosun gradually became warmer as it shrank. Did the protoplanets also become warmer as they coalesced? If so, why are they so much cooler today?

17. **Origin of the Solar System.** Astronomers have observed that all the planets of our Solar System revolve around the Sun in the same direction and in nearly circular orbits. Does the theory explaining the origin of the Solar System offered in this text account for this ordered rotation? Defend your answer.

18. **The Solar System.** What are the most common elements present on the Sun? How does this composition differ from that of the Earth?

19. **The Solar System.** Name the nine major planets that orbit around the Sun in order of their distance from the Sun. Name four other planetary bodies that are found in the Solar System.

20. **The Solar System.** Explain why the Earth is mostly solid matter even though it evolved from a cloud composed primarily of hydrogen and helium.

21. **The Sun.** Draw a picture of the Sun, labeling the core, the photosphere, the corona, and the chromosphere. Label the relative densities and temperatures of each region.

22. **The Sun.** What is the fundamental source of energy within the Sun? Is the Sun's chemical composition constant, or is it continuously changing? Explain.

23. **The Sun.** How does energy travel from the core of the Sun to the surface? How does it travel from the surface of the Sun to the Earth?

24. **The Sun.** Compare and contrast the core of the Sun with its outer surface.

25. **Sunspots.** Describe the formation of sunspots on the surface of the Sun. Why do sunspots appear black to an observer here on Earth?

26. **Telescopes.** Explain why a small telescope mounted on an orbiting spacecraft is sometimes more effective than a large telescope located on Earth.

27. **The Moon.** How do we know that the Moon was hot at one time in its history? According to modern theory, how was the Moon heated?

28. **The Moon.** Briefly outline the history of the Moon.

*29. **The Moon.** Suppose the oldest igneous rocks on the Moon had been formed when the Moon was one billion years old. What conclusions would we then draw about the geological history of the Moon? Could we positively answer the question, "Was the Moon heated by internal radioactivity or by external bombardment?" Defend your answer.

30. **The Moon.** Explain how we can learn about Earth's geology by studying the Moon.

*Indicates more difficult problem.

31. **Mercury.** Give a brief description of the planet Mercury. Include its surface temperature, type of terrain, speed of revolution around the Sun, and its magnetic fields.

32. **Mercury.** Why is the presence of a magnetic field around Mercury a curious phenomenon?

*33. **Mercury.** If Mercury rotated once every 24 hours as the Earth does, would you expect daytime temperatures on that planet to be higher or lower than they are today? Defend your answer.

34. **Venus.** Give a plausible explanation for the evolution of the atmosphere on Venus. Show how the Venusian atmosphere is responsible for the high temperatures on the planet.

*35. **Venus.** At one time Venus and Earth probably had similar environments, except that Venus was about 20° C warmer. If you could somehow cool the surface of Venus by 20° C, would conditions on that planet be likely to become similar to those on Earth? Explain.

36. **Mars.** Give three reasons why people have thought that intelligent civilized life exists on Mars. Basing your answer on the newest current information obtained from spacecraft, do you feel that such life does, in fact, exist? Defend your answer.

37. **Mars.** Discuss the evidence that indicates that the Martian atmosphere was once considerably different than it is today. Explain why this atmosphere could not have been similar to that of the Earth for long periods of time.

38. **Terrestrial planets.** Explain how the relative masses and distance from the Sun of Venus, Earth, and Mars led to markedly different environments on each of these three planets.

*39. **Terrestrial planets.** Imagine that three new planets were found between Earth and Mars. What could you tell about the past geological histories of each, given the following limited data? (a) Planet X: The entire surface of this planet is covered with sedimentary rock. (b) Planet Y: This planet's atmosphere contains large quantities of water, ammonia, methane, and hydrogen sulfide. (c) Planet Z: About one third of this planet is covered with numerous impact craters. Smaller craters can be seen within the largest of these. Another third of the surface is much smoother and scattered with a few small craters. The remainder of the planet has no visible craters but is marked with large topographic relief, mountain ranges, smooth plains, but no canyons or river basins.

40. **Jupiter.** Discuss the composition of the planet Jupiter. How does it differ from that of Earth?

41. **Jupiter.** Explain why the mass of Jupiter was an important factor in determining its present composition and structure.

42. **Jupiter.** About four billion years from now, the Sun will probably grow significantly larger and hotter. How will this change affect the composition and structure of Jupiter?

43. **Moons of Jupiter.** Compare and contrast the four Galilean moons of Jupiter. Discuss some similarities between the Galilean moon system and the Solar System as a whole.

44. **Saturn.** Compare and contrast Saturn with Jupiter.

45. **Meteoroids and meteorites.** What is a meteoroid? A meteorite? What effect do they have on Earth?

*46. **Meteoroids.** Astronomers once thought that perhaps meteoroids were fragments from a planet that formed and then exploded or was destroyed in a collision with another planet. Do you feel that such an origin is likely? Defend your answer.

47. **Comets.** Is a comet really hot, dense, and fiery? If so, what is the energy source? If not, why do comets look as though they are burning masses of gas?

---

*Indicates more difficult problem.

CHAPTER 17

In the past few decades, spacecraft have flown past, or landed on, six of the nine planets and relayed photographs and other types of data directly to Earth. While it is conceivable that rockets may be launched to one or more of the nearest stars sometime in the future, travel to the distant galaxies seems impossible. They are just too far away.

This chapter opens by explaining the techniques used to study distant objects in space. The structure and life cycle of a star and the origin of white dwarfs, pulsars, supernovae, and black holes are discussed. We then introduce galaxies, radio galaxies, and quasars. The chapter ends with a summary of relativity and current theory on cosmology, the study of the beginning and the end of the Universe.

"AS I UNDERSTAND IT, THEY WANT AN IMMEDIATE ANSWER. ONLY TROUBLE IS, THE MESSAGE WAS SENT OUT 3 MILLION YEARS AGO."

STARS, SPACE, AND TIME

17.1 INTRODUCTION

Throughout most of this book we have tried to explain physical phenomena in terms of concepts that we can relate to our everyday experience. But we cannot visualize very small objects such as atoms in terms of everyday experience, and classical physics does not apply adequately to them. Likewise, large objects and great distances are also difficult to comprehend. When we consider the mysteries of distant galaxies and the vast regions of intergalactic space, we simply cannot use common "household and garden" analogies, for these comparisons are generally inadequate. For example, some distant galaxies are over eight billion light years from the Earth. That means that light moving at 3×10^8 m/sec (186,000 mi/sec) must travel for eight billion years to reach us here on Earth. Think about it. The light we see now left this galaxy 3.5 billion years before our Solar System was even formed. It has been traveling all this time at 3×10^8 m (186,000 miles) *every second;* it hasn't hit anything during that time, and only now can it be seen.

Not only are distances in outer space incomprehensibly large, but forces are similarly unimaginable. For example, some dead and dying stars become compressed so severely that protons and electrons are squeezed together to form neutrons. If we are to comprehend these and other related concepts, we must release our imagination and let our thoughts fly beyond terrestrial standards of force, size, mass, distance, and time.

17.2 STUDYING AN UNKNOWN OBJECT IN SPACE

Look at the photograph shown in Figure 17–1. The small fuzzy dot in the upper center marked by the two solid lines is a distant galaxy. Best estimates indicate that there may be 100 billion stars in that galaxy, and that the entire galaxy is over 8 billion light years away from Earth. How can we know anything about an object that is so far away? The photograph that we see is the best available; there are no telescopes that can provide us with a sharper image. We will never, never be able to visit this galaxy, weigh it on some sort of conventional earthly balance, or collect samples for direct analysis.

One of the most useful tools available to astronomers is the study of atomic and molecular spectra. Recall from earlier chapters that an electron in an atom may absorb a photon of light and thereby be promoted to a higher energy level. However, an electron cannot absorb just any amount of energy; rather, it can absorb only those amounts that correspond to differences between its quantized energy levels. Similarly, the excited electrons may drop to a lower energy level, thereby emitting discrete quanta of light. Thus, atoms absorb and emit quanta of light in characteristic patterns. Recall that such a pattern is called a **spectrum** (plural: spectra). Now, each element has a characteristic spectrum and can be identified from it. If the spectrum of an unknown element matches that of neon, for example, the unknown must be neon.

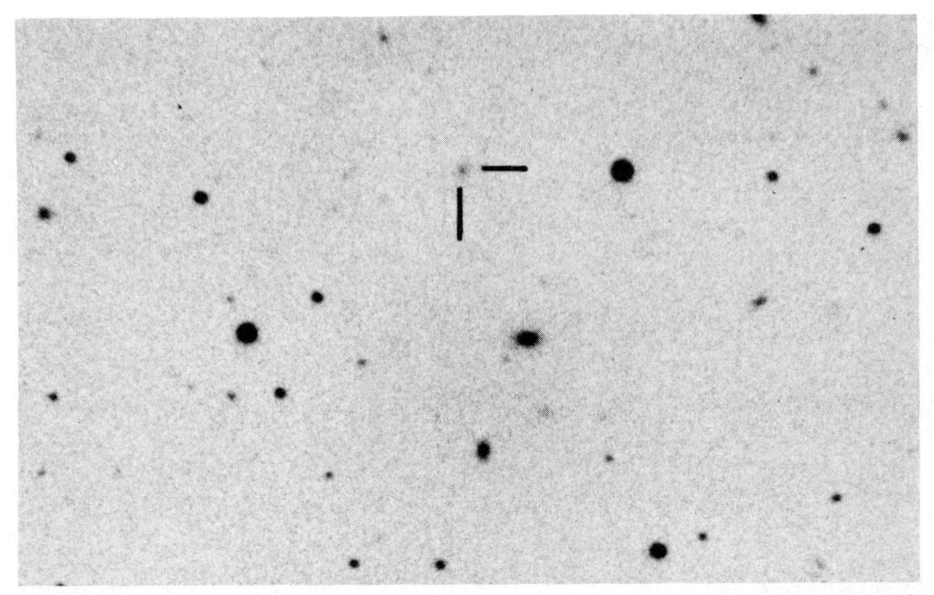

Figure 17–1. One of the farthest known galaxies, 3C 3431, is barely observable, even with the 4-m Kitt Peak telescope, as shown on this negative print. The object is believed to be over eight billion light years away. (From Pasachoff, Jay M: *Astronomy: From The Earth To The Universe.* Philadelphia, Saunders College Publishing, 1979.)

Light is emitted from the surface of a star as a continuous band over a wide range of frequencies. As this light passes through the outer layers, some of it is selectively absorbed by the various atoms. Therefore, an observer on Earth sees a spectrum showing lines of darkness crossing the band of the colors. This is called an **absorption spectrum.** Each dark line represents a frequency that is absorbed by some atom. Since a star contains many different gases, a stellar spectrum contains the superimposed images of many individual absorption spectra. By careful analysis, scientists can detect the types of atoms present in the star and their relative abundances.

Part of the absorption spectra of the Sun; similar spectra are observed from certain stars. (From Pasachoff, Jay M.: *Contemporary Astronomy.* Second edition. Philadelphia, Saunders College Publishing, 1981.)

Chemical composition is not the only information that can be obtained from absorption spectra. Elements absorb their different spectral lines at different relative brightness depending on their temperature, so we can also tell the temperature of the surface of a star.

There is also another way to determine stellar temperatures. Recall that if you heat a piece of iron it will start to glow dull red, then gradually become redder and change color to orange, and then to blue-white. Similarly, the overall color of starlight changes with temperature, so by studying the color of a star we can obtain an idea of stellar temperatures. This is an **emission spectrum.**

If certain kinds of atoms are located within a strong magnetic field, their electronic energy levels will be affected, and consequently their spectra will be altered. By studying the detailed structure of certain spectral lines, scientists can detect the presence and strength of magnetic fields on the Sun.

Atomic absorption and emission spectra, associated with the movement

The 100-meter radio telescope at Effelsburg, near Bonn, Germany. Note the tiny figures at the base of the right side of the telescope. (From Pasachoff, Jay M., and Kutner, Marc L.: *University Astronomy.* Philadelphia, Saunders College Publishing, 1978.)

of electrons in an atom or molecule, appear mainly in the visible, infrared, and ultraviolet regions of the spectra. In recent years, high- and low-frequency radiation has been studied extensively as well. Photons in the low, radio frequency range are emitted when free electrons are accelerated by an electromagnetic field. A normal star emits very weak radio signals, but some objects in space are powerful radio sources. Therefore, these objects must be quite different from stars, as we shall see later in the chapter. Similarly, X-rays are detected from objects in space that are powered by unusual types of energy sources.

Stars are all traveling about through space, and we can determine their speed relative to Earth by studying stellar spectra. To understand how this is done, let us think about sound waves for a moment. Have you ever stood by a train track and listened to a train speed by, blowing its whistle? As it approaches, the pitch of the whistle sounds higher than usual, and when it travels away from you, the pitch lowers. This changing pitch produces a characteristic sound. The same effect can be duplicated with an electric razor. If you turn on an electric razor, hold it still, and listen to it, it will produce a constant sound. Now move it quickly past your ear, and the pitch will change. This change in pitch is called the **Doppler effect** (Fig. 17–2). As explained in Chapter 11, a stationary object remains in the center of the circular waves it generates. The waves from a moving object will crowd each other in the direction of the object's motion. The object, in effect, is chasing its own waves. If we are in front of the moving object, we receive more waves per second (higher frequency) than we would if it were stationary, and similarly we receive fewer waves per second (lower frequency) if we are behind it.

The frequency of light waves also changes with relative motion. Certain spectral lines reaching us from a star that is flying rapidly away from Earth will appear at a lower frequency (closer to the red end of the spectrum) than would be expected if the star were stationary with respect to Earth. This frequency change is called the **red shift.** Similarly, light from stars traveling toward us will appear at higher frequencies and is **blue shifted.** Thus, the relative speeds of stars that are billions upon billions of kilometers away from us can be calculated.

In the 1920's an astronomer named Edwin Hubble noted that light from almost every object outside of our own galaxy is red shifted. Thus, all the gal-

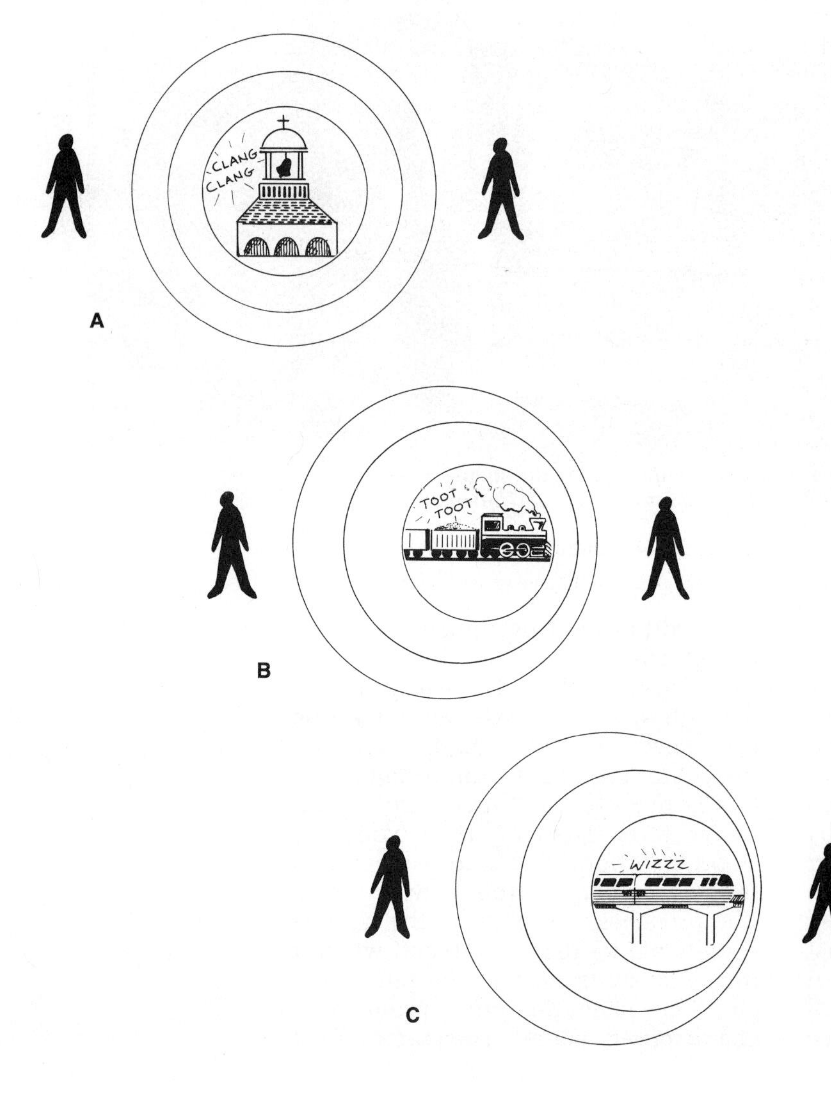

Figure 17–2. The Doppler effect. *A,* Noise is being produced by a stationary source (a church bell). Observers on either side of the church hear the same frequency of sound from the bell. *B,* A slowly moving train is, in effect, chasing its own waves, and an observer in front of it will hear the sound at higher frequency (more waves per second) than an observer who is stationed behind the train. *C,* The effect is enhanced if the observers listen to the whistle of a high speed train.

axies are flying away from each other; the Universe is expanding. Moreover, he observed that the most distant galaxies are moving outward at great speeds, while the closer ones are receding only slowly. This relationship has been quantified and is known as **Hubble's Law,** as shown in Figure 17–3. Using Hubble's Law, the distance of a distant object can be calculated simply by measuring its red shift.

The Sun and many stars are close enough and small enough so that we have learned much about their composition and their structure. They seem almost familiar to us. But many objects are so far away, so massive, so energetic, or so unlike anything we can observe on Earth that any complete understanding remains elusive. It is impossible to find something on Earth, put it on a laboratory bench, and say, "Aha, this is very similar to a galactic core, a quasar, or a black hole, so if I understand this I will understand what the unknown object in space is like." Recently computers have been used to construct theoretical models to predict the behavior of matter under the extreme conditions found in certain regions of space. But computers are only accurate if the data fed into them are accurate, and physicists are not sure that the equations or the numbers placed into the equations are correct.

> The Doppler effect was first explained for both light and sound waves by the Austrian physicist Johann Christian Doppler in 1842. The Doppler effect for sound waves was tested dramatically 3 years later by a Dutch meteorologist, Christopher Heinrich Buys-Ballot. He mounted an orchestra of trumpeters on an open railroad flatcar and noted the frequency shifts as they rode past him through the Dutch countryside south of Amsterdam.

Figure 17–3. The Hubble diagram for the galaxies Virgo, Ursa Major, Corona Borealis, Bootes, and Hydra. (From Pasachoff, Jay M.: *Contemporary Astronomy.* Second edition. Philadelphia, Saunders College Publishing, 1981.)

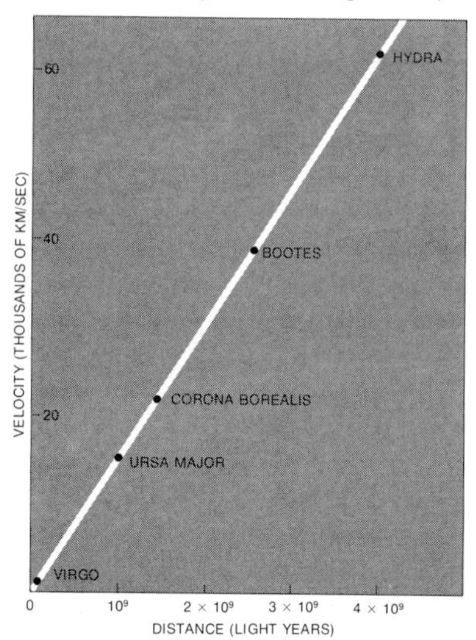

17.3 THE LIFE OF A STAR

An active star is a large, hot, spherical mass of gases that are so hot that nuclear fusion reactions are occurring within the central regions. Tremendous gravitational pressures pull these gases inward, yet the star does not collapse. In fact, the outer layers of most stars are diffuse and tenuous. They are less dense than the Earth's atmosphere at sea level. Therefore, some pressure must push outward against the force of gravity. As we learned in the last chapter, energetic photons and fast moving atomic particles released from the core push against the outer layers of gas and keep them from falling inward. Thus, the resultant density of a star is deter-

Figure 17–4. Equilibrium in a star.

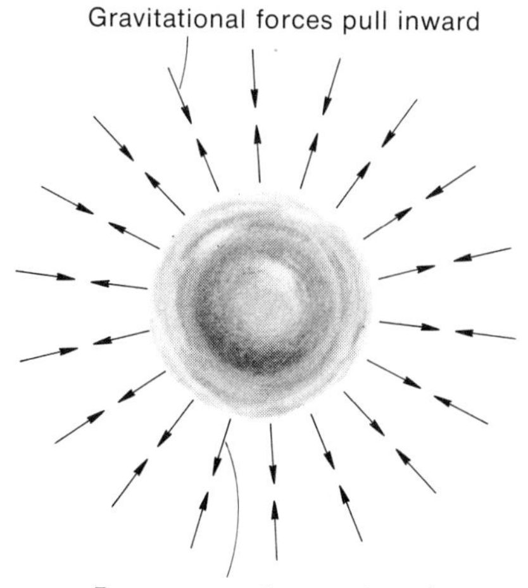

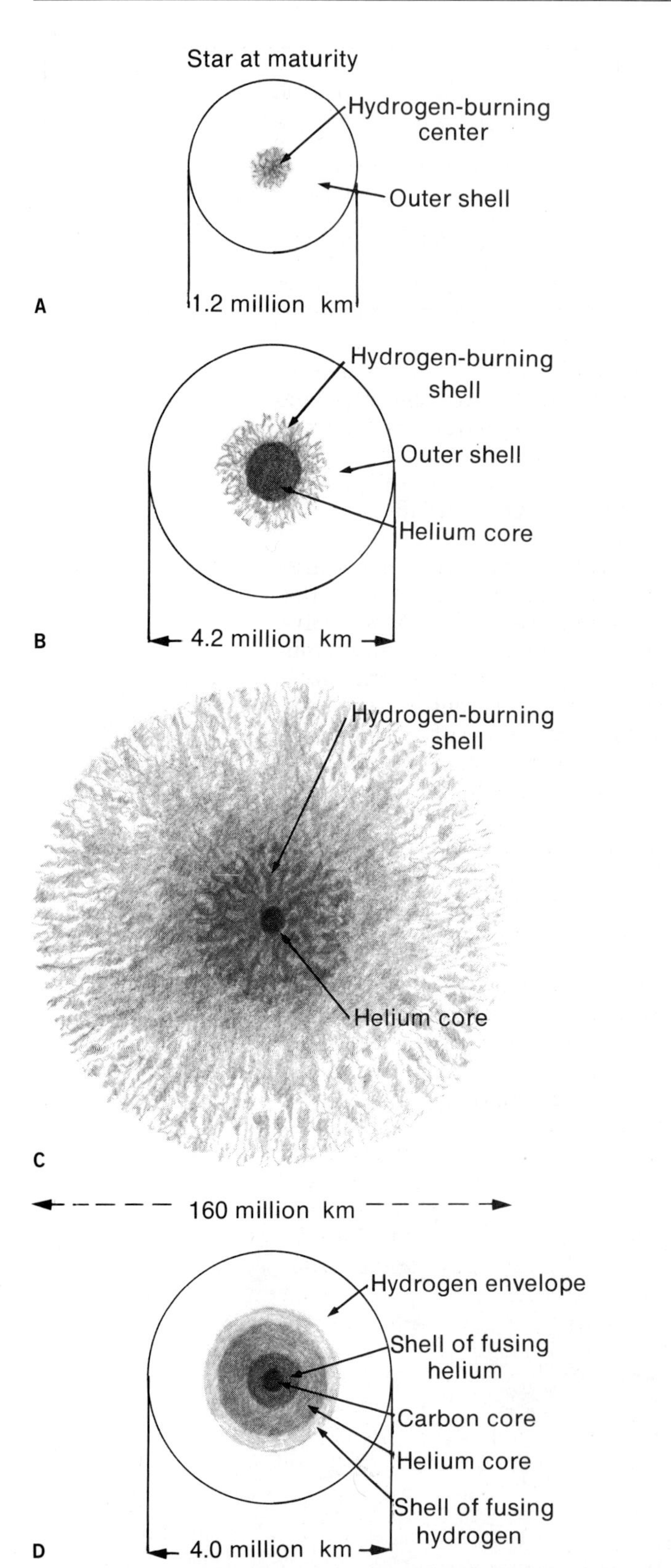

Figure 17–5. Aging of a star the size of our Sun. (In all cases the core region has been drawn larger than scale to show detail.)

mined by two opposing forces: the gravitational force pulling in and thermal pressure pushing out. These forces leave a star like the Sun in a dynamic equilibrium that can last for billions of years.

Over a period of many millions or billions of years, stars evolve, change, and die, and new ones are born. Throughout the life of a star the gravitational and thermal forces oppose each other until, as we shall see, the core finally cools and parts of the star collapse inward forever.

When a large diffuse cloud of cold dust and gas is pulled together by gravitation, it forms the early stages of a star, known as a **protostar.** As the particles move ever faster, they eventually reach the extremely high temperatures required for nuclear fusion to take place. (Remember, rapid motion is equivalent to high temperature.) At the onset of fusion, additional energy is released, and the gases move even more rapidly in all directions. These extremely energetic atomic particles push outward against the direction of the gravitational field. Therefore, the gravitational force pulling inward balances the thermal and radiation pressure pushing outward. At equilibrium, an average-sized star has a dense core surrounded by a less dense envelope (Fig. 17–5*A*).

The outer region of a star is considerably cooler and less dense than the core. The surface temperature of our Sun, for example, is only about 5800° C, whereas the temperature in the core soars to 15,000,000° C or more. At the relatively cool outer temperatures, hydrogen nuclei do not collide forcefully enough to fuse, so no energy is produced in these regions. Within the dense core, however, temperatures are high enough so that hydrogen nuclei fuse together to form helium, with the release of large quantities of energy.

As the star grows older, increasing quantities of hydrogen are being converted to helium. The helium nuclei do not fuse with each other at the temperatures of an average mature star. Recall that for fusion to occur, two nuclei must be pushed very close together. A hydrogen nucleus is simply a bare proton, so to fuse two of them we must overcome the electrostatic repulsion of one proton for another. However, each helium nucleus contains two protons, so in order for helium fusion to occur, a much greater repulsion must be overcome. As a result, the helium nuclei do not fuse at this time. A star the size of our Sun has enough hydrogen fuel to last for about 10 billion years. After that time, the outer shell still contains large quantities of hydrogen, but the central core is mostly hot helium (Fig. 17–5 *B*). The star now begins to behave quite differently than it did earlier in its life. Since little nuclear energy is produced in the central core, the core cools. When the core temperature decreases, the outward pressure that kept the star from falling inward also decreases and the central regions start to shrink under gravitational forces. This gravitational contraction causes the core to grow hotter. It seems to be a paradox that when the nuclear fire starts to diminish the core should get hotter, but that is exactly what happens, because some of the energy from the gravitational contraction is turned into heat. To repeat, *when hydrogen fusion ends within the core, the equilibrium of the star is upset so that the central mass is compressed by gravity and is therefore heated.* The heated shell of hydrogen around the helium core then "burns" more fiercely.* At this point the star is releasing hundreds of times as much energy as it did when it was mature. This intense energy output now causes the outer parts of the star to expand and become brighter. The star has become a **red giant.** This process is shown pictorially in Figure 17–5C. The outer regions have expanded so much that their density is very low, so low that it would be considered to be a vacuum in a physics laboratory on Earth.

Meanwhile, the inner core continues to condense under the influence of its gravitation and gets hotter and hotter until the critical temperature of 100 million degrees is reached. At this temperature, a new nuclear reaction starts; helium nuclei start to fuse together to form carbon, according to the reaction sequence shown in the next column. The helium fusion initiates several

*Don't forget: when we talk of stars, "burning" hydrogen refers to nuclear fusion reactions, not to ordinary chemical fires.

$$^{4}_{2}\text{He} + ^{4}_{2}\text{He} \rightarrow ^{8}_{4}\text{Be} + \text{energy}$$

$$^{4}_{2}\text{He} + ^{8}_{4}\text{Be} \rightarrow ^{12}_{6}\text{C} + \text{energy}$$

drastic and rapid changes. After a few hundred thousand years of instability, the star shrinks and then enters a new and stable phase. The newly structured core is now composed of fusing helium. Gradually, as increasing quantities of helium fuse to form carbon, the carbon starts to accumulate in the core just as helium had done during the earlier life of the star (Fig. 17–5*D*). After enough carbon has accumulated, the helium fusion in the core stops. If the star is of average size (e.g., if it has the same mass as that of our Sun), it will end its life peaceably. The helium fuel is gradually consumed, and the carbon core contracts. This gravitational contraction causes the gas to become hotter, but not hot enough to initiate fusion of the carbon nuclei. A star as massive as our Sun will eventually shrink so that its diameter will be approximately that of the Earth. Such a shrunken star no longer produces energy of its own and glows solely from the residual heat produced during past eras. The star is no longer kept from collapsing by thermal pressure. Rather, it has become so small that atomic particles are squeezed together. It is now only the strength of these particles, called the **degeneracy pressure,** that resists further compression. We say that the star has become a **white dwarf.** It will cool slowly over the course of tens of billions of years, but it will never change size again. No nuclear fire will cause it to expand, and the gravitational force isn't strong enough to resist the degeneracy pressure of the atomic particles, and cause it to contract.

Some stars do not die so peaceably. If the star is greater than four solar masses, the slowdown of helium fusion and the contraction of the resulting carbon core does not terminate in a white dwarf. Instead, as the core contracts slightly, the fusion reactions accelerate, and the outer regions expand into a second red giant phase.

The sizes of the white dwarfs are not very different from the size of the Earth. A white dwarf contains about 300,000 times more mass than does the Earth, however. (From Pasachoff, Jay M.: *Contemporary Astronomy*. Second edition. Philadelphia, Saunders College Publishing, 1981.)

After some time, the gravitational contraction of the carbon core will be intense enough to heat the core to such extreme temperatures that carbon nuclei begin to fuse, forming magnesium and other elements. After all the carbon is consumed, the star collapses again, and gradually new fusion reactions start building heavier and heavier nuclei. Thus, hydrogen is converted in steps to the heavier elements. The process continues until iron is formed. Iron is a very special element; two iron nuclei will not fuse together to release energy no matter how hot they are. Thus, once the core of a massive star is composed primarily of iron, a final and catastrophic event occurs. The star collapses under its own gravitation. The temperature reaches trillions of degrees within seconds, and the star explodes, hurling matter out into space. This exploding star is called a **supernova** (see Fig. 17–6). A supernova explosion is truly cataclysmic. For a brief period of time a single star shines as brightly as hundreds of billions of stars and can emit as much energy as an entire galaxy. To observers on Earth it appears as though a new brilliant star suddenly materialized in the sky, only to become dim and to disappear to the naked eye within a few months. Four of these events have been seen in our galaxy in the last 1000 years. A supernova explosion is violent enough to fragment many atomic nuclei, thereby shooting protons and neutrons about in all directions. Shock waves—giant sonic booms—race through the atmosphere of the star. Under these conditions, many of the nuclear particles collide with sufficient energy to fuse, thereby forming all the known elements heavier than iron.

Thus, in studying the evolution of stars, scientists learned how the natural elements were formed. We now believe that in the beginning of time, when the Universe was first formed, hydrogen was the predominant element. There was some helium, but there were few heavier elements. Within the cores of stars, hydrogen was converted to helium, helium to carbon, carbon to magnesium, and so on, until many elements, including iron, became abundant. Then, in giant supernova explosions, the rest of the elements were formed by fission and fusion of atomic nuclei and nuclear fragments. The death of a giant star is, in a way, only a beginning. A great number of nuclei are shot out into space. As countless supernova explosions occur in the course of time, the concentration of heavy elements slowly accumulates. Then, when conditions are favorable, the heavy elements mix with quantities of hydrogen and helium and condense into new stars and new solar systems. Our own Sun and the planet we live on is a condensate of supernova explosions that occurred billions of years ago. In a sense then, life itself is born out of the debris of dying stars.

Solar mass = the mass of our Sun (2×10^{31} kg),

used as a unit for the expression of the masses of other stars, nebulas, and galaxies.

A

B

Figure 17–6. *A*, Two views of a galaxy in Ursa Major. Note the supernova, indicated by the arrow in the second photograph. (Hale Observatories.) *B*, The "Crab" Nebula in Taurus. Remains of a supernova of 1054 A.D. (Hale Observatories.) *C*, Direct photographs of a region of space before and during a supernova explosion. (Courtesy of Lick Observatory.)

C

17.4 PULSARS—NEUTRON STARS AND BLACK HOLES

In a supernova explosion, not all the original matter is shot out into space. Some of it (perhaps half) remains behind, compressed into a tight sphere. In the 1930's, scientists tried to imagine the physical characteristics of the residual matter. If the sphere were more than 1.4 times as massive as the Sun, the gravitational forces would be extremely intense, so intense, in fact, that the star could not resist further compression in the same manner as a white dwarf. Instead, the electrons and protons would be squeezed together to form neutrons:

$$\text{electrons} + \text{protons} \rightarrow \text{neutrons}$$

The neutrons would then resist further compression and remain tightly packed. This ball of compressed neutrons is called a **neutron star.** A neutron star would be so dense—approximately 10^{13} kg/cm^3—that if the entire Earth were compressed to this extent, it could be placed inside a large football stadium.

It was not until 1967 that a neutron star was actually discovered, almost by accident. Jocelyn Bell Burnell, who was then a graduate student, was scanning the sky with a radiotelescope, studying radio emissions from distant galaxies. In one part of the sky she detected a radio signal that pulsed with a frequency of about one pulse every 1⅓ sec. If such a signal were fed into the speaker of a conventional radio, you would hear a beep, beep, beep, beep, evenly spaced at one beep every 1⅓ sec. There are many radio emissions arriving at Earth from outer space, but what made these particularly unusual was that they were (a) sharp, (b) regular, and (c) spaced only a little over one second apart. At first astronomers seriously considered that they might represent a signal from intelligent life, so they called the pulse signals LGM, for "Little Green Men." But when Burnell found a second similar pulsating source in a different region of the sky and discovered that the emission was over a wide range of frequencies, scientists ruled out the possibility of two widely divergent civilizations, each sending out similar bizarre signals in a manner that was wasteful of energy. Once it was established that the signals were of natural origin, the unknown pulsing sources were called **pulsars.** But naming the objects didn't help to describe them. What a puzzle! How do we study an object many trillions of kilometers away that emits no visible light, only radio signals like those shown in Figure 17–7?

The first step was to estimate its size. Of course, not all parts of an object in space are equidistant from Earth (Fig. 17–8). If a large sphere emits a sharp burst of radio signals from over its entire surface, some of the photons start off on their journey significantly closer to Earth than others and therefore will arrive sooner. A person on Earth listening to the radio noise will hear not a sharp beep but a more prolonged *beeeeeeep,* because it takes a while for all the photons to arrive. Alternatively, a signal from a small sphere will be much sharper, for the differences in distances are not nearly so great. The pulsar signals were unusually sharp, indicating that the source must be unusually small, perhaps 30 km in diameter. Was the source a starlike object only 30 km across? The smallest star previously recorded was a white dwarf 16,000 km in diameter, and a white dwarf, in any case, could not pulse so fast. Pulsation speed varies with density, and white dwarfs are not

Figure 17–7. Pulsar signals, as recorded by a radio telescope.

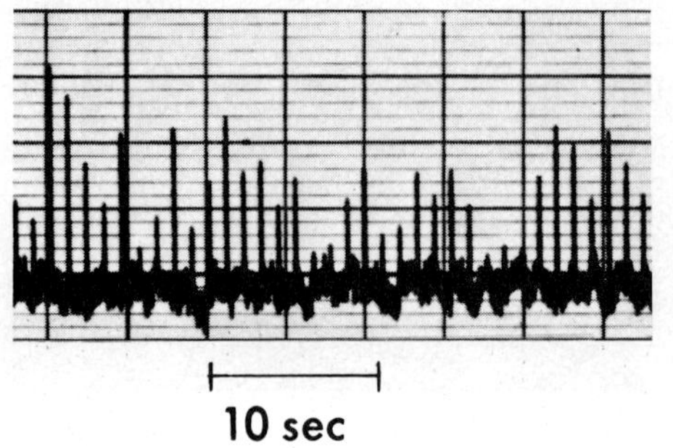

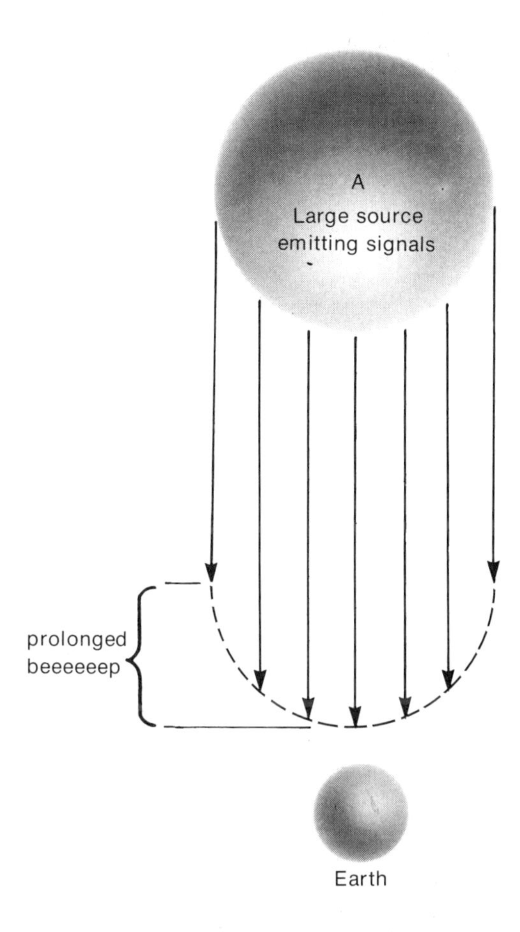

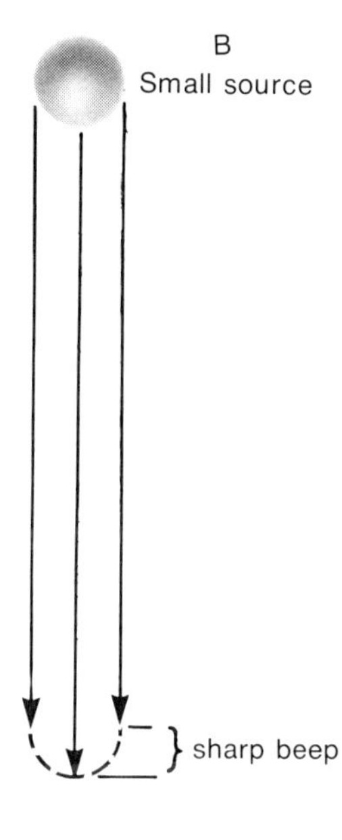

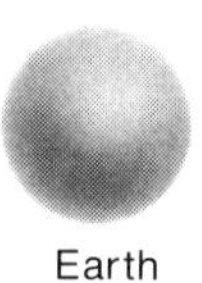

Figure 17–8. Sharp signal from a larger sphere (*A*) arrives over a longer time interval than a sharp signal from a smaller sphere (*B*).

sufficiently dense. Scientists then reasoned that the pulsar might be the long-searched-for neutron star. We now believe that when some sort of local electromagnetic storm occurs on the surface of a pulsar, a radio beacon is emitted. As the star rotates, this beacon will sweep around. We would see it flash by once at each rotation, just as a lighthouse beam flashes by ships at sea as the beacon rotates. When the Earth is in the path of a pulsar beam as it sweeps through space, we receive a pulse once every revolution. Since we receive a pulse once every 1⅓ sec, the pulsar star must rotate at this rapid rate. White dwarfs can again be ruled out as the rotating stars that cause the beam to sweep, since they are too big to rotate fast enough. But neutron stars could fill the bill. This suggestion is called the **lighthouse theory.** Thus, it is not only possible but also probable that pulsars are rotating neutron stars.

Then came the crucial test. Radio astronomers looked at the Crab Nebula, the location where a supernova explosion had occurred during the Middle Ages. They found a pulsar in exactly the same position that the supernova of 900 years ago had been. Thus a pulsar was found precisely where a neutron star should be. This made it even more convincing that pulsars must be neutron stars that are emitting radio-frequency energy.

To summarize briefly: When a small star dies, a white dwarf is formed. A neutron star—or pulsar—is formed when the nuclear fusion reactions have died in a larger star. After the supernova explosion, the remaining matter contracts under the influence of its own internal gravitation. In a pulsar this contraction continues until the neutrons themselves finally resist further compression.

What happens when a very large star dies? We believe that if the central core remaining after a supernova explosion is greater than three to five solar masses, the neutrons are not sufficiently strong to overcome the inward gravitational force. Then the star will

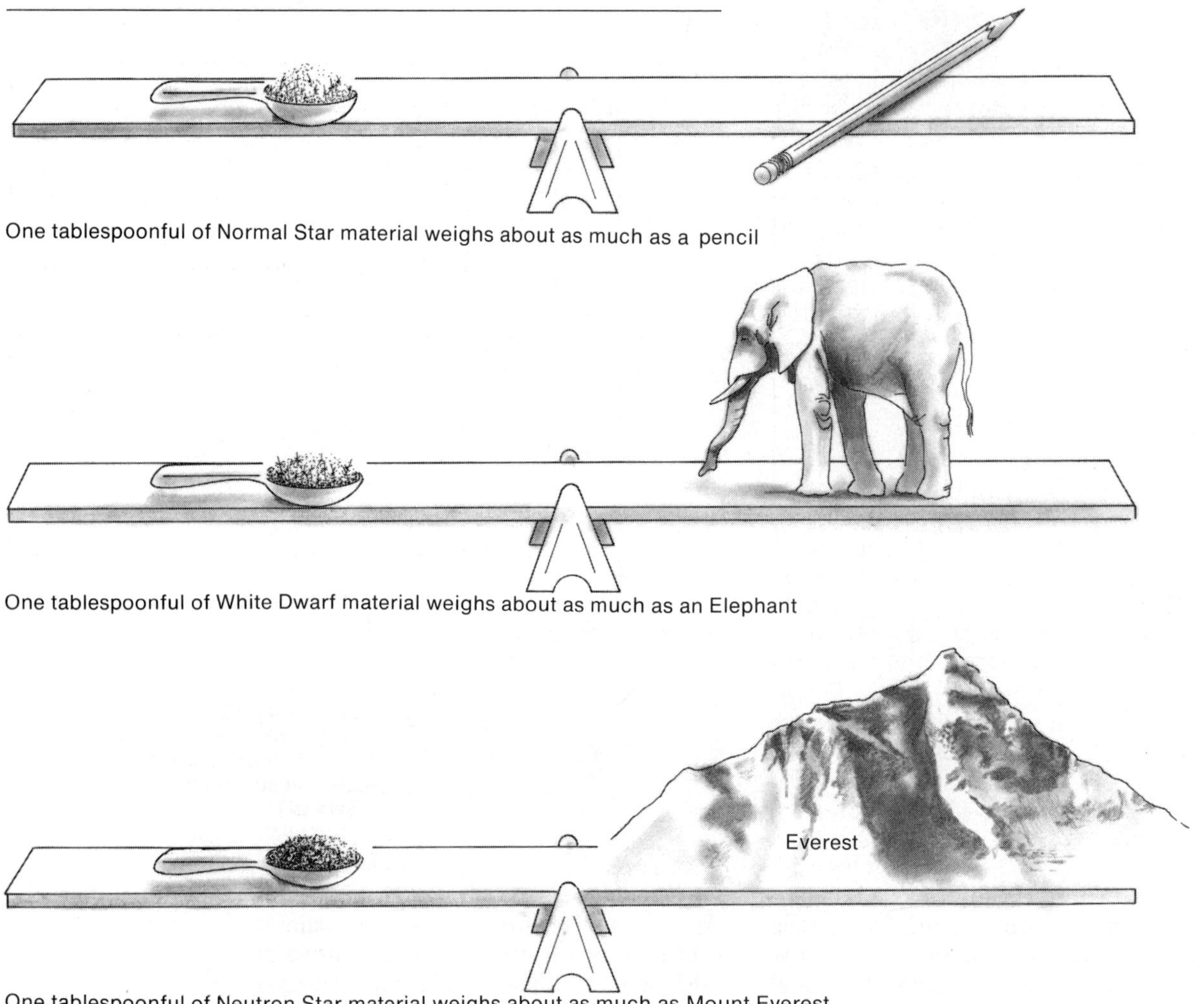

Comparison of the densities of some stellar bodies.

shrink to a size much smaller than a neutron star and become a **black hole.** Such a collapse is impossible to imagine in earthly terms. A tremendous mass, perhaps a trillion, trillion, trillion kg of matter, shrinks smaller and smaller. If known laws of physics are obeyed, this faint star will contract to the size of a pin head and then continue to shrink to the size of an atom, and then even smaller. Eventually it will collapse to a point of infinite density. Incredible! Can this really happen? We cannot tell. Perhaps as yet undiscovered physical laws control the behavior of particles under these extreme conditions. Physicists are a long way from comprehending fully what happens within a black hole.

A black hole is so small and so massive that it creates an extremely intense gravitational field. According to Einstein's theory of relativity (to be discussed in Section 17.5) a photon is affected by a gravitational field as though it had mass. As proof of this, light from nearby stars has been observed to be bent by the gravitational field of our Sun. If a star becomes dense enough, its gravitational field becomes so intense that a photon of light cannot escape. Thus, just as you cannot throw a ball from the Earth to outer space because it will fall back down, a ray of light cannot escape from an extremely dense object because it also will be pulled back downward. Since no light can escape such an object, it must always be invisible; hence the name black hole. If we shined a flashlight at a black hole, the light would simply be absorbed. It could never be reflected back to our eyes; therefore, we would never see the light. It would be as if the beam just vanished into space. Similarly, if a spaceship flew too close to a black hole it would be sucked in forever. No rocket engine could possibly be powerful enough to accelerate it back out, for no object can travel faster than the speed of light.

The search for a black hole has been even more difficult than the search for a neutron star. How do you find an object that is not only located trillions of kilometers away but is invisible as well and emits no energy in any form? In short, how do you find a hole in space? Although we will never see the black hole itself, we may be able to observe the effects of its gravitational field. Many of the stars in the Universe exist in pairs or small clusters. If two stars are close together they will orbit around each other like two dancers spinning in each other's arms. Even if one of these becomes a black hole, the two would still orbit about each other, and only one of the pair would then be invisible. The visible one would appear to be dancing around an imaginary partner. Astronomers have studied several stars that appear to vary in this unusual manner. In at least one case the invisible member of the pair is more than five solar masses. Since a normal star of five solar masses would be visible at that distance, the invisible partner is probably a black hole. However, observation of such movement is not complete proof that a black hole exists. The unseen partner could be some other object, such as a neutron star with a weak or non-existent radio signal, but theory indicates that a neutron star could not be so massive.

Astrophysicists have calculated that if a supergiant star were mutually orbiting with a black hole, great masses of gas from the supergiant would be sucked into the black hole, to disappear forever from view. As this matter

> "Now, here, you see, it takes all the running you can do to keep in the same place. If you want to get somewhere else, you must run twice as fast as that."
>
> The Red Queen, *Through the Looking Glass*, Lewis Carroll, 1871

> Apollo to Mission Control—
>
> "We are almost in reach of our goal,
> but our readings of g
> seem excessive to me,
> so we may be inside a black ho. . ."

An artist's conception of the disk of swirling gas that would develop around a black hole like Cygnus X-1 (*right*) as its gravity pulled matter off the companion supergiant (*left*). The X-radiation would arise in the disk. The painting is by Lois Cohen and is used courtesy of the Griffith Observatory. (From Pasachoff, Jay M.: *Contemporary Astronomy.* Second edition. Philadelphia, Saunders College Publishing, 1981.)

started to fall into the hole it would naturally accelerate, just as a meteorite accelerates as it falls toward Earth. The gravitational field of a black hole is so intense that matter would start to move at very high velocities—so high, in fact, that the gas particles would collide against each other with enough energy to emit intense X-rays. Thus, just as a falling meteorite glows white hot as it approaches the Earth, anything tumbling into a black hole would in a sense "glow" even more energetically—that is, it would emit X-rays. These X-rays might then be detected here on Earth. But, you may ask, if light cannot escape from a black hole, how will the X-rays escape? The answer lies in the fact that the X-rays are emitted from just outside the black hole. In this region, the gravitation would be strong enough to cause X-rays to be emitted from falling gases, yet the photons produced would be able to escape. It is as if matter being sucked into a black hole sends off one final message before being pulled into the void from which no message can ever be sent.

An important experiment, therefore, was to focus an X-ray telescope on portions of the sky where a star appeared to orbit around an invisible partner. Such telescopes must be located aboard space satellites, since X-rays do not penetrate the Earth's atmosphere. In a few instances, powerful X-ray signals emanating from the location of a double star have been recorded. The data are not yet conclusive, but as more evidence is being compiled, more scientists are becoming convinced of the existence of black holes.

17.5 GALAXIES AND INTERGALACTIC SPACE

Stars are not scattered randomly about in space, but rather are concentrated into various groups and collections of groups. Many stars exist in pairs, called **binaries,** or as multiple stars. The two or more stars in such a group are held together by mutual gravitation, and they orbit around each other. Then there are larger groups or **clusters,** containing as many as a million members, all held together and traveling through space in concert. Lone stars, binaries, and clusters are all bound together into central units called **galaxies.** A galaxy is a large volume of space containing many billions of stars all held together by their mutual gravitation. Several galactic shapes are shown in Figure 17–9. One of these types is a **spiral galaxy.** All spiral galaxies are quite large, for each one contains roughly 100 billion stars. Several arms radiate outward from the galactic center, giving the whole structure a shape like a thin disk with a ball in the center. The stars in the outer arms rotate around the core as if in a giant pinwheel.

Approximately one billion galaxies can be observed from Earth. If we map the distribution of galaxies, we find that they exist in clusters. Thus, just as there are galaxies of stars, there are also galaxies of galaxies. Such superclusters may contain up to 100,000 galaxies each. A typical group of galaxies may occupy a volume three million light years in diameter.

It is difficult to comprehend that all space between galaxies is virtually empty. As far as we know, there is almost nothing in these vast regions, not even tenuous clouds of dust and gas, just a stray hydrogen or helium atom or a photon or maybe a bare proton, neutron, or electron moving about here and there. Still, the amount of space between the galaxies is so large that this low density of material could conceivably add up to quite a lot of mass.

Our own Sun is one member of a spiral galaxy called the **Milky Way** (see Fig. 17–10). The disc of our galaxy is approximately 5000 light years thick and 100,000 light years in diameter. On a clear night you can see an edge-on view of the Milky Way as a diffuse but nearly continuous band of light stretching across the sky. Our Sun lies in one of the spiral arms of the Milky Way, 30,000 light years from the center. Here the stars are separated by great distances and very rarely collide with each other. Close to the center of the galaxy, however, conditions must be vastly dif-

Figure 17–9. *A,* A spiral galaxy in Ursa Major. *B,* A spiral galaxy in Virgo, seen edge-on. *C,* Barred spiral galaxy in Eridanus. *D,* Galaxy in Cancer. A source of radio noise. *E,* A spiral galaxy in Canes Venatici. Satellite galaxy in NGC 5195. (Hale Observatories.)

ferent. The concentration of stars in this region is perhaps one million times greater than is found in our own particular region of space. If we were to live on a planet circling one of these inner stars, we would never know nighttime, for the accumulated starlight from our near neighbors would provide light continuously. It is doubtful, however, that any life would have evolved in a

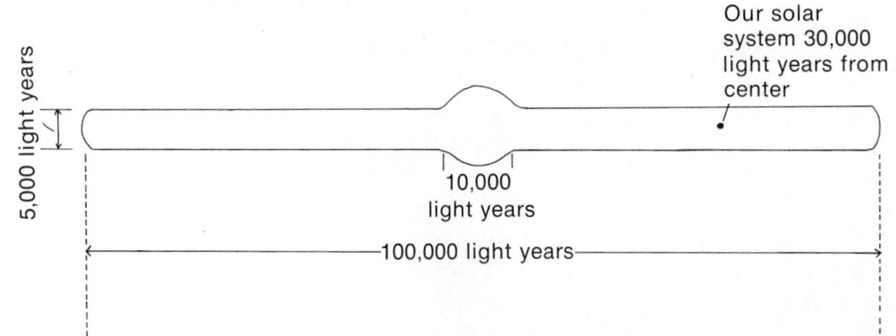

Figure 17–10. An edgewise view of the Milky Way galaxy.

solar system within this region, for collisions or near-collisions between stars are probably so frequent that a planet is likely to be ripped out of its orbit once every few hundred million years or so.

In the previous chapter we learned that the dominant objects in our Solar System are the Sun and the nine planets with their satellites. The rest of the void is largely empty—almost a vacuum—but not quite. Comets, asteroids, meteoroids, and atomic particles from the solar wind all travel through the Solar System. The vast volumes of space between the stars are likewise largely empty—but not quite. In general, there is less matter in interstellar space than within the Solar System, but large clouds of dust and gas do exist. You must understand that when we speak about such a cloud of dust in space it is ever so much more diffuse and tenuous than any rain clouds or dust storms you see within the Earth's atmosphere. Clouds that exist within the galaxy are several million times less dense than our atmosphere at sea level. An interstellar cloud consists mainly of atoms of hydrogen and helium, with traces of heavier atoms and a few simple molecules such as water, ammonia, or methylene. Even smaller quantities of more complex molecules such as ethylene have been found.

The concentration of dust is particularly high near the center of the galaxy. These clouds of matter appear to be streaming outward from the center at an extremely rapid rate. This motion implies that there was once an intense explosion occurring at the heart of the galaxy. Radio and X-ray emissions have been detected from this galactic core. Strong signals of these frequencies are not normally observed in ordinary stars. Thus, it appears that the nucleus of the Milky Way is more than just a dense collection of normal stars. Some

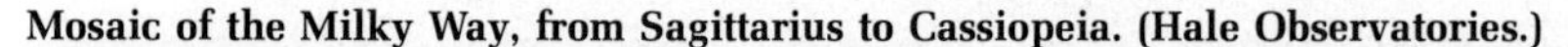

Mosaic of the Milky Way, from Sagittarius to Cassiopeia. (Hale Observatories.)

other type of energy source must be present, but no one can explain exactly what is happening.

According to one current theory, there was at one time a supermassive star located at the heart of our galaxy. The star was perhaps 10,000 times larger than our Sun. Such a mass would be highly unstable and must have exploded into a giant supernova, shooting dust far out into space and leaving a core that emits radio signals. Other astronomers have postulated that a giant black hole lies in the center of the galaxy and pulls stellar material inward in a vortex, ripping stars apart so that some matter is sucked inward and massive quantities of gas are ejected outward into space. The student should be aware that these proposals are simply working hypotheses. After one research team offers a suggestion, many scientists examine it in detail to see if all the available data can be satisfactorily explained. Gradually a more complete understanding is built up. But at the present time we have a long way to go.

The radio emissions from the Milky Way are not unique. Nearby spiral galaxies also emit radio signals, and some more distant galaxies are even more energetic. In 1940, astronomers discovered a distant object that only glowed dimly in the visible region of the spectrum but was an intense emitter of energy at radio frequencies. More than three times as much radio-frequency energy was radiated from this source than is emitted by the entire Milky Way galaxy at all wavelengths. These unusual objects appeared to be collections of stars of galactic scale and thus were called **radio galaxies.** Pictures of some radio galaxies show large lobes of gas that seem to be flying away from the central core (Fig. 17–11). Do these lobes represent material ejected from the center of a galaxy by a giant explosion? Perhaps. If so, the intense radio signals are being emitted by electrons that were accelerated many millions or hundreds of millions of years ago.

Many other radio sources have been detected in space. The most energetic of these are also the most mysterious. They are called **quasars,** short for quasi-stellar radio sources. Quasars exhibit tremendous red shifts, indicating that they are traveling very fast, some at speeds of over one-third the speed of light. According to Hubble's Law, these tremendous speeds mean that they must be very far away, as much as two to three billion light years from Earth. If quasars are, in fact, this distant, they must emit tremendous quantities of energy, perhaps 1000 times as much as the largest galaxies known. Despite their great energy output, quasars are quite small; most are

SOME ASTRONOMICAL DISTANCES

	Light Years
Earth to Sun	16×10^{-6} (about 8 minutes)
Earth to nearest star	4.3
Earth to center of Milky Way	30,000
Diameter of Milky Way	100,000
Earth to Andromeda galaxy	1,000,000
Earth to most distant galaxies	over 8,000,000,000

Figure 17–11. Messier 87. This galaxy is a source of radio emissions. The jet of gas may be a huge mass of material that has been ejected by a giant explosion in the galactic core. (Courtesy of Lick Observatory.)

less than 1 light year in diameter (recall that the Milky Way galaxy is 100,000 light years in diameter), and one has been found that may be as small as 1 light week in diameter.

What type of energy source could be so small yet so powerful? Various proposals have been offered. In many ways our concept of what could be happening inside a quasar is similar, at least qualitatively, to our concept of what may be happening inside an energetic galactic core. One theory states that quasars may be supermassive stars. Another is that they are formed by many supernova explosions in a galactic core. Many astronomers now think that quasars are powered by a central black hole. Remember that the light we see from quasars today is several billion years old, and thus a view of these objects is, in a sense, a window through time. Perhaps they represent some form of evolutionary protogalaxy in the making.

Some astronomers feel that none of these explanations is satisfactory. Instead, they argue that quasars must be much closer than Hubble's Law predicts. (If we detect a given quantity of radiation, it could be emitted from a powerful source that is far away, or from a less powerful source that is much closer.) If this is true, then much of astronomy would have to be rewritten, for Hubble's Law has been used to define intergalactic distances. If this scale is proved inaccurate, many of our present theories would have to be reevaluated.

This object appears stellar but is known to be not a star but a quasar. (From Pasachoff, Jay M.: *Contemporary Astronomy.* Second edition. Philadelphia, Saunders College Publishing, 1981.)

17.6 SPACE AND TIME—RELATIVITY

Everything in this whole ensemble of celestial objects is moving. A star moves about its particular region of a galaxy. Simultaneously, each galaxy appears to rotate about its center. Then all galaxies fly away from each other at fantastic velocities. How do you measure position and velocity in such a helter-skelter Universe? On Earth we measure velocity with respect to fixed points on the globe. Thus, if an automobile travels from Los Angeles to San Francisco (a distance of 690 km) in 10 hours, an observer along the route can easily determine that its average velocity is 69 km/hr northwest. But suppose that Los Angeles were moving towards Hawaii, San Francisco were whizzing along in the direction of Las Vegas, the magnetic pole headed toward Buenos Aires, and the observer who was attempting to calculate the motion were flying off to the Moon while simultaneously doing somersaults. How would you possibly calculate the velocity of the automobile? Even if you could do the mathematics, velocity is conventionally measured with respect to some fixed reference. If you say that a car is moving northwest, you are using the North Pole as a fixed reference; similarly the directions up, down, right, and left all assume that something somewhere is stationary. If everything is moving, as is our hypothetical example or as in the reality of space, such a fixed reference is lacking.

In the late 1800's, physicists reasoned that there must be a fixed reference somewhere in the Universe. Their reasoning was based on the fact that light seems to travel in waves. A wave is a disturbance, and all other known waves must travel in some medium. Sound may travel through air, water, wood, or any of a number of other materials, but it does not travel in a vacuum. It seemed illogical that light waves could travel in a vacuum, so it was postulated that a tenuous field of matter must pervade all space. This material was called the **ether.** If the ether could be detected, not only would it explain how light travels through space but it also would be a fixed reference with respect to which all motion could be measured. For many years the best experimenters in the world tried to measure the absolute speed of light through the ether. They reasoned that since the Earth must be traveling through the ether, there must be an "ether wind" blowing past us. If you aimed a beam of light into the ether wind, it should move slower than a light beam aimed crosscurrent, just as it is more difficult for a canoeist to meet an opposing current head-on rather than at an angle.

After years of the most careful research, it was shown that *the speed of light is the same in all directions, irrespective of the motion of the Earth!* A beam of light approaching us from any direction, at any angle, is always measured to travel at 3×10^8 m/sec. This observation was one of the most puzzling mysteries in all of physics. Think of it this way: Imagine that someone threw a ball at 50 km/hr. If a person were walking away from the thrown ball at 5 km/hr, the ball would approach him at a rate of 45 km/hr, and if he were moving toward the ball at 5 km/hr, the ball would approach him at 55 km/hr. But a beam of light approaches any observer at 3×10^8 m/sec, regardless of the motion of the observer. How could this be?

This question was answered 18 years later, in 1905, by a brilliant young physicist named Albert Einstein. But Einstein didn't tackle the puzzle directly; in fact, he may not have been aware of the experiment at all. At first Einstein considered only uniform motion; that is, movement of a body at constant velocity with respect to another body. He reasoned that if two people, traveling at different speeds, performed the same experiment, they should arrive at the same answer. In other words, all laws of physics should be the same in all bodies moving at constant velocity. For example, suppose that a horseback rider is galloping along a railroad grade at a speed of 25 km/hr, and a train on the track behind is traveling at a rate of 75 km/hr (see Fig. 17–12). The horseback rider would conclude that the train was catching up at a rate of 50 km/hr. Similarly, the engineer of the train would agree that the engine was overtaking the horse at a rate of 50 km/hr. As another example, the Earth is whizzing through space, but when you pour a cup of coffee, the liquid falls straight down into the cup under the force of gravity because the coffee, the cup, and the room are all moving together at constant velocity. Similarly, you can pour a cup of coffee successfully in an airplane. It doesn't matter that the craft is moving at, say, 700 km/hr with respect to the Earth, for within the cabin all objects are traveling along together, and the uniform motion of the airplane doesn't alter the laws of nature. Einstein summarized this observation by stating that all laws of nature are the same to all observers who are moving at constant velocity. This same relationship can be stated in different words: *All laws of nature are the same in all uniformly moving frames of reference.*

Albert Einstein was born in 1879 in Germany. His early career was unexceptional; he was an indifferent performer in grade school and in college. He finally obtained his Ph.D. in physics but remained unemployed for 2 years after graduation. Finally obtaining a job as a patent examiner in Berne, Switzerland, Einstein developed his theories in private, with little contact with the learned physicists of the day. In 1905 he published papers in three fields of physics: on the quantum theory of light, on statistical aspects of molecular theory, and on the special theory of relativity. His later contributions to physics, such as that of the general theory of relativity, continued to be of fundamental importance. He rapidly became highly regarded, held a series of important academic posts, and won the Nobel Prize for physics in 1921. In 1933, when Hitler came to power in Germany, Einstein, who had been head of his own research institute in Berlin for some time, was compelled to leave. He moved to the United States, where he remained at the Institute for Advanced Studies at Princeton until his death in 1955.

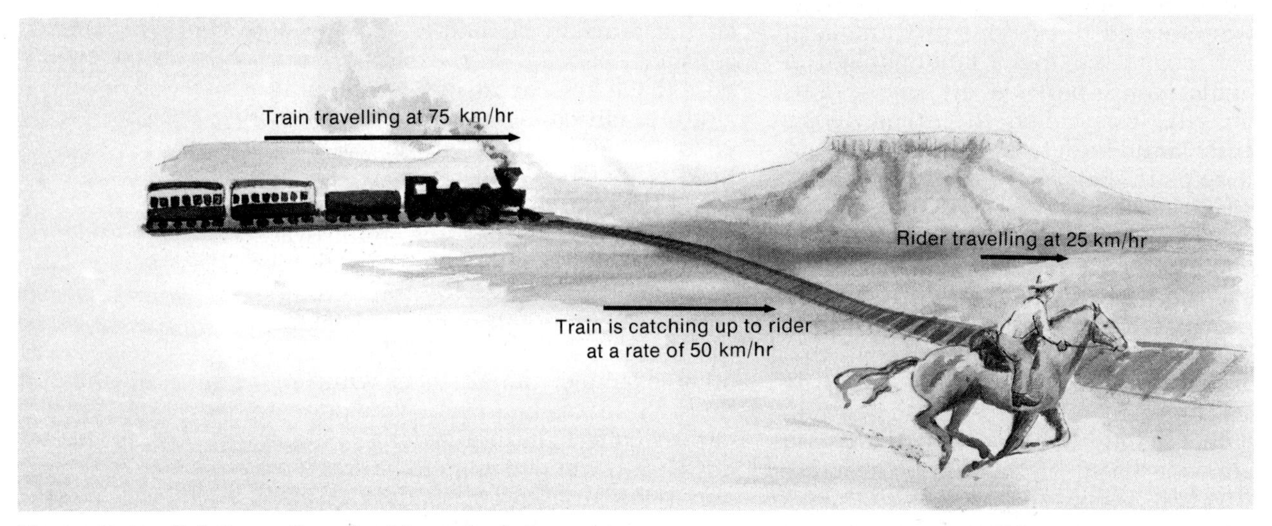

Figure 17–12. Relative motion of a rider and a train.

This statement is the first postulate of the **special theory of relativity.**

We solved the problem of the horseback rider and the railroad train simply and intuitively, but the situation is not so intuitive when we consider problems involving the speed of light. Recall that the speed of light is a fundamental, universal constant, 3×10^8 m/sec (Fig. 17–13). Thus, any experimenter anywhere in the Universe measuring the speed of light should arrive at the same answer. Don't ask for any explanation of this postulate—don't try to reason it out in terms of phenomena that you can easily observe or measure with rulers and stopwatches. It has helped physicists to explain many natural phenomena, and we have learned to accept it.

Now imagine that you are traveling away from Earth in a very fast rocket ship, one that moves skyward at a rate of 2×10^8 m/sec, nearly the speed of light. A communications station on Earth shines a beam of light toward your rocket. To an observer on Earth, light is leaving the planet at a rate of 3×10^8 m/sec. Since the rocket is traveling at 2×10^8 m/sec, light is catching up with the rocket at a rate of 1×10^8 m/sec (3×10^8 m/sec $- 2 \times 10^8$ m/sec). But what if the observer on the rocket ship were to measure the speed of this light signal. Since uniform motion doesn't change one's perspective of the Universe, and the speed of light is a universal constant, the astronaut would arrive at a value of 3×10^8 m/sec. To repeat, *the velocity of light in free space is finite and constant for all observers in all frames of reference.*

Now we have a problem. How can one observer see that light catches up

All laws of nature are the same in all uniformly moving frames of reference. A stewardess can pour coffee without spilling any in the cabin of an airplane that is traveling at speeds in excess of 800 km/hr because the woman, the coffee pot, the coffee, and the cup are all traveling at the same speed.

with the rocket at a rate of 1×10^8 m/sec while the moving observer sees the same photon of light approaching at 3×10^8 m/sec? Who is right and who is wrong? Einstein reasoned that both observers are correct. But they can both be right simultaneously only if the motion of the rocket somehow changed the traveler's perception of space and time. Imagine that some astronauts climb aboard the rocket with a ruler and a stopwatch and that the ship accelerates and then starts to travel very rapidly, at constant velocity, away from Earth. The astronauts in their rocket now exist in one frame of reference, and the people left on Earth exist in a second frame of reference. Within each frame of reference, everything is normal. In the rocket ship people can walk about, pour coffee, play Ping-Pong, and perform experiments. If they measure the speed of light, they arrive at a value of 3×10^8 m/sec. Similarly, on Earth people can walk, pour coffee, or play Ping-Pong, and if they measure the speed of light, they will arrive at the same value. However, space and time as determined by an observer on the rocket are different from those determined by an observer on Earth. *It is the magnitude of the meter and the duration of the second that appear different to the different observers in the different systems.*

Because the traveler's perceptions of space and time are different from those of an earthling, the traveler can observe that light is approaching at 3×10^8 m/sec while to the person on Earth the light is catching up with the rocket ship at a rate of 1×10^8 m/sec, and both experimenters *are* correct!

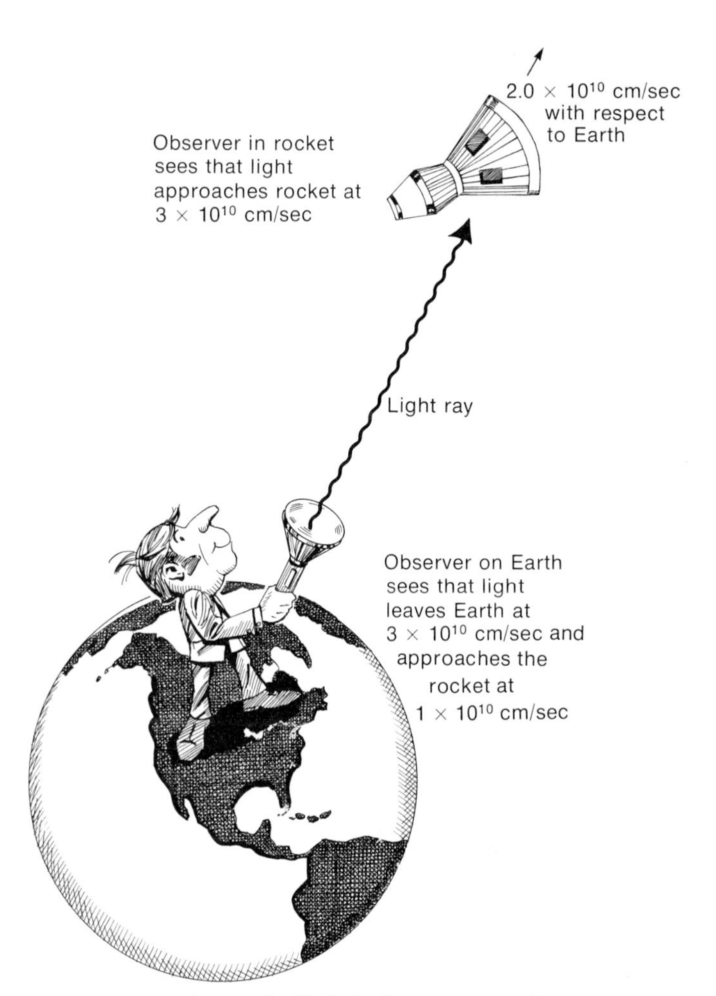

Figure 17–13. The speed of light is always measured to be 3×10^8 m/sec.

Time and distance are altered by motion.

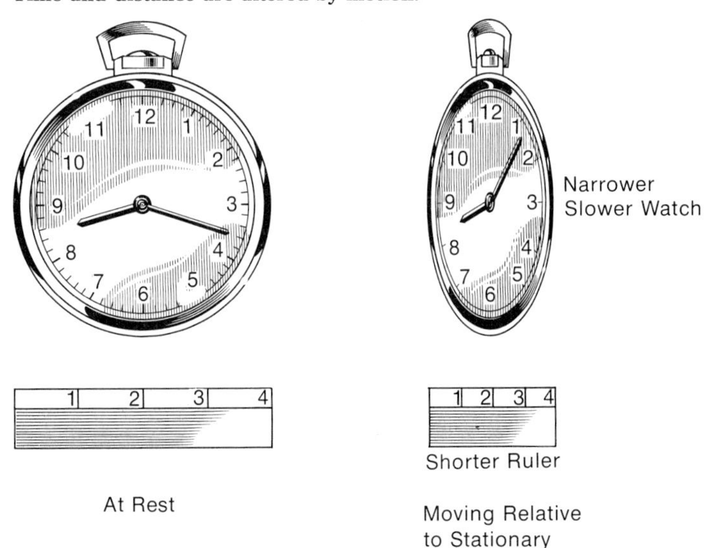

Contraction of Length

The lengths of objects appear to contract as they move by us at relativistic speeds; that is, at speeds close to the speed of light. Now, a person who is 175 cm tall on Earth would still measure 175 cm on a rapidly moving spacecraft, because both the person and his ruler are part of a single uniformly moving frame of reference. But to an observer *on Earth,* it would appear as though the astronaut and his or her meter stick had shrunk. This contraction occurs whenever one object travels past another, but it is significant only for speeds close to the speed of light. It is curious to know what would happen as the spacecraft approached the speed of light. According to Einstein's theory, the objects in the craft and the craft itself would continue to contract, approaching zero, as shown in Figure 17–14.

Dilation of Time

Just as distance is altered when two objects travel rapidly with respect to each other, so time and, in a larger sense, *space-time* are altered. Suppose that there were a pair of twins, each 25 years old. One was a traveling astronaut, while the other stayed at home. Now imagine that the astronaut twin boarded a rocket ship and headed out for distant galaxies, traveling at velocities very close to the speed of light. The twin in the rocket would exist in a different frame of reference from the Earth-bound twin, and time on the spaceship would slow down with respect to an observer on Earth. Upon the spaceship's return, the traveling twin would be younger than the other. Specifically, suppose that the rocket was traveling at 99.5 per cent of the speed of light. If the clock on the spaceship wall showed that 3 years had elapsed during the course of the journey, the traveler would have aged three years. The space wanderer would notice nothing unusual inside the rocket. On returning to Earth, however, the traveling twin would be only 28 years old (25 + 3). But, 30 years of Earth time would have elapsed during the journey and the other twin would be 55 years old (25 + 30)!

Figure 17–14. An object contracts as its velocity increases.

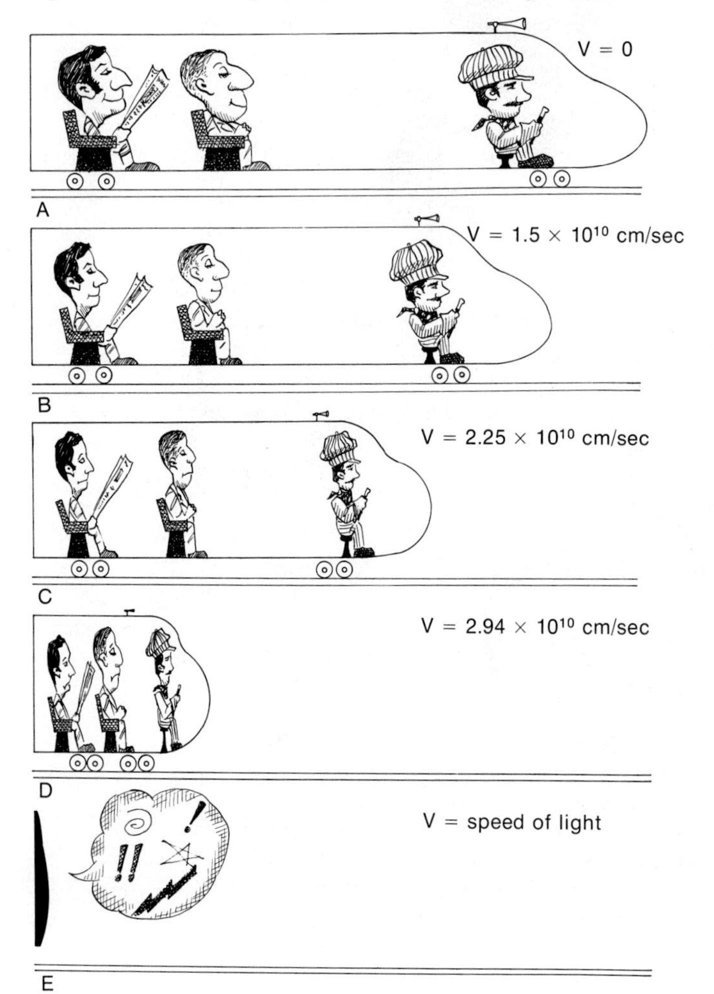

Several experiments have been performed that verify that time is not absolute. Thus for an observer at rest, atomic particles appear to decay more slowly when they are traveling very fast than they do at lower velocities. Or as another example, two extremely accurate clocks were placed one on each of two conventional airplanes. One plane flew around the world east to west and the other made the journey from west to east. Upon arrival at the starting point it was learned that the two clocks no longer read the same time. The act of motion itself caused one of the clocks to slow down by one billionth of a second relative to the other. Thus time is relative to space and velocity. There is no standard time. None. We each carry our own internal time with us. If you walk past me, you are not merely in a different portion of space, but in a different space-time as well.

Energy and Mass

Let us perform another thought experiment. Suppose that we had a small rocket ship that carried a limitless supply of fuel and that we started to accelerate the ship through free space. According to Newtonian mechanics, the acceleration of the rocket equals the force exerted by the engines divided by the mass of the craft, that is:

$$\text{Force} = \text{mass} \times \text{acceleration}$$

$$F = ma, \text{ and therefore}$$

$$a = \frac{F}{m}$$

Since the mass of the rocket is nearly constant (neglecting the depletion of fuel), a constant force would produce a constant acceleration. Therefore if we operated the engines continuously (producing a constant force), the rocket would move faster and faster forever. Thus, Newtonian mechanics predicts that it is possible to accelerate the craft to any desired speed.

We now believe that objects cannot, in fact, be accelerated indefinitely, but rather that there is a finite speed limit in the Universe. *No object can be accelerated to the speed of light.*

To understand why infinite speeds are impossible, recall that relativity theory predicts that time and distance are different in different frames of reference that are moving relative to one another. Einstein reasoned further that the mass of an object is affected by relative motion. He predicted that an object grows more massive as it travels faster, and as the speed approaches the speed of light, the mass approaches infinity. Since an infinite mass can be accelerated only by an infinite force, it naturally follows that no object can be accelerated to the speed of light. Thus, if we kept pushing our hypothetical rocket ship (or any other object), it would accelerate and simultaneously would become more massive. As it became more massive, it would be harder to accelerate. Some of the energy supplied is no longer being transformed into kinetic energy, but is being converted into mass. Thus, *mass and energy are different forms of the same phenomenon.* This equivalence is stated in the now-famous equation:

$$E = mc^2$$

Stated in words, energy equals the mass of an object times the speed of light squared.

Figure 17–15. Travels of a space wanderer.

While in theory you and I become more massive as we speed up on a freeway ramp or accelerate in any other manner, the change is far too small to measure. However, physicists have accelerated atomic particles to speeds in excess of 99 per cent of the speed of light and observed that their mass has increased measurably. Conversely, whenever energy is released, the mass of the system is decreased. Suppose, for example, that we burn a lump of coal in

The main accelerator tunnel at the Fermi national accelerator laboratory, Batavia, Illinois. The mass of particles accelerated in this chamber has been observed to increase as the speeds approach the speed of light. (From Merkin, Melvin: *Physical Science With Modern Applications.* 2nd ed. Philadelphia, Saunders College Publishing, 1980. Fermilab photo.)

air. The chemical equation for the reaction is

$$C + O_2 \rightarrow CO_2 + \text{heat}$$

Since the reaction releases energy, the mass of one molecule of carbon dioxide must be less than the combined masses of an atom of carbon and a molecule of oxygen. The lost mass is calculated to be about 10^{-13} g of matter for every gram of carbon burnt. However, this difference is too slight to be detected by even the finest balance. Nuclear reactions involve larger energy changes than do chemical reactions and consequently involve large changes in mass. When hydrogen is converted to helium during a nuclear fusion reaction, large amounts of energy are produced, and almost 1 per cent of the mass of the hydrogen is converted into energy. At that rate, the mass of the Sun decreases at a rate of 4½ million tons every second! (Fortunately for us, the Sun is massive enough to last for billions of years despite this loss of material.) Thus, mass is converted to the energy that radiates outward and provides us with light and heat.

> If 1 g of hydrogen could be converted completely into energy, and if that energy could be used 100 per cent efficiently, a 100-W light bulb could be kept running for 28,500 years.

17.7 COSMOLOGY—A STUDY OF THE BEGINNING AND THE END OF TIME

Humans have always looked to the heavens as a source of inspiration and mystery. In nearly every religion the Supreme Deity, the Ultimate Power, and the Great Unknowable reside in the vastness of space. During our brief look at astronomy we have studied many of the celestial bodies and some of the physics of the events that occur within our Solar System and the regions beyond. This knowledge that we have gained does not subtract from the mystery and wonder, for one can hardly contemplate the objects in space and the distances among them without being filled with awe. Perhaps the ultimate mystery, the great question that never ceases to boggle the mind, is "When did time and space begin, what was here before it, and when if ever will it end?" Cosmology is the study of the beginning and the end of the Universe. To contemplate cosmological questions, you must stretch your imagination even further than you have done previously in this chapter and attempt to comprehend new dimensions of space, time, and nothingness.

As part of our search for an ultimate beginning, we must search for signs that the Universe is progressively aging. If the state of the Universe doesn't change with time, we might be led to conclude that perhaps there was no evolution, no beginning, no start—ever. There are, in fact, two indications that the Universe is aging. The first is based on the quantity of elements heavier than hydrogen and helium in the stars and galaxies. We learned that within the core of the Sun and other mature stars, hydrogen is being converted into helium. As stars fade, change, and die amid giant supernova explosions, the heavier elements are gradually formed in increasing quantities. This conversion of hydrogen into other elements is essentially irreversible. No known process now occurring within the Universe breaks down large quantities of the heavier elements into hydrogen. Thus the chemical composition of the Universe is a type of evolutionary clock. We may reason that time began when all matter was hydrogen and helium and that the Universe will fade out and become cold when there is no more fuel for nuclear fusion.

A second marker of the passage of time is found in the movement of galaxies. Recall that all the galaxies are flying away from each other. If they are all flying away from each other, it seems reasonable to assume that they were all in the same location at some time in the past. Following this logic still further, we now believe that all matter in the Universe was once compressed into a single ball of infinite density. Since an observer on Earth sees everything moving away from him, does this mean that our own Milky Way is, by chance, the center of the Universe? No, not at all. There is no center. Think of a baker making a loaf of raisin bread (see Fig. 17–16). Imagine that each raisin is a galaxy and that the dough represents the empty space between them. As the dough rises, each raisin moves farther away from every other one. Any observer on any raisin always sees all the other raisins moving away and no one can truly be considered to be the center. This conclusion is somehow disquieting, and the student may ask, "If everything, all matter, was once in one spot, then that spot had to be the center." But, to repeat, that type of reasoning is not correct; there is no center. The formation of the Universe may have been the creation of space it-

A faint cluster of galaxies in the constellation of Pisces at a distance of well over four billion light years. (Hale Observatories.)

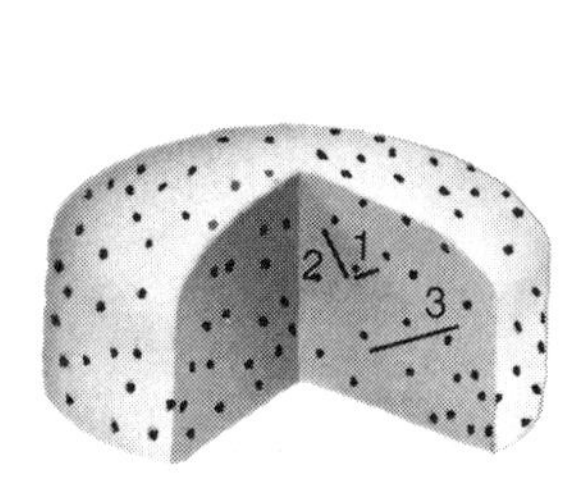

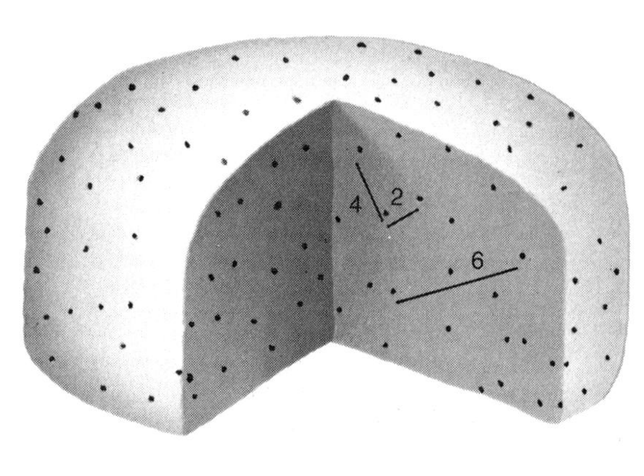

Figure 17–16. From every raisin in a raisin cake, every other raisin seems to be moving away from you at a speed that depends on its distance from you. This leads to a relation like the Hubble Law between the velocity and the distance. Note also that each raisin would be at the center of the expansion measured from its own position, yet the cake is expanding uniformly. For a better analogy with the Universe, consider an infinite cake; clearly, there is no center to its expansion. (From Pasachoff, Jay M.: *Contemporary Astronomy*. Second edition. Philadelphia, Saunders College Publishing, 1981.)

self; before the beginning there was nothing at all,—not even emptiness. Other theoreticians argue that there is an infinite amount of matter in the Universe. If this is true, then even if this matter were compressed to an infinite density, it had to occupy all space from the very beginning.

At some instant in time all the matter in the entire Universe exploded. This cataclysmic event, the **Big Bang,** was the beginning of the expansion. It marked the beginning of the Universe and the start of time. Since we know how far apart the galaxies are at present and approximately how fast they are moving, we can calculate backward through time and estimate how long ago it all started. Most current estimates place the Big Bang between 13 and 20 billion years ago. But not everyone agrees, and some new evidence seems to indicate that the Universe may be only half that age.

The most widely accepted theory of the formation of the Universe assumes that originally there was a huge hot ball of matter expanding rapidly into space. As matter expanded, it separated into galactic-sized agglomerations held together by mutual gravitation. These galaxies continued to fly apart, carried along by the expanding Universe. Meanwhile, within each galaxy, matter collected into stars, and the stars slowly aged. Supernova explosions ripped through dying stars to produce heavier elements, and, in at least one case, a Solar System was formed and life evolved.

Let us return for a moment to the Big Bang itself. This was no ordinary event such as we might observe if a supergiant firecracker or a massive star exploded. Explosions that we are familiar with start in a definite center and spread outward to engulf more and more matter. No. This must have been an explosion that started simultaneously everywhere, instantly filling all space with all matter such that from its very beginning every particle was flying away from every other particle. Theoretical physicists believe that about 1/100 of a second after the start of time the temperature of the Universe was about 100 billion °C. (Imagine. We actually think that we know what happened during that 1/100 of a second when the Universe was born!) Certainly, no molecules or even atomic nuclei could exist at these temperatures, and the Universe consisted of a uniform sea of atomic particles and photons. This homogeneous mass was so dense, and the available electron energy levels were so closely spaced, that photons could not travel far before they would be absorbed. But gradually the Universe cooled. After about one million years, particles were cool enough to condense together to form hydrogen atoms. At this point, photons left over from the Big Bang itself were no longer absorbed efficiently, for remember that hydrogen atoms can absorb light only at certain specific frequencies. These primordial photons dispersed unhindered into the void. About 15 billion years later, in 1965, two astronomers at Bell laboratories recorded a faint, low-energy radio signal that was evenly distributed throughout all of space. Most scientists believe that this radiation could only have been left over from the Big Bang itself. This discovery provides the main thrust of the evidence that substantiates the Big Bang theory.

Although scientists feel fairly confident that they know what happened at the beginning of time, they feel less sure about what will happen in the future. One possibility is that the Universe will continue to expand forever. Galaxies will continue to disperse and the space between them will gradually grow larger and emptier (Fig. 17–17). Simultaneously, fuel for stellar fusion reactions will be consumed so the energy output within each galaxy will slowly diminish. Eventually space will become emptier and emptier and only small bits of cold matter in a frozen void will remain. This version of the Big Bang theory assumes a beginning and an end.

Another possibility is that the expansion will eventually come to a halt. Not only are the galaxies flying away from each other but also they are being pulled inward by mutual gravitation. If the gravitational attraction is sufficiently large, it will gradually cause the galaxies to decelerate to a standstill,

The large horn-shaped antenna at the Bell Telephone Laboratories' space communication station in Holmdel, New Jersey. 3° K background radiation was discovered with this instrument. (From Pasachoff, Jay M.: *Contemporary Astronomy*. Second edition. Philadelphia, Saunders College Publishing, 1981.)

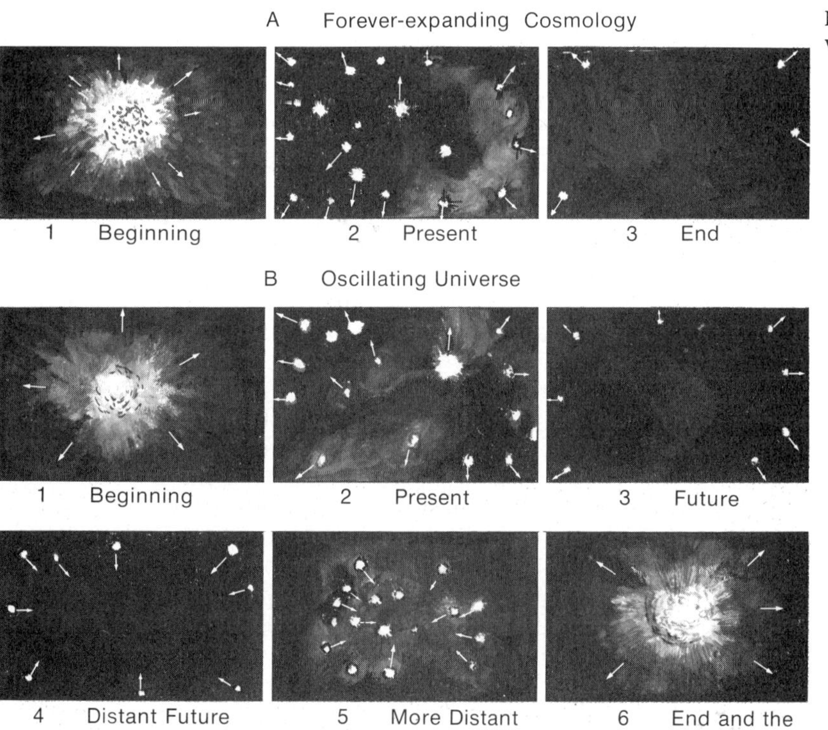

Figure 17–17. Formation of the Universe.

then accelerate back inward, falling closer and closer together until they all join together. All the galaxies, all the stars, and all matter itself would be unified once again. The gravitational forces within this volume would be incomprehensibly large, so intense in fact that we would expect all nuclei to be split and all matter to be converted into fundamental atomic particles. This giant agglomeration of matter containing all the mass of the entire Universe would be exactly identical to the mass that was present at the beginning of our current Universe. This dense matter would then "explode" again and begin expanding to form a new Universe. When we think about such an event, we speak of an oscillating Universe, which alternately expands and contracts indefinitely. In this version, the death of one Universe would simultaneously represent the birth of a new one. Thus the **Oscillating Universe cosmology** predicts innumerable beginnings and endings in an infinite continuum.

Will our Universe slowly expand into space and gradually fade into oblivion, or will it be pulled back together by its own gravitation so that all matter becomes reunified into a dense volume? Astronomers trying to answer this question have attempted to measure the density of the entire Universe. They reason that if they knew the density of the system, they could calculate its internal gravitation. Then, knowing the momentum of the receding galaxies, it would be possible to calculate whether they would be slowed down and drawn in again or whether they will escape into space and disappear into nothingness. A density of 5×10^{-30} g/cm^3 (approximately one hydrogen atom every four cubic meters) throughout the Universe would be sufficient to exert enough force eventually to pull the galaxies back together. It is very difficult to calculate the density of the Universe. It is relatively easy to count the number of stars in a given volume of space, but it is much more difficult to determine the mass of interstellar dust clouds or to count all the hydrogen atoms and stray photons drifting about through the intergalactic void. Or what about black holes; how many are out there anyway? Estimates of all these masses are available, and at the present time the weight of the evidence indicates that there is not enough mass to stop the expansion of the Universe. This conclusion is supported by another line of reasoning. Astrophysicists have detected the presence of a small amount of deuterium in interstellar space. This amount by itself is insignificant, but theory states that it was formed in the first 15 minutes after the Big Bang and so tells us about conditions at that time. The universe could not have been very dense then or else the deuterium would have fused into helium. This line of argument also strongly indicates that the Universe will expand forever, but this conclusion is by no means certain.

One hydrogen atom for every four cubic meters is very little matter. As a comparison, there are 8×10^{28} atoms per cubic meter in the core of the Sun and 2×10^{20} atoms in the same volume of the Earth's atmosphere at sea level.

17.8 EPILOGUE

In a search for the origin and conclusion of the Universe, we have thought about events that must have occurred many billions of years ago, or that will occur many billions of years from now. We have tried to extend our vision across expanses of space, and in our imagination we have traveled to the very edge of what is known and beyond.

Let us ask this final question: Have we gone beyond the merely unknown and perhaps encroached on the unknowable? The Big Bang cosmologies assume a beginning—a small, dense, hot proto-universe. Can science ever address itself to the question of how that Universe originally appeared, or where it came from? If there were nothingness before, what was nothingness like, or even what do we mean by "before"? If we live in an oscillating Universe, we may not need to ask about the ultimate beginning, for perhaps there was none; perhaps matter has been expanding and contracting for all of past time. But if our Universe is not oscillating, if it is a unique "one-shot" affair, then one has to ask why are we so special? What went on before, and what will be after?

CHAPTER OBJECTIVES

Understand how atomic spectra are used to determine various physical characteristics of an object in space. Study the history of a large and a small star, and know how a white dwarf, a neutron star, and a black hole are formed. Know what a galaxy is, the dimensions of an average galaxy, and what radio galaxies and quasars are. Think about Einstein's theory of special relativity. Understand the Big Bang cosmology and the difference between the forever expanding and the oscillating Universe theories.

KEY WORDS

Red shift
Hubble's Law
Red giant
White dwarf
Degeneracy pressure
Supernova
Neutron Star
Pulsar
Lighthouse theory
Black hole
Galaxy
Spiral galaxy
Milky Way galaxy
Radio galaxy
Quasar
Ether
Uniformly moving frame of reference
Special Theory of Relativity
Length contraction
Time dilation
Cosmology
Big Bang cosmology
Oscillating Universe cosmology

FORMULA TO KNOW

$E = mc^2$

TAKE-HOME EXPERIMENTS

1. **Stargazing.** If you are studying this chapter in the winter or the spring, look toward the southern sky and locate the constellation Orion. (Refer to the star chart at the end of Chapter 16.) Look carefully at the corner stars Betelgeuse and Rigel. What color are they? From this information alone, what can you tell about their temperatures? Referring back to the text material, discuss the past history of Betelgeuse.

If you are studying this chapter in the summer or the fall, locate the star Antares located in the constellation Scorpio. What color is it? Answer the questions posed in the previous paragraph.

PROBLEMS

1. **Spectra.** What is an absorption spectrum? How is it formed in a star? What information can be obtained from it?

2. **Radio astronomy.** Discuss some similarities and differences between a radio signal and one in the visible or ultraviolet region. What information can be obtained from each?

3. **Doppler shift.** What is the Doppler shift? Would the waves from a speedboat traveling through the water exhibit Doppler shifts? If you were in front of the moving boat, would you observe more waves, fewer waves, or the same number of waves per unit time than if you were behind the boat? Explain.

*4. **Doppler shift.** Many of the stars in our galaxy exhibit spectra that are blue shifted. Does this invalidate Hubble's Law? Explain.

5. **Studying outer space.** In recent years, astronomers have learned a great deal about our universe by studying radio, X-ray, and

*Indicates more difficult problem.

other invisible radiation. Do you think that more information could be gained by building large microphones to detect the sounds of giant explosions in space? Defend your answer.

6. **Reactions within a star.** What is the primary source of energy of a star like our Sun?

7. **Reactions within a star.** Hydrogen burns in air according to the following equation: $2H_2 + O_2 \rightarrow 2H_2O$. Is the chemical combustion of hydrogen an important process within a star? Why or why not? Explain.

8. **Structure of a star.** Explain why the density of the gases near the surface of the Sun is less than the density of gases near the surface of the Earth, even though the gravitational force of the Sun is much greater.

9. **Life of a star.** Briefly trace the evolution and life history of a star.

10. **Life of a star.** Explain why the core of a star becomes hotter when the nuclear fusion reactions diminish.

*11. **Life of a star.** What could you tell about the past history of a star if you knew that its core was composed primarily of carbon? Explain.

12. **Life of a star.** Compare and contrast a white dwarf with a red giant. Can a single star ever be both a red giant and a white dwarf in its lifetime? Explain.

*13. **Life of a star.** Would you be likely to find life on planets orbiting around a star that was composed solely of hydrogen and helium? Explain.

14. **Supernova.** What is a supernova? Do all stars eventually explode as supernovae? Explain. What is a neutron star? Do all supernovae lead to the formation of neutron stars?

*15. **Pulsars.** Explain why the pulsar signals detected by Jocelyn Bell Burnell could not have originated from (a) a star, (b) an unknown planet in our solar system, (c) a distant galaxy, or (d) a large magnetic storm on a nearby star.

*Indicates more difficult problem.

16. **Black holes.** What is a black hole? Why are they hard to find? Do you think that one could be hidden in our Solar System? Explain.

*17. **Black holes.** Some astronomers believe that there are black holes flying through space. Would such objects represent a hazard to a rocket ship traveling to distant stars? Could the crew of such a rocket detect a black hole well in advance and avoid a collision? Explain.

18. **Galaxies.** What is a galaxy? What is the approximate diameter of the Milky Way galaxy, and how many stars does it contain? What holds together the individual parts of the galaxy? Discuss.

19. **The Milky Way galaxy.** What evidence do we have that indicates that the center of our galaxy was once the scene of a violent explosion?

20. **Outer space.** Describe the following collections of stars: binaries, clusters, and galaxies. Are galaxies random collections of stars? Explain.

21. **Quasars.** What is a quasar? How much energy is released by a quasar compared to the energy released by a normal galaxy? Briefly discuss the possible energy source of a quasar.

22. **Astronomical distances.** What is the diameter of the Milky Way? How far is it to the nearest galaxy? How far is it to distant galaxies? Give your answer in light years, kilometers, and miles.

*23. **Densities.** Below is a list of different environments found in the Universe. Arrange them in order of increasing densities: (a) intergalactic space, (b) the core of the Sun, (c) the corona of the Sun, (d) the region of space between planets in our Solar System, (e) galactic space, (f) the Earth's atmosphere at sea level.

24. **Relativity.** A person driving from Los Angeles to San Francisco is said to be moving northwest. But such a simple description ignores the fact that the person is rotating with the Earth, orbiting the Sun, and simultaneously flying through intergalactic space. Would it be more accurate to define the net motion of the car as the sum of all these independent earthly celestial movements? Explain.

25. **Ether.** What is the ether? How did scientists search for it? What is the significance of their findings? Discuss.

Rule 1

In addition or subtraction, the value with the fewest decimal places will determine how far the significant figures should be carried in the answer:

308.7810 g	(4 decimal places)
0.00034 g	(5 decimal places)
+10.31 g	(2 decimal places; the fewest)
319.09 g	(2 decimal places)

Rule 2

In multiplication and division, the number of significant figures in the answer is the same as that in the quantity with the fewest significant figures:

$$\frac{3.0 \times 4297}{0.0721} = 1.8 \times 10^5$$

There are two significant figures in 3.0, whereas 4297 has four significant figures, and 0.0721 has three significant figures. Therefore the answer, 1.8×10^5, can have only two significant figures.

Rule 3

When a number is "rounded off" (nonsignificant figures discarded), the last significant figure is increased by 1 if the next figure is more than 5, and is unchanged if the next figure is less than 5. If the next figure is exactly 5, you can toss a coin to determine whether to leave the last significant figure unchanged or increase it by one:

$4.6349 \rightarrow 4.635$	(four significant figures)
$4.6349 \rightarrow 4.63$	(three significant figures)
$2.815 \rightarrow 2.81$ or 2.82	(three significant figures)

Example 1

Evaluate the expression

$$V = 4.4 \times \frac{311.8}{273.1} \times \frac{760}{784 - 3}$$

Answer: **There are two significant figures in the number 4.4; therefore the answer will have two significant figures. Note that the −3 is not a factor in multiplication or division. Thus**

$$V = 4.4 \times \frac{311.8}{273.1} \times \frac{760}{781} = 4.8884328$$

(by pocket calculator)

Now round off to two significant figures

$$V = 4.9$$

B DIRECT PROPORTIONALITY AND INVERSE PROPORTIONALITY

Two variable properties are said to be directly proportional to each other when a change in one of the variables produces a proportionate change in the other. If one variable is doubled, the other doubles; if one triples, the other triples. An example is Charles' law (Section 7.5), which states, "The volume of a gas is directly proportional to its absolute temperature." The expression is

$$V \propto T$$

(The symbol $\propto$ means "is proportional to.") The accompanying graph illustrates such a relationship. In the example shown, a sample of gas at 100 K occupies 2 L. If we double the absolute temperature, to 200 K, the gas volume also doubles, to 4 L.

In an inverse proportionality, when one variable changes by a given factor, the other variable changes by the *reciprocal* of that factor. For example, Boyle's law (Section 7.5) states that "the volume of a gas is inversely proportional to its pressure." Thus, if the pressure of a sample of gas is doubled (that is, multiplied by 2), the volume of the gas is halved (that is, multiplied by $\frac{1}{2}$). In the accompanying graph, the volume of the gas is 1 L at 0.4 atm^{-1} ($atm^{-1} = \frac{1}{atm}$, or reciprocal atmosphere). At double this value, 0.8 atm^{-1}, the gas volume is also doubled, to 2 L. But the *pressure* has actually been halved (from $\frac{1}{0.4}$, or 2.5 to $\frac{1}{0.8}$, or 1.25). Thus the relationship shows that the volume is inversely proportional to the pressure.

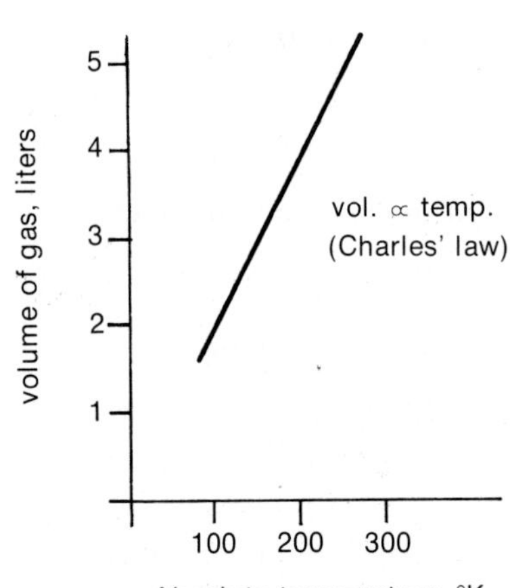

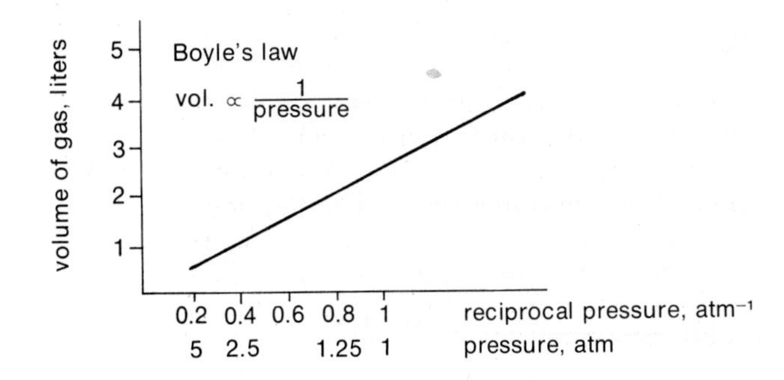

C CONVERSION BETWEEN FAHRENHEIT AND CELSIUS TEMPERATURE SCALES

The following equations express the relationship between the Fahrenheit and Celsius temperature scales.

$$°C = \frac{5}{9}(°F - 32)$$

$$°F = \frac{9}{5}(°C) + 32$$

The use of these equations is shown in the two examples below.

Example 2
Convert 85°F to °C

Answer: $°C = \frac{5}{9}(85° - 32)$

$= \frac{5}{9}(53°)$

$= 29.4°C$

Example 3
Convert 85°C to °F

Answer: $°F = \frac{9}{5}(85°) + 32$

$= 153° + 32$

$= 185°F$

D DERIVATION OF KINETIC ENERGY EQUATION

A moving body has energy of motion, or **kinetic energy.** Energy is the capacity to do work, and a moving body can do work by colliding with a stationary body and forcing it to move. Let us consider how much energy a stationary body can gain as it is accelerated at a uniform rate; this energy will be its kinetic energy.

Let m = mass of body
0 = original velocity
v = final velocity
d = distance the body travels as its velocity changes uniformly from 0 to v
t = time

Then,

change in velocity = final velocity − initial velocity
$= v - 0$
$= v$

acceleration of body

$$= \frac{\text{change in velocity}}{\text{time}} = \frac{v}{t}$$

average velocity of body

$$= \frac{\text{final velocity} - \text{initial velocity}}{2}$$

$$= \frac{v}{2}$$

distance traveled by body

= average velocity × time

$$d = \frac{v}{2} \times t$$

Dividing both sides of the above equation by t, we have

$$\frac{d}{t} = \frac{v}{2}$$

The kinetic energy of the body is the energy it gains from the work done on it.

$$\text{Work} = \text{force} \times \text{distance}$$

$$\begin{aligned}\text{Kinetic energy} &= \text{force} \times \text{distance} \\ &= \text{mass} \times \text{acceleration} \times \text{distance} \\ &= m \times \frac{v}{t} \times d \\ &= m \times v \times \frac{d}{t}\end{aligned}$$

But $\frac{d}{t} = \frac{v}{2}$ (from equation above for distance traveled by body) Therefore,

$$\begin{aligned}\text{Kinetic energy} &= m \times v \times \frac{v}{2} \\ &= \frac{1}{2} mv^2\end{aligned}$$

E THE DECIBEL SCALE; A MORE MATHEMATICAL TREATMENT

Physicists have created a unit that defines a tenfold increase in sound intensity, and named it a **Bel,** after Alexander Graham Bell. If the sound of a garbage disposal unit is 10 times as intense as that of a vacuum cleaner, it is one Bel more intense. A rocket whose sound is a million, or 10^6, times as intense as the vacuum cleaner is therefore 6 Bels more intense. This definition leads to the following relationship:

Difference in intensity between two sounds, X and Y, expressed in Bels

$$= \log_{10}\left(\frac{\text{sound intensity of X}}{\text{sound intensity of Y}}\right)$$

It happens that the Bel is a rather large unit, so that it is convenient to divide it into tenths, or decibels, dB, as follows:

$$1 \text{ Bel} = 10 \text{ dB}$$

Then,

Intensity in dB

$$= \text{intensity in Bels} \times \frac{10 \text{ dB}}{\text{Bel}}$$

Therefore,

Difference in intensity between two sounds, X and Y, expressed in decibels, dB

$$= 10 \log_{10}\left(\frac{\text{sound intensity of X}}{\text{sound intensity of Y}}\right)$$

Finally, it is very convenient to start our scale somewhere that we can designate zero, and the most convenient point is at the softest sound level which is audible to the human ear. We will call this level zero decibels. We can now write our equation for the decibel scale as follows:

Intensity in dB of any given sound

$$= 10 \times \log_{10}\left(\frac{\text{intensity of the given sound}}{\text{intensity of a barely audible sound}}\right)$$

Example 4

The sound of a vacuum cleaner in a room has 10 million times the intensity of the faintest audible sound. What is the intensity of the sound in decibels?

Answer:

$$\left(\frac{\textbf{sound intensity of vacuum cleaner}}{\textbf{faintest audible sound}}\right) = \mathbf{10{,}000{,}000}$$

$$\mathbf{\log 10{,}000{,}000 = 7}$$

$$\begin{aligned}\textbf{Sound intensity} &= \mathbf{10 \times \log 10{,}000{,}000} \\ &= \mathbf{10 \times 7} \\ &= \mathbf{70\ dB}\end{aligned}$$

Example 5

What is the intensity in decibels of the faintest audible sound?

Answer: **This had better turn out to be zero, which is what we promised the log scale would provide:**

$$\left(\frac{\text{intensity of the faintest audible sound}}{\text{intensity of the faintest audible sound}}\right) = 1, \text{ and } \log 1 = 0$$

Thus,

$$\text{Sound intensity} = 10 \times \log 1 = 10 \times 0 = 0 \text{ dB}$$

Example 6

Referring back to Example 3, page 329, if the sound level in a library is 30 dB, and the sound level of a rustling leaf is 10 dB, what will be the sound level in the library if we bring in the rustling leaf?

Answer: The difference between the two decibel levels is 30 − 10 = 20 dB. Substituting this in the equation,* we have

$$20 = 10 \log \left(\frac{\text{sound intensity of library}}{\text{sound intensity of leaf}}\right)$$

$$\log \left(\frac{\text{sound intensity of library}}{\text{sound intensity of leaf}}\right) = \frac{20}{10} = 2$$

$$\frac{\text{sound intensity of library}}{\text{sound intensity of leaf}} = \text{antilog } 2 = 10^2 = 100$$

Now, if $x/y = 100$, then $x + y = 101\,y$.

*See log table, Appendix G.

Therefore,

$$\frac{\text{sound intensity of library + leaf}}{\text{sound intensity of library}} = \frac{101}{100} = 1.01$$

Difference in dB levels between library + leaf and library alone

$$= 10 \log 1.01 = 0.04$$

Therefore the decibel level of the library with the rustling leaf is 30 dB + 0.04 dB = 30.04 dB. So, you see, the leaf hardly makes any difference.

Example 7

On takeoff a certain SST aircraft is judged to sound like 50 subsonic jets all taking off at the same time. How much louder is this SST than one subsonic jet? How much louder are 50 jets than 1 jet?

Answer

Difference in intensity between 1 SST and 1 subsonic jet

= difference in intensity between 50 jets and 1 jet

$$= 10 \times \log_{10} \left(\frac{\text{sound power of 50 jets}}{\text{sound power of 1 jet}}\right)$$

$$= 10 \times \log_{10} 50$$
$$= 10 \times 1.7 = 17 \text{ dB}$$

The calculation tells us that 50 jet planes or their equivalent with reference to sound (one SST) are 17 dB louder than one jet plane.

F HANDY CONVERSION FACTORS

To Convert From	To	Multiply By	
Centimeters	Feet	0.0328 ft/cm	
	Inches	0.394 in/cm	
	Meters	0.01 m/cm	(exactly)
	Micrometers	1000 μm/cm	(")
	Miles (statute)	6.214×10^{-6} mi/cm	
	Millimeters	10 mm/cm	(exactly)
Feet	Centimeters	30.48 cm/ft	(exactly)
	Inches	12 in/ft	(")
	Meters	0.3048 m/ft	(")
	Micrometers	304800 μm/ft	(")
	Miles (statute)	0.000189 mi/ft	
	Yards	0.3333 yd/ft	

To Convert From	To	Multiply By	
Gallons (U.S., liq.)	Cu. centimeters	3785 cm^3/gal	
	Cu. feet	0.133 ft^3/gal	
	Cu. inches	231 in^3/gal	
	Cu. meters	0.003785 m^3/gal	
	Cu. yards	0.004951 yd^3/gal	
	Liters	3.785 L/gal	
	Quarts (U.S., liq.)	4 qt/gal	(exactly)
Grams	Kilograms	0.001 kg/g	(exactly)
	Micrograms	1×10^6 μg/g	(")
	Ounces (avdp.)	0.03527 oz/g	
	Pounds (avdp.)	0.002205 lb/g	
Inches	Centimeters	2.54 cm/in	(exactly)
	Feet	0.0833 ft/in	
	Meters	0.0254 m/in	
	Yards	0.0278 yd/in	
Kilograms	Ounces (avdp.)	35.27 oz/kg	
	Pounds (avdp.)	2.205 lb/kg	
Liters	Cu. centimeters	1000 cm^3/L	(exactly)
	Cu. feet	0.0353 ft^3/L	
	Cu. inches	61.03 in^3/L	
	Cu. meters	0.001 m^3/L	(exactly)
	Cu. yards	0.001308 yd^3/L	
	Gallons (U.S., liq.)	0.264 gal/L	
	Ounces (U.S., fluid)	33.81 oz/L	
	Quarts (U.S., liq.)	1.0567 qt/L	
Meters	Centimeters	100 cm/m	(exactly)
	Feet	3.2808 ft/m	
	Inches	39.37 in/m	
	Kilometers	0.001 km/m	(exactly)
	Miles (statute)	0.0006214 mi/m	
	Millimeters	1000 mm/m	(exactly)
	Yards	1.0936 yd/m	
Miles (statute)	Centimeters	160934 cm/mi	
	Feet	5280 ft/mi	(exactly)
	Inches	63360 in/mi	(exactly)
	Kilometers	1.609 km/mi	
	Meters	1609 m/mi	
	Yards	1760 yd/mi	(exactly)
Ounces (avdp.)	Grams	28.35 g/oz	
	Pounds (avdp.)	0.0625 lb/oz	
Pounds (avdp.)	Grams	453.6 g/lb	
	Kilograms	0.454 kg/lb	
	Ounces (avdp.)	16 oz/lb	(exactly)
Ounces (troy)*	Grams	31.1 g/oz (troy)	
	Ounces (avdp.)	1.097 oz (troy)/oz (avdp.)	
Pounds (troy)	Grams	373 g/lb (troy)	
	Ounces (troy)	12 oz (troy)/lb (troy) (exactly)	

*The price of gold and other precious metals is commonly quoted in troy weight. Note that a troy ounce (31.1 g) is heavier than an avdp. ounce (28.35 g), but a troy pound (12 troy oz) is lighter than an avdp. pound (16 avdp. oz).

G LOGARITHMS TO THE BASE 10 (THREE PLACES)

N	0	1	2	3	4	5	6	7	8	9
1	000	041	079	114	146	176	204	230	255	279
2	301	322	342	362	380	398	415	431	447	462
3	477	491	505	519	532	544	556	568	580	591
4	602	613	623	634	644	653	663	672	681	690
5	699	708	716	724	732	740	748	756	763	771
6	778	785	792	799	806	813	820	826	833	839
7	845	851	857	863	869	875	881	887	892	898
8	903	909	914	919	924	929	935	941	945	949
9	954	959	964	969	973	978	982	987	991	996

ANSWERS TO NUMERICAL PROBLEMS

Chapter 1

1. 10^3 or 1000; 10^2 or 100; 10^3 or 1000; 10^6 or 1,000,000; 10^3 or 1000.
3. 33¢
4. 3×10^{10} cm/sec or 30,000,000,000 cm/sec.
5. Approximately 3.3 yd.
6. 379 m, or 3.79×10^2 m.
7. 3.2×10^6 cans.
9. 1.8 m or 180 cm.
10. 4830 km.

Chapter 2

2. 6.67 km/hr.
3. 2700 m; 2.7 km.
4. 71 km/hr.
7. 4 km/hr east; about 6.3 km/hr south southwest.
8. 83 km/hr south.
24. $2 \times 10^5 \frac{m}{sec^2}$.

Chapter 3

1. 1.6×10^6 J.
5. 2.5×10^3 J; 7.8 m/sec.
6. 1.5×10^5 J; 7.4×10^4 J.
7. 7.4×10^3 J.
10. 4×10^4 cal; 40 kcal; 1.68×10^5 J; yes.
19. 8.9×10^4 kg m/sec.
21. 57 m/sec in the opposite direction in which the bullet is traveling.

Chapter 5

7. 117,800 volts; 2200 volts; 119,890 volts.
11. (a) 10 ohms; (b) 12 volts.
13. 484 ohms, 242 ohms, 242 ohms, 121 ohms, 48 ohms, and 15 ohms.
14. 167 W
24. (a) Current in wire = 0.1 amp; power in 20-ohm resistor = 0.2 W; power in 100-ohm resistor = 1.0 W.
    (b) Current in 10-ohm resistor = 11 amp; power through the 10-ohm resistor = 1210 W; current in the 50-ohm resistor = 2.2 amps; power through the 50-ohm resistor = 242 W.
    (c) Current in the 100-ohm resistor = 0.18 amp; power through the 100-ohm resistor = 3.2 W; current in the 10,000-ohm resistor = 1.8×10^{-3} amp; power through the 10,000-ohm resistor = 0.032 W.
    (d) Current in the wire = 0.0109 amp; power in the 10,000-ohm resistor = 1.18 W; power in the 10-ohm resistor = 0.00118 W; power in the 100-ohm resistor = 0.0118 W.
51. 200 loops; 10 loops; 100 loops. 5 amps; 100 amps; 10 amps.

Chapter 6

2. 10^{-5} sec.
8. (a) 3×10^{-14} m; (b) 10^7 sec^{-1}; (c) 0.331 m; (d) 3×10^5 m or 300 km.

Chapter 7

4. O-18: 8, 18, 10;
   Sr-90: 38, 90, 52;
   U-233: 92, 233, 141;
   I-131: 53, 131, 78;
   Cl-35: 17, 35, 18;
   Ra-226: 88, 226, 138.
14. (a) 32;
    (b) ${}_{13}Al$: 2, 8, 3;
    ${}_{14}Si$: 2, 8, 4;
    ${}_{15}P$: 2, 8, 5;
    ${}_{16}S$: 2, 8, 6;
    ${}_{17}Cl$: 2, 8, 7;
    ${}_{18}Ar$: 2, 8, 8.
19. (a) 233 K, 283 K, 546 K;

(b) $-268°$ C, 0° C, 727° C
(c) -3 K and $-300°$ C.
20. (a) 24 L, 48 L;
(b) 600 mL.
22. 6 mL, 3 mL, 24 mL.
26. (a) (i) 16 cm^2; (ii) $4\pi cm^2$ or 12.57 cm^2; (iii) 3.43 cm^2; (iv) 21.4%.
32. (a) 16.650 J; (b) 12,810 J; (c) 24,672 J.
(These numbers may be rounded off to 1.67×10^4 J, 1.28×10^4 J, and 2.47×10^4 J.

Chapter 8
2. (a) 6; (b) 7; (c) 21; (d) 13; (e) 22.

Chapter 9
3. (a) 4; (b) 3; (c) 10; (d) 11.
4. When conc. of H^+ is 1 mol/L, pH = 0; at 10 mol/L, pH = -1.
13. $C_{18}H_{12}$.

Chapter 10
3. (a) $^{28}_{14}Si$; (b) $^{10}_{4}Be$; (c) $^{95}_{41}Nb$; (d) $^{41}_{20}Ca$.
4. 2 hr; 16 cps.
5. (a) 150 yr.
6. (a) 224 yr.
7. (a) 1 mg.
10. (a) $^{30}_{15}P$; (b) $^{238}_{93}Np$; (c) $^{138}_{53}I$; (d) $^{206}_{82}Pb$; (e) $^{133}_{49}In$; (f) $^{85}_{36}Kr$.
27. (a) 11,460 yr; (b) 17,190 yr.
28. 48 yr.

Chapter 11
3. 0.334 m.
10. 30 dB.
12. 1,000,000,000 or 10^9.
13. (a) 100,000,000 or 10^8; (b) 10,000 or 10^4.
14. 73 dB.
15. -10 dB.
21. 501 m/sec.

Chapter 12
26. 1.25 m (long arm) +0.25 m (short arm) = 1.50 m.

Chapter 17
27. 4 km/hr away from each other; canoeist 2 km/hr south; walker 2 km/hr north.
28. (a) 1000 km/hr; (b) 2500 km/hr; (c) 1001 km/hr; (d) 2501 km/hr.
29. 3×10^8 m/sec in all cases.

GLOSSARY

absolute humidity—See **humidity.**
absolute zero—The coldest possible temperature; no substance can be cooled below this temperature. On the Kelvin scale absolute zero is zero kelvin, or 0 K. The equivalent temperature on the Celsius scale is $-273.15\,^{\circ}C$.
absorption spectrum—See **spectrum.**
acceleration—The change in velocity of an object per unit time. Acceleration is a vector quantity. A body is accelerating when it is speeding up, slowing down, or changing direction.
acceleration due to gravity—The acceleration of a freely falling body under the influence of the Earth's gravitation at sea level. This term is symbolized by the letter g and is equal to approximately $9.8\ m/sec^2$.
acid—A substance that can supply hydrogen ions (protons) to another substance, known as a base.
acid mine drainage—Water pollution that results when water flowing through a mine reacts with sulfur compounds to produce sulfuric acid. The acid washes into streams and watercourses and disrupts normal aquatic life cycles.
adiabatic—A process that occurs without loss or gain of heat.
adiabatic cooling—Cooling process that occurs without loss or gain of heat. Under certain conditions, a rising air mass may cool adiabatically. If no heat is transferred, a rising air mass will expand and, as it expands, it performs work and therefore cools.
adsorption—The process by which molecules from a liquid or gaseous phase become concentrated on the surface of a solid.
air mass—A large body of air that has approximately the same temperature and humidity throughout.
air pollution—The deterioration of the quality of air that results from the addition of impurities.
albedo—A measure of the reflectivity of a surface, measured as the ratio of light reflected to light received. A mirror or bright snowy surface has a high albedo, whereas a rough flat road surface has a low albedo.
alloy—A material composed of a metal intimately mixed with other metals or small concentrations of certain nonmetals such as carbon or silicon. An alloy has different physical characteristics from any of its individual components.
alpha particle—The nucleus of a helium atom.
alternating current (ac)—An electric current that oscillates in a wire. When an alternating current is established in a wire, electrical energy is transported, but the electrons themselves do not move in a concerted direction. See also *direct current.*
amino acid—A compound whose molecules contain both amino and carboxylic acid groups. Amino acids are the building blocks of proteins.
ampere—A measure of electrical current equal to the movement of one coulomb of charge past a given point in a wire in one second.

$$1\ \text{ampere} = 1\ \text{coulomb/sec}$$

amplifier—A device designed to increase the power of an electrical signal without affecting its form.
amplitude (of a wave)—The magnitude or height of a wave, measured as the distance between the zero point of the wave to the point of maximum displacement. The amplitude is one half of the vertical distance between the crest and the trough.
anaerobiosis—The biological utilization of nutrients in the absence of air.
angle of incidence—When a light ray is beamed onto a surface, the angle of incidence is defined as the angle between

the light ray and a line drawn perpendicular to the surface.

anode—The positive terminal in a vacuum tube. The electrons emitted by the cathode are collected at the anode. In an electrochemical cell, the anode is the electrode where oxidation (loss of electrons) occurs.

arch—A curved construction used for spanning an opening. An arch is built so that a downward force is transmitted as a horizontal force to the outer supports of the structure.

asteroid—One of the small planetary bodies that orbits the Sun. Asteroids range in size from less than 1 km to 1000 km in diameter.

asthenosphere—The uppermost boundary of the Earth's mantle. It is between 100 and 400 km thick. The asthenosphere is plastic and semifluid. See also *core, crust, mantle.*

atmosphere—The predominantly gaseous envelope that surrounds the Earth.

atmosphere (Standard pressure)—The pressure exerted at sea level by a column of mercury 76 cm high. This corresponds to the normal pressure exerted by the Earth's atmosphere at sea level.

atom—The fundamental unit of the element.

atomic nucleus—The small positive central portion of the atom that contains its protons and neutrons.

atomic number—The number of protons in an atomic nucleus.

aurora borealis—A luminous display appearing in the Northern Hemisphere that occurs when high-energy cosmic rays and other high-energy radiation approach the Earth and ionize atoms and molecules in the upper atmosphere. Such a display in the Southern Hemisphere is called the *aurora australis.*

autotroph—An organism that obtains its energy from the Sun, as opposed to a *heterotroph*, which is an organism that obtains energy from the tissue of other organisms. Most plants are autotrophs.

Avogadro's law—Equal volumes of all gases (at the same temperature and pressure) contain the same number of molecules.

background radiation—The level of radiation on Earth from natural sources.

barometer—A device used to measure atmospheric pressure.

barometric pressure—The pressure $\left(\frac{\text{force}}{\text{area}}\right)$ exerted by the atmosphere.

base—A substance that accepts protons from an acid. The reaction is said to neutralize the acid.

bel—Ten decibels.

beta particle—An electron emitted from an atomic nucleus.

Big Bang—An event that is thought to mark the beginning of our Universe. The theory assumes that some 10 to 20 billion years ago, all matter that was to form the galaxies exploded into space from an infinitely compressed state. See also *oscillating universe cosmology.*

biogas—Combustible gas (mostly methane) produced by anaerobic fermentation of organic matter.

biosphere—The life-supporting portions of the Earth and its atmosphere.

black hole—A small region of space that contains matter packed so densely that an intense gravitational field is created, from which light cannot escape. Since no light can ever leave a black hole, it always remains invisible.

Boyle's law—The volume of a gas (at constant temperature) is inversely proportional to its pressure.

branching chain reaction—A chain reaction in which each step produces more than one succeeding step.

breeder reactor—A nuclear reactor that produces more fissionable material than it consumes.

British system—A system of measurement formerly used in Great Britain, now used almost exclusively in the United States. It differs from the Système International d'Unités (SI system) in that the foot is used as the fundamental unit of length, the pound as the unit of force, and the degree Fahrenheit as the unit of temperature.

brittle—Easily fractured when stressed or struck. Brick is brittle. Brittle is the opposite of *ductile.*

bushing—A part of an electric motor or generator that makes electrical contact between the moving and the stationary parts of the motor.

calorie—A unit of energy used to express quantities of heat. When calorie is spelled with a small c, it refers to the quantity of heat required to heat 1 gram of water 1°C. (This definition is not precise, because the quantity depends slightly on the particular temperature range chosen. The gram calorie, normal calorie, mean calorie, and thermochemical calorie are all precisely defined, but they are nearly the same, and their differences need not concern us.) When Calorie is spelled with a capital C, it means 1000 small calories, or one kilocalorie, the quantity of heat required to heat 1000 grams (1 kilogram) of water 1°C. Food energies for nutrition are always expressed in Calories.
cam—An eccentric wheel that is used to open and close automobile valves according to a precise timing schedule. Cams are also used in a great many other mechanical applications.
carcinogen—A cancer-producing substance.
catalyst—A substance that influences (usually speeds up) the rate of a chemical reaction and that can be recovered from the reaction mixture.
cathode—The negative terminal in a vacuum tube that emits electrons. These electrons then travel across free space toward the anode. In an electrochemical cell, the cathode is the electrode where reduction (gain of electrons) occurs.
centrifugal force—An outward force rising in reaction to a centripetal force when an object is in circular motion.
centripetal force—An inward, "center-seeking" force that is necessary to hold an object in circular motion.
chain reaction—A reaction that proceeds in a series of steps, each step being made possible by the preceding one. See also *branching chain reaction.*
Charles' law —The volume of a gas (at constant pressure) is directly proportional to its absolute temperature.
chelating agent—A molecule that can offer two or more different chemical bonding sites to hold a metal ion in a clawlike linkage. The bonds between chelating agent and metal ion can be broken and reestablished reversibly.
chemical bond—A linkage that holds atoms together to form molecules. See also *covalent bond.*
chemical change—A transfer that results from making or breaking of chemical bonds.
chemical energy—The energy that is absorbed when chemical bonds are broken or that is released when chemical bonds are formed. A substance that can release energy by undergoing chemical reactions is said to have chemical energy.
chemical formula—A combination of symbols of elements that shows the composition of a molecule or a substance.
China Syndrome—A facetious expression referring to a nuclear meltdown in which the hot radioactive mass melts its way into the ground towards China. While a meltdown through the Earth to China is, of course, impossible, an accident in a nuclear power plant may potentially lead to a situation where a hot radioactive mass melts its way through the containment structure into the earth, contaminating neighboring environments and groundwater supplies.
chromosphere—A turbulent diffuse gaseous layer of the Sun that lies above the photosphere.
climate—The composite pattern of weather conditions that can be expected in a given region. Climate refers to yearly cycles of temperature, wind, rainfall, etc., and not to daily variations. See also *weather.*
closed system—A system that is isolated so that no mass can enter or leave.
cochlea—A snail-shaped structure in the inner ear, which contains a fluid that vibrates in response to sound waves.
coherent light—A beam of light in which all the component waves are traveling in phase, at the same frequency, and in exactly the same direction. Coherent light is produced by a laser.
comet—A celestial body moving about the Sun, usually in a highly elliptical path or orbit. Comets appear to have a fairly dense core surrounded by a "fuzzy," "fiery" halo, but in actuality, comets are quite cold. When a comet approaches the Sun, the force of the solar wind blows matter outward from the comet, forming a long "tail."

compass—A device that consists of a small, freely rotating magnet that aligns itself with the Earth's magnetic field and is used to indicate direction for navigation and other uses.

compound (compound substance)—A substance that consists of a fixed composition of elements and has a fixed set of properties.

compressive stress—See *stress.*

condensation—Conversion of vapor to liquid.

conduction (of heat)—The process by which heat energy is transmitted directly through materials. Conduction occurs because energetic molecules move rapidly and collide with neighboring molecules. Kinetic energy is transferred during the collision process and the neighboring molecules accelerate and become energetic, or "hot."

conduction band—A group of electronic energy levels spaced so closely that they form a practically continuous energy band. Conduction bands are typical of metals.

conductor (electrical)—A material that offers little resistance to the movement of electric current.

continental drift—The theory stating the continent-sized masses of the Earth's crust are slowly moving relative to one another.

control rod—A neutron-absorbing medium that controls the reaction rate in a nuclear reactor.

convection—The process by which heat energy is transmitted through gases and liquids by the action of currents that circulate in the fluid.

cooling pond—An open, shallow lake used to provide cool water for an electrical power plant or other factory.

cooling tower—A large structure used to cool water from an electrical power plant or other factory. The hot water is pumped to the top of the tower and allowed to fall downward and is cooled by air flowing upward from the bottom. In the wet process, the cooling is aided by evaporation.

core (of the Earth)—The central portion of the Earth, believed to be composed mainly of iron and nickel. See also *asthenosphere, crust, mantle.*

Coriolis effect—The deflection of air flow caused by the rotation of the Earth.

corona—The luminous irregular envelope of highly ionized gas outside the chromosphere of the Sun. See also *photosphere.*

cosmic ray—A form of radiation consisting mainly of high-speed atomic nuclei and other atomic particles that move through space and frequently strike the Earth's atmosphere.

cosmology—The study of the origin and the end of the universe.

coulomb—A unit quantity of electricity that equals the amount of electricity possessed by 6.24×10^{18} electrons.

Coulomb's law—The force of attraction (or repulsion) between two charges is directly proportional to the product of the charges and inversely proportional to the square of the distance between them.

covalent bond—A chemical bond between atoms that is characterized by shared electrons.

crankshaft—A basically U-shaped rod that is used to convert up-and-down or back-and-forth motion to rotational motion.

crest—The highest point in a wave.

critical condition—A condition under which a chain reaction continues at a steady rate, neither accelerating nor slowing down.

critical mass (in a nuclear reaction)—The quantity of fissionable material just sufficient to maintain a nuclear chain reaction.

crust (of the Earth)—The solid outer layer of the Earth; the portion on which we live. See also *asthenosphere, core, mantle.*

crystalline solid—See *solid.*

cyclone (for air pollution control)—An air cleaning device that removes dust particles by throwing them out of an air stream in a cyclonic motion.

cylinder (of an automobile)—In an automotive engine, a cylinder is a round hole bored in the engine block. The piston moves within the cylinder.

decibel (dB)—A unit of sound intensity equal to $\frac{1}{10}$ of a Bel. The decibel scale is a logarithmic scale used in measuring sound intensities relative to the intensity of the faintest audible sound.

degeneracy pressure—The strength of the atomic particles that holds a white dwarf star from further collapse.
density—Mass per unit volume.
deoxyribonucleic acid—See *DNA*.
detergent—A cleaning agent that acts by serving to bind water molecules to molecules of grease or other soiling substances.
deuterium—Isotope of hydrogen with mass number of 2. Also called "heavy hydrogen."
dew—Moisture condensed from the atmosphere, usually during the night, when the ground and leaf surfaces become significantly cooler than the surrounding air.
diamond—A hard, brilliant, crystalline form of the element carbon.
direct current (dc)—An electric current moving in one direction only. When a direct current moves through a wire, electrons travel progressively through the wire. See also *alternating current*.
distillation—A process in which a liquid is vaporized and the vapor condensed to a liquid again.
DNA—A substance consisting of large molecules which determines the synthesis of proteins and accounts for the continuity of species.
doldrums—A region of the Earth near the Equator in which hot, humid air is moving vertically upward, forming a vast low-pressure region. Local squalls and rainstorms are common, and steady winds are rare.
dome—A three-dimensional curved structure. A dome transmits downward force to lateral forces spread out over the entire base.
Doppler effect—The observed change in frequency of light or sound that occurs when the source of the wave is moving relative to the observer.
ductile—Easily bent or deformed when stressed. Ductile is the opposite of *brittle*. A ductile material can be drawn out to form a wire.
dust—An airborne substance that consists of solid particles typically having diameters greater than about one micrometer.
dust mulching—An agricultural practice of pulverizing the surface of the soil to enhance its capillary action and thereby draw underground water up to the root zone.
eardrum—A membrane in the ear canal that vibrates when sound waves enter the ear. Also called the *tympanic membrane*.
earthquake—A sudden traumatic movement of part of the Earth's crust.
ECCS—Emergency Core Cooling System in a nuclear reactor.
eclipse—A phenomenon that occurs when a heavenly body is shadowed by another and therefore rendered invisible. When the Moon lies directly between the Earth and the Sun, we observe a **solar eclipse;** when the Earth lies directly between the Sun and the Moon, we observe a **lunar eclipse.**
ecology—The study of the interrelationships among plants and animals and the interactions between living organisms and their physical environment.
ecosystem—A group of plants and animals occurring together plus that part of the physical environment with which they interact. An ecosystem is defined to be nearly self-contained so that the matter which flows into and out of it is small compared to the quantities which are internally recycled in a continuous exchange of the essentials of life.
elastic wave—A wave that manifests itself as a series of compressions and expansions of an elastic medium. Sound waves are elastic waves.
elasticity—The property of a body that enables it to change its length, width, or shape when the body is stressed and then recover its original shape when the stress is removed.
electric charge—The quantity of electricity or electric energy within a substance or on its surface. It is a measure of the excess or deficiency of electrons.
electric circuit—A complete path of conducting materials that allows electric current to flow. See also *parallel circuit, series circuit.*
electric current—A concerted and continuous movement of charged particles in response to a potential gradient.
electric field—A condition of space in the vicinity of a charged body. If a charged body is placed in an electric field, it experiences a force.

electrical force—The force that results from the interaction of charged bodies. Electrical force is repulsive if the bodies carry like charges (++ or −−) and is attractive if the bodies are oppositely charged (+− or −+).
electrical potential—See *volt.*
electromagnet—A device consisting of an iron core wrapped with wire that is magnetized when a direct current is passed through the wire.
electromagnetic field—The combined electric and magnetic fields produced by an oscillating charged particle or particles.
electromagnetic spectrum—The entire range of electromagnetic radiation.
electromagnetic induction—The induction of an electric current in a wire when a magnetic field changes near the wire or when the wire moves through a magnetic field.
electromotive force (emf)—An energy source that maintains a potential difference (measured in volts) between two points in an electric circuit.
electron—The fundamental atomic unit of negative electricity.
electostatic precipitator—A device that electrically charges particulate air pollutants and attracts them to an oppositely charged surface so that they can be removed easily.
element—A substance all of whose atoms have the same atomic number.
ellipse—A closed curve construction such that the sum of the distance from the two foci to the edge of the curve is always the same for any point on the curve.
emission spectrum—See *spectrum.*
energy—The capacity to perform work or to transfer heat. See also specific types of energy, *chemical, kinetic, nuclear,* and *potential.*
engineer—A person capable of applying scientific principles to the design, construction, and operation of practical devices such as roads, bridges, buildings, machinery, or industrial or electrical equipment.
entropy—A thermodynamic measure of disorder. It has been observed that the entropy of an undisturbed system always increases during any spontaneous process; that is, the degree of disorder always increases.
equinox—Either of two times during a year when the Sun shines directly overhead at the Equator. During the equinox, every portion of the Earth receives 12 hours of daylight and 12 hours of darkness.
erosion—The process by which parts of the Earth's surface are transported to new locations by water, wind, wave, ice, or other natural agents.
ether—A medium thought by early physicists to pervade all space. The existence of the ether was disproved by the Michelson-Morley experiment. (In chemistry, ether is an organic substance that vaporizes readily.)
evaporation—Conversion of liquid to vapor.
excited electron—An electron in an atom or molecule that has been promoted to a higher energy level and therefore exists in an excited state.
excited state—A state of an atom or molecule in which one or more electrons have absorbed energy and exist in higher energy levels. See also *ground state.*

fatigue—The tendency of a material to fail after repeated stress.
fault—A crack or weak point in the Earth's surface; a potential site of earthquake activity.
fault creep—The gradual nontraumatic slippage of land surfaces past each other.
field of force—See *electric field.*
First Law of Thermodynamics—See *thermodynamics.*
fission (of atomic nuclei)—The splitting of atomic nuclei into approximately equal fragments.
flywheel—A heavy disc or wheel mounted on a shaft of a piece of machinery. The rotational inertia of the flywheel tends to smooth out any irregularities in the motion of the machinery and maintains smooth movement of the shaft.
fog—The low cloud formation usually formed when warm, moisture-laden air is cooled on contact with land or water.
food chain—An idealized pattern of flow of energy in a natural ecosystem. In the classical food chain, plants are eaten by primary consumers only, pri-

mary consumers are eaten by secondary consumers only, secondary consumers by tertiary consumers only, and so forth.

force—Any influence that causes or tends to cause a body to accelerate. Force is commonly measured in newtons in the SI system and pounds in the British system.

freezing—Conversion of liquid to solid.

Freon—A trade name of the Dupont Company that refers to the class of chlorofluorocarbons. The compounds that may be implicated in stratospheric pollution are Freon-11 ($CFCl_3$), and Freon-12 (CCl_2F_2).

frequency—The number of wave disturbances (can be measured as the number of crests) that pass a given point in a specific amount of time. Frequency is usually expressed in cycles/sec, or hertz. 1 Hz = 1 cycle/sec.

friction—The sum total of all the forces that oppose the motion of one body past another when the two are in contact.

frontal weather system—Weather systems that develop when air masses collide.

fulcrum—The support or point of rest of a lever.

full moon—See *phases of the moon.*

fundamental frequency—The lowest frequency of a musical sound. See also *overtone.*

fusion (of atomic nuclei)—The combination of nuclei of light elements (particularly hydrogen) to form heavier nuclei.

Gaia—The ancient Greek goddess of the Earth. This word has recently been used to describe the biosphere and to emphasize the interdependence of the Earth's ecosystems by likening the entire biosphere to a single living organism.

galaxy—A large volume of space containing many billions of stars, all held together by mutual gravitation.

gas—A state of matter that consists of molecules that are moving independently of each other in random patterns.

gasohol—A mixture of gasoline and alcohol that can be used as an automotive fuel.

generator—A device that produces electrical power when a coil of wire is rotated in a magnetic field. Generators must be powered by some external source of energy. In most commercial applications, steam or flowing water drives a turbine, and the generator is connected to the spinning shaft of the turbine.

geodesic dome—A type of structure first designed by Buckminster Fuller that is built of a series of triangular units leaning inward to form a dome.

geothermal energy—Energy derived from the heat of the Earth's interior.

glacier—A large mass of flowing ice. A glacier usually takes the form of a river of ice.

glass (or glassy solid)—A rigid state of matter in which the atoms or molecules are randomly arranged.

gluon—A hypothetical fundamental subatomic exchange particle that holds quarks together.

graphite—A soft, black form of the element carbon that consists of crystalline layers which can slide past one another.

gravitation—A universal force of mutual attraction between all bodies.

gravitation, acceleration due to—See *acceleration due to gravity.*

Great Red Spot—A large atmospheric storm on the surface of Jupiter that was first observed over 300 years ago.

greenhouse effect—The effect produced by certain gases, such as carbon dioxide or water vapor, that causes a warming of the Earth's atmosphere by absorption of infrared radiation.

ground state—A state of an atom or molecule in which all the electrons are in their lowest allowed energy levels. See also *excited state.*

ground wire—See *system ground.*

half-life (of a radioactive substance)—The time required for half of a sample of radioactive matter to decompose.

Hall-Héroult process—The industrial process for manufacturing aluminum by the electrolysis of bauxite.

heat—A form of energy. Every object contains heat energy in an amount that depends on its mass, its temperature,

and the specific heat of the materials of which it consists.
heat engine—A mechanical device that converts heat to work.
heat of fusion—The heat required to melt 1 g of a solid at constant temperature.
heat of vaporization—The heat required to vaporize 1 g of a liquid at constant temperature.
heliocentric—The theory, now known to be true, that the Sun, and not the Earth, is the center of the Solar System.
hertz (Hz)—A unit that measures the frequency of a wave form. When one crest of a wave passes a given point every second, that wave is said to have a frequency of one hertz.

$$1 \text{ hertz} = 1 \text{ cycle/sec}$$

heterotroph—See *autotroph.*
hologram—A three-dimensional photograph produced using laser light.
horse latitudes—A region of the Earth lying at about 30° north and south latitudes, in which air is moving vertically downward, forming a vast high-pressure region. Generally dry conditions prevail, and steady winds are rare.
Hubble's Law—A law that relates the red shift of an object outside our galaxy to its distance from Earth. See *red shift.*
humidity—A measure of the amount of moisture in the air. **Absolute humidity** is defined as the amount of water vapor in a given volume of air. **Relative humidity** is defined as the ratio of the amount of moisture in a given volume of air divided by the total amount of moisture that can be held by that volume at a given temperature.
humus—The complex mixture of decayed organic matter that is an essential part of healthy natural soil.
hydrocarbon—A compound of hydrogen and carbon.
hydroelectric power—Power derived from the energy of falling water.
hydrological cycle (water cycle)—The cycling of water, in all its forms, on the Earth.

igneous rock—Rock formed directly from cooling magma.
impulse—The product of the average force acting on a body multiplied by the time required for that force to act.

$$\text{impulse} = \text{force} \times \text{time}$$

incineration—A process by which solid wastes are burned. Sometimes the heat produced is utilized for space heating or to produce steam to generate electricity.
inertia—That property of a body that compels it to remain at rest or at constant velocity unless forced to change. More force is required to accelerate a body with a lot of inertia than one with less inertia.
infrasound—Elastic waves of frequency below the minimum for human hearing (about 50 Hz).
insulator—A material that offers substantial resistance to the movement of an electric current.
interference—A process whereby two or more waves combine when they reach a single point in space at the same time. The new wave is formed by the addition of the wave components.
ion—An electrically charged atom or group of atoms.
ionic bond—A chemical bond formed by attraction between oppositely charged ions.
isoelectronic structures—Atoms or ions that have the same electronic composition, such as F^-, Ne, and Na^+.
isomers—Different substances that have the same molecular formula, such as ethyl alcohol and dimethyl ether, both C_2H_6O.
isotopes—Atoms of the same element that have different mass numbers.

joule—The fundamental unit of work in the SI system.

$$1 \text{ joule} = 1 \text{ newton-meter}$$

kelvin—The SI unit of temperature. One kelvin is the same as a difference in temperature of 1 °C. The Kelvin temperature scale starts at 0 K, which equals −273.15° C.
kinetic energy—The energy possessed by a moving object.

$$KE = \frac{1}{2} mv^2$$

terial constructed of a mesh of steel embedded in concrete.
relative humidity—See *humidity.*
relativistic speeds—Speeds close to the speed of light.
respiration—The process by which plants and animals combine oxygen with sugar and other organic matter to produce energy and maintain body functions. Carbon dioxide and water are released as by-products.
revolve—To orbit a central point. A satellite revolves around the Earth. See also *rotate.*
roasting—The conversion of a sulfide ore to the oxide by means of oxidation in air.
rotate—To turn or spin on an axis. A top rotates. See also *revolve.*
rotational inertia—That property of a body that compels it to resist any changes in the speed of its rotation.
rotational motion—The movement of an object around an axis of rotation.

Sahel—A semi-arid region in North Africa just south of the Sahara Desert.
San Andreas fault—A large earthquake fault running north and south through the state of California.
sanitary landfill—A repository for solid wastes in which various measures, such as compaction and the use of sand or earth barriers, are taken to guard against environmental disruption.
scrubber—An air pollution control device that dissolves air contaminants in a liquid (usually water) by mechanical means, solvent action, chemical reaction, or some combination of these processes.
sea breeze—A local wind caused by uneven heating of land and ocean surfaces.
Second Law of Thermodynamics—See *thermodynamics.*
secondary treatment (of sewage)—The removal of impurities from water by the digestive action of various small organisms in the presence of air or oxygen.
sedimentary rock—Rock formed from compressed sediment.
sediments—Small particles of mineral and organic matter deposited by erosion.
seismograph—A device used to detect earthquakes.
seismology—The science of measuring and recording the shock waves of earthquakes.
semiconductor—A material that is neither a good conductor nor a good insulator. Semiconductors are used in the construction of transistors.
series circuit—An electrical circuit with two or more resistors arranged so that the electric current travels through each one of them in turn.
shearing stress—See *stress.*
shooting star—See *meteor.*
short circuit—A phenomenon that occurs when a circuit is completed with materials of low resistance only. Because the resistance is low, a great deal of current is allowed to flow, and large quantities of heat are generated.
SI system—See *Système International d'Unités.*
sine wave—A smoothly oscillating symmetrical wave form that is produced by a pure tone. Mathematically it is defined as a wave described by the following equation: $y = \text{sine } x$.
sinusoidal—Having the character of a sine wave.
slag—The product produced in the metallurgy of iron by the reaction of lime with sandy impurities. Slag is mostly calcium silicate, which floats on the molten iron and is skimmed off.
solar cell—A semiconductor device that converts sunlight directly into electricity.
solar collector—A device used to collect solar energy and concentrate it for useful purposes such as space or water heating.
solar design (passive)—A series of design features used in building construction to capture solar heat without the use of mechanical collection systems.
solar eclipse—See *eclipse.*
solar energy—Energy derived from the Sun.
solar wind—A stream of atomic particles shot out into space by violent storms occurring in the outer regions of the Sun's atmosphere.
solid (crystalline)—A rigid state of matter in which the atoms or molecules are arranged in an orderly pattern.

solstice—Either of two times per year when the Sun shines directly overhead furthest from the Equator. One solstice occurs on or about June 21 and marks the longest day of the year in the Northern Hemisphere and the shortest day in the Southern Hemisphere; the other solstice occurs on or about December 22, marking the longest day in the Southern Hemisphere and the shortest day in the Northern Hemisphere.
sonic boom—The sharp disturbance of air pressure caused by the reinforcing waves that trail an object moving at supersonic speed.
sonic speed—The speed of sound.
specific heat—The amount of heat energy required to raise the temperature of one gram of a substance 1° Celsius.
spectrum (electromagnetic)—A pattern of wavelengths into which a beam of light or other electromagnetic radiation is separated. The spectrum is seen as colors, or is photographed, or is detected by an electronic device. An **emission spectrum** is obtained from radiation emitted from a source. An **absorption spectrum** is obtained after radiation from a source has passed through a substance that absorbs some of the wavelengths.
speed—The distance traveled by an object in a given time interval.

$$\text{speed} = \frac{\text{distance}}{\text{time}}$$

speed of light—The speed traveled by an electromagnetic wave in a vacuum. The speed of light is a universal constant: 3×10^8 m/sec.
standard atmosphere—See *atmosphere (standard pressure.)*
steady state—A condition in which the inflow of material or energy is equal to the outflow.
steel—A type of metal alloy consisting mainly of iron mixed with small amounts of carbon and other materials.
strain—The distortion that results when an object is stressed.
stratosphere—A layer of air of fairly constant temperature that lies just above the troposphere. See also *mesosphere, thermosphere.*
stress—The force exerted on an object divided by the area over which the force acts.

$$\text{stress} = \frac{F}{A}$$

tensile stress—A stress that tends to pull an object apart.
compressive stress—A stress that tends to squeeze an object inward.
shearing stress—A stress that tends to slide one portion of an object laterally past the other.

strip mining—Any mining operation that operates by removing the surface layers of soil and rock, thereby exposing the deposits of ore to be removed.
subduction—A process whereby one continental plate is forced downward during a collision with another.
sublimation—Direct conversion of solid to vapor.
subsonic speed—Less than the speed of sound.
sunspot—A cool region of the Sun formed by intense magnetic disturbance. We observe sunspots as dark blotches on the surface of the Sun.
superconductor—A material that offers almost zero resistance to the flow of electric current. Superconductivity is shown by certain materials when they are cooled to temperatures close to absolute zero.
supernova—A star that has collapsed under intense gravitation and then exploded, hurling matter into space and sometimes emitting as much energy as an entire galaxy.
supersonic speed—Greater than the speed of sound.
synergism—A condition in which a whole effect is greater than the sum of its parts.
synfuels—An abbreviation for synthetic fuels. Any fuel that is manufactured by a chemical conversion from one type of fuel to another. The gasoline produced by conversion of coal or extraction of oil shale is a synfuel.
system ground—The wire on an electrical appliance that connects the entire system to ground. This wire protects a person using the appliance by shunting the electric current to ground in the event of a short circuit.

Système International d'Unités (SI)—Commonly called the metric system. A system of measurement used in all scientific circles and by lay people in most nations of the world. The standard units in the SI system are: length—meter; mass—kilogram; time—second; electric current—ampere; temperature—Kelvin, or °C; luminous intensity—candela; and amount of substance—mole. See also *British System.*

tar sands—Sand fields that bear organic materials that can be converted into petroleum products.
tectonic plate—A large, continent-sized piece of the Earth's crust that may move and collide with other tectonic plates.
temperature—A measure of the warmth or coldness of an object with reference to some standard. Temperature should not be confused with heat. Heat is the quantity of energy possessed by a body; the temperature is just a measure of how hot or cold it is.
tensile stress—See *stress.*
terrestrial planets—Mercury, Venus, Earth, and Mars; the four innermost planets of our Solar System that are all relatively small, dense, and rocky.
tertiary, or "advanced" treatment (of sewage)—Any of a variety of special methods of water purification, such as adsorption or reverse osmosis, which are more effective than simple physical or biological processes for specific pollutants.
thermal pollution—A change in the quality of an environment (usually an aquatic environment) caused by raising its temperature.
thermodynamics—The science concerned with heat and work and the relationships between them.
  First Law of Thermodynamics—Energy cannot be created or destroyed.
  Second Law of Thermodynamics—It is impossible to derive mechanical work from any portion of matter by cooling it below the temperature of the coldest surrounding object.
thermonuclear reaction—A nuclear reaction, specifically fusion, initiated by a very high temperature.
thermosphere—An extremely high and diffuse region of the atmosphere lying above the mesosphere.
tidal currents—Ocean currents that are powered by the movements of the tides. These currents are usually found close to shore or to island systems.
tidal energy—Energy derived from the movement of the tides.
tides—The cyclic rise and fall of ocean water caused by the gravitational force of the Moon and, to a lesser extent, by the gravitational force of the Sun.
trade winds—The winds that blow steadily from the northeast in the Northern Hemisphere and southeast in the Southern Hemisphere between 5° and 30° north and south latitudes.
transformer—A device that changes the voltage of a circuit but does not by itself produce electric power.
transistor—A semiconductor device used in most modern amplifier and switching circuits. The transistor acts as the heart of a circuit that amplifies a signal without changing its form.
translational motion—The movement of an object such that the entire object travels from one place to another.
transmutation (of elements)—The conversion of one element to another.
tritium—Radioactive isotope of hydrogen with mass number of 3.
troposphere—The layer of air that lies closest to the surface of the Earth and extends upward to about 12 km. See also *mesosphere; stratosphere; thermosphere.*
trough—The lowest point in a wave.
truss—A structured frame made up of a series of triangular members that is used to span a space and carry a load.
turbine—A mechanical device consisting of fanlike blades mounted on a shaft. When water, steam, or air rushes past the blades, the shaft turns, and this mechanical energy can be used to generate electricity.
tympanic membrane—See *eardrum.*

ultrasound—Elastic waves of frequency above the maximum for human hearing (about 15,000 Hz).
uncertainty principle—The theory that tells us that we cannot know both the

position and the energy of an electron at the same time.

valence—The chemical combining capacity of an element. Specifically, the "common valence" of an element is the number of hydrogen atoms that combine with one atom of that element.
vector quantity—A quantity that has both magnitude and direction. Velocity, force, and acceleration are all vector quantities.
vein (of rock)—A thin layer of one type of rock embedded in a dominant rock formation.
velocity—A description of the speed of a body and its direction of motion. Velocity is a vector quantity.
viable—Capable of living.
vibrational motion—The movement of an object or a portion of the object back and forth without any permanent displacement away from a fixed position. The motion of a struck tuning fork is vibrational.
volcano—A fissure in the Earth's crust through which lava, steam, and other substances are expelled.
volt—A measure of the electric potential energy per unit charge.

$$\text{volt} = \frac{\text{electrical energy}}{\text{unit of charge}}$$

Voltage is a potential and must always be measured with respect to some other point.

watt—The SI unit of power.

$$1 \text{ watt} = \frac{1 \text{ joule}}{\text{sec}}$$

wave—A periodic disturbance in some medium. A wave carries energy from one point to another but there is no net movement of materials. Electromagnetic waves are qualitatively different from all other waves in that they can be propagated in a vacuum.
wavelength—The distance between successive disturbances of the same type in a wave, such as between neighboring crests.
weather—The temperature, wind, and precipitation conditions that prevail in a given region on a particular day. See also *climate*.
weathering—The sum of processes that fracture and decompose surface rock.
weight—The force of gravity acting on a body.
white dwarf—A stage in the life of a star when fusion has halted and the star glows solely from the residual heat produced during past eras. White dwarfs are very small stars.
work—The energy expended when something is forced to move. Work is defined as the force exerted on an object multiplied by the distance that the object is forced to travel.

INDEX

Key to abbreviations:

box = marginal box
ff = following pages
fig = figure
mrg = margin
prb = problem
tbl = table
exp = experiment
ftn = footnote

P

Q

R

S

T

U

V

W

X

Y